26th Nov. 1998

For Haydn with best wishes.

Donald E. Scott.

BLOOD BROTHERS

David E Scott

MINERVA PRESS
LONDON
MONTREUX   LOS ANGELES   SYDNEY

BLOOD BROTHERS
Copyright © David E Scott 1997

ISBN 1 86106 097 1

First published 1997 by
MINERVA PRESS
195 Knightsbridge
London SW7 1RE

Printed and bound in Great Britain by
Antony Rowe Ltd, Chippenham, Wiltshire.

BLOOD BROTHERS

The people of Crete unfortunately make more history than they consume locally.

from *The Jesting of Arlington Stringer*

During Crete's turbulent history no period was more vicious and bloody than the island's occupation by the Germans and Italians between June 1941 and April 1945.

D E Scott, 1996

This book is dedicated to my long-suffering and understanding wife

Contents

Prologue   11

BOOK ONE   13

One
The Railway Halt at Bialowieza   15

Two
Saint Teresa *Frauhaus Klinik*,
Munich, December 14th 1918   33

Three
The Grünbergs, Aalbrücke, 1918 – 1931   51

Four
The Schmidts, Munich, 1918 – 1932   57

Five
Grossmunde Farm, May – September 1930,
The Blood Brother Ceremony.
Grünbergs; Aalbrücke to London, October 1931   70

Six
Gerhardt Schmidt, Munich Nazi Party, 1919 – 1939,
Manfred Schmidt, Military Academy, 1936 – 1938   82

Seven
Pusey Street School, 1932
Rotherhithe Grammar School, 1932 – 1936   100

Eight
The Oxford Experience, October 1936 – June 1939   114

Nine
The Train to Winterberg, Erica, January 1939
Parachute School at Minden; Heinz Schneider;

Recruitment of Fritz Schultz   130

Ten
Lieutenant David Green, July 1939 – December 1940
Commando Training; Bronwen   159

Eleven
The Sitzkrieg, September 1939 – May 1940
Attack in the West; Schiphol – May 1940   185

Twelve
The Grand Parade, 4th July 1940
Paris, July 1940 – January 1941
The Wooing of Lise Frank   220

Thirteen
The Long Train Journey, Lübbecke to Athens,
April – May 1941   263

Fourteen
Captain David Green's Trip to Athens
Crete before the Invasion, April – May 1941   278

Fifteen
Hotel Grande Bretagne, Athens, May 15th 1941
German Assault on Crete, 20th May – 2nd June, 1941   317

Sixteen
The Defenders of Crete, May 20th – June 2nd, 1941
Rape at Piskopiano
Heraklion Airfield, 3rd June, 1941   344

Seventeen
The Desert War, June 1940 – December 1942   361

Eighteen
Commando Recruitment, Cairo
Bronwen in North Africa, August 1942   397

Nineteen
Six Months in the Wilderness, June – December 1941
SS Rehabilitation Hospital, Havel, Berlin
The Sex Hotel   418

BOOK TWO   451

Twenty
Organisation of German Resistance,
Eastern Crete, 1942 – 1943   453

Twenty-One
The First Six Weeks at Piskopiano   477

Twenty-Two
Eastern Crete, January – February 1943
Meeting with Cpl Dai, 1st March 1943   499

Twenty-Three
The Ambush, April 27th, 1943   519

Twenty-Four
Eastern Crete, May – June 1943
Attack on Vai   535

Twenty-Five
Eastern Crete, July - August 1943
Call to Festung HQ
Trouble at the Kibbutz   558

Twenty-Six
Eastern Crete, November, 1943
Loss of Courier
Obliteration of Pirgia and Piskopiano   584

Twenty-Seven
Eastern Crete, January 1944
Attack on Submarine Pens, Heraklion   605

Twenty-Eight
Eastern Crete, February – April 1944
Death of Captain Schubert and Samaritis
Abduction of General Kreipe   617

Twenty-Nine
Eastern Crete, May 1944 – March 1945
The Cheese Huts at Häraso   637

Thirty
Festung Elounda, October – December 1944
Slaughter on Krikri   651

Thirty-One
Codforce in Festung Elounda
Christmas Eve 1944   676

Thirty-Two
The Final Act, Christmas Day 1944   688

Thirty-Three
The Beachcombers' Find   709

Epilogue   719

Prologue

The German airborne assault on Crete during the last eleven days of May 1941 was one of the bloodiest battles in the history of modern warfare comparable to the conflict at Stalingrad and the carnage of the early days of the Battle of the Somme in 1915. German airborne assault troops suffered horrendous casualties during the first three days and over a thousand out of four thousand paratroopers killed in action fell victim to Cretan *andartes*, much to the surprise of the German High Command, who had predicted the population would welcome the invaders with open arms. After their swift victory over the British and Dominion forces German reprisals, ordered by *Reichsmarschall* Goering, were both swift and ruthless. Cretan civilian fighters fled into the vast mountain ranges in central Crete where, for the first year, they rampaged in bands continuing the Cretan tradition of family vendettas and sniping and ambushing the occupying forces. By the summer of 1942, by a process of amalgamation and coercion, definitive groups became identifiable throughout Crete, each led by a *kapitan*. The picture was further complicated by the emergence of two factions, the Nationalists who were dedicated to Cretan independence after the war, and the Communists who sought affiliation with ELAS forces on the mainland. Eastern Crete, including Heraklion, was garrisoned by German and Italian forces and with the collapse of Mussolini's dictatorship in September 1943 the Italians virtually became prisoners of their German compatriots. In late 1942, into this cauldron of intrigue and violence two young officers, at one time blood brothers, arrived, one, the German, to command counter-resistance forces in Heraklion and the British officer to lead a team of six commandos in subversive activities. This book relates the history of their early days in Germany, the blood brother ceremony, their separate education and military careers, their love lives and their final confrontation on the sun-baked island of Crete.

BOOK ONE

Chapter One

The Railway Halt at Bialowieza

Isaac Grünberg half-crouched behind the leeward corner of a wooden cattle shed as he attempted to light a pipe, cupping his mittened hands around the bowl to protect the spluttering match from gusting winds and snow flurries. The icy wind blew from the east biting through Isaac's threadbare overcoat and cutting through his thin frame to the bone. He shivered as his shaking, numb, stiff fingers made futile attempts to light the tobacco in his pipe. The brief flicker of a lighted match revealed a thin, cracked face and blue-beaked nose above a black moustache and a borscht-stained, grey goatee beard. He cursed gently to himself and eventually managed to light his pipe and inhaled the acrid smoke. He coughed briefly and explosively three times and then straightened his body leaning back against the wooden shed and attempting to draw his meagre frame into the fabric of the wood to shield his body from the biting, tearing, and overpowering coldness.

Taking stock of his surroundings, he looked out through slit-like eyelids and quietly cursed Kowalski, the station minder, who had sold him the foul tobacco for an exorbitant price of two roubles. At that very moment Kowalski was huddled over a kerosene lamp in his house some twenty yards away and Isaac could see the dim shadow of light in the living room through the frosted window. The railway station lay forty yards to the right of the station master's house and consisted of a fifty yard wooden platform with an open-ended wooden hut at its centre, surmounted by a metal eagle crest of the Czarist monarchs. Bialowieza had for centuries been a hunting lodge for Russian royalty.

The grey snow-laden light of early afternoon was quickly fading and it would soon be pitch dark. The red glow in Isaac's pipe abruptly expired and, with a sigh, he returned his pipe to his right-hand coat pocket, coughed once more and began to shiver uncontrollably. The hunger pangs which had been lurking near the surface again reasserted themselves and these, combined with the muscular contractions of his cadaverous frame, made Isaac feel wretched and miserable. He made a mental note that later he would confront Pan Kowalski and demand more meat and vegetables in the borscht he provided for Isaac and his wife. They had been in this godforsaken railway halt for two whole days. He reckoned that Pan Kowalski must be making a fortune in roubles from the foul home-made tobacco and meatless borscht which he sold to the hapless Grünbergs.

The wind continued gusting and occasionally howling bringing in its wake showers of fine snow which settled on Isaac's black felt hat, his eyebrows, beard and his black woollen overcoat. In between the windy gusts Isaac's ears picked up the sounds of Kowalski's shepherd dog whimpering and growling near the door of the house. He was also conscious of his wife's quiet moaning inside the cattle shed and, from time to time, of footsteps on the wooden floor. Anna had been in labour for two whole days and Pani Kowalski, for a considerable financial consideration, had agreed to act as midwife. She was more humane than her obdurate husband and took time and trouble to be with Anna most of the day, administering to her needs as best she could. Mme Kowalski, a smiling, dumpy, grey-haired woman of sixty years, had produced six children of her own and appeared to be well-versed in the intricacies of childbirth, predicting that Isaac's infant would arrive before midnight.

His mind again wandered to his own misery and uncomfortable situation. He could hear and feel his teeth chattering and his bones and joints grating and the violent shuddering produced by the muscular contractions of his thin body. He thought about re-entering the warmer fodder-shed, but could not bring himself to face the agony of watching his poor Anna suffering violent uterine contractions, gritting her teeth and smiling wanly between gasps, vainly trying to suppress the shouts of agony which emanated from her dry, cracked lips. Isaac stamped his feet, coughed abruptly, squinted into the enveloping gloom and pulled his overcoat firmly around his body. He closed his eyes, swayed gently and made a conscious effort to control the damnable shivering. He thought that with God's blessing and Pani Kowalski's assistance he would be a father within the next few hours.

Isaac's mind wandered back through the years, recalling his father's funeral and his early years in the Ukraine. He closed his eyes firmly to eliminate the sting from the cold blast, thrust his hands into the pocket of his great coat, leant back against the shed wall and started to sway gently on his feet and quickly dozed.

Isaac was born in 1880, the son of Abraham Grünberg boot-maker in the village of Laremenov some two hundred miles from Kharkov and twenty miles south of the small town of Sverdlovsk. The village straddled both banks of a narrow stream and both halves were connected by a rickety wooden bridge, which often subsided into the icy waters during the heavy snows and freezing winter months. The Jewish community occupied most of the west bank whilst the Ukrainians lived mainly on the eastern side. The whole village was under the dominance of His Honour Simonov, a land owner, who lived in a resplendent mansion three miles to the north of Laremenov.

Isaac's father plied his trade as a shoemaker and occupied a three-roomed dwelling in the centre of the small collection of Jewish houses. His workshop was a primitive lean-to wooden contraption at the back of the house. Isaac remembered his father with affection. He was a strict disciplinarian and leader of the forty strong Jewish community in Laremenov. Schooling was organised within the community and tuition in Hebrew was undertaken for an hour each day. Russian was spoken only during contact with the inhabitants across the river or when the landlord paid his monthly visits to collect rents and dues. By and large the Jewish inhabitants of Laremenov were practically self-sufficient.

Isaac grew into a strong, lean, sinewy young man and at the age of thirteen, after his barmitzvah, started learning his father's trade. Abraham Grünberg died from pneumonia in the winter of 1900. Isaac, then twenty years old, took over his father's trade and became an industrious shoemaker, well able to cope with the needs of his Jewish brethren and selling his wares in increasing quantities to the Ukrainian community across the river. His business prospered and his wealth accumulated for the next fifteen years. He was cared for by his mother until 1913 when she died and thereafter, from the age of thirty-three, he lived a solitary bachelor's existence. The community matchmaker attempted an arranged marriage on a few occasions but Isaac eluded her ploys and seemed idyllically content to be a bachelor, caring for his own needs.

Following in his father's footsteps, Isaac took an active part in organising the Jewish community and by his late twenties had been elected to the Committee of Elders. By the outbreak of the Great War in 1914 he was recognised as the leader of the Jewish commune at Laremenov.

The war in the west had little impact on the Jews at Laremenov. Many Ukrainians from the eastern bank volunteered for military service and went away to fight the Austro-Hungarians in Poland. In early 1916 His Honour Simonov and a troop of twelve mounted guards visited the village. Recruits were enlisted from able-bodied male Ukrainians but no one in the Jewish sector volunteered to serve in the Czarist army. Isaac reasoned that they were pacifists at heart and had no obligation to enlist. Within a few weeks his reasoning changed and he felt that he should rally to the aid of his country of birth in a non-combatant capacity.

Joseph, an unmarried son of the village farmer, was of the same mind and the two agreed to volunteer and enlist. In the summer of 1916 they walked north to Simonov's mansion carrying their meagre belongings in canvas bags. The landowner accepted their services as cooks to his military detachment. Due to a shortage of uniforms the two Jews, Isaac and Joseph, went to war in their work-day clothes. Only the officers were clothed in anything resembling a military uniform.

The detachment, fifty strong, left for Sverdlovsk in June 1916 and marched northwards gathering recruits in the towns and villages as they progressed. The officers rode ahead whilst the soldiers struggled along in their wake in a straggling irregular column. The kitchen equipment, food, and medical supplies were piled on an old cart drawn by two scrawny horses which brought up the rear of the column where Isaac and Joseph rode with a kindly, portly, old sergeant. When the column reached Kharkov they were ordered to camp for the issue of uniforms and arms and for training and re-grouping with similar units from other parts of the Ukraine.

Eventually the 35th Ukrainian division was deployed as a reserve unit for the main battle which was then in progress eight hundred miles to the west. Movement of this army towards the front line was slow and ponderous. The 35th was not in position in the Pripet marshes, forty miles north of Rovno, until November 1916 and by this time the severe Russian winter had arrived and fighting had virtually come to a standstill. Isaac and Joseph were fortunate in that they had warmth and food to ensure their survival through the harsh Russian winter. Many of the foot soldiers and most of the horses died during the severe winter of 1916-17.

With the advent of spring the fighting recommenced. At that time echelons of fresh troops were arriving at the front, troops with a different outlook on the war. They preached new doctrines and advocated rebellion against officers loyal to the Czar. They were the rudiments of the Red Army and the revolutionary spirit of these indoctrinated young men spread like wildfire amongst the demoralised infantry men. They actively preached mutiny against White Russian officers and desertion if no other method of insurrection proved effective. The troops of the 35th Ukrainian reserve division were ready and willing participants in their schemes and in August 1917 the entire division threw down its arms and walked eastwards away from the battle front.

Isaac and Joseph and their friendly sergeant kept the field kitchen intact and retreated with the disorganised rabble feeding them at various points along the route with victuals acquired from farmers and houses in the vicinity of the retreat. After twelve long and weary weeks they reached Kharkov. During the tenth week of the retreat the two horses died and the field kitchen had to be abandoned. Isaac and Joseph then made their way on foot southward towards Laremenov arriving in a sorry state, virtually bundles of rags and bone, in early November 1917.

The two young Jews became heroes in the village for a short while. Isaac resumed his occupation and control of the Committee of Elders and village life again assumed its habitual monotony. News of the overthrow and murder of the Czar Nicholas II and his replacement by a presidium, with Lenin at his head, hardly caused a ripple on the surface of the calm village life of Laremenov. Simonov never returned from the war and was believed to have been killed in action. Isaac knew the truth. He had witnessed the shooting of His Honour, the colonel, and three other officers during the rout and retreat from the Pripet marshes.

In January 1918 a new face arrived and took up residency in Simonov's mansion and also took control of the village of Laremenov and its surrounding lands. Alexis Gordanovitch was a peasant from Kiev and became the commissar for Laremenov, introducing new doctrines and creating a commune in the area. All the inhabitants and the surrounding farms were ordered to pool their resources and to support each other. There were no monetary payments. The state did not levy a rent, or taxes, but expected to cull a third of the produce from all the industries of the commune. Isaac had to barter his boots and shoes for food, clothing and oil, on a scale determined by Commissar Gordanovitch and his henchmen. The penalty for non-cooperation in this scheme was deportation to the inhospitable eastern states of Russia. The penalty for stealing was death.

The Jewish community suffered considerably under this regime and it became apparent to Isaac that survival of the Jews in Laremenov was endangered. In March 1918, after due consultation with the matchmaker, he married Anna the thirty year old elder daughter of the village farm and Joseph's sister. Isaac's reason for marrying after a long bachelor life was simple. He had resolved to leave Laremenov at the first opportunity and to travel west to Munich where he had a cousin with whom the Grünberg family corresponded once a year at Passover. A wife would be an asset in setting up a new home in Germany. He also had the urge to father a child, preferably a son. His union with Anna was happy and uncomplicated and, reluctant at first to leave, she soon came to share Isaac's views she realised she was pregnant.

The Commissar's demands were ever increasing and the Jewish commune became progressively more depressed and poor. They were not openly persecuted but there was a distinct undertone of discrimination against them in the excessive demands made by Alexis Gordanovitch and his commissars. In August 1918 Isaac and Anna and two other families with relatives in western Europe planned their trip to the west. The party consisted of six adults and five children between the ages of seven and thirteen. The Grünbergs collected their belongings into one shabby canvas bag and Isaac carefully packed the family Bible, a *Magen* David and two silver candlesticks, inside his valise. The money which he had earned over many years' hard labour was secreted in a pocket inside his black overcoat. There were various family complications with other members of the group and the party, now reduced to four adults and three children, left Laremenov on the first week of November 1918. By this time, Anna's pregnancy was well advanced, but she insisted on proceeding westwards for the sake of her unborn child.

The party had to walk twenty-four miles to the nearest rail junction at Sverdlovsk. They travelled northwards slowly in an open-sided cattle wagon frequently sharing their accommodation with the creatures for which the carriage had originally been designed. The weather was getting palpably colder, daylight hours shorter, and the autumn sun appeared only irregularly during the three day journey to Kharkov. The miserable journey had affected Joseph's family more than the Grünbergs. The three children spent the last two days huddled together in the wagon for warmth, alternately wailing and crying, and accompanied in their misery by Joseph's wife. By the time they reached Kharkov station the bedraggled group was thoroughly demoralised and Marta wanted to return by the first available train. They settled in a wooden waiting room at Kharkov station where there was an ineffective wood-burning stove for warmth. Isaac was anxious to carry on at the first opportunity but Joseph was hesitant and concerned about proceeding further with his wife and children reluctant to do so and determined to return to Laremenov. No amount of persuasion could change Marta's mind despite energetic pleas from Isaac. The party remained in the waiting room at Kharkov station for two days and during this time Joseph himself started wavering and losing his resolve to continue. On the third day snow flurries heralded the onset of heavy snowfall from the leaden skies and this completely broke Joseph's will. With Isaac's blessing the Geldberg family left Kharkov later that evening and retraced their steps southwards to their home in Laremenov.

On the following day Isaac and Anna boarded a passenger train for Lvov, paying the engine driver and guard in roubles. The coaches were a little more luxurious than the goods wagon of their previous journey. Each coach was divided into eight sections by wooden partitions and each section seated eight persons on hard planks. There was no form of heating or toilet facilities apart from one communal bucket at the rear end of the coach. The train was crowded and Isaac had to bribe the guard with ten roubles to secure a seat for himself and Anna. The train journey lasted eighteen hours with many stops to refuel the age-worn locomotive with dry wood for the boiler. Snow fell incessantly blurring the outlines of the surrounding countryside and drifting on to the railway lines, impeding the locomotive's progress. The station at Lvov was in a dilapidated state after the battles that had raged in the town during the war and Isaac was pleased to find a train leaving for Poland three hours after their arrival.

The locomotive for Krakow was much smaller than the Kiev/Lvov engine and the coaches were correspondingly smaller, each section seating six people. The main bulk of passengers from Kiev left the train at Lvov and Isaac and Anna procured a compartment to themselves, paying the guard before the journey commenced. By the time the train left Lvov the compartment was already freezing. Isaac wrapped Anna in blankets and he huddled close to her for body warmth. Anna remained impassive during the seemingly interminable journey towards the Polish border and they spoke very little as the train intermittently started and shuddered to a halt mainly for re-fuelling the old locomotive, negotiating inclines and clearing snowdrifts from the line. Ten hours after leaving Lvov the guard with his lamp walked the length of the train announcing that in a few minutes they would cross the Narevko river into Poland. But the river remained unseen in a blanket of snowdrifts and ice which obliterated the landscape.

About an hour after crossing the river Anna suddenly bent forward and clutched at her abdomen. The pain lasted only a few seconds and Isaac reassured her that she probably had hunger pains. Thereafter Anna remained wide awake and the sharp stabs in her abdomen brought a grimace to her face every twenty minutes or so. Isaac became increasingly concerned about his wife and, despite their ignorance and inexperience in these matters, they both agreed that the pains might indicate premature arrival of their child. At the next stop for re-fuelling Isaac hailed the guard and explained his predicament. The guard, sullen and obviously unhappy, suggested that the Grünbergs should get off the train at the next halt in Bialowieza. He explained that the train had made a detour off the main Lvov/Krakow line because of the conditions on a section of the main line ahead and that the station minder at Bialowieza would look after them. Isaac demurred, wishing to get Anna into some sort of comfort and warmth.

The couple arrived in Bialowieza in complete darkness, chilled to the marrow, and enveloped in a blizzard. After a hasty conversation on the platform between the guard and the station master the Grünbergs were ushered away through the deep snowdrifts toward a two-roomed house. The train departed behind them in a hazy spray of steam, spluttering, puffing and panting its way along the railway line away from the halt. As they reached the door to the house the noise from the overloaded locomotive had blended imperceptibly into the dark, gloomy night.

On entering the house the Grünbergs were confronted by a short, stout, grey-haired, middle-aged woman, huddled in front of a wood-burning stove and restraining a vicious looking Alsatian dog. The station master, Kowalski, kicked the dog firmly in the rump, sending it cowering and whimpering into the corner of the room and in a strange language explained to his wife the reason for the sudden appearance of the Grünbergs. Mme Kowalski moved away from the fire and invited Isaac and Anna to warm themselves at the stove, preparing hot tea for the travellers and setting a pot of borscht stew on top of the stove to re-heat. As Anna and Isaac sat huddled silently together near the source of warmth, with hot mugs of tea in their numbed hands, another uterine pang grabbed Anna causing her to wince and Pani Kowalski gave her a knowing smile and a gentle tap on the forehead.

Pan Kowalski stood near the bare wooden table and eyed his guests with interest. He was a short stocky man with broad shoulders and a pot belly. The lower part of his face was completely ensheathed in an unkempt beard surmounted by two piercing black eyes and rugged cheeks. His only concession to indicate his status in life was a ragged blue cap with a semblance of faded gold braid around its peak. The black eyes took on an air of cunning as he surveyed his unexpected guests. He spoke quickly and briefly to his wife, picked up the lantern, turned and again toed the dog into the corner and, by gesticulating with his hand, indicated to Isaac that he wished him to enter the other room in the dwelling. Isaac followed Kowalski into an icy-cold bedroom which contained a small table and a low divan bed. Kowalski closed the door, placed his lantern on a rickety table, turned to face Isaac and, by opening his left hand and striking the palm with his right forefinger, indicated that he wished to come to a financial arrangement. Pointing at Isaac with his left forefinger and holding his right hand above his shoulder with fingers outspread he conveyed that the daily cost for shelter and feeding of Isaac and Anna would be five roubles each. Pan Kowalski then cupped his hands together and carried them downward over his protuberant abdomen and held up both his hands with four fingers outstretched. The cost for Anna's confinement would be a further eight roubles a day.

Isaac felt bewildered and vulnerable but he was in no position to argue with the unsavoury Pole. He looked around the dingy bedroom with its coarse, dirty bed sheets and grubby table and surmised that this was the best arrangement he could make for his beloved Anna. A curt nod of his head indicated his agreement whereupon Kowalski extended his left hand with palm upwards and with his right hand made dipping motions towards the extended palm. Isaac realised the Pole wanted payment in advance, an exorbitant demand for eighteen roubles a day. His store of roubles were secreted in the lining of his great coat and, as he moved his hand to undo the buttons under the watchful eye of the station master and his fingers started fumbling with the lining of the coat, Kowalski turned on his heel and walked out of the room. Isaac withdrew his money pouch and placed eighteen roubles on the table near the lantern. Within a minute Kowalski returned carrying an earthenware jug and two mugs which had been used for tea in the other room. His eyes widened briefly at the sight of the remaining roubles which Isaac was hastily scooping into his leather pouch.

He poured vodka into the tin utensils, a large measure for himself and a smaller one for Isaac and, with a curt grunt, downed the spirit in one gulp and immediately refilled his mug. Isaac took a tentative sip of his vodka and spluttered and coughed, choking as he felt the red hot liquid run down his gullet into his stomach. Kowalski kept drinking rapidly and refilling his own tea mug with mechanical regularity, whilst Isaac was only able to take a small sip which produced burning in his chest. He replaced the cup on the wooden table and Kowalski did likewise, secreting the half empty jug in his overcoat pocket. Both men returned to the living room and joined the women. Borscht broth and black bread were dispensed by Pani Kowalski in wooden bowls and consumed whilst they sat huddled around the stove in the centre of the living room.

After eating Kowalski made puffing gestures indicating and inviting Isaac to smoke with him. Pipes were produced, bowls filled, and the two men puffed contentedly, herded as close to the fire as possible. A little later the Pole produced a tin of dark tobacco and handed it to Isaac but with two fingers extended asking for payment. Isaac accepted the tobacco and had to turn his back on the others whilst he delved in his coat lining to recover two roubles and pay the station master.

Anna's contractions had abated considerably but she felt tired and nauseated by the smoke in the living room. Pani Kowalski sensed her discomfiture and, after a few brief words with her tipsy, belching husband, they both rose and left the room via the back door taking blankets and a lantern with them.

Mme Kowalski returned in twenty minutes inclining her head sideways indicating that the Grünbergs should follow her. Isaac and Anna, wrapped in blankets, walked out into the driving snow lead by Pani Kowalski carrying a lantern. Within twenty yards they came to a wooden outhouse and on entering Isaac perceived that he was in a cattle shed, the odour of the animals' urine and excreta pervading all else. The left side of the outhouse contained straw and fodder for the animals and on the straw in the corner the Kowalskis had made a bed with the blankets. There was a low wooden partition in the middle of the outhouse and on the other side Isaac heard the unmistakable sound of cattle rustling and chewing. In the middle of the storage section there was a wood-burning stove and in the other corner a supply of dry wood. Pani Kowalski left a bell near the makeshift bed and then withdrew to her quarters for the night.

Isaac felt cheated that he had not been offered a bedroom in the house for his ten roubles but the little outhouse was warmer than the interior of Kowalski's dwelling, the stove producing a warm glow and an adequate source of heat for the size of the stable, augmented by the body heat of the cattle on the other side of the wooden partition. Anna was exhausted. There were no further abdominal cramps and, fully clothed, the Grünbergs lay huddled together wrapped in blankets on a litter of straw and slept deeply and soundly for the rest of the night.

In the morning they were given tea and black bread with goats' cheese. Kowalski appeared and claimed a rouble for fuel to replenish the stock of wood from a stockpile at the side of the house. The Grünbergs remained in their small cell and kept themselves warm in the blankets. The three cows on the other side of the partition were docile companions, only showing some interest in life when Kowalski came to feed them around midday. In the evening Pani Kowalski brought the inevitable borsch stew followed by her husband who staggered drunkenly into the cow-shed claiming his nineteen roubles in advance for the next day. No trains passed through Bialowieza that day and Kowalski indicated that possibly the heavy snowfall had blocked the railway lines in the vicinity of the halt. Isaac felt depressed and gloomy at the thought of a further delay in this remote and dismal location. During the second night Anna shook Isaac's shoulder and, in the dark, directed his hand to her abdomen where he felt a sudden tensing of the muscles which coincided with a gasp of pain from her lips and they both knew that labour was commencing. After two hours he rang the bell and a disgruntled Pani Kowalski eventually came across to the outhouse. She briefly examined Anna's abdomen, 'tut tutted' and departed. The labour pains continued all night and throughout the next day. Pani Kowalski became more attentive as the day wore on and by tea time she had placed a bowl of hot water on the stove and had inserted some grubby white sheets under Anna's body. The pains were now severe and frequent and poor Anna kept gasping, shouting and crying in agony. No sooner had one severe contraction receded than another started and Isaac crouched beside his wife holding her hand and murmuring words of comfort whilst Mme Kowalski busied herself with preparation for the birth of his child.

By the evening Isaac could no longer cope with situation and his wife's torment and when Pani Kowalski indicated with a shrug of her left shoulder and a nod of her head that he should withdraw for a while he was glad to accept the suggestion. Giving Anna's hand a quick squeeze of affection and encouragement he left the cattle shed closing the door behind him. He thought at first to go across to Kowalski's house but the growling dog and inhospitable greedy nature of the station master changed his mind. He sought the leeward side of the outhouse and, after many futile attempts, managed to light his pipe. Half a minute later his pipe bowl was cold and empty and Isaac leaning, against the wooden wall of the cattle shed, fell into a light sleep.

Isaac returned to consciousness with a start. His head had fallen on to his chest and the ultimate sensation that he was slipping forwards woke him abruptly. He jerked his head backwards, felt a sharp pain in the back of his neck and attempted to open his eyes, but the eyelashes were firmly encrusted and frozen together. His whole body felt stiff and rigid and he had no sensation whatsoever in his lower limbs. His hands were thrust deep into the overcoat pockets, the right still clutching the cold bowl of his pipe. Isaac worked his fingers free from the pipe and lifted his hand to gently massage his frozen eyelids.

He then became fully aware of a strange noise, a bleat or a squeal, very similar to the cry of a new-born lamb. His ears became attuned to the howling wind and clatter of roof slates and then he heard the squeal again from within the hut. This time, unmistakably, it was a baby's cry. The realisation that Anna had given birth struck him forcibly and he lurched blindly forwards crying, "Anna, Anna," his voice carried away in the swirling snow storm. He struggled painfully through the deep snow around the side of the hut, feeling his way by touching the walls of the shed, and still shouting "Anna, Anna," with every strenuous step. At last his right eye opened and he was able to grasp the door latch and enter into the dimly lit cow-shed.

Pani Kowalski stood near the stove with a bundle of linen in her arms and tears streaming down her face. Isaac staggered to the bedside where Anna, with her eyes closed, lay gasping for breath. He knelt by the litter and took her hand in his own. Her nether regions were covered with blood, liquor and afterbirth and he felt nauseated by the unaccustomed sickly odour of human blood and placental tissues. He bent forwards and gently kissed Anna on her forehead which was cool and damp with fine perspiration running in droplets down her face. Anna briefly opened her eyes and gasped through cracked lips, "Isaac, we have a son."

She then closed her eyes and her head fell backwards on to the pillow. Isaac remained kneeling and praying, "Thank God for Anna, thank God for my son, thank God for my Anna and my son."

A further squeal from within the bundle of sheets in Pani Kowalski's arms brought Isaac to his feet. He turned and walked stiffly to the stove in the centre of the hut. Pani Kowalski held the bundle towards him and he took it gingerly in both arms, clutching the small packet to his snow covered coat. The Polish midwife gave him a brief smile, hurried across to the litter and busied herself cleaning up Anna and disposing of the afterbirth. Isaac gently uncovered his new-born son's face. The infant's face was red and wrinkled with a pale brown crust on his forehead, eyes tightly shut and a small hand wandering aimlessly around half-closed lips. He gently bent forward and kissed the baby on his forehead producing no evident reaction.

After ten minutes Mme Kowalski straightened herself and washed her hands in the blood-stained, lukewarm water in the bucket. She then directed her attention to the new-born infant lying in Isaac's lap. She exposed his abdomen where, to Isaac's horror, the umbilical cord still stretched like a blue-black entrail from his navel. Pani Kowalski securely tied the cord and the redundant portion was cut off with rusty scissors and discarded into a bowl which held the placenta. She then firmly wrapped the baby in a sheet and blanket and took him to the litter next to his exhausted mother. Pani Kowalski turned to face Isaac, gave him a brief smile, and strode out of the shed back to her own house taking the bucket containing the afterbirth with her.

Isaac sat on a wooden bench huddled in his overcoat and extending his hands to the wan warmth emanating from the stove. Gradually the icy chill in his lower body and back thawed and he felt pleased and proud as he persistently glanced at Anna asleep with their new baby. He reflected that the infant's name had not been predestined. Anna had insisted that it should be David if it were a boy. He wished for no other name for their son. Isaac closed his eyes and silently prayed, thanking God for his good fortune in giving him Anna and for allowing them to have a healthy son and heir. Later he reflected on their present difficulties and of the long journey ahead. Anna slept for one hour and was awakened by the crying infant. She instinctively picked up the baby, baring her right breast to feed her hungry son, a contented smile on her tear-stained face and Isaac gazed in wonderment at this inbred response of a mother to her hungry new-born.

The blissful situation was rudely interrupted by the sudden entry of an inebriated and truculent Kowalski who took no notice of the child but glowered and beckoned to Isaac. A wave of his hand at the new arrival and four extended fingers indicated the fee for keeping David and another wave of the hand over the bed in general was the fee for Pani Kowalski's midwifery – another twelve roubles. The Pole's extended palms indicated that he demanded immediate payment of sixteen roubles for the confinement. Isaac had no option but to comply and again had the indignity of searching in the lining of his coat to extract the roubles. Kowalski's hound was free outside the shed door, growling, and scratching on the door panels, waiting to enter. Once he had secured payment Kowalski departed and an hour later his wife appeared with hot soup, black bread and hot tea and the Grünbergs finally settled down for their first night together as proud parents. Isaac and Anna, both exhausted, slept soundly, Anna's rest interrupted at two-hour intervals by urgent feeding demands from the new-born baby.

During the night the wind abated and next morning the sky was clear and sunny. The cow-shed was buried almost to its eaves in snow drifts. Mid-morning Isaac left the hut and struggled through the deep drifts to Kowalski's house. He was unable to see the railway line or the station hut in the white vastness that surrounded him. He knocked at the door of the house clutching the family Bible in the left pocket of his overcoat. The Alsatian was first to arrive with a snarl on the other side of the closed door and a hefty kick and guttural shout from Kowalski sent the dog spinning across the room. The door opened and the scowling Pole faced Isaac, who, using sign language, indicated that he wished to have pen and ink. Kowalski's scowl faded and a cunning look reappeared in his penetrating black eyes. Dispensing with formalities he held up four fingers – four roubles for the use of pen and ink. Isaac gave him the money. He entered the bedroom and sitting on an uneven bench at the table opened the Bible. Inside the cover were records of his Grünberg ancestors and he now added the name and place of birth of his own son, David:

> David Isaac Grünberg. Born 22nd November 1918, Bialowieza, Poland.
> Father, Isaac Grünberg. Mother, Anna (née Geldberg.)

Pan Kowalski produced a bottle of vodka and two mugs and poured a liberal portion into each. Pointing westwards and making puffing noises he attempted to ascertain Isaac's future plans. Isaac looked around the living room and his eyes settled on a roughly drawn map, with crenated brown edges, nailed to the wall in the darker corner of the room which showed, in red, the railway communications in southern Poland. Russia was on the right hand side and Germany on the left. The stop at Bialowieza, incongruously, was marked in bold red capitals while other major rail terminals were entered in ordinary script. Isaac smiled inwardly at the thought that Kowalski's vanity attributed such importance to his minor station in the Polish railway system. Kowalski stood at his side and belched loudly, emitting an odour of stale tobacco and vodka. Isaac pointed to Bialowieza and then ran his finger across the map to Krakow, Worclaw and along the splintered brown edge to Dresden in Germany.

Kowalski threw his arms in the air and shouted, *"Germania, Germania."*

He turned abruptly on his heel and walked to the table drawer rummaging among piles of string and old newspaper until, triumphantly, he produced a wad of greenish brown notes. He laid them on the table and invited Isaac to examine them, holding the lantern aloft and shouting, *"Germania, Germania."* There were twenty-one thousand Deutschmark notes on the table. Kowalski's dark eyes filled with cunning and greed as he fondled the notes and inspected each one in the light repeating, *"boom-boom, Germania boom-boom, Germania"*, indicating that the money had been acquired during the German occupation of Bialowieza in 1916 and 1917.

A request for roubles inevitably followed; five hundred roubles for all the German money, for all the twenty-one thousand Deutschmarks. Isaac was bewildered by the noughts on the German notes and, ignorant of the true value of the mark, agreed to the transaction after a few moments thought and hesitation. He retrieved the leather money bag from inside his overcoat and poured the contents on the table counting five hundred coins and handing them to a triumphant Kowalski and replaced the leather pouch, now containing twenty-one thousand marks and fifty roubles, in his inside pocket. Kowalski saw the transaction as an excuse for a further refill of vodka which he disposed of hungrily in three large gulps whilst Isaac's vodka remained untouched on the table. Isaac turned towards the door murmuring goodnight in Hebrew and, with a courteous nod of his head to Pani Kowalski, left the house and crossed the path to his own quarters.

Anna was sitting up in the corner of the shed breastfeeding her ravenous infant. She asked no questions about his absence of over an hour and was content to have her baby and husband with her once more. With pride Isaac showed her the entry in the family Bible and she smiled with pleasure. The day wore on without incident but no trains arrived in Bialowieza that day or on the following day.

Warmer weather produced a gradual thaw converting the white blanket of snow into a morass of slush and mud. On the fifth day of their arrival in Bialowieza a piercing whistle heralded the approach of a train. Kowalski ran around shouting and cursing and made his way to the station platform to await the train's arrival. Isaac collected their meagre belongings and his canvas bag, ensured that David was comfortably cocooned in his own blankets, and trudged across to the platform, Anna following and cradling her son in her arms. Pan Kowalski was in animated conversation with the guard and eventually a price of twenty-five roubles was agreed to take the Grünbergs to Krakow. After a desultory handshake with the unsavoury station master Isaac and Anna boarded the train. Pani Kowalski was nowhere to be seen.

The Grünbergs were accommodated in a wagon carrying timber and straw. After five hours they arrived in Krakow in good spirits and negotiated the next trip to Worclaw in a relatively comfortable passenger train with no other travellers in their compartment. There was a three-hour delay in Worclaw and, late at night, they boarded a train bound for Dresden. The journey took ten hours and they crossed the border into Germany at Görlitz on the morning of 28th November 1918. In Görlitz there was a delay for a perfunctory search by German border guards but no questions were asked.

In Dresden Isaac went to purchase his fare to Munich. He presented a thousand Deutschmark note in payment, but the station *Direktor* laughed shouting to his colleagues, *"Soldat Deutschmark."* This produced a chorus of laughter and ribald remarks and the *Direktor*, taking the banknote from a bemused Isaac, tore it into shreds and threw the paper money into a blazing fire. Isaac realised that his wad of notes, Kowalski's paper money, was worthless. He cursed under his breath and produced his remaining roubles. The *Direktor* again laughed and pushed the money back across the counter.

Isaac was mystified and felt helpless when he realised that he had been duped by Kowalski and that his roubles were not negotiable in Germany. He returned to Anna almost in tears. She was pensive for a few moments, then rummaged in the canvas bag and produced the *Magen* David and chain and, without a word, handed it to Isaac. Her eyes bade him return to the *Direktor*'s office and barter the family heirloom in return for their rail fare to Munich.

Despite the recent armistice and the ravages and losses of the Great War, train travel in Germany was both efficient and punctual. A twenty-two hour journey took them from Dresden through Chemnitz, Zwickau, Marktredwitz, Nuremberg and, on the morning of 1st December, they reached Munich. Isaac left Anna and the baby in a comfortable, warm station waiting room and walked across the square to the main post office. There he wrote his name on the edge of a newspaper and, using sign language, learnt that there were evidently no Grünbergs in Munich but one of the postmen responsible for deliveries to Aalbrücke, a village forty miles to the north, knew of a Grünberg who kept the ironmonger's and *Postamt*. On the following day, the 2nd December 1918, the Grünbergs travelled in the rear of a green post office delivery van, sitting amongst the canvas sacks and parcels and arrived in Aalbrücke on a dark, dank and dismal December evening at the end of a long and arduous pilgrimage.

Chapter Two
Saint Teresa *Frauhaus Klinik*, Munich, 14th December, 1918

Gerhardt Schmidt emerged from the main entrance of St Teresa's *Frauhaus Klinik* from the comparative warmth of the vestibule into the raw, cold night. Winter had come early to Bavaria. The side-walks and side-streets were covered with a layer of fine snow and the night air was impregnated by alternate flurries of sleet and snow. The concrete steps leading from the entrance to the street were dimly lit and coated with a fine veneer of ice. Gerhardt took great care in descending to the street, holding on to the hand rail and concentrating on each step, as he clumsily negotiated his way to the snow-covered pavement. At street level he paused and took a deep breath, glad to be away from the antiseptic smells of the *Klinik*, the arrogance and hostility of the Matron, Frau Bernard, and the screams and intermittent sobbing of his young wife Helga.

At four o'clock that morning Helga had complained of abdominal cramps and, though both were inexperienced in these matters, it seemed that Helga's pregnancy was coming to term. By six o'clock Gerhardt realised that his wife might be in labour and by this time she was shouting and screaming. Gerhardt dressed her in a fur coat, thick stockings and fur-lined boots and, wrapping her in a blanket, walked her to the *Klinik* in Graubenstrasse a matter of a mile and a half away from his flat. Helga did not accept the walk with equanimity. She complained, and swore, as the pains came and went. Gerhardt was very pleased to get her into the *Klinik* and eventually into a private room which would cost him one thousand marks a day. He could ill-afford the payment but there was no other alternative except that Helga could have had the baby at home under the care of a midwife.

Matron Bernard at the *Klinik* was at first patronising, then short-tempered, and finally, by mid-afternoon, openly arrogant and rude. The Matron, in her early sixties, was tall, thin-faced and wore pince-nez glasses. Her white collars were high and starch-stiff, and she wore a small crenated white beret on top of her head giving her an austere authoritative look becoming to a lady in her high position. Matron Bernard's high-pitched, piercing voice made it quite clear to all and sundry who was in command at St Teresa's *Klinik*. Helga had a long day in and out of pain. She was not the best of patients and tended to scream and thrash about when the slightest abdominal colic made her uncomfortable. Matron Bernard would have none of this. By teatime she had administered large doses of opiate to the patient and Gerhardt, sitting at her bedside, observed Helga slip into a befuddled state and later into a deeper comatose sleep. He stayed at Helga's bedside for a further hour but, apart from an occasional whimper, she did not stir.

At six o'clock Matron Bernard appeared and commanded Gerhardt to leave and go home as she did not expect any developments that night. The Matron added that should anything happen during the night the *Klinik* would send a courier to fetch Gerhardt from his apartment. This, she hastened to add, was part of the *Klinik*'s service and was supplied at extra cost to the patient. Gerhardt acceded to the Matron's superior advice and, giving Helga's right hand a squeeze which evoked no response, he left the private room and made his way out of the *Klinik* with the Matron's parting words ringing in his ears – *"Guten nacht Herr Schmidt, schlafen sie gut."*

On the street Gerhardt suddenly felt the chill. It had been reasonably warm in the *Klinik* but outside the temperature was sub-zero. He pulled his leather cap down over his face, tucked the collar of his heavy overcoat under his chin, and plunged his gloved hands deep into its pockets. He turned towards his apartment and, having walked a few yards, stopped and assessed the situation. Helga would be asleep for a few hours and according to the Matron the baby would not be born until the next day. He was tired, cold and hungry and longed for the companionship of his habitual friends. There was only one place in Munich that could offer him sanctuary at this particular time. So he turned on his heels, retraced his steps and, walking past the *Klinik,* made his way to the end of Graubenstrasse on to the main Kaiser Allee which led him to Marienplatz in the centre of Munich.

Gerhardt Schmidt was thirty-one years of age, born in 1887 on a large farm on the banks of the River Aal, about forty-four kilometres north-east of Munich. He was the eldest son in the family and had a younger brother, Joachim. As a baby Gerhardt was premature and puny and had a congenital squint and a deformed right foot. He was always sickly and the local doctors treated him for tuberculosis for two years between the ages of seven and nine. He consequently missed schooling for many months at a time and his parents provided him with private tuition at the farmhouse.

Gerhardt had a quick and perceptive brain and revelled in manipulating figures and mathematics. When it became evident to the parents that he could not physically become a farmer he was encouraged to develop his mathematical abilities. Having missed schooling for most of his young life, at the age of seventeen, he secured employment on a part time basis at the local school teaching mathematics to six and seven year olds. After four years of living at home and teaching at Aalbrücke Primary School he was offered a banking post in Ismaning, a small town about twenty-five kilometres north-east of Aalbrücke. His superiors at the bank found him fastidious, correct and polite, with no sense of humour. He had no vices or extravagances that might be expected of a young man in his prime. He remained in the bank at Ismaning until the early part of 1913 when, at the age of twenty-six, his *Direktor*, through personal contacts, found him a position as junior clerical officer in the *Rathaus* in Munich.

Throughout these years in Aalbrücke and Ismaning Gerhardt had been living at home with his parents. His young brother Joachim, broad shouldered and strong as an ox, had taken over the task of running the farm. Gerhardt was envious of Joachim, jealous of his strength and ability to perform physical tasks and of his outgoing and generous personality. Joachim, on the other hand, had no scholastic attributes having left school at the age of fourteen and was proud of his brother's achievements in schooling and banking and now on his appointment in Munich. Gerhardt's underlying frustration was the fact that his home, Grossmunde farm, which, as an elder brother was rightly his, had ended up in Joachim's hands. In 1911 both Gerhardt's parents died of influenza and the will incontestably confirmed Joachim Schmidt as the rightful owner of Grossmunde farm.

Gerhardt arrived in Munich in early October 1913. For the first eighteen months he lived in digs with a Frau Denzler on the northern outskirts of the city and about four kilometres from the *Rathaus*. At all times he dressed in a fashion becoming an official of the Council of Munich. He prided himself on his sartorial appearance, dressed in a dark suit and waistcoat, festooned with his father's gold watch and chain and a cut-back starched collar and white shirt. The whole ensemble was completed with a black bowler hat and a black ebony cane. This immaculate appearance was, however, marred by the physical attributes of the man himself. Gerhardt was about five feet six inches in height, of slim build, with a thin wizened face, a sharp protruding nose, and his dark eyes were permanently shielded by metal-rimmed glasses. The left eye deviated internally and, to hide this feature, the left lens of his glasses was lightly frosted. A black moustache guarded the upper margins of his small measly mouth which, in turn, partially covered an irregular array of yellowish-black teeth.

His attempts to hide the worst features of his facial physiognomy were partially successful but nothing could conceal nature's ravages to his right leg which was under-developed. Gerhardt had to wear a platform boot on his right foot and, in order to walk, he swung the leg from his hip and dipped the left side of his pelvis. Years of walking with this loping type of gait had produced a permanent curvature of the lower spine which, even when standing erect, had the effect of tilting Gerhardt sideways, like the leaning tower of Pisa. With these deformities it is not surprising that Gerhardt rarely smiled.

Gerhardt enjoyed his daily journey to and from work on the No. 47 tram car and made a point of offering a seat to ladies and elderly folk. He preferred to stand as, on sitting down, his right trouser leg rose to reveal a boot-clad club foot. For this reason he was unable to wear spats. At work Gerhardt was punctual, industrious and courteous to his superiors. He started as a general office boy but the senior clerk in the department soon realised his potential and made him a junior clerk in the first month. His meticulous ability to keep the books soon came to the notice of the *Direktor* and Gerhardt was moved to the census department as deputy to the senior clerk, who was in fact five years younger than himself. There he remained for a whole year.

During the early months of 1914 war clouds were gathering over Europe and talk of a conflict between Germany and France was rife. In late July Kaiser Wilhelm found an excuse to take Germany to war against Russia and France with the murder of the Austro-Hungarian Prince Ferdinand in Sarajevo and, when Belgian neutrality was violated, England also declared war on Germany on 4th August, 1914. The *Rathaus* now became a centre of military activity and recruitment for the armed forces. The corridors and offices buzzed with excitement and high-ranking officers were forever present in the building in discussion with the *Bürgermeister* and, in particular, the census department seeking suitable candidates for enlistment into the armed forces.

Gerhardt became indispensable in these proceedings due to his intimate knowledge of eligible males available in Munich and even, on a few occasions, indicating to the officers where the *schwerpunkt* of a recruiting drive might be most effective. The military personnel, his own department and the *Bürgermeister* came to lean heavily on Gerhardt.

Gerhardt was not slow to offer his own services to the armed forces but his physical disabilities were so evident that his enlistment was never seriously considered. Not so with his colleagues of military age in the *Rathaus*. They, in fits of bravado, enlisted like lemmings which resulted in Gerhardt's rapid promotion. By January 1915 Gerhardt Schmidt had become *Direktor* of the census department, one of the three official *Direktors* to the *Bürgermeister*. In his new position he could afford his own quarters, and moved to No. 14 Grünewald Strasse in March 1915. The first-floor, two-bedroomed apartment in a stone built house was only a mile distant from the *Rathaus*. The lower floor was occupied by the Hellers, an old retired couple who owned the property. This was the apartment in which Gerhardt sustained a bachelor existence for three years and the apartment where he took his seventeen year old bride Helga, in May 1918.

Cold, hungry and dispirited, Gerhardt clomped purposefully down Graübenstrasse. Germany had lost the war and, since this disaster, food, clothing and fuel were in short supply and the value of the Deutschmark was plummeting. His nose felt pinched and icy cold and his glasses were covered with a veneer of frozen mist. He used the stick in his gloved right hand to help his gammy leg over the uneven snow-covered pavement of the dimly lit street, with only one gas lamp in working order. He turned into the main Kaiser Allee where the gas lamps were functioning at intervals of one hundred metres and the minimal increase in illumination lifted his spirits to some extent. His pace quickened slightly, within the limitations of his disability, as he anticipated with pleasure the warmth and comfort of his *Bierkeller* in Marienplatz and the prospects of a solid meal of broth, bread, bratwurst and sauerkraut, washed down with a stein of beer and, tonight, liberally laced with a few shots of schnapps.

There were very few Munich citizens abroad that night or any other night for that matter. Losing the war had thrown the whole of Germany into a state of apathy and dejection and most of the local inhabitants were huddled around their meagre fires bemoaning their country's defeat. The Hofbrauhaus, once a centre for festivities, communication and comradeship between the military and civilian population during the war, was often almost deserted. Poor old Willi Klinsman, the bachelor proprietor of the *Keller*, complained incessantly of the lack of trade, comestibles and of the severe weather.

Gerhardt mused on these thoughts as he laboriously shuffled along the last five hundred metres of his journey to the *Keller*. He thought about his achievements at the *Rathaus* since his arrival in 1913. Returning warriors, his superiors in 1913, were now reclaiming their posts and the *Rathaus* was in a state of upheaval and intrigue, as they battled and jostled with the *Bürgermeister* for a return to their previous seniority and rank over and above those who had not enlisted. The *Bürgermeister*, Herr *Direktor* Müller, under pressure, conceded here and conciliated there but in one decision he was adamant. The population census department would remain under the control of *Direktor* Gerhardt Schmidt. Gerhardt permitted himself a fleeting smile as he thought that he was in sole command of his beloved census department and justifiably so. Had he not spent most of his working hours collecting and collating data from the whole of Munich and its environs over the past four years? He whispered a stifled, "*Ja*", under his breath and gave an imperceptible nod of his head.

In 1913 the records of the census department were grossly inaccurate and incomplete and only included household owners in greater Munich itself. Gerhardt realised that many of the larger houses were sub-let and there were no records of tenants who, for various reasons, wished to remain anonymous and pay their dues to the landlords and not in state taxes. Similarly the landlords did not wish to reveal this source of extra income. Gerhardt's staff in 1914 were three in number, a very junior clerk and typist, a spinster, Frau Striker, who acted as librarian and archivist and had been employed at the *Rathaus* for twenty years and the large, rotund, but highly efficient Frau Meninger, a secretary and deputy *Direktor*. With the *Bürgermeister*'s blessing and Gerhardt's insistence that it would increase revenue from taxes, a full house-to-house census of greater Munich was proposed and also a pastoral census of surrounding towns, hamlets and farms within a forty mile radius of the city. This formidable task was undertaken by Gerhardt and Frau Meninger and took eighteen months to complete. Gerhardt insisted that the census should also take into account the ethnic origins of the population.

The records were duplicated and Gerhardt kept his own files and census returns for the non-Germanic population. On reviewing the returns in 1916, he was considerably surprised at the number of aliens domiciled in the Munich area, notably Italians, Turks, Austrians and Jews. The slaughter of German infantry on the Western Front during 1914 led to recruitment drives at regular intervals during the ensuing four years and these campaigns were organised through the *Bürgermeister* at the *Rathaus*. Herr Müller presided at meetings with the visiting military officers but soon co-opted Gerhardt, and sometimes Frau Meninger, on to the committee as their knowledge of population distribution became paramount in the recruitment campaign.

Gerhardt was honoured to be included on such an important task and very rapidly became the organiser of each new campaign. He soon developed a poor opinion of most of the military recruiters. They were invariably Prussian, often titled, arrogant and bedecked with splendiferous uniforms, on the assumption that their haughty and military presence would entice men to flock to the colours and enlist for service in the Kaiser's armed forces. Moreover these resplendent puppets expected to be fêted and entertained lavishly. Herr Müller felt it his duty to act as host to the visitors and, after committee, Gerhardt was duly dispatched back to his census department to ruminate and delve further into his voluminous archives.

One of the Prussian recruiting officers who visited Munich in October 1917 was different from the rest. Captain Count Erich von Bulow realised that the brain behind the recruitment drive was in fact Gerhardt Schmidt. After the first committee he made a point of going downstairs to the census department, formally thanking the *Direktor*, and asking if he could join Gerhardt for a drink.

At six o'clock the incongruous pair made their way to the Hofbrauhaus, Gerhardt hobbling alongside the erect trim figure of the Count, dressed in a dark green uniform with a red *kepi*. Gerhardt never forgot the grand entry they made into the packed *Keller* and the introduction to Willi, who stood rooted to the spot, eyes bulging, fawning, and ostentatiously wiping his hands on his blue striped apron and the back of his hand on his drooping moustache. Count von Bulow cut a dashing figure. He was short, some five feet five inches tall, slim, and had a trim military moustache and a twinkling blue right eye. The socket of his left eye, reputedly gouged out by a piece of shrapnel at Verdun, was protected by a black eye-patch. That night in the Hofbrauhaus a mammoth drinking session took place. Backs were slapped, songs were sung, steins of beer were downed and Willi dispensed ample supplies of schnapps and cognac, as alternative chasers. After the Count had departed for Nuremberg, Gerhardt's standing and importance in the eyes of the patrons of the Hofbrauhaus was elevated and he never let Willi and the clientele forget the best night of the war and his part in bringing his friend, Captain Count von Bulow, to the *Keller*.

Short of breath, Gerhardt arrived at the Hofbrauhaus, where a dim light was visible through the frosted window. He shuffled slowly down three steps and then through a revolving door to the comparative warmth of the main lounge and hobbled across to his seat in an alcove to the left of the bar, near the newspaper rack. Unbuttoning his coat he took off his cap and gloves, wiped his misted glasses on a handkerchief and sat down, rubbing his hands vigorously to restore circulation. As usual these days there were very few patrons in the bar, no papers in the reading rack, and the gas pressure in the wall light was low, failing to illuminate the alcove completely.

"*Guten abend* Herr *Direktor* Schmidt. *Wie geht es mit* Helga?"

Willi Klinsman stood a few paces in front of Gerhardt, his corpulent frame blocking Gerhardt's view of the bar. Gerhardt, preoccupied with rubbing his hands together, looked up:

"*Nicht gut* Herr Klinsman," and explained that Helga was in labour.

Willi assumed a conciliatory attitude. After all was he not Helga's adopted uncle and had he not brought her to the Hofbrauhaus as a serving girl. His red, podgy cheeks screwed up in a grimace of sympathy and his moustache drooped even further down the side of his face, his eyes becoming mere slits as he appeared to be fighting back his tears, at the same time impulsively wringing his hands in the folds of his blue and white striped apron. Gerhardt explained that according to the matron the event was scheduled for tomorrow. Willi offered the hospitality of the inn to Gerhardt and brought a large glass of schnapps and a stein of foaming beer to his table. A portion of black bread and salami followed and a plate of bratwurst and sauerkraut. This was indeed superb hospitality as the food that Willi provided was in short supply in post-war Germany.

That evening there were only four other customers in the bar sitting separately at the tables and skulking over their beers, bread and cheese. There was no conversation whatsoever and, as Willi's services were not in demand, he deserted his usual position behind the bar, pulled up a chair, placed a bottle of schnapps on the table, and, levering his capacious rear into a seat, sat opposite Gerhardt who was slowly eating his meal.

"Herr Schmidt, how long is it since you married Helga? I believe it was in May? The baby is coming early and will be small. Helga is a strong girl of good country stock. I should know. After all I am her uncle. God willing she will have an easy childbirth. *Nicht wahr?*"

Gerhardt merely nodded. Willi refilled the glasses with schnapps, and both men swallowed the fiery fluid in one gulp.

Willi continued, "Do you remember Helga arriving here? You are a fortunate man to have married such a pretty and healthy young woman, Herr Schmidt. She will provide many more babies for you."

He paused to refill the glasses again. Gerhardt felt an inner warmth permeating through his body as the alcohol took effect. He was conscious that Willi was droning on about last Christmas when Helga had arrived in Munich but he let his mind wander and the memories of Helga's appearance in the Hofbrauhaus came flooding back.

Gerhardt moved from his digs in the north of Munich to his apartment in Grünewald Strasse in the Spring of 1915. The apartment was situated only two kilometres from the *Rathaus* and he walked to and from work each day. His punctiliousness did not allow him to leave the *Rathaus* before six o'clock. A brisk walk of around four hundred metres to Marienplatz on his way home brought Gerhardt to the Hofbrauhaus and it became his invariable practice on six days of the week to call for a drink and a meal and peruse the daily papers and discuss progress of the war with Willi and his customers. Willi set his pocket watch at the time that Gerhardt arrived each evening – eleven or twelve minutes past six o'clock. Willi's greeting, *"Guten abend,* Herr *Direktor* Schmidt" always evoked the same response from Gerhardt, *"Danke gut,* Herr Klinsman," complimented by a touch of the ebony cane on the brim of his bowler hat. Gerhardt then sat in his usual seat in the dark alcove near the left end of the bar, illuminated by a wan gas lamp, and within easy reach of a daily news sheet.

Gerhardt's culinary needs were extremely unpretentious; black bread, broth, bratwurst with sauerkraut, and occasionally a schnitzel or a beef steak, all washed down with two steins of foaming ale and a schnapps to round off the repast. At 7.30 p.m. Gerhardt took his leave and returned to his bachelor apartment in Grünewald Strasse. He went to bed at 9 p.m. and then woke again at 6 a.m. and, after a light breakfast of bread, cheese and coffee, took the short walk to the *Rathaus*, arriving at precisely 7 a.m.

In the evenings at the Hofbrauhaus discussions revolved around the daily war news and every campaign, every battle or skirmish, was analysed in detail. Willi and his clientele, a mixture of retired artisans, business men and army personnel on leave, listened attentively to Gerhardt's opinions. After all, was he not in a position of trust and power, meeting daily with important army officers in the *Rathaus*. He should know what is going on at the front.

Herr Brander, a retired banker, was heard to comment one night, "It is a pity that Herr Schmidt has been declared unfit to serve the Kaiser. If he could get to the front he would teach our generals a thing or two."

The last fifteen minutes of these bar room discussions was inevitably an appraisal of the previous days horrendous casualties, with commiseration for any local families who had lost sons or fathers in battle. The gloom produced by these statistics was dispelled by news of German advances on the Western and Eastern fronts. A German advance or the capture of a town, village or field was an indication for an extra schnapps "for the road." During the discussions Gerhardt was able to inform his eager listeners of the success of recruitment drives arranged and organised by himself. He often commented that, in order to maintain a fit and active Army, conscription would have to be introduced in Germany. His drinking companions disagreed, pointing out that there were enough young men more than willing to enlist and become cannon fodder for Kaiser Wilhelm's armies. Gerhardt insisted that conscription was the only way to force enlistment from ethnic races living in Germany but exhibiting a strong reluctance to volunteer for military service. In particular the Italians, Austrians, and Turks were conspicuous in this respect.

Gerhardt's lifestyle was by now stereotyped. In his own estimation he was one of the twenty most important people in Munich. He often recalled the respect and the feeling of importance and power he experienced when he conducted a census in his own home village. The citizens of Aalbrücke were amazed that the unprepossessing, deformed young man who left home in 1913 now returned in a position of great power and travelled with his female secretary in a chauffeur driven car. Gerhardt's uncomplicated bachelor life continued until the Christmas of 1917 when Helga appeared on the scene and became Willi Klinsman's barmaid at the Hofbrauhaus.

During Christmas week 1917 Herr Wilhelm Klinsman had emerged from behind his bar holding the hand of a pretty seventeen year old, buxom blonde, announcing, "Gentleman, I introduce Helga to you. She is my niece from the country and will be my new barmaid. Helga will start work tonight. I will ask her to first look after my best customer, Herr *Direktor* Schmidt from the *Rathaus*."

The customers gave a brief cheer and then started clapping. Helga blushed red as she was taken to Gerhardt's table by the beaming Willi, who gave Gerhardt a brief bow and a click of the heels and left the blushing and shaking Helga at his table.

Gerhardt was furious, and yet, as he peered over the top of his paper and saw the gorgeous, shaking apparition in front of him he took pity on the pretty young girl and even felt a pang of emotion. The faint aroma of lavender and womanly earthiness further stimulated his masculine senses. He behaved formally and asked

Fraulein Helga to get him his usual order. As Helga retired to get the food Gerhardt noted with pleasure the curvature of her buttocks and the full, almost masculine, contour of her exposed calves. His emotions were further aroused when she leant forward to serve his soup and he had a long glimpse of the rounded alabaster globes of her full, turgid breasts. He averted his gaze to Helga's face and was pleased to note her clear blue eyes, set wide apart in a round peasant's face, and a generous smiling mouth, her head surmounted by a crown of golden blonde hair, plaited at the back.

Gerhardt was smitten. He could not keep his eyes off Helga. When he paid his bill he made certain that he left a five pfennig tip under the plate. In the apartment that night he was unable to Helga off his mind and all next day in the *Rathaus* he was impatient for six o'clock to come along. And so it continued through the Christmas period and into the spring of 1918. Gerhardt's consorting with Helga was kept on a formal basis; it was always "Herr *Direktor* Schmidt" on Helga's part and "*Mein gnädige* Fraulein" in reply from Gerhardt. By mid-January Gerhardt realised he was in love with the beautiful young, fully rounded and excitingly aromatic, Helga. As the weeks passed Helga's confidence as a serving wench grew by leaps and bounds and she soon started innocuous flirtations with the customers. Gerhardt's jealousy festered but he kept himself under control and continued to show proper respect for the young country girl.

Christmas 1917 and New Year 1918 was a particularly quiet time on the Western Front. There was some talk of peace and a stop to the carnage that had already cost Germany a million and a half men and the majority of Germans wanted an end to the war with complete victory for themselves. Over Christmas and the New Year many soldiers were home on leave and celebrating groups of young men frequented the Hofbrauhaus. They irritated Gerhardt by making remarks directed at Helga. She gave as good as she got. One tall, fair-haired sergeant, home for a long convalescent leave after an injury to his foot, took particular interest in her and, with Willi's permission, started paying court to the young barmaid. In early March Sergeant Hans Kholer was arrested and taken back to the front to be tried as a deserter. At first Helga appeared to be distraught but, with bovine resilience, she soon bounced back into her former good spirits and, with renewed vigour, continued flirting with customers and with a stream of young soldiers home on leave from the Front.

Helga was by now putting on weight, had a blooming glow, and Gerhardt's perceptive sense of smell detected that the aroma around the woman had changed.

She had a passion for sweets and, once a week, Gerhardt brought her a box of *schokolade*, a rare commodity in war-torn Munich. Helga responded with a bright red blush and a curtsey and "*Vielen dank,* Herr *Direktor* Schmidt.*"* Willi, who had noted Gerhardt's interest in Helga, commented, "The Herr *Direktor* is like a lovesick bull!"

One evening in March he had a word with Gerhardt indicating that Helga was very grateful for his kindness and for the *schokolade* and would be honoured if Herr *Direktor* would take her out for a walk on her night off. Gerhardt readily acquiesced, but in view of his position and standing at the *Rathaus*, it would not be seemly for him to be seen in public with Helga. A supper was arranged for Helga and Gerhardt in Willi's lounge on the first floor of the Hofbrauhaus.

Gerhardt never forgot that evening on Easter Saturday 1918, when he, at the age of thirty, lost his virginity. Suitably fortified with schnapps he entered the lounge to find Helga standing in her best Bavarian costume beside a table laden with cooked meats, bread and cheese and she had already started eating from a box of chocolates. The room was unbearably warm and Gerhardt was invited to take off his jacket and waistcoat and to loosen the collar of his shirt. Similarly Helga undid the top buttons of her costume which revealed the upper halves of her full, rounded breasts. The food was consumed rapidly, laced liberally with sips of fiery schnapps.

Gerhardt felt light-headed and his memory of subsequent events remained unclear. Helga took the initiative. Unbuttoning her tunic and undoing her waistband she stepped out of her costume and advancing towards Gerhardt, topless but still wearing her blue bloomers, she kissed him on the mouth whispering, "*Danke* Herr *Direktor, danke* Herr *Direktor.*"

Gerhardt found his hands fondling her breasts and his lips rapidly closed around her upturned, turgid nipple. Helga kept pushing her pelvis on to Gerhardt's chest and became frenzied, tearing at his shirt and undoing his trouser buttons. Her probing fingers managed to pull down his trousers and braces and then his long johns. Helga made Gerhardt stand on his feet and pushed him backwards on to the couch. Without further ado the blue bloomers were discarded and Helga mounted Gerhardt, guiding his small erect virgin penis into her vagina and cooing, "Oh, Herr *Direktor*, oh, Herr *Direktor*."

Gerhardt's recollection of the event was of a mound of pink flesh above him oscillating upwards and downwards and within twenty seconds of initial penetration a suffocating climax, whilst Helga kept whispering, "*Wunderbar* Herr *Direktor*, *wunderbar*."

When Helga had disengaged herself Gerhardt observed her nakedness with its folds of abdominal fat and turgid breasts which were contained with difficulty by the stiff calico of her Bavarian costume. They both dressed without talking. Gerhardt, somewhat ashamed of his action and yet elated by the experience, descended the stairs and, with a brief nod to Willi, left the inn. Willi stood behind the bar with a twinkle in his knowing blue eyes and thought, 'Well done Herr *Direktor*. You are not the first. I have been there myself and so have many others.'

Gerhardt and Helga continued to meet in Willi's room once or twice a week and sometimes in the evenings, if the bar was quiet, they would slip upstairs for ten minutes or so. The other customers knew what was going on. They were also aware that one or two other favourite clients were allowed upstairs with Helga when the Herr *Direktor* was absent. Willi had the field to himself after closing the Hofbrauhaus late at night.

One evening in early May Willi invited Gerhardt to his office behind the main bar. "Herr *Direktor* Schmidt, Helga is pregnant and she tells me you are the father."

Gerhardt was taken aback and at the same time thrilled that he had fathered a child. Gerhardt's decision was both abrupt and practical. "If this is true, and if Helga will have me, I will marry her."

Willi already knew that Helga would accept, as she was six weeks pregnant and anxious to have a father for her unborn child despite the knowledge that the baby had not been conceived by Gerhardt. It could be himself or the dashing deserter Sergeant Hans Kholer or one a number of young bucks on leave who had, for a small fee, been allowed to use Willi's room to service the rapacious Helga.

A wedding was quickly arranged. Gerhardt and Helga were married in the *Rathaus* in a civil ceremony on the 20th May 1918. Gerhardt's brother Joachim, red-faced in an ill-fitting dark suit with a stiff collar, accompanied by Valtraut, his diminutive, thin, childless wife, were in attendance while 'Uncle' Willi gave the bride away.

For the occasion Willi had managed to get a grey coat and trousers around his corpulent frame but could not find a collar or waistcoat to fit his immense bulk and consequently wore a red cravat and a large handkerchief in his top pocket. The ceremony took only ten minutes. The wedding party returned to the Hofbrauhaus where a small breakfast had been prepared in one of the back rooms. Joachim was distinctly uncomfortable in the setting and his timid wife spoke not a word. Gerhardt was evidently besotted with his new bride.

Willi, in good spirits, proposed a few perfunctory toasts and Gerhardt made a brief speech to welcome Helga into the Schmidt family. Joachim conceded that Helga was a suitable choice as she came from good farming stock. There was no definite evidence to support this statement as none of Helga's family were present and only Willi knew that she was from an orphanage in Partenkirchen, near the Austrian border. The wedding breakfast lasted about an hour. Joachim and Valtraut departed first to catch a bus back to Aalbrücke and, as is traditionally customary, Willi and two co-opted customers walked Gerhardt and Helga to the apartment at No. 14 Grünewald Strasse where they were ushered into the flat by the attendants banging on a large drum and crashing cymbals.

For the first two months Helga's sexual ardour remained unabated. Gerhardt forbade her to return to the Hofbrauhaus and she spent most of her time in the apartment devouring mountains of chocolate and listening to music from an old gramophone. Helga grew rapidly in size. By July intercourse happened less frequently on Helga's assertion that it would be bad for the baby. Gerhardt understood and in early August intercourse ceased and Helga's attitude toward him changed completely. She had never been house-proud and left all the cooking and cleaning to Gerhardt. Now she took to staying in bed until late morning and became morose and introspective and hostile towards Gerhardt. He did his best to cope with the work at the *Rathaus*, to look after his apartment and to prepare lunch and an evening meal for Helga. Consequently he had to hurry home after work and only rarely called at the Hofbrauhaus.

By September 1918 the last major German offensive on the Western Front was petering out and it became evident that the Germans might lose the war. Gerhardt's concern about Germany's fate was compounded by his intense concern about Helga who, by now, was of enormous proportions, eating him out of house and home, with a continuing passion for chocolate which was only obtainable with great difficulty and at great cost. The Armistice was signed on the 11th November 1918 in Versailles. That evening the Hofbrauhaus was almost deserted and Willi was ominously quiet behind the bar counter. After two quick schnapps Gerhardt left the deserted inn to return to his cheerless apartment and to the gluttonous, silent Helga.

Gerhardt did not visit the Hofbrauhaus again until the 13th December, the night before the birth of his son. After his drinking session with Willi, Gerhardt stumbled and slithered along an erratic, drunken path to his apartment. Tired and befuddled he lay fully clothed in the spare bedroom where he had been relegated by Helga during the last three months of pregnancy and immediately fell asleep. He was awaken about an hour later by a loud banging on the apartment door. His head was aching and, with an unsteady gait, he crossed the lounge to open the door. Outside, clothed in a large fur-lined overcoat and fur cap, covered with fine snowflakes, stood an elderly caretaker from the *Klinik*.

"Come immediately with me, Herr *Direktor* Schmidt. Your baby is arriving."

Gerhardt dressed quickly and, taking his cane in his left hand, hurried as expediently as possible alongside the bent old gentleman to the *Klinik*. He could hear Helga screaming from the entrance hall. A nurse with bedraggled spiky hair and a dirty grey smock came towards him.

"Your baby is on the way but I think there will be a delay. Please sit in the waiting room."

The violent screaming seemed to have stopped and Gerhardt, still not fully awake, nodded off to sleep. His head lolled forwards revealing the top of his balding pate and his steel-rimmed glasses fell to the floor between his feet.

Gerhardt Schmidt woke with a start, conscious that there was another person in the waiting room. His myopic eye saw a blurred image in long skirts, surmounted by a dirty white blouse, encasing a portly, middle-aged lady with greying hair. Gerhardt fumbled in his pocket and then stooped to pick up his glasses, thrusting them firmly on his nose. He instantly rose to his feet shouting at the midwife, "Sein fuß, sein fuß."

He reached forwards and almost tore at the blankets that surrounded the sleeping infant. The midwife, mystified and uncomprehending, allowed the blanket to unwrap and at once Gerhardt thrust his hands between the folds and delivered the infant's legs into view. The baby's feet were perfectly well formed. He gave a deep sigh of relief and only then looked at the plump, red, crinkly face of his son. The baby had a perfect body and a surge of relief overcame Gerhardt who, for the first time since boyhood, broke down and wept loudly blowing his nose in his red pocket handkerchief. He took a minute or so to compose himself, gave the stony-faced midwife a brief smile, and crossed the hallway into the labour ward where Helga lay on the maternity bed like a large stranded walrus. He thought she looked revolting but crossed the room and held her hand for a brief moment. She immediately drew her hand away and, moaning, turned away from Gerhardt and lay on her side. Rather formally he said, *"Danke"* to his wife and then left the *Klinik* to celebrate in the Hofbrauhaus. For the first time in his life he became very drunk and had to be assisted home to his apartment by his cronies who had participated in the free celebration.

The following morning he woke from his stupor with a dreadful headache and was immediately sick on the bedroom floor. The recollection of the previous night's activities returned gradually to his befuddled brain. A cerebral image of his large wife and the baby registered quickly and then he thought the baby boy had no name. Gerhardt dressed quickly, took a few mouthfuls of cold black coffee, felt nauseated once more and then ran as best he could to his office in the *Rathaus*. There in copperplate handwriting he made an entry in the register:

Schmidt, Manfred Joachim, born December 14th 1918, Parents, Gerhardt and Helga Schmidt. No. 14 Grünewald Strasse, Munich.

The *Bürgermeister* signed the registration certificate. His son would be called Manfred. Later that morning at the *Klinik* he told Helga of his decision. She seemed completely indifferent to the news and was miserably pleading to be taken home to have a good meal, as the *Klinik* food was, *"Schlecht, sehr schlecht."* Two days later the Schmidts left the *Klinik* and walked to their flat, Gerhardt proudly carrying his son, wrapped in a blanket, in his arms. Willi Klinsman at the Hofbrauhaus was one of the first to be informed that the Schmidt's son would be christened Manfred Joachim. Willi wondered to himself – why not Hans or Wilhelm or a host of others who had caroused at his *Keller* and serviced Helga.

Chapter Three

The Grünbergs, Aalbrücke, 1918 – 1931

The village of Aalbrücke is located on the banks of the River Aal, a tributary of the Vils, forty-five kilometres north east of Munich and fifty-two kilometres south of Nuremberg. At the end of the Great War its population was in the region of eight hundred. Simon's ironmongery shop and post office was located on the western bank near a rickety wooden bridge, which spanned the river, where he lived on the premises with his wife and two teenage daughters. The sudden arrival of Isaac, Anna and a baby was both unexpected and, in many respects, unwelcome. Simon knew of a family connection in the Ukraine but there had been little communication between the two branches of the family for over twenty years.

Having welcomed Isaac and Anna over a samovar of tea the subject of their future plans arose. As it was evident to Simon that his cousin would not be returning to the Ukraine he explained that there were ten other Jewish families in Aalbrücke, mainly concentrated on the west bank of the Aal. Accommodation would be an immediate problem as the shop took up most of the floor space in his own household and for a few days Isaac and Anna could use his daughters' bedroom to look after and feed the baby whilst a search was made for more suitable quarters. Isaac, Anna and David spent their first night in Aalbrücke in a clean room and in a comfortable warm bed.

Within a few days Simon's two, rather shy, teenage daughters and his wife Gerda had become completely captivated by the baby. After a week it became evident to Simon that his newly acquired relatives would not be moving house. Behind the shop there were two sturdily built out-houses, one of them partly used as a storage space for

Simon's ironmongery implements. The out-houses were requisitioned, scrubbed and cleaned, and sparsely furnished with a bed, table and chairs and a wood-burning stove. Isaac moved his family into the new accommodation where they had privacy but continued to take their main meals at Simon's table.

The question of work for Isaac was simpler to solve. Arrangements were made for him to resume his skilled occupation as soon as possible as Aalbrücke did not have a shoemaker. The tools of his trade were acquired from the widow of an elderly village cobbler who had died a few years previously and one-half of the second out-house was converted into a workshop. Within a fortnight Isaac happily returned to work at the only occupation he had mastered as a young man. At first he was limited to making boots and shoes for Simon's family and other Jewish brethren in the village. The quality of his products soon brought orders from villagers across the river who were pleased not to have to travel to Ingolstadt or Munich for their footwear.

Anna was unhappy and longed to return to her birthplace in the Ukraine. She was pleased that Isaac prospered but could not bring herself to share his enthusiasm for their new neighbours and surroundings. Apart for a few simple words of thanks and greeting, Anna and Isaac defiantly refused to master the German tongue. The language of their house and home, and of David's childhood, was Hebrew with a smattering of Ukrainian words of endearment. Anna's only pleasure in life was to watch her David developing and growing into a fine healthy boy and to share the rewards Isaac derived from his increasing prosperity and from his elevation in stature within the Jewish community at Aalbrücke.

The front of Simon's post office overlooked the road on the west bank of the Aal whilst the out-houses at the rear faced the wide open fields and hedgerows of the largest farm in the area owned by Joachim Schmidt. The younger brother of two boys, Joachim, in accordance with German rural tradition, had inherited the three hundred acre farm in 1913 when his parents died of influenza. His herd of one hundred and twenty cattle, reared on the lush and fertile fields of the Aal valley, were the pride of the district and a renowned prize herd in the area. After his father's death Joachim had married a neighbouring farmer's daughter, Valtraut, thereby acquiring a wife and further valuable grazing acreage for his ever-expanding herd. Joachim and

Valtraut Schmidt were childless. They were a devoted couple who longed for an heir and the arrival of a boy at the post office, on the border of their farm, was an exceptionally fortuitous event. The fact that the infant was Jewish was of no relevance to the simple-minded, homely Schmidts.

Valtraut manufactured any excuse to call at the *Postamt* to lavish her maternal instincts on the baby and always brought milk, yoghurt and cheese as small gifts from her dairy, much to Anna's discomfiture and jealousy. Joachim's visits to the *Postamt* and to the shoemaker in the out-house also became more frequent. His business instincts were aroused when he witnessed the skill of Isaac's work. He commissioned a pair of calf-skin boots for himself, insisting that he would provide the hide from one of the calves in his herd. Three times a year a cull of calves occurred on the farm to provide veal for the meat markets at Ingolstadt and Munich. The skins were commonly discarded, but Joachim saw an opportunity of earning a few extra marks by selling the hides to the shoemaker. A designated hide was treated and preserved in tannic acid for two weeks, prior to increasing its pliability by kneading and the final product, two perfect, shiny, soft-leather jack boots, were a work of art and the envy of all adult males in Aalbrücke. The boots were comfortable, watertight and perfect footwear for a working farmer. Other orders for the specially designed calf-leather boots matured rapidly and Isaac now devoted most of his time to this aspect of his trade. Isaac's industry provided Joachim with a ready and profitable outlet for the large number of calf-hides he produced each year. Space became a problem in Isaac's out-house and, by agreement, Joachim allowed him to use a barn at the farmhouse as a tannery. Regular contacts between the farmer and the shoemaker blossomed into friendship although the lack of a common language presented difficulties.

In June 1921 Isaac met Joachim's brother who was paying a short day visit to the farmhouse. Gerhardt's demeanour towards Isaac was abrupt and almost insulting, much to Joachim's displeasure. The meeting was brief and terminated when Gerhardt limped out of the tannery towards the farmhouse. The following day Joachim enquired whether Isaac could make a special pair of leather boots for his brother, designed to conceal the deformity of Gerhardt's club foot. Gerhardt had the foresight to leave a pair of his old boots at the farmhouse as a model. Fashioning the special pair of boots taxed

Isaac's ingenuity to the full but, by trial and error and incorporating a wooden stock in the right boot, he produced a magnificent pair of jack boots in shiny, black, soft leather with glowing polished toe caps. Within a few months Joachim was receiving coded bulk orders from Munich for Gerhardt's special leather boots. Isaac's industry and Joachim's recommendation and contacts with his brother produced a lucrative income and by 1926 he was able to purchase a four-roomed cottage next to the *Postamt*, still using his expanded workshop in the out-houses and the tannery at the farm.

Despite their move to a new home Anna remained unhappy and became physically emaciated, introverted and completely dependent on Isaac. He, on the other hand, blossomed and became a proxy rabbi and a patriarch of the Jewish fraternity in Aalbrücke. Five other Jewish settlers were involved in service industries; one a tailor, one a market gardener, one a dairy farmer, and one, his own cousin, the local postmaster and ironmonger. They all had grown-up children, but little David was the baby and newcomer in their minuscule community. Isaac, as acting rabbi, led the services on Saturday in the saddler's house and supervised religious instruction and Hebrew classes for the young people on a Wednesday afternoon. He soon became the spokesman and leader of his small band of brethren.

David Grünberg grew up in this community. His early childhood was spent within the protective embrace of his mother, cousins, uncle, Auntie Gerda and, at the farm, of Herr Schmidt and *Mutti* Valtraut. He grew into a lean young boy with dark black hair, an aquiline nose and penetrating grey eyes. His early days were centred around the *Postamt* and later in the cottage next door. By the age of five he was allowed to visit the farm, ride horses, watch the cows being milked, and generally enjoy the simple hospitality of a Bavarian farmhouse offered by Frau Valtraut and her husband. He became friendly with the dogs, the horses, the geese and the cow-herds on the farm and his love for farm life persisted after he started as a day pupil at kindergarten. There he rapidly learned to read, speak and write German fortifying the rudimentary knowledge he had acquired from the Schmidts. His indoctrination into the Jewish faith and its theology commenced early so that, by the age of seven, he was proficient in speaking, reading and writing both German and Hebrew.

Joachim Schmidt took a particular interest in the young boy recognising his interest in animal husbandry. He understood that

David's father and uncle were too busy to spend time with David and that his mother, in her misery, did not wish to partake in his education and interests outside the house. To all intents and purposes Joachim and Valtraut Schmidt adopted David as a son of their own. Joachim taught David the art of farming, methods of herding and milking cows, and the rudiments of caring for and nurturing the animals on his farm.

David attended the elementary school at Aalbrücke from the age of seven years. He was an exceptionally quick learner and became rapidly proficient in German and basic English. His grasp of mathematics, geography and biology were uncanny but his comprehension of history was marred by the tuition he received in the Hebrew classes and, even at an early age, he was unable to differentiate between the teaching at home and at school. These discrepancies were further accentuated by a change in the attitude of the masters in the classrooms.

In 1929, at school assembly, the pupils were instructed to sing nationalistic songs rather than traditional hymns. Later that year and in early 1930, school history lessons were heavily weighted with German history and the struggle for freedom of the German people, future hopes for the German race and the spread of German influence and colonisation throughout Europe. This propaganda left grave doubts in the mind of the sensitive eleven year old Jewish boy. He realised that he was a German subject, almost by birth, but certainly by residence and was unable to reconcile the philosophies of the Jewish faith and of his Hebrew teachers with the nationalistic doctrines of his German schoolmasters. David was perplexed and confused and found no answers from his father or Jewish elders who exhorted him to continue with his traditional belief in Judaism.

Joachim Schmidt, who had no political or nationalistic aspirations, continued to be his mentor and friend and urged David to persevere with his work on the farm. He rose early to guide the herd to their grazing pastures and every evening after school returned to the farm for milking. At such times he completely forgot classroom indoctrination and the political whirlpool which seemed to be enveloping Germany in 1930 and 1931.

As he grew older his day was equally divided between his classes and schooling and helping Uncle Joachim on the farm and, during school holidays, he spent most of his daylight hours in the fields and the farmhouse. Uncle Joachim, wise in the ways of the countryside, taught him to fish for eel and to tickle trout in the stream and to hunt and set snares for rabbits and hares in the hedgerows and wooded glades. Isaac approved of his son's interest in the farm and of his relationship with Joachim and Valtraut as it kept the boy out of his way during his long arduous working hours. Anna suffered in silent anguish at the continual absence of her only boy from the house. The Grünbergs were together as a family only on the Sabbath when David was forbidden to visit his adopted Uncle and Aunt. On Sabbath day David felt repressed and longed for Sunday to come along so that he could escape to Grossmunde farm and to the welcoming arms of Joachim and Valtraut Schmidt.

Chapter Four
The Schmidts, Munich, 1918 – 1932

The Schmidts and their three day old son returned home to their apartment at No. 14 Grünewald Strasse on the 16th December 1918. Their son was healthy and voracious, demanding frequent feeds from his mother and Helga soon announced her displeasure at having to breastfeed and having her mealtimes and sleep interrupted. Manfred was quickly weaned off the breast and Helga's lack of interest in the baby's welfare and her insatiable desire to lie in bed all day worried Gerhardt considerably. With the aid of Frau Heller the maternal tasks of feeding, changing and caring for the baby were accomplished while his depressed wife remained in bed most of the day and night, rising only for essential reasons and for meals. Manfred thrived and grew into a gangly, fair-haired, blue-eyed boy. Academically backward and deprived of maternal affection, he relied on his father to tender to his every need.

The growing boy spent most of his childhood in the apartment and nearby park cared for by a series of nannies, while Gerhardt was at work at the *Rathaus* and whilst his mother lived a life of gluttony and fantasy in the seclusion of her bedroom. At the age of five years Manfred started at kindergarten. He was the tallest boy in his class and was also the most uncoordinated and awkward pupil at ball games and athletic activities and only average in scholastic ability. He grew into an introspective boy, short-tempered and with a tendency to bully his smaller compatriots. He seemed incapable of making friends and was frequently the 'odd man out' during ball games and organised school activities. The pattern continued when he moved up to junior school in Munich. His position in the class was nearer the foot than the top of the scholastic ladder and his frustration at his inability to concentrate and learn quickly, goaded by the taunts of *"Dummkopf"* from his classmates, frequently produced outbursts of rage and hysteria culminating in uncontrollable crying fits. These motivated his schoolmates further and led to intensification of their taunts and jibes.

Manfred's forte was complete obedience to his tutors and this trait, and his physique, made him a teacher's pet and an automatic selection as a school prefect. His proud father ensured that Manfred was always perfectly turned out in school uniform with polished shoes and slicked-back blonde hair. Manfred's duties as a prefect were to supervise the lines of other pupils at assembly and school meals and to ensure that everyone entered on the roster at roll-call remained in class for the rest of the day.

Early in 1929 the daily pattern of education in German schools changed imperceptibly. In the morning assembly German national songs were introduced and one study period each day was dedicated entirely to German history and to the rise of National Socialism. Manfred was an avid student, enthralled by details of past German conquests and of the struggle for power currently happening in Bavaria and Berlin. Munich was the epicentre of the revolution and the names of the National Socialist leaders, Hitler, Hess, Goering, von Ribbentrop and Ernst Röhm were emblazoned on Manfred's fertile young mind. His interest in the Nazi movement was further nurtured at home by his father, who hinted from time to time that he held a high position in the Munich Nazi Party. The ten year old boy came to believe in the concept of Nazism and worshipped its leaders as heroes who would liberate the German *herrenvolk*. When the Party or its leaders were mentioned in classes a fixed, glazed, almost fanatical look appeared in Manfred's deep blue eyes.

During the winter of 1930 Manfred had contracted pneumonia and was confined to his bed for three months. His recovery was slow and he was unable to return to the junior school for the spring and summer terms of 1931. The nanny and Gerhardt took care of the ailing boy who had lost a considerable amount of weight and by the end of his illness in March 1931 he looked like a scarecrow, emaciated and hardly filling his brown drill-shirt and *lederhosen*. Gerhardt, delighted with his son's recovery, bought him a wide leather belt and a sheath and dagger with a swastika emblazoned on its hilt. Manfred was overjoyed with the gift which, according to his father, was presented by the Führer himself. Manfred wore the belt all day and at night time the dagger lay reverently on the pillow beside his head.

Gerhardt's concern for his son's health led him to arrange for the boy to convalesce for the summer months of 1931 at his brother's farm in Aalbrücke. At first Manfred was not enamoured with his impending enforced holiday at Grossmunde farm but, as a dutiful son, he had learned to obey his father's orders. As the day of departure approached, he could summon very little enthusiasm at the prospect of living with his Uncle Joachim and Aunt Valtraut. He had only a vague mental recollection of his relatives in Aalbrücke. They had visited the apartment at No. 14 Grünewald Strasse in 1925, when he was seven years of age, to discuss business matters with his father.

Aunt Valtraut, he recalled, was a short, bespectacled, dumpy person with greying hair and a fine black moustache on her upper lip. She kept hugging and cuddling Manfred, much to his displeasure. Her breath smelt of peppermint, her clothes of camphor, and she had a black hairy mole on the right side of her chin, which caused stabs of sharp pain in his cheek when she kissed him. Uncle Joachim was squat and broad shouldered, with a wide open, round, weather-beaten face, thinning blond hair and enormous rough, hard-skinned hands. He was distinctly uncomfortable in his town clothes and stiff, starched collar. Manfred compared the men, and wondered how two completely different persons could be brothers. He also wondered why Uncle Joachim had two sound legs while his own unfortunate father stumped and hobbled his way around the apartment. He would soon be meeting his Uncle and Aunt again and the thought filled him with trepidation and concern that his aunt might not have lost her proclivity for hugging and kissing. But he genuinely looked forward to seeing his smiling amiable uncle. The trip to Aalbrücke would at least get him away from the confines of the flat in Grünewald Strasse, from his strange, depressed mother and from his dull authoritarian and humourless father.

On the morning of the 21st May, 1931 Gerhardt picked up his son at the apartment in an official black chauffeur-driven Opel. Manfred dutifully kissed his mother on her forehead, receiving no indication of affection in return, merely a grunt and a sigh from the large flabby women with bedraggled hair lying on the huge bed. He picked up his canvas valise and, smartly dressed in his brown drill shirt and *lederhosen* and proudly displaying his polished brown belt and its shining dagger, he threw his bag on to the floor of the Opel and climbed imperiously into the back seat of the car. The journey from

No. 14 Grünewald Strasse to Grossmunde farm at Aalbrücke took nearly two hours.

Gerhardt Schmidt: Munich: 1918 – 1933

When Gerhardt had brought his son and wife home from the *Klinik* he felt a surge of pride at his achievement in producing a healthy boy but was perturbed about Helga.   She did not seem to be very interested in the baby and breast-feeding was a distinct chore. Helga's appetite had not been impaired by her recent pregnancy and hospitalisation and by the fourth day at home she stopped breastfeeding. Thereafter Gerhardt fed his baby on the bottle. He had a week off work to settle his family in the apartment and towards the end of that week it was apparent that Helga could not manage the baby on her own.   He secured the services of a nanny from one of the adjacent apartments to look after Manfred during the day and during the night Gerhardt tended to the needs of his voracious infant son and also had to cope with Helga's tantrums and insatiable appetite.

At the end of the week Gerhardt returned to work in the *Rathaus* and immersed himself in the laborious task of recording data collected in the *Reichsland* census office during his absence. Life settled once more into its usual humdrum pattern. In due course an assistant was appointed to his department, a veteran of the war, who had lost a leg at Verdun. Further promotion prospects within the *Rathaus* were not good and Gerhardt was content to keep his meticulous census files up to date and to bide his time. He called at the Hofbrauhaus on his way home from work for a stein or two of beer and a glance at the daily news sheets. Customers came and went over the years but Gerhardt Schmidt remained a faithful and respected client in the old *Bierkeller* in Marienplatz.

In the spring and summer of 1920 the evening clientele at the Hofbrauhaus changed radically.   A motley crowd of young and middle-aged men, all dressed in brown shirts, began frequenting the bar. Their leader was a burly, arrogant, loudmouth giant of a man, with an ill-fitting shirt, jodhpurs and scuffed jackboots. Ernst Röhm commanded attention from his followers by shouting, blustering and blaspheming.   The Brownshirts and their undisciplined shouting, carousing and swearing drove away most of the regular customers but Gerhardt held his ground. Had he not been a regular customer at the

Bierkeller for seven years. The Brownshirts did not bother Gerhardt to any great extent, but some of them looked disdainfully at his departing figure when he limped away after his nightly drink. A hint from Willi Klinsman that Gerhardt's limp was a relic of the war mollified their attitude to the strange, timid man who sat alone in the midst of their drunken carousing. One evening Röhm crashed on to a chair next to Gerhardt and brought him a stein of beer, making an incomprehensible and ineffectual apology for the behaviour of his followers. Gerhardt answered politely *"Danke Sehr* Herr *Kapitan."* Thereafter the contacts between Gerhardt and the Brownshirts were of a formal and polite nature.

One evening in the autumn of the same year Gerhardt observed the entry into the Hofbrauhaus of seven men, identically dressed in black raincoats. The central figure of this group was shorter than the others and, under his hunting hat, he had sleek, black hair parted on the left side of his forehead, a small black moustache confined to his upper lip, and piercing, commanding blue eyes. The revelling Brownshirts were commanded to silence by Röhm who became servile and fawning as he shook hands with Adolf Hitler. With a nod of his head Hitler, his friends and Ernst Röhm walked through into the back room of the *Bierkeller.* Gerhardt left before they re-appeared and in the meantime the Brownshirt group around the bar were silent and subdued, overcome by some mystic reverence for the strange man in a black overcoat who had invaded and interrupted their drinking. A few weeks later Adolf Hitler again appeared with many more henchmen and, having collected Röhm from the bar, went into the back room, The Brownshirts remaining at the bar obediently downed their steins and walked out into Marienplatz leaving Gerhardt and two other customers in the *Keller.* By the autumn of 1921 the Brownshirts had left the Hofbrauhaus but Hitler and his followers were frequent visitors and the fawning Röhm appeared for the meetings in an ill-fitting suit draped around his massive frame and a small feathered hunting hat balanced precariously on top of his balding skull. As the men arrived for these meetings Gerhardt learned to recognise other members of Hitler's entourage – Hess, Goering, Rosenberg, von Ribbentrop, Himmler, Goebbels and von Schneider.

During the second week of June 1921 the numbers at one meeting were too large to be accommodated in the rear room, and Gerhardt and four other regulars were politely asked to leave the *Bierkeller.* As

Gerhardt limped out through the door he felt a tap on his shoulder and turned to face the piercing deep set eyes of Rudolf Hess. Hess asked politely if Gerhardt would like to speak to the Führer who had asked to meet a fellow soldier wounded on the Western Front. Gerhardt agreed and a few moments later stood near the podium shaking the limpid hand of Adolf Hitler. Hitler's clear blue eyes mesmerised Gerhardt, seemingly piercing into his soul, and from that moment onwards he was completely captivated by the man. After a few mundane high-pitched platitudes about the war, Hitler asked if Gerhardt wished to enlist in the Nazi Party. Gerhardt's reply came as a surprise to himself. He realised he was speaking but had no control over the words, *"Jawohl, mein Führer."* Another congratulatory handshake and the interview was over.

The assembled party members discarded their raincoats to reveal grey-coloured uniforms, with black belts, black jackboots and swastika armbands. After singing a nationalist song at attention the gathering was given a forty minute address by the Führer. The content of the speech was soon forgotten but Gerhardt was overwhelmed by the Führer's oratory. After brief addresses by four other officers on the podium, including Hess and Goering, the meeting ended with another rousing song and, as Hitler and his officials left the dais, the party members stood to attention, right arm raised in front of the body in salute, chanting '*Heil* Hitler.'

The next meeting was scheduled for a month later when Gerhardt and many others signed enlistment cards and received a black armband emblazoned with a red swastika. The armband was placed on his left sleeve by Rudolf Hess, officially confirming Gerhardt Schmidt's membership of the Nazi Party, member number 1,993.

Increase in membership rendered the Hofbrauhaus too small for Party meetings and the next one was arranged at the Burgerbraukeller, a larger establishment on the outskirts of Munich. For his second party meeting Gerhardt had purchased a grey button-up tunic with the swastika armband on his left sleeve and jodhpurs and for the first time in public he wore the gleaming soft leather jackboots which his brother Joachim had given him the previous year. During the two mile walk to the Burgerbraukeller his uniform was concealed beneath a button-up black raincoat. Gerhardt felt self-important in his regalia and, due to Isaac's ingenuity in fashioning the jackboots, walked with only a mildly perceptible limp. The meeting at the Burgerbraukeller took the same pattern as on previous occasions, Hitler's speech and exhortation to the Party to work and strive for a glorious and unified Germany being the highlight of the evening. Gerhardt returned home in a frenzy of patriotism, proud of his membership of the Nazi Party and completely besotted by the charisma and eloquence of his Führer, Adolf Hitler.

Nazi Party Diary, The Beer Hall Putsch, 9th November 1923

Gerhardt's involvement with the Nazi Party and his unquenchable faith in the Führer, received a sudden jolt on November 9th 1923. At that time Bavarian affairs were in the hands of a triumvirate composed of Gustav von Khar, the State Commissioner, General Otto von Lossow, Commander of the Reichswehr, and Colonel Hans von Seisser, Chief of the State Police. Gustav Stressemann, the German Chancellor, decreed that reparations to the Allies should recommence and that active resistance in the Ruhr should cease. The Bavarian Cabinet and the Nazi Party were strongly opposed to the Chancellor's proposals and Hitler saw his opportunity to overthrow the Weimar Republic by seizing power in Bavaria. On November 9th an opportunity to act came unexpectedly at a meeting of the triumvirate with three thousand businessmen in the Burgerbraukeller. When the meeting began Röhm's SA Brownshirts surrounded the building and posted machine-gunners at the entrance and exit to the beer hall. Hitler, carrying a pistol, fought his way through the beer-quaffing burghers on to the stage and pushed von Khar aside declaring, "The National revolution has started. The Reich Government has been overthrown and, as I speak, the army and police have joined the Nazi Party and are marching on Munich."

At gunpoint Hitler ordered von Khar, von Lossow and Seisser into a private room, whilst Goering took the stage and mollified the stunned and disbelieving audience. In the private room Hitler tried to persuade the triumvirate to join him to form a Bavarian government with Field Marshal von Ludendorf as the chancellor, but to no avail. Hitler left the three brooding officials and returned to the stage to announce that the triumvirate were in full agreement and that, with their co-operation, a National Socialist Party had been established. At that precise moment Field Marshal von Ludendorf appeared in the Bierhall. Furious at first to hear that Hitler had used his name to try and coerce the Bavarian Government to join the Nazi Party, he soon relented and used his considerable powers of persuasion on the triumvirate. They returned to the stage one by one and pledged their allegiance to the new National Socialist Party, led by Adolf Hitler and von Ludendorf. The assembled audience cheered loudly. Adolf Hitler had won the day.

At that point news reached the Bierhall of a clash between regular army engineers and Röhm's stormtroopers and Hitler and von Ludendorf left the Burgerbraukeller to deal with the skirmish. Up to now the takeover by Hitler had been a bloodless coup but, if fighting broke out between the SA and regular troops, a civil war could ensue and the Nazi Party had insufficient manpower to withstand the might of the Weimar Army. At eleven the following morning, the 10th November, Hitler and Field Marshal von Ludendorf marched at the head of some three thousand stormtroopers towards the War Ministry in the centre of Munich and the engineers' barracks, where Röhm and his SA were surrounded by Reichswehr *detachments. Ludendorf led the SA column down a narrow street guarded at one end by a detachment of one thousand armed police. The police would not give way and a fusillade of shots were fired.*

The SA turned tail and ran for cover. Only Field Marshal von Ludendorf remained erect and unflinching. Goering was wounded in the thigh and three policemen and sixteen Nazis lay dead in the street. Adolf Hitler fled from the scene. The Bierhallputsch ended in disorder and fiasco and, as a result, the Nazi Party was disbanded. Hitler was arrested two days later in a country house and came to trial on the 26th February 1924. The trial lasted twenty-four days and was dominated by Hitler who mesmerised the jury and the world press. He was sentenced to five years imprisonment but the sentence was commuted to nine months and during his time in Landsberg Prison, and with Rudolf Hess's assistance, he wrote Mein Kampf, *the doctrinal handbook of Nazism. Hitler was eventually released on the 20th December 1924 and again took up the reins and plotted to reform his now defunct Nazi Party.*

Gerhardt Schmidt had no prior knowledge of the Bierhallputsch and missed the meeting and confrontation in the Burgerbraukeller. News of the bloodless coup was received with great enthusiasm in the Hofbrauhaus. Party members revelled and caroused into the early hours, their joy constantly re-enforced by wildly exaggerated eye-witness accounts by some of the SA troopers returning from the Bierhall. One of the troopers insisted that he had "seen with his own eyes" Adolf Hitler shooting a police guard dead when the policeman tried to prevent their Führer reaching the stage. For the first time in many years Gerhardt struggled home inebriated and sank into a drunken coma on the living room sofa. He was late for work the following morning, not only from the after effects of alcoholic excess, but also from the meticulous care with which he proudly donned his Nazi tunic and armband. At breakfast he tried to explain the enormity of the occasion to his five year old son but the boy was unable to comprehend the magnitude of the events which were occurring in Munich. As he walked to the *Rathaus* he was sorry that he had to wear his overcoat as he wanted to show everyone that he wore the Party uniform with pride and, as he limped down Köenigsallee, he felt ten feet tall.

In the *Rathaus* that morning very little work was done. Uncertain as to whether his job was secure the *Bürgermeister* closeted himself in his room, and other non-Party members wandered around sullenly discussing events of the previous night, frightened for their own safety and job security. Gerhardt lorded it over the rest. There were only two other Nazi Party members in the *Rathaus* and they congregated in Gerhardt's office plotting and planning for the future and, by lunchtime, urged on by his colleagues Gerhardt was certain that he would become the next *Bürgermeister* of Munich. The *Rathaus* Nazi triumvirate had lunch at the Hofbrauhaus where Willi, always prone to fly with the wind, treated them royally. Early in the afternoon the mood changed when news arrived about the fiasco at the engineers' barracks and at the War Ministry. The non-Party *Rathaus* employees now took their revenge with sneers and jibes.

"The bastard turned and ran when the bullets started to fly. And where is he now? Hiding in a pigsty we have no doubt!"

Gerhardt was devastated by the news of his Führer's defection. How could a great man like Hitler turn and run? But he must have had his reasons for doing so. Probably saving his own life for a future sacrifice in the cause of National Socialism.

Gerhardt removed his armband and other Nazi insignia, put on his overcoat and skulked off home where he locked himself in his small bedroom and cried and sobbed until he fell into a fitful sleep. He stayed away from the *Rathaus* for a whole week. Two days later Hitler was arrested and taken to Landsberg Prison to await trial for treason. Gerhardt submissively returned to the *Rathaus* and expected to lose his job as his two Nazi colleagues had been summarily dismissed on the day after the Bierhallputsch. The *Bürgermeister* ordered that Gerhardt could remain in the *Rathaus* but would lose seniority and would revert to a position of Senior Clerk in the census department. Hitler's trial on the 26th February 1924 and his release from Landsberg on the 24th December the same year raised a glimmer of hope in Gerhardt's breast that the Party might be resurrected. But throughout 1925 and 1926 it seemed that the glorious concept of a Third Reich was rapidly fading into history. A few clandestine meetings were held in the Hofbrauhaus and Burgerbraukeller during 1927 and 1928, but it took the depression of 1929 to resurrect Nazi ideology and recruit Germans in their thousands into the Party. Hitler returned to power with a vengeance in 1929 and thereafter the Nazi Party prospered.

During 1929 the Party's popularity amongst the citizens of Munich grew in leaps and bounds and Party members, Gerhardt included, were confident enough to walk the streets of Munich in uniform. These were indeed heady days which Gerhardt savoured to the full. The *Bürgermeister* was at first openly hostile to Gerhardt's resurgent affiliations but, in the face of the growing strength of the Nazis, he became more docile and was removed from office in October and replaced by a Nazi sympathiser, Herr Konrad Widemayer, who lost little time in purging non-Nazi staff at the *Rathaus* and appointing Gerhardt as his private secretary. Gerhardt left the *Reichslands* Department and moved upstairs to a magnificent new office next to the *Bürgermeister*'s rooms. He had a staff of three under-secretaries, all Nazi Party members, and the use of a black chauffeur driven staff car. He took his private ethnic files with him from the *Reichslands* Bureau and kept them under lock and key in his new department. In the Party and at frequent meetings in the Burgerbraukeller Gerhardt became a notary, keeping minutes of proceedings. One of the reasons which led to Hitler's incarceration in 1924 was the clandestine nature of the activities of the Nazi Party and the lack of records of their meetings. This was now rectified. Gerhardt kept two sets of minutes, one of the true nature of the proceedings and the other, often vastly different, for publication in the German and world press.

Gerhardt Schmidt was now an important person in the Nazi hierarchy in Munich and in the office of administration of the city of Munich. He remained in this important office until his death in 1939.

Whilst Gerhardt's political career blossomed during 1929 and 1930 his personal domestic life waned. The gargantuan Helga had become bedridden and mentally deranged and the best medical advice available in Munich was unable to solve her problems. Eventually, in early 1928, the unfortunate woman was committed to an asylum on the outskirts of Munich. Gerhardt visited her weekly but eventually the futility of such visits became apparent and he resigned himself to a monthly trip.

Manfred refused to visit his sick mother and appeared completely indifferent to her mental illness, never asking to see her or enquiring after her health and completely eliminating her from his young mind. This attitude was an extension of the indifference he had felt when his mother lay in her bed day after day and month after month, in the apartment at No. 14 Grünewald Strasse. She had never been a true mother and he was unable to comprehend that his mother's post-natal depression gradually and inexorably progressed to dementia, necessitating her permanent removal to a Munich asylum where she committed suicide on Christmas Eve, 1929. Manfred did not attend her funeral. With the typical resilience of youth he was able to dismiss his mother completely from his mind. He lived in awe of his disciplinarian, humourless father. There were very few intimate exchanges between father and son and, as a result of his family background and loveless childhood, he became rather a shy boy with a tendency to release his inward frustration in tantrums and bouts of crying in the seclusion of his own room.

In the summer holidays of 1929 Gerhardt took his eleven year old son to an executive meeting of the Party in the Hofbrauhaus and presented the boy to Adolf Hitler. This meeting with the Führer was the highlight of Manfred's childhood. Every day, for months after the brief contact, he daydreamed of his idol and of the aura of greatness which seemed to envelop Adolf Hitler. His last thought and silent prayer at night was for the thin, round-shouldered, moustached man with piercing blue eyes and dressed simply in a grey tunic, black denim trousers and black boots; the Führer, his Führer. His father, realising that Manfred was besotted with the Party leader began letting him hear about the confidences and intrigues of prominent members in the Munich Nazi Party.

Shortly after resumption of Party meetings in the Hofbrauhaus in the spring of 1926, Rudolf Hess showed a great interest in Gerhardt's boots, admiring the shine, the line and the softness of the calf-clinging leather. Gerhardt arranged for a pair of Hess' old boots to be sent to Aalbrücke and within a fortnight a brand new made-to-measure pair was delivered to Hess. Subsequent orders arrived thick and fast. Within three months all the Party executive were shod with Gerhardt's special jackboots. The interest in the jackboots culminated in a special surprise presentation of a pair to Adolf Hitler on his fortieth birthday on the 20th April, 1929. The Führer was immensely pleased with the gift and, when he enquired about the source, he was told that the craftsman was Gerhardt Schmidt's relative in Aalbrücke and the Party Executive thought this to be true. Only Gerhardt knew that the orders for the jackboots were executed by a Jew using his brother Joachim as retailer. Gerhardt had no conscience about this situation arguing that, although the craftsman might be Jewish, the leather originated from good German livestock.

After his release from gaol in December 1924 the Jewish problem occupied much of Hitler's time and thoughts and his anti-Semitic feelings became abundantly evident to the Party Executive and members. Hitler's request for a detailed list of Jewish families in Munich produced an immediate response from his notary, Gerhardt Schmidt, and the secret ethnic files in Schmidt's office in the *Rathaus* were produced at the next meeting. In 1929 the executive ordered a census of Jewish citizens and family units for an area of fifty kilometres surrounding Munich. With the blessing of Herr Widemayer, the recently appointed *Bürgermeister*, Gerhardt commenced on a systematic and progressive census of the surrounding areas in widening circles, around Munich.

Gerhardt felt all-important in his Party uniform and polished black leather jackboots and the arrival of his chauffeur-driven black Opel in the more remote villages always caused a stir and aroused interest and respect amongst local inhabitants. In accordance with instructions from the Nazi Executive Committee Gerhardt kept a separate ledger of Jewish residents in Munich and surrounding villages and towns. As the circle of his attention widened he spent two or three days away from his office, staying overnight at a *Gasthaus* at the expense of the

Munich ratepayers. After fourteen months of research, by 1930, his records were near completion but there were a few minor centres to the north and east still unvisited, including his own birthplace in Aalbrücke. Gerhardt's plans for a census visit to Aalbrücke would serve a dual purpose. His son would benefit from a few months recuperation in the clean atmosphere of his brother's farm in Aalbrücke and the census visit would be an ideal opportunity to take him to Grossmunde farm.

Chapter Five

Grossmunde Farm, May – September 1930
The Blood Brother Ceremony
Aalbrücke to London, October 1931

Since the Christmas holiday of 1929 David had not been to Aalbrücke school. He was the youngest and the only male Jewish pupil at the school but two others, both girls, continued to attend. The process of Nazification had proceeded to such an extent that, at every lesson, the children were required to stand at attention and reciprocate the teachers' Nazi salute and sing Party songs. Most of the lessons were curtailed and more and more time devoted to the history of Germany and to the development and political aims of the Nazi Party. The doctrines propounded by the teachers were based on Adolf Hitler's dictates and *Mein Kampf*, written by Adolf Hitler whilst in captivity in 1924, was the book for compulsory reading throughout the school. The serious-minded young Jew objected to this indoctrination but his father begged him to acquiesce and follow the rest of his classmates.

David had a stubborn streak and during the week leading up to the Christmas holiday he refused to stand on his feet for the salute and to sing Party songs. On the third occasion, and two days before the end of Christmas term 1929, he was sent home in disgrace and finally a letter of expulsion followed in the New Year. David's further education was essentially self-tuition at home. He continued studying German and Hebrew and started reading English. He soon mastered the written word, but conversational English was a different matter as there was simply no one in Aalbrücke to help him. Uncle Simon at the *Postamt* had been to college for one year and helped him with arithmetic. David had an active and retentive mind, quick to learn and grasp facts, and he found that three hours' hard study each day was sufficient to cover all subjects. Consequently he had plenty of opportunity to visit the farm and spent time working and helping Uncle Joachim.

Joachim was fully aware of the boy's expulsion from school but, with peasant logic, concluded that the event would not change anything and, in particular, his feelings towards the Jewish family he had befriended. Joachim and Valtraut had no firm opinions about the Nazi Party. They were very fond of young David and regarded him as a son, a replacement for the boy which he and the barren Valtraut could not produce. Added to this David was a pleasant and reserved young lad who worked hard on the farm and had a natural empathy with other workers and with the livestock. Joachim wondered what his brother Gerhardt in Munich would think about all this. He knew Gerhardt was heavily embroiled with, and a full member of, the Nazi Party. Furthermore, he appeared to be bringing up his son as a young Nazi. Gerhardt's last letter at Christmas had been full of information about the glory of Nazism and about his own important position in the Party, adding that his plans for Manfred were that, at thirteen years of age, he would enlist in the Hitler Youth.

The sad news was that Manfred was quite ill. In early September 1929 he had contracted pneumonia, from which he had not recovered fully. Gerhardt asked if the boy could spend the summer months on the family farm in Aalbrücke. Joachim and Valtraut were ecstatic at the thought that they would have a 'boy of their own' to care for and feed. They had hardly seen anything of their nephew since he was born. He would be very welcome at the farm and Valtraut redecorated and refurbished a bedroom with large glass windows and a balcony overlooking the fields and a perfect view of the *Munde* at the end of the long meadows.

Gerhardt's letter ended in a formal manner. In his capacity as *Direktor* of the census department at the *Rathaus* he would visit Aalbrücke on official business and would bring Manfred and his luggage to the farm in the official car. The letter did not even ask about Joachim or Valtraut's well-being. Nevertheless the prospect of having a young boy, a surrogate son, living in Grossmunde farm for three or four months during the summer filled them both with joy.

In mid-March Joachim informed David of his nephew's impending holiday. He was careful to stress that Manfred was a very sick boy and, though they were roughly the same age, he might not be able to run about the farm or go fishing, swimming and hunting with David. Joachim felt that these activities might be possible later when Manfred was stronger and hoped David would be a good friend and companion to his nephew. The shy young Jew readily agreed. It was the least he could do to repay his kindly benefactor and his Auntie Valtraut.

April 6th, 1930 was a fine, sunny, spring morning. David busied himself in the cow-shed and Joachim, in a clean shirt, with Valtraut in a starched white apron and cap, fussed around the entrance to the farmhouse. Punctually at twelve noon the black chauffeur-driven Opel arrived at the farmyard and, bumping over the cobblestones, came to a halt outside the farmhouse door. The peak-capped chauffeur held the back door open and Gerhardt emerged wearing a black coat displaying a red Nazi armband, followed by a tall, pale-faced, blond-haired boy wrapped in a thick woollen blanket. After perfunctory greetings on the doorstep the two visitors were ushered into the farmhouse and the chauffeur returned to his car, taking his place behind the steering wheel. David withdrew into the cow-shed and kept an eye on the house.

After twenty minutes Gerhardt and Joachim emerged and a few words were spoken. The brothers gave each other a muted hug. Gerhardt saluted and '*Heil* Hitlered' and, turning about, limped to the car and took his place in the back seat. The car turned in a wide arc on the farmyard and the driver gave a toot on the horn as they drove out through the gate, Gerhardt sitting bolt upright in the back seat not glancing left or right. Joachim watched the departing car, standing on the spot on which he had said farewell to his brother, gently shaking his head and muttering "*Nein, nein*" under his breath. He then crossed the yard and entered the cow-shed.

"David, my nephew Manfred is poorly and you cannot visit him today. Perhaps in a week or so he will be well enough to see you."

David nodded that he understood. Joachim had a quick look at a cow about to calf, prodded its haunches and turning on his heels walked out into the sunny yard calling over his shoulder, "*Ich will frühmorgens sie geschehen.*"

David again nodded his acquiescence and then departed for home, wondering about the sick-looking boy he saw being bundled into the farmhouse.

A week dragged into a fortnight before Valtraut ushered David into the sick room. Manfred, clad in a voluminous brown dressing gown, sat in an armchair at the window overlooking the sun-drenched farmyard and fields. The River Aal could be seen meandering its lazy course through the undulating fertile meadows and the hump of the Munde stood out on the far distant horizon. Manfred stood wavering at attention and gave David a brief nod, *"Ich bin Manfred."*

David stood awkwardly in the middle of the bedroom, fingering his cap, *"Ich bin David."*

On a low table in front of Manfred an atlas of the world was open, and also a large tome depicting in graphic detail German armaments, tanks, guns, rifles, grenades, aeroplanes and naval vessels. An open page revealed a photograph and a detailed diagram of Germany's latest cruiser, the *Prinz Eugen*, and the book was undoubtedly displayed to impress the visitor. Valtraut hovered in the background and then left the boys together speaking as she turned to leave: "David – only ten minutes, *bitte.*"

Manfred invited David to inspect his atlas and the photographic records of Germany's military might. David pretended to show an interest in the books and spent two or three minutes leafing through the atlas and military treatise. David asked if Manfred enjoyed the view. The boy from Munich replied that it was *"Fantastiche,"* especially as he rarely saw wide open fields in Munich. David then outlined the geography of the farm, pointing out good sites for grazing the cows, spots for fishing and swimming in the Aal and, finally, his secret hideout in the wooded area on a hillock at the northern end of the largest grazing meadow on the farm. He promised that when Manfred was stronger all these places would be their playground. Valtraut entered the bedroom carrying a bowl of steaming broth and David took the cue and left the house.

David visited Manfred regularly, hardly missing a day, and saw that with Valtraut's expert nursing and feeding the blond patient was getting visibly stronger and within a further week he was able to dress and sit downstairs. Manfred wore his *lederhosen*, a brown shirt, a brown belt with a large brass buckle and a dagger with its swastika-inscribed handle, in its sheath on his left hip.

By the end of April, Manfred was able to sit outdoors in the shade of the cow-shed protected from the breeze. He watched the farmhands milking and wandered around the outhouses nestling in the four corners of the yard. When standing erect Manfred was a good six inches taller than David. He was, however, painfully pale and thin and his clear blue eyes stuck out like organ stops from their sockets. Beneath the *lederhosen* his long white legs protruded like broomsticks and his knees appeared abnormally large and bulbous.

In mid-May Manfred went into the fields with David. At first the walks were confined to fetching the cows from the meadows but it soon became apparent that Manfred was not comfortable in the presence of livestock. He was timid and ill at ease and would not enter the field if Bruno, the bull, was present. David mingled happily with the cows, knew them by name, and handled the herd without fear. During the next few days the boys went further afield exploring the upper reaches of the Aal where it tumbled down in a cascade from a rocky outcrop. Just below the waterfall there was a sizeable pool. David stripped to his underpants and plunged into the deep water, swimming across the pool, but Manfred only ventured to remove his shoes and socks and dunked his feet in the ice-cold water.

David noticed that Manfred appeared to be uncoordinated and awkward in his movements and, if there was any obstacle on the path, he invariably tripped over it and stumbled. David was conscious that his friend's timidity held him back and limited his searches for trout to tickle amongst the rocks in the Aal, in case he encountered an eel. The river in May and June abounded with eel on their migration up-stream. Similarly when the boys caught a rabbit, or hare, in a snare Manfred refused to touch the animal in case it was still alive. Though Manfred became a little bolder as the weeks went by, he never lost his innate fear of handling or touching animals or fish in the wild. Whenever they played hide and seek, cowboys and Indians, or, as Manfred preferred, Frenchies and German stormtroopers, David nearly always won. Manfred refused to go far into the woods, or into a cave as he was too frightened of encountering snakes and other imaginary predators. Similarly when it was his turn to do the stalking his clumsiness and lack of ability to read the topography of the terrain quickly give away his position. Manfred always insisted on representing the German troopers in these daily 'battles' and this led to a great deal of acrimony between the boys. Within a few weeks a combination of Auntie Valtraut's food, physical exercise and abundant sunshine produced a remarkable change in Manfred. His legs became stronger, his tanned face fuller and the exposed areas of his forearms and legs went a deep mahogany colour.

The previous year David had constructed a den on top of the rocks which formed the boundary to the Aal waterfall. The den was built from reeds and canvas and, in the heat of day, made a shady nook from which the boy could see the river Aal meandering gently through the meadows towards the farmhouse. The only approach to the hideout was by a stiff, almost perpendicular, climb up a rock face. Manfred attempted this climb on a few occasions but, because of his temerity, inherent awkwardness and fear of heights, he was unable to accomplish the climb. David scampered up the rock face with ease and in order to help Manfred fixed a rope outside the den but, even so, Manfred was unable to negotiate the climb. On these occasions the boy from Munich became morose and sulky and almost tearful. For most of the time the two boys enjoyed each other's company, free from parental restriction, free from school and free to roam around the farm hunting, fishing, bathing and hiking. And so their idyllic existence continued day in and day out throughout the hot summer months of 1930.

On two or three occasions Manfred intimated to David that he had met the Führer and that, during the following year, he would be enlisting in the Hitler *Jungend*. He felt that even at his age he should be doing all he could to serve the Führer and the Fatherland and all his friends in school in Munich would be enlisting. It would be a happy time in camps in the summer months and, at the age of fourteen, he would be allowed to fire a rifle. Was this not exciting? David replied that he thought it might be but there were no Scouts or Hitler Youth cadres in Aalbrücke and, in any event, he knew his father would not allow him to join any youth organisations. So there was no point in thinking about it.

Manfred's convalescent holiday was coming to an end and his father was due to pick him up at the end of August. A few days before he was due to leave Manfred mastered enough courage to pull himself up the rope and into the den and suggested they should repeat the visit on the following day. On that particular day Manfred appeared dressed in his Hitler Youth uniform complete with brown shirt, *lederhosen* and the swastika-hilted dagger in his belt. David busied himself with watering the herd and by the time he had scaled the rocks into the den Manfred was already in the hideout. David found him sitting at the back of the den clasping his knees and sobbing quietly, alternately dabbing his eyes and his knees with a blood-soaked handkerchief. During the ascent and without David's help Manfred had managed to scrape his knee caps and tear his lederhosen on the sharp rocks. David settled down beside him and the two boys sat in silence for fully two minutes.

David noticed that for the first time in many weeks the sharp pointed swastika dagger was in its sheath in Manfred's belt. The sobbing gradually ceased. Manfred, with a handkerchief firmly pressed to his right knee, was the first to speak in a low faltering tone, "*Du bist mein besten Kamerad,*" then a long pause, "I know you are a *Juden* and my masters in school tells us that we must not be friends with Jews. But I want to be your friend."

David nodded indicating that he understood and Manfred continued "I saw a Hitler *Jungvolk* film before I came here and it showed the Hitler Youth becoming blood brothers by cutting their hands and mixing blood. Would you, David, become my blood brother?"

On impulse David replied "*Ja, Manfred.*"

He felt some affection for this tall, gangly, uncoordinated and emotional young Aryan who had been his closest companion and only playmate for three months. Manfred unsheathed the Nazi dagger. After a few tentative stabs at the front of his palm he became tearful again and David gently took the dagger from his sobbing companion and immediately plunged the sharp tip of the blade into the front of his right wrist producing a small venous ooze. He then took Manfred's right hand and placed his own palm on the blood-soaked handkerchief on Manfred's right knee. Manfred smiled and they clasped their right hands in a firm grip for a whole minute. When the hands were uncoupled Manfred's smiling light blue eyes looked directly at David.

"*David, nur wir sind Blütbrüders.*"

Very little else was said that morning. The boys felt a closeness which neither of them had previously experienced in their lives and they returned to the farmhouse hand in hand. Goodbyes were said and Joachim and Valtraut looked on with pleasure at their happy smiling faces. The following day the chauffeur-driven Opel came to pick up Manfred and whisked him away to Munich, leaving David sad at the loss of his summertime companion.

*

A year later, on the 12th September 1931, a black "official" Opel came to halt in the yard at Grossmunde and sitting in the back were the bowler-hatted Gerhardt and at his side Manfred, dressed in his brown-shirt uniform of the Hitler Youth, complete with a forage cap and a Nazi armband. David stood at the door of one of the outhouses and witnessed the unexpected arrival of the car. Joachim and Valtraut were not in the yard to greet the visitors. David's first impulse was to rush to the car to greet his blood brother. An unseen hand held him back, as Manfred emerged from the car and looked straight through David without a flicker of recognition in his steely blue eyes. Manfred then joined his father and they walked stiffly towards the farmhouse door where an excited Valtraut appeared, fluffing her hair and patting her apron. Valtraut's attempt to smother Manfred with kisses was met with stern resistance and a stiff Nazi salute, replicated by his father at his side. By now, Joachim stood at Valtraut's side and looked crestfallen at the sight of his nephew bedecked in military clothing.

The Schmidt family disappeared into the house and David returned to his chores in the cow-shed, badly shaken and utterly dismayed. After twenty minutes Gerhardt and Manfred reappeared and with a perfunctory salute turned on their heels, re-entered the car and were driven away, neither giving a backward glance. Joachim, dejected, slowly crossed the farmyard to join David.

"I have some bad news for you David and for your family. My brother, who as you know is an official in the *Rathaus* in Munich, tells me that the Nazi Party are expelling all Jewish persons from Munich and from this area. He told me that Aalbrücke will be selected for 'cleansing' in October by a special squad of stormtroopers. Please go home now and send your father across to see me. I am sorry, David. My brother Gerhardt asked me to let your family know so that you could get away from Aalbrücke before the soldiers come. Go home now, David."

News of the impending purge of the Jews was so devastating that Isaac Grünberg began immediate preparations to move his family westwards into France. He called to see Joachim later that afternoon. They spoke together for twenty minutes and shook hands very firmly before parting company. That evening Isaac convened a gathering of

Jewish elders in Aalbrücke. They were all agreed that over the past year there had been a dramatic fall-off in trade from the German community on the other bank of the Aal. Isaac, in particular, had noticed a decline in demand for his calf-leather boots. Curiously there had been only a slight diminution in trade with his Munich clients. The elders decided on a wait and see policy. Isaac opted to leave Aalbrücke at the earliest opportunity. He would take his family to Aachen where the Grünbergs had a family connection.

The Grünbergs bade a sad farewell to their friends of twelve years standing on the 27th September, 1931. David's parting from the Schmidts was prolonged and poignant. There were many hugs and kisses from a tearful Valtraut who had baked a cake and two dozen delicious meat pies for the occasion. Joachim Schmidt was also near to tears. He repeatedly hugged David and, as a parting gift, gave him a silver watch and chain, a beautiful timepiece and a Schmidt family heirloom.

Isaac Grünberg had amassed a sizeable fortune during his twelve years in Aalbrücke but, due to the depression and devaluation of the mark, the true value of his money was considerably diminished. On September 27th the family travelled in comfort by train to Aachen and the journey was completed easily in one day. At the station they were met by Ben Levi, bald and bespectacled, with piercing dark eyes, who was a successful advocate and lived with his wife in a large house on the outskirts of the town. Isaac and Anna were uncomfortable in their new surroundings but David found the house interesting and enjoyed the large garden at the back and the walks along the well-manicured streets and avenues of suburban Aachen.

The town was situated astride the German/Belgian border and the Nazi influence was prominent amongst the local community. Uncle Ben urged the Grünbergs to move on as there was no work for Isaac and schooling for David would present difficulties. Ben Levi had already helped many Jewish families to move on to France and England from Aachen and, as a lawyer, he was able to provide these families with authenticated documents and, in particular, certificates of sponsorship and introduction. His contact in London was Dr Heinz Mulheim, a middle European doctor in practice in London's docklands. At first Isaac could not be persuaded to leave as he and Anna spoke no English and David, although he had studied English at school, could only claim to have a passing acquaintance with the language.

Gradually, under the sheer weight of reason and economics, it was evident that a move would have to be made. Isaac was assured by Ben Levi that Dr Mulheim in London would find him suitable work and that the education available in England was second to none. Ben Levi prepared the necessary documentation for the Grünbergs. He had an important motive for wishing the Grünbergs out of his house. Born in Aachen he was now a respected lawyer and a loyal Belgian citizen and the presence of a very orthodox and practising Jewish family in his home might compromise his credibility with the authorities and with the German speaking inhabitants on the eastern bank of the Maas.

The papers took three weeks to prepare and when they were ready and the tickets and vouchers purchased the Grünbergs left Aachen for London on the 19th October 1931. Ben took them to the railway station and, as the train was moving slowly away, allowed himself a few moments of ethnic self-indulgence when he considered that he had helped this Jewish family and many others to make a new home away from the encroaching and oppressive clutches of the Third Reich. In particular he was pleased that young David, already proficient in Hebrew and German and to a lesser extent in English and mathematics, would have a future in a British democracy. Ironically when the German juggernaut swept through the Low Countries in May 1940 the first two citizens in Aachen to be arrested and deported to a concentration camp in eastern Germany were Herr and Frau Levi.

The Grünbergs travelled in a comfortable train from Aachen via Maastricht and Brussels to the port of Antwerp. After an uncomfortable night ferry crossing from Antwerp on the Royal Harwich Ferry they found themselves wallowing in a dense fog in the Thames with foghorns blaring and visibility reduced to twenty yards. They eventually disembarked on Wapping Wharf at 11.30 a.m. on Tuesday 21st October 1931. On the dark side, in the swirling, cold fog, the ship's passengers were formed into two groups, a smaller queue for British citizens and the Grünbergs took station in a line forming in front of a placard illuminated by a single light bulb – "Immigrants and Aliens".

A large man in a heavy blue overcoat and peaked cap took a quick look at their papers and murmuring "Ah Dr Molly" sent them into a wooden hut where they were issued with two blankets each, soap and a towel and then directed to shed No. 29. The shed proved to be a large warehouse sub-divided by flimsy wooden partitions into a dozen separate cubicles and serviced by temporary washrooms and a primitive bucket latrine at one end. Isaac, Anna and David spent an uncomfortable twenty-four hours in the shed. They were given a meal of bread, cheese and hot soup in the evening and again mid-morning and on the following day at lunchtime Dr Molly arrived with a sergeant of police and a nondescript man in a grey suit representing the immigration authorities. Each of the four families were interviewed in turn and the Grünbergs were last in line.

Dr Heinz Mulheim was a short, dapper grey-suited man with twinkling, piercing, green eyes and a bushy mane of grey hair. He spoke with a curt middle-European accent. David acted as interpreter for the Grünbergs and after a few routine questions Dr Molly came to the unassailable conclusion that Isaac would be suited for a job in Mr Geldman's factory in Pusey Street, only three hundred yards north of Wapping Wharf. Furthermore, temporary accommodation was available on the third floor of the factory and the location was suitably near Pusey Street Primary School for David's education. When he had finished with the immigration formalities Dr Molly escorted the Grünbergs to the Geldman factory.

Mr Geldman was a large, flabby, balding and bespectacled individual with deep sunken eyes and a blotchy skin. He welcomed the Grünbergs warmly and proudly showed them around the two working floors of his factory which was producing tunics and overalls for post office employees and for the armed forces. He had no work for a shoemaker and Isaac Grünberg would have to learn new skills and, if he were prepared to act as night-watchman, he could have the flat on the third floor rent free. The 'flat' consisted of four rooms; two bedrooms, a kitchen/living room and a separate toilet and bathroom. The rest of the rooms on the third floor were storage space for rolls of denim and cloth which were used in the factory two floors below. The windows in the flat overlooked Pusey Street on one side and a green area and playing fields at the rear. Anna's heart sank when she saw the state of the living accommodation offered but the Grünbergs had no choice. Over the succeeding three days some hard work, scrubbing and polishing, converted the derelict rooms into reasonable living and sleeping quarters. Gas-lighting was only available on the ground and first floors and the Grünberg's flat was illuminated by two oil lamps. Within a few days Isaac had started his dull, laborious work on the sewing machines in the factory. At night he patrolled the floors below twice between dusk and dawn.

After a fortnight Dr Molly called with an education officer to interview David and arrange for his further education. It was decided that he could not proceed immediately to a secondary or grammar school and that he would need six months' probation at a primary school prior to sitting an entrance examination. The primary school selected was two blocks away from the flat on the eastern side of Pusey Street, wedged in between the main road in front and the Shadwell dock basin at the rear. David was to start his schooling after the Christmas holidays on the 5th January 1932. In the meantime he would celebrate his barmitzvah. David's barmitzvah on his thirteenth birthday on the 22nd November was a very quiet affair. The Grünbergs had not met many of the local Jewry and Isaac reserved the synagogue in Wapping Lane for the ceremony and had planned a simple celebratory meal in their flat. Mr and Mrs Geldman had other ideas. They arranged for the Grünbergs, the Mulheims, the Rabbi from the synagogue in Wapping Lane and their own Rabbi in Golders Green to gather at their house in Hampstead where a sumptuous meal was provided. David was allowed a taste of the celebration wine, his first ever encounter with alcohol. The combination of wine and travelling across London in the Geldmans' motor car made this a memorable day for the young man. On the night of his barmitzvah he went to bed tired and content and, for the first time, he felt completely at home in his new environment.

Chapter Six

Gerhardt Schmidt, Munich Nazi Party, 1919 – 1939
Manfred Schmidt, Military Academy, 1936 – 1938

Nazi Party Diary

In September 1919, Adolf Hitler, still assigned to the List Regiment, appeared on the scene in Munich where he attended a meeting of German workers at the Hofbrauhaus. Together with an assortment of unemployed misfits and discharged servicemen, including Anton Drexler, a drunken homosexual officer, he took the lead in forming a Party of National Socialism which later developed into the Nazi Party. On 24th February 1920 Hitler produced a twenty-five point programme for adoption by his fledgling Party, which appealed to unemployed workers and the downtrodden peasants of Munich. The two significant points in Hitler's portfolio were union of all Germans in a greater Germany and denial to Jews of public office and citizenship in Germany and the eventual expurgation of all Jews and other aliens from German soil.

In the post-war years Bavaria was in turmoil, demanding separation from Chancellor Stressemann's Berlin Government. Ernst Röhm and his Brownshirt gang of rowdies enlisted in the Nazi Party in 1920 and became its strong arm squad. Röhm's Sturmabteilung (SA) Units were to play a significant part in the ensuing struggles for survival of the embryo Nazi Party. The Hakenkreuz was designed as an emblem for the Party by Hitler himself and swastika armbands were issued to members and to new enlistments after the autumn of 1921.

Gerhardt Schmidt received his armband from Rudolf Hess on the 1st June, 1921. Gerhardt was purely and simply a Party member who enjoyed the oratory and brouhaha of political meetings in the Hofbrauhaus *and the charismatic personality and dedication to the cause of the Führer. He was indeed a very minor cog in the machinery of the National Socialist Party. By now many prominent political and military figures joined ranks with Hitler. In late 1920 and early 1921, Rudolf Hess, Alfred Rosenberg, Dietrich Eckhart, Hermann Goering and Julius Streicher, a depraved sadist and anti-Semite, all enlisted. Alfred Rosenberg became editor of the Party's propaganda newspaper the* Volkisher Beobachter *and Hermann Goering assumed command of the SA. Hitler's personal entourage included his bodyguard Max Amann, a sergeant in the List Regiment, Ulrich Graf, Christian Webber and Heinrich Hoffman, the lame court photographer. The Nazi Party grew rapidly in strength and membership throughout 1922 and 1923, under protection of the ruthless SA, and become a formidable force in Bavaria. Nazism was becoming rampant in southern Germany but outside of this area and in the world at large very little recognition had been granted to the emerging Party. Benito Mussolini and Fascism in Italy were regarded as a greater threat to world peace than the comic looking Bavarian ex-corporal who was inciting the German population to overthrow the Weimar Republic.*

When the Bierhallputsch occurred on the 9th and 10th November 1923 Manfred was nearly five years of age. He was growing into a tall, fair-skinned, blond-haired, blue-eyed, long-legged youngster. His mother was perpetually depressed and morose and conversations with her husband and son were monosyllabic. Gerhardt despaired of her ever improving and had spent a lot of money on medical advice and various hydrotherapy and vitamin treatments but Helga would never co-operate and refused to take medication. Gerhardt had not had any sexual contact with his wife since Manfred's birth. His main concern was the complete lack of interest Helga showed in her son. She would not even touch Manfred and if the boy fell at play or started crying she turned her back on him and walked away. Young Manfred could not understand his mother and missed the natural contact which he might have expected from her. He concentrated his affection on

'Papi' showering him with kisses and hugs when he returned home from work.

During the daytime Gerhardt had arranged for a housekeeper to look after the boy and take him out to play in the park and to the shops. Frau Heller who lived downstairs was a great help and stood in for the housekeeper when she was sick or indisposed and when Herr Schmidt was late coming home from work. Helga could not abide having another person in the apartment during the day. She shouted and swore at the unfortunate housekeepers and occasionally physically attacked them which led to a succession of disgruntled helpers leaving the Schmidt apartment. Frau Heller was a linchpin in the young boy's early childhood. 'Helli' was always there to pick up the pieces and comfort the boy and, in all ways, acted as Manfred's surrogate mother.

At this time Gerhardt had three interests in life – the Nazi Party, his job as *Direktor* of the Census Department at the *Rathaus* and his blond Aryan son. After work and supper he sat the young boy on his knee and told him about his work at the *Rathaus* and about the famous men he met in Party meetings. He told Manfred about Hess, Goering and Röhm, but mainly about Adolf Hitler. He taught Manfred to execute a Nazi salute and made a small replica Nazi armband for him out of pieces of cloth from the needlework basket. The story of the Bierhallputsch was retold time and time again, Gerhardt stressing the courage of the Führer and General Ludendorf in the uprising. By the time Manfred started kindergarten he was well indoctrinated in the Nazi cult. His father promised that, one day, Manfred would meet the Führer in person

Manfred disliked kindergarten intensely. Having no brothers or sisters and no other young children near the apartment he was not used to mixing with boys of his own age and became a loner. The kindergarten teachers found him pleasant and obedient but very slow to learn to read and write. By the time he moved to junior school in Munsteralle, two blocks away from the apartment, he was academically considerably behind his contemporaries. His attitude to the teachers continued to be servile and polite but he was unable to integrate with his classmates and, in particular, he found it impossible to communicate with girls in the class and took great pains to avoid contact with them. All day at school he thought about getting home to No. 14 Grünewald Strasse and his tolerant 'Papi' and caring 'Helli'.

The evenings at the apartment were only spoilt for him when he had to go into his mothers room to bid her *"Guten nacht"*. Sometimes there was a replying grunt from the large mound of flesh under the bedclothes. More often that not his nightly salutation met with stony silence. As the years went by young Manfred came to hate this nightly incursion into his mother's bedroom sanctuary.

In the spring of 1926 Adolf Hitler returned to the Hofbrauhaus *in Marienplatz to resurrect his Nazi Party in Munich. After his arrest and subsequent incarceration for nine months during 1924 the Party had gone underground but Hitler was now determined that it should survive by constitutional means, not relying on military force or a putsch to achieve its aims. He soon became confident and in a speech in February 1927 reiterated his threats to the State and was banned from public speaking for two years. During this time he concentrated his energies in recruitment. In 1925 there were roughly twenty-seven thousand paid up Party members but this number was increased to one hundred and seventy thousand by 1929. During this period Hitler's visits to Munich became less frequent and between 1927 and 1930 he spent his time travelling the length and breadth of Germany on recruitment drives and, in between, resting at his villa at Berchtesgaden in the Bavarian Alps. In 1927 Ernst Röhm, the SA leader, broke his partnership with Hitler and, disbanding the SA, left Germany to become a colonel in the Bolivian Army. The Nazi Party was now lying dormant, without a leader who could speak in public and without armed strength for protection and intimidation of opponents.*

Between 1925 and 1929 Gerhardt remained *Direktor* of the census department at the *Rathaus*. During this period he had to conceal his affiliation to the Nazi Party and never wore his insignia in public. He acted as a notary at party meetings which were again resurrected at the Hofbrauhaus or the Burgerbraukeller, depending on the number of attenders. At one such meeting in the Hofbrauhaus in June 1927, with Hess's permission, he brought Manfred to be introduced to the Führer. Hitler stood in the middle of the floor as Gerhardt ushered Manfred towards him. The nine year old boy was shaking but stood rigidly at attention and gazed directly into the Führer's blue eyes. Hitler took his hand and then gently patted his head.

"Your son Herr *Direktor* Schmidt? A good strong boy. He will make an excellent soldier for the Third Reich."

He then gave Manfred's hand a final squeeze, turned on his heels and mounted the platform to start the meeting. Gerhardt, with an arm around Manfred's shoulder, took the boy outside.

"Is the Führer not a great man, Manfred?"

"Ja, Papi, he is like a god. I shall never forget this meeting with mein Führer."

Manfred walked home to the apartment in a daze. He slept soundly dreaming about his encounter with the great man who looked and acted like God and who held the destiny of the German nation in his hands.

Resurgence of the Nazi Party occurred with exceptional rapidity, starting late in 1928 when Germany, in common with all other nations of the world, entered the great depression. The value of the Deutschmark plummeted and unemployment was rife. Hitler estimated and guessed correctly that the time was right for a further attempt to take over Government in Germany. A general election was called for 14th September, 1930 and a well-oiled Nazi organisation swung into action concentrating its campaign on the unemployed, homeless, and starving millions and on the youth of Germany. The Nazi Party with a total of six and a half million votes became the second largest party in Government. Munich was the hotbed of Nazism and, on its return to power, the local party in Bavaria became immensely powerful.

As a long-standing member of the Party Gerhardt Schmidt's fortunes prospered. Throughout 1929 he had been wearing his Nazi armband to work despite protests from the *Bürgermeister* who was deposed in January 1930 and replaced by a Nazi-sponsored Mayor, Herr Konrad Widemayer. In June 1930 Gerhardt was appointed *Direktor* and Secretary of a new Nazi headquarters at the Braunhaus in Munich. Within the Party this was a prestigious appointment and signified great changes in the lifestyle of the Schmidt family. The Braunhaus was located about half a mile from Marienplatz and was the centre for political and military organisation of the Nazi Party in Bavaria. Herr *Direktor* Schmidt was responsible for the smooth running of Party headquarters and when he left the *Rathaus* he made certain that all his census data was transferred to his new office.

After the Nazi success in the 1930 September elections and on Hitler's instigation the bombastic and uncouth Colonel Röhm was invited back to Munich to reform and retrain the SA battalions which were again beginning to use force to achieve the Party's political ends. Much to Gerhardt's dislike, Röhm and Heinrich Himmler, who was Commandant of the Schutzstaffel (SS), established their headquarters in the Braunhaus. Of necessity Gerhardt had to put up with the arrogant, sadistic and homosexual SA leader and in this he was greatly helped by the conciliatory attitude of Rudolf Hess, Supreme *Kontroller* of the Munich Braunhaus between 1931 and 1934. In recognition of the importance of his position Gerhardt Schmidt was given a car and a chauffeur for his own personal use.

Due to his father's eminence in the Munich Nazi Party Manfred found that when he transferred from junior to senior school in November 1930 his new classmates treated him with awesome respect. He was not taunted or bullied and the teachers promoted him as a typical example of pure Aryan manhood. He was never chastised and his indifferent scholastic performances were overlooked. Not surprisingly the twelve year old boy became swollen-headed and took to wearing his Nazi armband and dagger to school, without protestations from his tutors. Nazi classroom indoctrination was taking hold rapidly and each day started with an assembly, singing the Horstwessel song and *Deutschland Uber Alles* and pledging fidelity to Germany and the Führer. A visit to the school by Baldur von Schirach stimulated interest in the Hitler Youth movement and a cadre of young volunteers enlisted, Manfred Schmidt the youngest and proudest of them all.

Geli: 18th September, 1931

At eight o'clock on the morning of September 18th 1931 Gerhardt Schmidt sat behind an ornate desk in his comfortable office suite in the Braunhaus. A large portrait of Adolf Hitler in his brown shirt uniform adorned the wall behind him and on each side of the desk were two Nazi pennants on standards. A cup of steaming coffee lay untouched near his right hand as he scanned through reports received over the telephone by the night-time operator. After scrutinising each message he carefully placed the papers in order into one of four boxes on the desk for the attention of Hess, Himmler, Röhm and for his own action, depending on the degree of urgency. This task took him nearly an hour by which time the coffee was cold and he pressed the buzzer and asked Ingrid, his middle-aged, stony-faced secretary, to bring him a second cup. Before the coffee arrived a telephone operator burst unannounced into the office brandishing an urgent message.

Gerhardt gazed in disbelief at the curt message: *"Geli ist tot."*

He shouted for Ingrid and, when she appeared, asked her to find out if Hess, Röhm or Himmler had arrived in their offices. He suddenly remembered that Hess had left with the Führer the previous day to attend a Party rally in Nuremberg. As Ingrid was moving quickly out of his office Gerhardt added, "Don't bother with Hess, he's with the Führer in Nuremberg."

He then curtly dismissed the operator and told her not to discuss the telephone message with anyone. Gerhardt sat erect in his chair thinking hard as to how he would deal with this unprecedented catastrophe. In the summer of 1929 Adolf Hitler introduced a bright loveable young lady to the Party hierarchy. Her name was Geli Raubal, reputedly the Führer's niece. Hitler brought her from Vienna and had provided her with a large furnished apartment in Munich. She accompanied him to nearly all official functions and receptions and most of the senior Nazis in Munich had little doubt that Hitler was besotted with her. When Geli was around he was a different person, laughing, smiling and cracking jokes in the presence of his beloved niece. And now she was *'tot'*. When, where, how and why? As Gerhardt wrestled with these questions Himmler burst into his office.

"Vas ist loss Herr *Direktor?"* The ferret-like short-sighted, moustached leader of the SS demanded an answer.

Gerhardt repeated, *"Geli ist tot."*

Himmler acted quickly. Geli's address was known at the Braunhaus and the Munich police chief was alerted and ordered to make his way immediately to her home. Turning on his heel Himmler strode out of the office, *"Kommen sie mit* Herr Schmidt. *Schnell."*

Gerhardt and Himmler were the first to arrive at the apartment. The housekeeper, crying and wailing, met them at the bottom of the stairs. She had heard a shot in the early hours of the morning and at around 7.30 a.m. found her mistress lying on the floor in a pool of blood. She had immediately telephoned the Braunhaus. Gerhardt complimented the housekeeper on her swift action and stumbled up the stairs behind Heinrich Himmler.

In the bedroom they found the beautiful Geli, dressed in her night-gown, lying on the floor, her shattered skull surrounded by a pool of dark congealed blood and a pistol near her outstretched right hand. There was no need to examine the body. Geli was obviously very dead and the body very cold. *Obergruppenführer* Schneidhuber, the police chief, burst into the room with a flurry and, sizing up the situation, ordered everyone out of the room except Gerhardt and Himmler. He stood squarely in front of the two officials from the Braunhaus.

"We must do everything to conceal the nature of this poor girl's death for the sake of our beloved Führer. He must not be allowed to suffer more than necessary. It is clearly suicide. I will arrange for the body to be moved to the mortuary immediately and have this place cleaned up. You gentlemen should return to the Braunhaus and contact the Führer. He must be told of this tragedy as soon as possible."

Gerhardt Schmidt and Heinrich Himmler drove back to the Braunhaus in complete silence. Once inside the building Himmler turned to Gerhardt.

"You, Herr Schmidt, must inform the Führer. I wash my hands of this and do not want anything more to do with it," and with that he strode downstairs and out of the building. Despite his ruthlessness and depravity Heinrich Himmler was morally straight-laced and, from the beginning, strongly disapproved of the Führer's alleged incestuous involvement with his beautiful young Austrian niece.

Gerhardt spent the rest of the morning telephoning Nuremberg trying to contact Hitler's entourage. He spoke to the Führer in the early afternoon. Hitler's reaction was complete disbelief.

"*Nein, nein* Herr *Direktor*, there must be a mistake. Tell me this is not true. Oh *mein Gott*...! I will return to Munich immediately."

Gerhardt met the Führer and Hess at Munich airport and accompanied them to Geli's apartment. Hitler thanked Gerhardt for his handling of the delicate situation and, devastated with grief, was driven to Obersalzburg for complete rest and, for a few months after Geli's death, he remained inconsolable in his mountain retreat at Berchtesgaden.

Nazi Party Diary

As the world depression progressed the Weimar Republic crumbled leading to the election and resignation of successive governments in Germany during 1931 and 1932. The elections of July 1932 left the Nazis holding 320 seats in the Reichstag, not an overall majority, but sufficient to make them the largest party with nearly thirty per cent of electoral votes. On January 15th 1933 a local electoral success at Lippe gave Goebbels a chance to celebrate a great Nazi victory and this minor success impressed the waverers in the Weimar government. Largely due to von Ribbentrop's influence, the state secretary Meissner, the President's son Oscar von Hindenburg and Franz von Papen were recruited into the Nazi fold. On 30th January, 1933 von Papen took Hitler and his supporters to the Chancellery to meet the President, Field Marshal von Hindenburg. The President agreed that for the good of the Fatherland a coalition government should be formed, with a Nazi cabinet in control and Adolf Hitler Chancellor of the Third Reich. The last 'free' election in Germany was held on the 5th March 1933.

By liberal use of SA Stormtroopers under Röhm and Himmler's SS Battalions other political parties were harried and rival electioneering meetings were broken up in disarray. Goebbels' propaganda machine worked around the clock to produce a Nazi majority in the next Parliament. On 27th February, 1933 the Reichstag burnt to the ground, a Communist atrocity against National Socialism claimed Goebbels, who blamed the arson on a Dutchman named van der Lebbe. The backlash all over Germany was horrendous. Communist sympathisers were hounded, arrested, beaten, tortured and incarcerated and often shot without trial. On March 23rd, in the wake of the great fire, Hitler pushed an enabling act through Parliament devolving all the powers of the Reichstag on to himself. Though these powers were meant to be temporary they were never relinquished by Hitler and, on this day, the Führer became the undisputed leader and dictator of the Third Reich.

Early in 1930 Rudolf Hess held a secret meeting in the Braunhaus with the Munich deputy leaders to discuss the Führer's edicts for a New Order in the Third Reich. The main principle of the New Order was the subjugation, incarceration, exportation and elimination of non-Aryan ethnic groups throughout Germany. The specific arrangements for identifying these 'undesirables' were outlined by Hess.

"In Munich we already have a census compiled by our *Direktor,* Gerhardt Schmidt, and I ask him now to extend his survey to include towns, villages and rural areas within a fifty kilometre radius of the city. I need not add that the results of the census will be kept in secret here at the Braunhaus. Comrades, we are indeed fortunate in having such an expert in the field working with us."

All eyes and nods of approval were directed towards Gerhardt who felt elated and proud that his work in the *Rathaus* had been acknowledged by the deputy leader of the Nazi Party. At the conclusion of the meeting Gerhardt pored over a wall map of Munich and its environs. The fifty kilometre circle which he drew on the map included Aalbrücke. With great efficiency and aided by a private secretary, Giesela Sturmkopf, Gerhardt spent the next year travelling daily through towns and villages within a fifty kilometre circle compiling a census of German citizens and a separate secret list of non-Aryan and Jewish residents. By the end of March 1931 his census was near completion and Aalbrücke was one of the last few villages requiring a visit. Dispensing with the services of Frau Sturmkopf for the day he seized the opportunity of taking Manfred with him to Grossmunde farm.

Nazi Party Diary
Ernst Röhm, 30th June, 1934

In February 1934 Ernst Röhm proposed to the Nazi cabinet that his two and a half million SA. Stormtroopers should be amalgamated with the SS and the Abwehr and the whole should be a people's army under his command. The regular army commanders, in particular General von Brauchitsch, rejected the plan out of hand and received Hitler's support.

Hitler could not afford to antagonise the Reichswehr generals. Röhm refused to be pacified and continued rearming his SA troopers and at the same time openly antagonising the senior generals in the German High Command, who were supported by the ailing and dying President Marshal von Hindenburg. Hitler had his eye on the presidency. In return for the High Command's support of his candidacy he offered a reduction in Himmler's SS Army by two-thirds, control of Röhm's ambitions and a guarantee that the Wehrmacht *would be expanded and become the main military force in the Third Reich.*

Admiral Raeder readily agreed and, after consultation with senior Reichswehr *generals, a 'deal' was arranged. Within the Nazi Party Goering and Himmler were openly antagonistic to Röhm. Herr Himmler was commander of the black uniformed SS, but still under Röhm's overall command. Goering appointed Himmler Chief of the Prussian Gestapo to include his SS troops. Hitler feared that the SA. might revolt and he ordered that they should all go on leave for the month of July 1934. In mid-June Röhm, accompanied by a few of his senior officers, went on sick leave to Hotel Hanslbauer on Lake Tegernsee and Gerhardt Schmidt was instructed to keep an eye on the motley band of SA officers. Meanwhile throughout May and June Hitler had been under considerable pressure from Marshal Hindenburg, Goering, Himmler and the German Abwehr generals to disband the SA Stormtroopers and remove Röhm from office.*

On the 29th June Gerhardt Schmidt informed Martin Bormann, who was with Hitler at a rally in Bad Godesberg, that the SA in Munich were re-mobilising and a similar message arrived from Berlin. A plane carrying Hitler and Goebbels left Hangelar airfield near Bonn at 2 a.m. on June 30th and flew directly to Munich, where they were met at the airfield at 4 a.m. by Gerhardt Schmidt. Hitler descended the aeroplane steps in his crumpled brown raincoat and floppy black hat and returned Gerhardt's salute.

"What's happening here in Munich, Herr *Direktor*?"

Gerhardt replied, "Mein Führer, on your direction some twenty SA officers have been arrested and are being held in the Ministry of Interior to await your arrival. Major Walther Buch and Adolf Wagner carried out the arrests and they are also holding *Obergruppenführer* Schneidhuber, the police chief."

The party entered the black limousine, Hitler and Goebbels in the back seat and Gerhardt in the passenger seat. Hitler leant forward.

"And what about Röhm?"

"We have been keeping him and his companions under observation since he arrived here three weeks ago. He hardly ever leaves the hotel but has been seen in Wiessee on a few occasions. He has not visited Munich."

"Well done Herr Schmidt. You have acted according to my wishes. Now let us drive to the Ministry first and then on to Tegernsee."

They drove in silence to the Ministry of Interior where loyal party members held captive the Munich SA leaders, including the chief of police. The fleet of cars then left for Tegernsee, some forty kilometres to the south, where they arrived just after dawn on the 1st July. Gerhardt Schmidt saw the Führer and Goebbels enter the hotel and a short while later two naked men were dragged out on to the lawn and summarily shot in full view of the motorcade. An hour later Hitler and Goebbels emerged and were driven quickly away back to headquarters in Munich. Röhm was arrested by SS officers and taken to Stadelheim Prison on the outskirts of Munich. Gerhardt returned to his desk at the Braunhaus where reports were coming in of a massacre of one hundred and fifty SA officers in Berlin at the *Kadet* Academy in Lichterfelde, ordered by Goering and Himmler. Later that day a report arrived from Stadelheim Prison that Röhm had committed suicide. Goebbels called at the Braunhaus in the early evening and commended Gerhardt on the way he had handled the insurrection.

In reality Röhm had been shot in his cell by two SS officers. During that day, the 1st July, nearly six hundred officers and Commanders of the SA were executed. Hitler had effectively destroyed the SA and its homosexual bombastic commander and in its place he gained allegiance from the Army and Navy. Gerhardt described the purge to sixteen year old Manfred, explaining that the drastic actions were justified to ensure survival of the Nazi regime and outlining his own part in the events of the day. By now Manfred was a sergeant in the Hitler Youth Movement and glorified in the resolution showed by the Führer in dealing with Röhm and his mutineers and revelled in the important part that his own Papi had played in the bloody purge of the SA in Munich. The world came to know the purge of Ernst Röhm's SA as the night of the long knives.

Manfred Schmidt. Hitler Youth. Military Academy

In 1929 Baldur von Schirach introduced the concept of a Hitler Youth Movement to the Nazi Party executive and, though his proposals were well-received by Hitler, they were not generally accepted by the Cabinet. He persevered and in the later part of 1930 introduced a youth programme for German boys and girls based on the scouting movement. Originally the joining age was fourteen but by 1932 a *Jungvolk* section was introduced for boys aged between ten and fourteen. Entry into the *Jungvolk* and Hitler Youth entailed swearing an oath of allegiance to the Führer. The Hitler Youth section in Manfred's secondary school became active in the spring of 1930, but his illness during that winter and subsequent convalescence delayed his recruitment into the programme until October 1931. His contemporaries at school were urged to volunteer for the Hitler Youth as depicted on posters showing a shadowy picture of Adolf Hitler in the background and the strong positive picture of a blond, blue-eyed youngster in the foreground. The captions on the posters read *"Jungend dient dem* Führer", "Youth serve the Führer."

Manfred's academic progression in school was mediocre and his aptitude at sports indifferent but the pomp and ceremony of the parades, dressed in a brown tunic, black trousers and brown forage cap, captivated his imagination. He became a fanatic Nazi and was rapidly promoted to the rank of sergeant. At the age of seventeen he was elected *kapitan* of his school and senior leader of the Hitler Youth Corps in Munich. Undoubtedly his promotion to both these positions were largely dependent on his father's powerful position in the Nazi Party. The tall, humourless, serious-minded Manfred decided at the age of sixteen, and with his father's full blessing, that he would dedicate his life to the Fatherland and the Führer and that he would pursue a career in the regular German army or the SS. Gerhardt was extremely proud of his son. He looked so manly and strong in his Hitler Youth uniform and Gerhardt was completely overcome with emotion when he was an official guest on the back row of the rostrum with other Nazi dignitaries at the Nuremberg Rally in July 1935 when his son led the march past of the Munich Youth Corps.

In April 1936 German troops re-occupied the demilitarised Rheinland and in the summer of the same year Manfred left his secondary school and enlisted in the Grafelfing *Kadet* Academy where he spent two years completing his general education and introduction into the Officers Corps of the German Army. Life at the Academy was an extension of the discipline, parading and training he had received with the Hitler Youth. One visiting lecturer in 1938 impressed Manfred immensely. *Hauptmann* Kurt Student had been attached to the Condor Legion in Franco's war in Spain and had first-hand experience of the use of parachute troops in battle. *Hauptmann* Student predicted that in the German Army of the future *Fallschirmjagger* units would be invaluable for surprise attacks behind enemy lines, combined with softening up of defences by Stuka bombardment from the air, as happened in Guernica in April 1937, an assault in which the captain had led the airborne forces. These surprise attacks led to instant success and did away with the prolonged battles of attrition which had been a pattern of trench warfare in the last Great War.

Another speaker, Major Erwin Rommel, expounded the theory of the use of tanks in great numbers supported by stormtroopers to punch holes in enemy defence lines and surround defenders, breaking them up into small pockets, which could then be easily subjugated and conquered. These blitzkrieg lightning attacks were to be the pattern for future action by the armies of the Third Reich.

Manfred graduated from Grafelfing *Kadet* Academy in May 1938, twentieth in order of merit out of a group of eighty *Kadets*. His father attended the passing-out parade and proudly watched his son march at the head of his section saluting General Ludwig Beck who had been invited to command the parade. Despite Gerhardt's connections he had been unable to secure a place for his son in the SS, mainly due to opposition from Heinrich Himmler. On 21st September 1938 Lieutenant Manfred Schmidt was posted as a section commander to the Twelfth Bavarian Hussars stationed at Augsburg.

German troops occupied Sudeten territory in Czechoslovakia in October 1938. Early in the same month Berlin informed Gerhardt Schmidt that Colonel Count Erich von Bulow would visit Munich on a recruitment drive for the Parachute Brigade. Gerhardt was directed to make every facility available at the Braunhaus and to alert all *Wehrmacht* and SS units of the impending visit and its purpose. With the co-operation of local army commanders Gerhardt produced a three day timetable for the paratrooper colonel's visit and also arranged for his car and chauffeur to be at the Count's disposal. Gerhardt looked forward with anticipation to meeting von Bulow whom he remembered fondly from the previous occasion when the Count, then a captain, had been on a recruitment campaign in 1917.

When Colonel Count Erich von Bulow arrived at his office on the 30th October Gerhardt was completely taken aback. Before him stood a short, elegantly dressed, sprightly man in his early fifties sporting a bristly grey moustache and a black eye-patch covering his left eye. His left arm was missing and an empty sleeve was pinned to his left breast pocket near his Iron Cross and his Knight's Cross. There was a placid smile on his face and his blue right eye twinkled brightly beneath the peak of his gold-embroidered cap. After a cordial exchange of pleasantries the Count sat casually in a chair and, after asking permission, lit a long cheroot.

Count von Bulow, an aristocratic Prussian officer and a descendant of the famous Baron who fought with the British against Napoleon at Waterloo, had a chequered history. Volunteering in 1914 he served as an officer in the Verdun campaign where he lost his left eye. It was reported at the time that the cause of the injury was a piece of flying shrapnel. The truth of the matter was that he lost his eye in a duel for a lady's favour whilst on leave at Belfort. His left arm was amputated in 1937, crushed by a tank during the Spanish Civil War, when he was an observer with the Condor Regiment. Again it was reported that he had suffered the injury in a fierce tank battle. The truth was that his arm was amputated by the tracks of a tank when, in a drunken stupor, he had fallen asleep under the vehicle.

Within ten minutes the Count left the Braunhaus to start his recruitment campaign and returned in the evening at 7 p.m., slightly inebriated but in excellent spirits. He had recruited five soldiers for his Parachute Regiment that day which, he assured Gerhardt, was a good result as, in general, very few Abwehr or SS personnel showed any enthusiasm for enlisting.

"Gerhardt, where can we eat and have a few schnapps? What about the *Bierkeller* we visited together when I was last here in Munich in 1917?"

Gerhardt thought quickly and decided that the Hofbrauhaus would probably not be suitable for the colonel who obviously liked good food and wine. Since Helga's death Gerhardt had not been frequenting the Hofbrauhaus very often. He managed a visit once or twice a month. Due to his elevation to a position of seniority in the Nazi Party and his increased income he preferred to dine in one of the more fashionable restaurants around the *Rathaus* where he was more likely to meet high-ranking officials and army officers. He recommended one of his favourite eating places, the Restaurant Den Berliner, but the wily old colonel would have none of it and insisted on going to Willi Klinsman's establishment.

At 7.30 p.m. the colonel strode purposefully across the cobbled Marienplatz with Gerhardt, limping slightly, finding difficulty keeping up with his fast-walking pace. By the time they reached the Hofbrauhaus Gerhardt was quite breathless but the Count, obviously very fit and agile, leapt down the steps, through the revolving doors and into the main lounge followed ten seconds later by the panting *Direktor*.

Willi came from behind the bar to welcome Gerhardt and his important guest, clicking his tongue and wiping his hands on his blue-striped apron.

"Welcome, welcome, Herr Colonel. Welcome Herr *Direktor* Schmidt, the first drinks are on the house."

The schnapps kept coming thick and fast, backs were slapped, tales were told and the old favourite wartime songs were sung, whilst in between the carousing the Count entertained them with his stories of war, lovemaking, fighting, surviving and dying. What a great night! Afterwards Willi averred that it was the best night they had ever had in the Hofbrauhaus, thanks to *Direktor* Schmidt who had brought this military genius, this raconteur, this man's man, into his inn.

The following day Colonel Count von Bulow made a few more recruiting calls and dined in splendour with the commanding general of the *Abwehr* garrison in Munich. On the third day the Count was due to leave for Nuremberg. Gerhardt asked if he could stay overnight to meet his son. Lieutenant Manfred Schmidt was due home on weekend leave. The Count agreed provided they could again dine and drink in the Hofbrauhaus on the Friday night.

As arranged the proud father took Manfred, formally dressed in his mess kit, to the Hofbrauhaus to meet his friend Colonel von Bulow. The older officer, fortified by liberal tots of schnapps with the ever-attentive Willi hovering in the background, mesmerised and captivated the young Lieutenant.

"Manfred, we need you in the *Fallschirmjagger*. You are just the man I need. If you agree to enlist I will personally make sure you become my aide at brigade headquarters. Think about it."

Before the night was through, and with a slightly befuddled brain from the effects of the schnapps, Manfred indicated he would be proud to join the Parachute Regiment and serve under such an illustrious and dashing commander as the Count. Gerhardt was overjoyed and his active brain already envisaged his son's progress and promotion to a high rank within the *Fallschirmjagger*. The deal was sealed with a firm handshake and a toast to *"Die Fallschirmjagger."* By the end of the evening the whole party was inebriated and Colonel von Bulow scribbled something indecipherable on the back of an envelope, crushed it into his tunic pocket and with a *'Heil Hitler'* and a ramrod straight spine, marched slowly and unsteadily out of the Hofbrauhaus to return to his billet in the garrison barracks.

On the following day Gerhardt was uncertain the Count would fulfil his promise and commented, "He is an officer and a gentleman, but I fear the bargain was made when the Count was in a bad state and he may have forgotten by today."

Manfred was more optimistic.

"Papi, I know the colonel will keep his word."

Manfred was quite correct. In late November his commanding officer in Augsburg was informed that, "Lieutenant Manfred Schmidt will transfer to the Eighth Parachute Regiment at Lübbecke, date of transfer – 10th January 1939."

The commanding officer re-read the telegram, shrugged his shoulders and commented, "Lieutenant Schmidt, I can't understand why you wish to leave a crack unit like the Twelfth Bavarian Hussars to serve with this crackpot, rabble-rousing outfit. However, the order comes from High Command and I have no alternative but to agree to it. I wish you luck. You are dismissed!"

Manfred saluted, turned on his heel and marched out into the barrack square pleased that in the New Year he would become an officer in Colonel von Bulow's regiment.

Christmas leave of 1938 was the last time Manfred would be at home with his father. They celebrated modestly and for the first time in ten years he attended a church service on Christmas day. He dined on two occasions at the Den Berliner with Marianne Widemayer, the tall, blonde, but rather plain, daughter of the Nazi *Bürgermeister*. There was little romance in these meetings. Manfred was awkward and ill at ease in the girl's presence and the evenings always ended on Marianne's doorstep with a hug and a peck on the cheek, though the girl herself wanted to pursue matters further. For a few days in the

New Year Manfred returned to the Hussars. On 9th January he left Augsburg to commence his training with the Eighth Parachute Regiment.

Chapter Seven

Pusey Street School, 1932
Rotherhithe Grammar School,
1932 – 1936

The school in Pusey Street was a typical Victorian grey-stone building in the shape of a letter 'T'. The transverse limb of the 'T' faced on to the street and was contained within high railings with two large granite pillars and an archway protecting the main entrance. This part of the school housed three classrooms for the higher grades. The vertical limb of the 'T' had two classrooms for infants and first-formers. A sloping school yard, constructed of tarmac and gravel, lay at the back of the building on each side of the junior classrooms. At the very bottom of the yard there was a containing wooden fence which had, at its centre, a small gate leading to a narrow strip of ground cultivated as a vegetable garden. A small wooden storage shed for garden tools and agricultural implements had been erected at the entrance to the vegetable garden. By long-standing tradition the infants and first-formers used the playground on one side of the vertical 'T' limb and on the other side the girls of form three and four used the upper part of the yard for netball, whilst the boys of the same forms were allocated the lower half nearest to the boundary fence between the yard and the vegetable garden. This section of the playground was the undisputed domain of the big boys of the upper forms.

When David entered the school in January 1932 there were, in all, ninety-four pupils and in view of his age he was placed in the fifth form. The quiet, shy Jewish boy was at first shunned by his school mates who made ribald remarks about his difficulty in speaking

English and his German accent. Nicknamed the 'kraut' he learnt quickly and within a few weeks had outstripped his classmates in all subjects, including English.

David's acceptance amongst the senior boys was slow in maturing. The king and undisputed leader of the senior gang of fourth and fifth-formers at the school was Biffo, an unprepossessing, dark, squat and muscular Brylcream-haired boy of fourteen of dubious parentage. Biffo ruled the roost and was undoubtedly the ring leader and 'Boss' of the senior pupils and the ringmaster of the senior boys' patch in the school yard. At his age, Biffo should have left school, but the depression in Britain was at its height and more so in the London dockland area where there were no jobs available. The orphanage had persuaded the school authorities to accept Biffo at least until the end of the summer term to keep him off the streets and Biffo regarded his last year in school as 'doing time'.

The inevitable confrontation between Biffo and David occurred in the boys' urinal. After the usual jostling and verbal abuse David was pushed hard against the toilet wall whilst he was still urinating. David's warm urinary stream trickled down Biffo's trouser leg and on to his knees and boots. With a shout of "You bastard kraut" Biffo lunged at David aiming a blow at his head. David ducked to avoid the flailing fist and turned away from Biffo who jumped on his back enveloping his shoulders with his strong muscular arms. David instinctively hit backwards with the point of his left elbow and felt the sharp bony prominence sink into Biffo's midriff. Biffo gasped and started slipping downwards towards the ground. David used his elbow again as his adversary was falling and struck Biffo squarely on the point of his pug-like nose. There was a squelching noise and a loud yelp of pain from Biffo who fell to his knees onto the urine soaked floor holding his traumatised proboscis. Biffo shouted, "You shouldn't have done that. It was a dirty trick. You'll pay for this you fucking kraut."

David ran out of the toilet while Biffo's mates tried to console their stricken, bleeding leader. "It wasn't a fair fight. You'll get him next time, Biffo."

Contrary to expectation the fight in the WC was not a prelude to further confrontation. Biffo, cunning if not very bright, thought he might have met his match and a few days later invited David to join his gang. The kraut became a member of Biffo's clique, not through any desire on his part but rather to placate the ferocious little leader and keep the peace. David's scholastic ability impressed Mr Fairclough, the headmaster, who was convinced that David would be a candidate for entry to Rotherhithe Grammar School. Thereafter the headmaster and his senior staff concentrated their efforts on grooming David for the entrance examination which would take place in June. David sailed through the examination and came second in order of merit for the borough of Wapping. Three other pupils from Pusey Street, a boy and two girls, were also successful but came way down the list. Even Biffo was impressed with David's achievement and grudgingly gave him a compliment. "Well done, kraut. We showed them didn't we?"

At the beginning of the summer term a fourteen year old girl arrived at Pusey Street School before entering the unknown wide world outside. Her father had lost his job on the Great Western Railway in Ealing and had managed to secure a shunter's post in the London docks. Mary Louise O'Rourke was no beauty. She had a plain face, black hair and flashing dark eyes. The top part of her body was flat with no evidence of pubertal breast development. From the waist down she was over-developed and had large protruding buttocks and short stumpy, hirsute legs. Her mother attributed Mary's development in this area to the fact that her father had been an all-Ireland hurling champion. Mary Louise was not a scholar. Like Biffo she was in Pusey Street 'doing time' until the end of term when she could leave school and earn a living in some way or other, probably as a waitress or a housemaid. Though scholastically backward her one attribute was in the playground where she proved to be a very aggressive, and often dirty, netball player, so much so that the other girls refused to play with her.

Mary Louise turned her attention to the boys' games in the lower yard. This was Biffo's domain and the games that were played by the boys were directly under his control. One week it would be football, the next cricket, or French cricket, and this summer term Biffo had decreed that the game played should be tip and run, a form of cricket where the batsman, if he strikes the ball with the bat, has to run a statutory fifteen yards. Biffo's variation on the game was that the 'running' batsman could be obstructed or brought down in his run by any of the fielders. Very few batsman completed a run except, of course, Biffo himself. It would be unthinkable for a fielder to run down the gang leader and Biffo, in full flight wielding a cricket bat, was a formidable obstacle to tackle. Mary Louise, the supreme competitor, disobeyed the 'rules' and very few running batsmen, including Biffo, evaded her ferocious tackles. The boys came to regard Mary Louise as a 'sport' and within a week or two she had become a 'sport' in a sexual capacity which earned her the nickname 'Mary Loose'.

Mary Louise, at the age of thirteen years, had lost her virginity on an Ealing school trip to Southend-on-Sea. Whilst the seniors paired off, bought candy floss, wore 'kiss-me-quick' hats and went to the dark back seats of the cinema to kiss and grope, Mary Louise found herself left out and alone. She ate her sandwich lunch on the beach amongst a group of third form girls and afterwards complained of stomach ache and returned to the school bus which was parked in a large field on the outskirts of the town. The charabanc was deserted and Bill, the driver, was nowhere to be seen. Mary Louise retraced her steps and walked back towards the promenade. Outside the Lamb and Flag she saw Bill standing in the doorway with a frothing pint of Worthington bitter in his right hand and, by his look, she assumed that this was not the first pint he had consumed that day.

When Bill saw the peculiar, ugly, bird-like little girl dressed in her school uniform he downed his pint, came out of the pub and accompanied her back to the charabanc. Bill insisted that Mary should lie down on the back seat and loosen the buttons on her blouse and the waistband of her skirt. Having satisfied himself that the girl was comfortable he left saying that he had matters to attend to in Southend and Mary concluded that he was returning to the Lamb and Flag. The driver locked the bus and Mary Louise settled down to rest and sleep on the back seat of the aged charabanc.

"How are you now love?"

Mary woke with a start to see Bill bending over her, swaying to and fro and smelling of beer.

"Where's the pain?"

Mary indicated her lower abdomen.

"I'll rub it better," Bill volunteered, lifting her blouse and vest and inserting his large grubby fingers under the elastic of her bloomers gently massaging the painful area.

The sensation was pleasant and Mary guided the probing fingers lower where they became enmeshed in her tangled mass of pubic hair.

Bill's probing now became more insistent and, encouraged by Mary's pleas of, "lower, lower", he finally reached the area between her legs, aided and abetted by Mary's forward pelvic thrust. Bill was now undoing his trouser buttons clumsily and Mary gazed in awe at the size of his erect penis which, as if by a miracle, appeared in his left hand. Mary touched the penis and gently fondled it. The urgings from her nether regions were now becoming more intense and, as Bill covered her body with his own, she guided the erection into her area of genital pleasure. Bill was no longer gentle and he pushed forward violently using short sharp jabs with his hard penis. Suddenly Mary experienced an excruciating pain as penetration occurred. She gave a short sharp yelp but, as the pain subsided, she felt her whole lower body full of his erection which was now pumping in staccato bursts until finally the man above her shouted and yelled in ecstasy, his whole body reverberating.

Mary, incongruously, felt proud of the fact that she could produce such a reaction in a mature male. She felt a wetness between her thighs and an internal feeling of diminution in the size of the penis within her. Bill stood up abruptly and, wiping his blood-stained penis with a handkerchief, replaced it in his trousers.

"Best not to tell anyone about this, love. If you do I'll make trouble for you."

With that he returned to the front of the charabanc, sat on a seat and almost immediately fell asleep. Mary took off her vest and cleaned herself inserting the bloody garment in the carrier bag which once held her luncheon sandwiches and a bottle of pop. She would account for the blood stain on her vest to her friends by saying that her period had started.

Mary reflected on the experience. It had not been unpleasant and she decided she would want more of that as soon and as often as possible. Mary Louise was surprised at how soon her sexual urges returned. About an hour after defloration she wanted sex again. Not knowing how to entice the sleeping driver into action she decided on a bold full-frontal approach.

Knickerless and holding her blouse aloft she approached Bill and, shaking his shoulder, inserted her open legs at the man's half open eyes. Bill, rudely awakened, was amazed to be looking straight at a bleeding orifice surrounded by a black, bushy halo. He responded appropriately and on this occasion Mary sat astride his erection and attempted to be the lead artist in the sexual concerto. The second time was better than the first for Mary. When the rest of the school party returned she was ensconced on the back seat of the bus, smiling blissfully, and reassuring all who asked that her tummy pains had now settled down.

After the school trip to Southend Mary continued to further explore the mysteries of sex. The O'Rourkes were staunch Catholics and, as the teaching of the Church was clearly that intercourse should only be used for procreation, she arranged to visit her Auntie Molly, an unmarried far-distant cousin of the O'Rourkes who had a flat in Lambeth. Auntie Molly had a live-in lover, or more correctly a pimp, and, unbeknown to the O'Rourkes, Molly was a prostitute who plied her trade around the Elephant and Castle.

She instructed Mary in the mysteries of the safe period, *coitus interruptus*, contraception, male and female masturbation and the female orgasm. After two visits Mike, the pimp, was offered as a practical teacher. Mike was not a great lover, not interested in foreplay and a wham-bam practitioner which only partially satisfied Mary's lust. Mike regarded her as a potential addition to his harem when she was of age. Mary used to visit the Lambeth flat most weekends and, as this was Molly's busiest time of the week, she was alone with the wham-bam pimp for prolonged periods.

After leaving Pusey Street School Mary Louise intended to emulate Aunt Molly who seemed to be well-off and earning a comfortable living by merely being nice to men, just as she had been to Bill on the charabanc in Southend. In the meantime she was determined not to work and to enjoy herself as frequently and as often as she could in the company of the 'boys' in school and Mike in the Lambeth flat.

After a fortnight at Pusey Street Mary Louise was certain that none of the senior girls liked her. Because of her dark swarthy complexion and black eyes she had been nicknamed the 'gypsy' by the other girls. The gypsy soon became disillusioned with the pace and vigour of girls' netball and joined the senior boys at play in the lower yard. This was Biffo's patch and tip-and-run was the game of the term. At first Biffo and the boys were contemptuous of the thin ugly-looking little girl but her athletic ability soon won their approval. The games-master, supervising the yard at playtime, had no objections to Mary joining the senior boys as she looked perfectly capable of looking after herself. In any event he did not want any hassle to interrupt his chance of having a couple of fags, out of sight, behind the outdoor toilets.

Biffo was Mary's prime target. She reckoned that if she could conquer Biffo the rest of the gang would be chicken feed. Tip-and-run was played with a cricket bat and a tennis ball and the striker had to run if the bat came into contact with the ball and could be dismissed if either of the fielders hit the runner or the wicket. Biffo came running down the pitch wielding his bat to ward off anyone who dared obstruct his pathway. He was ten yards short of 'home' when Mary Louise tackled him from the side with a crunch that reverberated around the playground and he hit the ground with a loud thud which completely winded the boy.

As he recovered his senses Mary Louise was astride his thighs, her hands pressing his shoulders into the ground. He started to move to dislodge the girl but became pleasurably aware of the movement of her body. Mary Louise was pushing and grinding her pelvis into Biffo's groin. They lay in this position for half a minute, while the rest of the gang gathered around fearing that their leader had been mortally injured.

Mary Louise whispered in Biffo's ear, "What about it Biffo? Do you want a shag? In the shed!"

Biffo could feel his desire growing down below. They crouched and ran for the shed, sheltered from view by the surrounding group of boys. Biffo and Mary Louise were only in the shed for two minutes. Biffo emerged with a sly smile on his pug-like face.

"Did you do it Biffo? What was it like Biffo?" the gang enquired.

David kept himself away from the whole incident pretending the cricket bat needed urgent repair. For the next two weeks Biffo got his 'oats' every day. He had managed to acquire a condom from an older boy at the orphanage which was kept hidden, washed and dried each day, under a pile of flower pots. In order to allay any suspicion about the activities in the shed the rest of the boys continued with the game while Biffo and Mary Louise were copulating.

After a while Biffo became concerned that some members of the gang might split to the other children, or worse, to the headmaster. With Mary's eager collaboration he concocted a plan of initiation for each member of the gang followed of course by his own daily ration of sex. Mary offered the boys full sex, or masturbation, depending on her menstrual cycle and an estimation of her safe period. Mary's playground tackle was the indication of selection for her sexual favours on the day and the identity of the candidate had already been pre-destined by Mary and Biffo. David was the third boy to be gently tackled by Mary and ushered into the dimly lit shed. He was both petrified and strangely excited; petrified because he had no sexual experience and excited at the thought of what lay ahead. In any event he could not say no and risk accepting the wrath of the whole gang and in particular Biffo.

"Come here, kraut."

Mary Loose was sitting on a small table, naked from the waist down. She opened her legs slowly and deliberately to reveal the blackness of her perineal area with a vertical pink slash at its centre. There were no preliminaries. Mary expertly undid his trouser buttons and massaged his genitalia, quickly producing an erection which she then guided in between her legs, whereupon she started a vigorous pelvic gyration using the maximum power of her formidable buttocks. For David the next thirty seconds was a complete blur.

"Fuck me Kraut. Fuck me Kraut," Mary entreated.

All of a sudden he felt his penis was exploding, coupled with a sensation that he might be urinating between the girl's legs. He ended with two or three sharp thrusts of his own accompanied by a paroxysm of grunting. Mary Loose knew what had happened. She gave David a brief peck on the cheek.

"Get out Kraut. Send Biffo in. I'm ready for him now!"

David emerged from the copulating shed to the plaudits of the rest of the gang, shamefaced and near to tears. In two weeks it was David's turn again. This time Mary Loose would only allow masturbation which she achieved in a quick and non-gentle manner. The whole procedure took only twenty seconds, Mary diverting the seminal stream to intermingle with other stains on the floor of the shed, evidence of weeks of hard graft on Mary's part. She laughed, "Kraut spunk" and, as David left the shed in disgust, Biffo was eagerly awaiting his turn outside the door fingering the communal condom.

In late May matters came to a head. A short, fat, bespectacled, timid boy from the forth form, Leonard Plumpton had, for the past week or two, been showing an unusual interest in the goings-on at the bottom of the yard. Biffo felt that Lennie was getting too inquisitive and that the boy mighty betray the gang and expose Mary Loose's

108

activities to the authorities. He was made target for the day. Biffo pulled the protesting boy into the shed and held him there and, when confronted with Mary's nether nudity, Lennie burst into tears and started wailing loudly. Biffo took Lennie's trousers down and held him whilst Mary tried hard to arouse the boy's sexual interest, but to no avail. Lennie continued to cringe, wail and bawl. In the end Biffo held the boy between Mary Louise's legs as she managed to rub the tip of his flaccid penis in the voluminous bushy black brush of her femininity.

"Lennie, you've done it now. You are a member of our gang. Don't forget this is all a secret."

Lennie ran out of the tool shed weeping uncontrollably. Biffo remained behind to have a 'quickie' and partially satisfy Mary Loose's sexual ardour. On the following day in school all hell was let loose. At assembly the headmaster announced that there was a very grave matter to be resolved. The junior classes were dismissed but the fourth and fifth forms of both boys and girls were detained.

"Mr Plumpton came to see me this morning and made a serious complaint. Yesterday his son Lennie was sexually abused by two members of the fifth form. I want these two pupils to come on to the stage now."

No one moved. Mr Fairclough repeated his request. No one stirred but there were a few sidelong glances in Biffo's direction.

"Very well then," continued the Headmaster, "I will name the two culprits. I want Mary Louise O'Rourke and Billy Wendro to come up here immediately."

The allegations were repeated by the headmaster and they were not denied or confirmed.

Mr Fairclough continued, "This is a most serious offence that you have committed. You are both expelled and I don't want to see either of you again in this school."

Biffo and Mary Loose left the podium together. At the top of the steps Mary, smiling, half lifted her skirt to expose her muscular hairy left thigh above the elasticated black stockings and bobbed her buttock towards the headmaster in a gesture of defiance and insolence. Together they left the assembly room and the school premises. The scandal of Biffo and Mary Loose lingered on for the rest of the summer term. It did not affect David's application to his work and he attained one of the top three slots and a scholarship entry to Rotherhithe Grammar School.

*

From his home David was able to walk to Pusey Street School but getting to Rotherhithe involved a half mile walk to Wapping Pier, a ferry crossing of the Thames to land near the Mayflower Inn, and a half mile walk down Salter Road past the Church of St Mary. A scholarship ensured that his school fees and books were paid for and his father had only to provide a dark-blue school uniform and cap, a satchel and gym shoes and six pence a week for school meals. The grammar school was large and impressive, built of red brick, and had three playing fields at the rear. His fellow pupils were more refined than those at Pusey Street; no jibes of 'Kraut' or 'Jew' and, in fact, more than a third of the pupils at the school had Jewish ancestry. Rotherhithe Grammar School had four regular grades and two higher grades, upper and lower sixth. All the regular grades had streams A, B, C and D and, in view of his scholarship results, David was allocated to Form 2A.

The Form master was Mr David Evans MA, an Oxford graduate and Classics Master for the whole school. David Evans, a bachelor, irreverently called Daima by his pupils, was a short, rotund man always scruffily dressed with a red, rounded, blotchy face and a prominent large, pock-marked nose. He had a gentle lilting voice which contrasted sharply with his piercing dark brown eyes, shielded by thick horn-rimmed spectacles. Born in Treorchy in the Rhondda and destined for a life in the coal mines, by dint of an active brain and perseverance, he won a scholarship to New College Oxford and read Classics. He was a man of strong conviction, passionately fond of his beloved Classics, his Welsh heritage and the Eisteddfod, Socialism, rugby football, choral singing and Brains bitter. The latter passion could be said to be his only serious vice. Every night after school and at weekends he downed six or seven pints in the Angel Inn located between Jamaica Road and Hope Surface Wharf which was within walking distance of his lonely digs in Salter Road where, in a frugal manner, he catered for his simple needs. He had never married and was not interested in females. On a Sunday he occasionally went to the Welsh Baptist Chapel in Castle Street and only missed school on the occasion of the Welsh National Eisteddfod and the Munich *Bierfest* in October.

Within a few months of David's arrival at school Daima realised that he had an exceptional brain in Class 2A. Latin was one of the main languages during the first term and David was well ahead of his classmates.

"Would you consider doing Greek as well as Latin David?" asked Mr Evans one morning. "I mean would you think about doing Greek as an extra subject? I will coach you privately."

Without hesitation David agreed. David Evans MA was overjoyed. Here was a boy, who, if his brain didn't blow a fuse, was definite material for a classics scholarship to his old college at Oxford. The boy could already read and write German and Hebrew and would certainly make the grade in Latin and, if David Evans had anything to do with it, could be taught Greek.

"Right," said Mr Evans, "We'll start on a little Greek now but at the end of the term I will see your parents to discuss your future education."

Daima had found a young brain with an exceptional capacity for languages and to celebrate his 'find' he had an extra pint of Inde Coope and Alsop at the Angel that night, lamenting that they didn't sell Brains at the miserable dockside pub!

During Christmas week 1932, by appointment, David Evans MA arrived in the Grünberg's flat in Pusey Street. David's mother fussed around with her teapot and cakes but the visitor was not hungry and only had one cup of tea. Isaac Grünberg sat impassively at one end of the kitchen table with David between the two men acting as interpreter. Mr David Evans explained his mission and his intention for David's further education.

"Mr Grünberg, I want to groom your boy in Latin, Greek and Hebrew to get him into Oxford University which, as you know, is the leading college in Britain and in the world. I know it's a long time ahead but, to be sure we are successful, I need to start work next term."

Isaac nodded that he understood and agreed.

"One other thing," added the Welshman. "For peculiar reasons that I can't explain it would be an advantage if David's surname were changed, sort of anglicised."

Isaac did not agree. David himself was taken aback by the request as he saw no reason to change his name just to go to university. But perhaps Daima knew best.

"We'll leave things as they are at present," added Mr Evans and Isaac agreed again with a nod.

They parted company with a firm handshake, the tallish thin bearded Jew and the small, rotund, charismatic Welshman, knowing that they both were working towards David's future education and career in his country of adoption.

David's four years at Rotherhithe passed very quickly. Apart from his parents' company at home and the ritual synagogue attendance on Saturday there was very little social life. On occasion he persuaded his father and mother to take him out on Sunday, to the Tower of London, to the Palace and changing of the guards, to the British Museum and very rarely to Speakers' Corner at Hyde Park where he heard prominent speakers being heckled by a discriminating audience. He once heard Sir Leonard Moseley speak and, even at the age of sixteen, felt that the presence of a Fascist in the British democratic system was unbelievable. One Sunday night he was uplifted by a combined Welsh choir of unemployed miners singing in harmony – 'Cwm Rhondda', 'Sanctaidd' and 'Land of my Fathers'. On the sports field David had limited talent for soccer and cricket and, much to Daima's disappointment, no talent for rugby football. He was able to swim fairly well thanks to his early experiences in the Aal and took on the sport competitively representing his Grammar school at a few minor galas. His forte was in the classroom where he excelled at languages and had a natural proclivity for mathematics and physics. By the time he was in form 4A Daima announced that he had taught David all he knew and that the boy should now be entered for a scholarship to Oxford.

During his teenage years at Rotherhithe Grammar School David had little contact with girls. The Geldmans had taken the trouble to introduce him to a timid and introspective niece of theirs but he could not find any common ground with the shy Jewish girl and by now Mary Loose was an event in the distant past.

Daima felt some responsibility for David's existence outside school. He took David to a Wales and England rugby match at Twickenham in March 1935. The game itself made little impact on David but Daima went berserk. Fortified by a few pre-match pints he sang 'Land of my Fathers' with enthusiasm and conviction and then immediately started abusing the surrounding English supporters. It was meant to be light-hearted banter but David feared that there might be a premature end to the match if Daima continued to insult his English adversaries. Wales lost by six points and Daima was completely devastated and deflated on the way home. They called in numerous pubs, David waiting outside, as Daima continued his analysis of the game.

"If only Wooler or Viv Jenkins had kicked a goal then Wales would have been in with a chance and would have beaten the English bastards."

The day out was capped on the Central line between Tower Hill and Whitechapel Stations when Daima was violently sick. Thereafter David had to support him home to his flat in Salter Road and explained to the landlady that Mr Evans had been taken ill. The landlady showed very little concern for the drunken schoolmaster. Mr David Evans MA apparently frequently turned up in a dishevelled and inebriated state.

In May 1935 David sat his London Matriculation Examination. He passed with distinction in eight subjects, mainly languages and literature and had credits in three others. Daima advised further education in the lower sixth, concentrating on Latin, Greek and Hebrew and an attempt at the Oxford entrance scholarship in June 1936. The two day examination was conducted in the Great Hall at New College and Daima, at his own expense, took the adolescent boy to Oxford, where they put up in the Old Parsonage Hotel on College Green. David Evans MA was at home in Oxford. He spent his days meandering from pub to pub and usually arrived back at the Old Parsonage late at night, red-faced, belching and humming Welsh hymns, re-living past glories. Daima's cup was full to overflowing when news came in mid-July that David had passed his entrance examination with flying colours and had obtained a full Classics scholarship to New College. Daima celebrated David's success with a mammoth binge which lasted two days. David, now approaching his eighteenth birthday, was set to start his academic career at New College Oxford in Michaelmas Term 1936.

Daima continued giving advice, "You will enrol under the name of David Green. I have fixed this for you with the Dean of the College. You will keep the name Grünberg until you are eighteen and then it

will be changed by deed poll. You must persuade your father that this
is the right course to adopt."

David listened attentively to the advice of his tutor and mentor.
Had not Mr Evans been correct in all his prognostications up to now.
He owed the lovable rogue a lot and this advice seemed reasonable,
though he was certain that his father and the Geldmans would object
strongly. There was no alternative. In September 1936 David
arranged that, at the age of eighteen, by deed poll, he would have his
surname changed from Grünberg to Green.

Chapter Eight

The Oxford Experience,
October 1936 – June 1939

David travelled to Oxford on the 10.45 a.m. GWR train from Paddington on a misty Monday morning in October. His father accompanied him to the station to wish him well and, amidst a flurry of '*shaloms*' and hugs, the bearded parent held on to his son as long as possible. His last instruction in Hebrew to David was:

"Keep the faith, trust in God and go to the synagogue."

David's old valise was quite heavy as, apart from the dark suit and starched collar he wore, his father had bought a second dark-grey pin-striped suit and a second-hand dress suit, essential for dining-in nights at the Oxford college. He walked from London Street station to New College lugging his heavy valise and sweating, despite having to push forward through a cold drizzle. He entered the main gate of the college and reported to the head porter in the lodge who read out his name from a paper sheet on a clipper board.

"David Green, you're in No. 12 Plato. The servant will carry your bag upstairs. Welcome to New College, Sir."

Billy, the servant, was a wizened arthritic man in his early sixties who had great trouble in negotiating the narrow winding stone stairway and at the same time humping the valise from step to step.

"Your room is in the attic, Sir," Billy explained and, as they passed two open doors, No.s 9 and 10 on the third floor, David heard voices in each room. "The Honourable Percival Cavendish is in room 9 and Mr Bertram Woolford is in room No. 10. They will be your nearest room-mates, Sir."

David's attic room was small, spartan and cold, heated by an antiquated gas fire with a washstand in one corner. Billy explained that the lavatory and bathroom were on the landing on the floor below.

David started unpacking but kept his black overcoat on for warmth. As he was arranging his washing utensils and towel on the washstand, a loud imperious voice from below bellowed, "Hey, you up there, in No. 12. Come down and let's meet you. We're having a drink to celebrate safe arrival."

David edged his way slowly down the attic steps and, knocking on the open door, entered.

"Well, what in hell's name have we here? An undertaker no doubt! I'm Percy Cavendish, Perce to my friends, and that good looking fella is Bertie Woolford, call him Wooley."

David extended his hand stiffly in turn to both. "I'm David Grün..." he hesitated. "Green. I'm here to do Classics."

"Ah a clever bastard what d'ya think Wooley? Well work does not start for a week so let's drink and be merry!"

The Honourable Percy Cavendish turned to a table, picked up a bottle of Moët et Chandon, popped the cork and filled three glasses. Perce proposed a toast:

"To all three of us and to happy days in this college for the next three years." Wooley added with a smile, "Special luck to the undertaker. May he get three firsts."

They raised their glasses and drank a toast. David surveyed his companions whilst sipping champagne. The Honourable Percy Cavendish, an old Etonian, was tall, thin with slashed-back, centrally parted, dark hair, an aristocratic aquiline nose and a monocle dangling on a gold chain around his neck. The monocle was purely for affectation, only worn when Perce was in a temper. By contrast Bertram Woolford had a wide, open, pleasant, smiling face, blond hair and blue eyes. He was stockily built and a rugby player of renown having captained Charterhouse and the English schoolboys for the past two years. Both were dressed in almost identical clothes – long, thread-worn, brown jumpers, baggy corduroy trousers and an Oxford university scarf coiled around their necks. David felt overdressed and uncomfortable in their company but, after a refill, he thawed out and removed his overcoat.

The Honourable Percy Cavendish's room was twice the size of David's. It had a separate bedroom and a commodious reception room heated by a blazing coal fire. The floor was carpeted in contrast to David's room which was covered with cracked linoleum. A second champagne cork popped and the three men were now chatting amicably. Percy's father was Lord Cavendish and the Honourable Percy was heir to a title and to a hereditary seat in the House of Lords.

"A damn bad show with all these death duties and the House of Lords is as dead as the proverbial dodo. Let's drink again – to the present."

Bertie Woolford was the son of Sir Francis Woolford, a well known explorer and botanist and now President of the Royal Geographic Society. Wooley was reading medicine and would certainly play rugby for Oxford and was reputedly an English international prospect. Both Perce and Wooley were over a year older than David. The 'get to know each other' session came to an abrupt halt when David suddenly felt sick. He had to rush across the room to the washbasin and spewed out his stomach contents, mainly champagne and bile. Perce and Wooley laughed.

"I wonder what other use we could have for the washbasin? The undertaker has christened it for us," said Perce fingering his monocle.

David's head was spinning. He was compulsively sick twice in his own room before lying fully clothed on his bed and falling into a stuporous sleep.

David woke at around 7 a.m. with a splitting headache to find Billy wheezing his way around the room bringing a pot of tea to his bedside.

"Good morning, Sir." Billy turned his attention to the washbasin with its rim of encrusted vomit, "Tut, tut, what a mess! Nothing like the mess in his Lordship's in No. 10."

After a quick wash David hurried down to breakfast in the refectory which was already full of eager-faced freshmen. By tradition the meal was taken in complete silence apart from a few platitudes and muted requests for the condiments, toast or tea. His drinking companions from the previous night were not present. He met them later, just before 10 a.m., in the corridor leading to the assembly hall. They were both unshaven, dishevelled, unkempt, wearing the same clobber as on the night before. Perce spoke first.

"Hello Undertaker. When I woke this morning, I thought there might be a job for you!" with a brief guffaw. "The point of this morning's exercise is to enrol and get a tutor and take my advice – don't join any of the tedious societies, except Wooley of course who must join the rugby section. He's an international player did you know?"

David had been advised by Mr David Evans MA to get Randolph Collingwood as a tutor. Daima believed that Collingwood was getting on a bit but was still the best Classics don at Oxford. David was interviewed by three dons and happily secured Randolph Collingwood as his personal tutor for the first year. Behind the trestle tables, dotted around the hall, sat the secretaries of various societies touting for members. David showed an interest in the swimming section and the debating society and enrolled in both. In one corner of the great hall he found his Lordship in animated conversation with the secretary of the Outdoor Activities Section, which included orienteering and climbing.

As David approached the table, Perce said, "Come here Undertaker. What do you think of this? Only two members at present in this society. Let's join and increase membership by one hundred per cent and swan around the country at weekends. The enrolment fee is only a shilling."

As David and Perce left the assembly hall together they met up with Wooley and a friend from Harrow and, on Perce's insistence, they repaired to the Pied Piper for a lunch of faggots and peas, washed down with a few pints of beer. David was again sick in the pub and for the second time in two days had to be helped up to his quarters amidst much levity from Perce and Wooley. The pattern established on the first two days did not persist. Whilst Perce and to a lesser extent Wooley, kept drinking heavily, David learnt to pace himself. Nevertheless he was always invited to Perce's drinking sessions and parties and invariably attended for his own education and entertainment. The Honourable Percy Cavendish was uncommonly generous and paid for all the food and drink consumed by the three undergraduates.

The three freshmen became firm friends, commonly referred to by other undergraduates as the PUW Group – the Perce, Undertaker, Wooley Group. The Honourable Perce was a very complex character. Despite his aristocratic background he was a rabid socialist, a royalist and an agnostic. He was reading politics and economics whilst Wooley, on the other hand, was a Tory which was not surprising as his father had, until recently, been Conservative Member of Parliament for Salisbury. David was apolitical and officiated as an umpire in the prolonged and heated debates which frequently raged between the two political adversaries. David's education in the social graces escalated rapidly under Perce's tutelage. On dining-in nights he wore his ill-fitting tails with an air of confidence, suggesting to others that his dress was a deliberate form of eccentricity calculated to draw attention. The Honourable Perce approved heartily and who would disagree with the leader and spokesman of the PUW Group.

By long established tradition in New College one dining night each month was Masters' night. The Master, Sir Arbuthnot Commins, was a Classics scholar and had long ago ordained that the proceedings on his dining-in night should be conducted in Latin. The PUW Group and two guests from No. 3 and No. 6 Plato were well into the second champagne bottle when the Honourable Perce, immaculate in his tails, stood with a glass in one hand and his monocle firmly secured in his left socket.

"Do ye know tonight is Masters' night? Old Sir Arbuthnot and his cronies will have a great time chattering to each other in that blasted dead language. David, you are our Classics expert and I intend to challenge in port tonight and nominate you to reply. What do ye think?" as he turned and looked at David.

"Don't rely on me but I'll have a shot at it. I'll try not to let you down, Perce," David replied.

"Splendid, splendid." Perce unhitched his monocle. "That's all settled."

They then applied themselves to consuming a third bottle of champagne before walking down to the refectory. The format of the dinner was, and had been for centuries, that the grace and loyal toast were proposed in Latin by designated undergraduates. The top table, about twelve in all, the Master, dons and tutors, challenged the undergraduates to quote from the Iliad, Homer, or to speak in Latin for one minute on a specific subject without making grammatical errors. The undergraduates were allowed to nominate their speaker. The prize was a round of port wine or beer bought by the losers. The college Master was the sole arbiter of the contest. Similarly the undergraduates challenged and nominated a specific tutor, or don, to reply in Latin. The invariable penalty, if the top table won, was a round of vintage port. The first nominated don was on his feet, challenged to list seventeen Latin prepositions.

"*A, ab, absque, coram, de, palam, clam, cum, exore, sine, tenus, pro* and *prae, suber, subter, sub* or *in.*"

David nudged Honourable Perce who leapt to his feet shouting, "Challenge, challenge *in porto nominatum* David Green."

David spoke on behalf of the undergraduates, "*Exore* is not a preposition. It is a combination of two adverbs, '*ex*' and '*e*'."

David's challenge was upheld by the Master amidst cheers from the undergraduates and an issue of port all round from the top table, Perce insisting that it should be vintage. The dons challenged David to speak for one minute on "*Muris, muris* the mouse." This he accomplished with ease and grammatical perfection and on this occasion the top table nominated beer from the undergraduates. At one similar dinner later that year the Honourable Percy Cavendish was nominated to say grace. In case of emergency David had jotted down a few suitable graces but had not managed to get Percy to learn any off by heart. Perce stood with his head bowed and his crib card beside his soup plate.

"*Benedictus, benedicat. Levator labiae superioris aliquae nasi. Christum Dominum, Amen.*"

There were a few smirks from the medical students and classics readers in the hall and disbelief and consternation on the top table. Percy sat down confused.

"What's that all about?"

"Literally," said David, "Your grace means the muscle which elevates the corner of the mouth and side of the nose."

Percy guffawed. Sir Arbuthnot Commins was not best pleased by the outrage that had been innocently committed by Perce and ordered that he should be gated for a week. Percy himself, however, was highly amused by the incident.

"Jolly good prank, don't ye think? Well done Undertaker. Have some more champagne?"

One evening early in January 1937 the PUW Group had a special meeting in No. 10 Plato. Perce, slouching in his favourite armchair with his monocle in position, looked vexed.

"Do you know the Outdoor Activity Society is all to pot? They're bloody useless. Only eight members. We only had one outing last term and that was a walk between the Trout at Woodstock and the college, not using or crossing a main road. A piece of cake. I did it with my eyes closed. In fact I've done it often after a good binge in the Trout! The club needs a kick up the arse and I shall be the one to do it. I am going to form a rock climbing section. We'll advertise for customers. You and I David will start the club. Dear old Wooley is in line for captaincy of rugby or something like that and can't come this weekend. They're playing some club from London called the Bees or something."

"The Wasps," Wooley interjected.

"Wasps, Bees, what does it matter? They're all cauliflower-eared louts to boot." Without waiting for David's agreement Perce went on. "I'll get some gear and on Friday we'll pop up to north Wales in the Lagonda and do some climbing. That's settled."

Then he immediately changed the subject. On Friday after lunch, the Lagonda, laden with climbing gear, left New College with Percy at the wheel. He was an erratic driver but there were few other cars on the road and he negotiated the trip safely. As the soft-topped Lagonda was not draught-proof the two passengers were well wrapped in heavy overcoats, leather caps, goggles and gloves but, even so, the frosty January winds bit into their clothing and by the time they reached snow-covered Snowdonia both were frozen to the marrow. They put up for two nights at the Tyn-y-Mynydd Arms, about a mile distant from the base of Mount Snowdon. Nancy, the short, dumpy, grey-haired proprietress of the pub fussed over her young customers as they thawed out in front of a spitting log fire downing large brandies. There were two locals in the bar that night.

"Come far?" a standard Welsh greeting to travellers.

"Oxford," was the reply.

"*Rhydychen, Duw, Duw* a long way. College boys?"

"Yes," replied David on behalf of the rock climbing section of Oxford University whilst Perce was still inseparably attached to his brandy glass.

"We've come to climb Snowdon tomorrow."

"Climbers, *Duw, Duw*. Not good weather. A bit dangerous. Be careful and good luck boys."

Nancy prepared a meal of hot soup, bread and cheese and thus, suitably fortified, they went to bed.

Next morning they woke to find it snowing hard. After a hearty breakfast Perce announced, "What do ye know David? As we've come all this way we'd better have a go at dear old Snowdon. It's expected of University rock climbers. What?"

Well wrapped up and festooned with ropes, pitons and climbing sticks they sallied forth in the general direction of the mountain. It took them over two hours to reach the foot of the mountain and climb to a spot designated by Perce as base camp where they rested while Perce consumed nearly the whole of his brandy filled hip flask.

"David, what do ye think? We won't get much further today."

David agreed. They rested for half an hour and then, in driving snow, retraced their steps to the Tyn-y-Mynydd Arms where they arrived at mid-afternoon. That evening at the bar, attended by the smiling Nancy, one of the locals with some expertise in English asked, "Get to the top then?"

Perce replied, monocle in position, "Driven back near the top by heavy snow do ye know?"

The locals nodded sympathetically. After a few rounds, all bought by Perce, the locals became more friendly. Conversation was in broken English but the singing which ensued was all in Welsh, melodious and soporific. The rock climbers staggered upstairs at about 9 p.m. with the harmonious strains of *Âr hyd y Nôs* echoing in their ears. Next day the Lagonda accomplished the hazardous return journey to Oxford where later that week Perce announced to the Outdoor Activities Section:

"Two members of the Rock Climbing Section made an attempt on Mount Snowdon last weekend and were defeated by adverse conditions whilst within sight of the summit. Further attempts will be made later this month."

None of the other members, or for that matter anyone else at Oxford University, could challenge the statement. David smiled inwardly whilst basking in the glory of their attempted climb of Wales' highest mountain. Other attempts did occur. The Honourable Perce and David, or ''is Lordship and Dai' as they were known in Tyn-y-Mynydd, returned to Snowdonia again and again. With practice their climbing technique improved and they managed to scale the difficult western side of Snowdon in October 1937. David, in particular, developed an affinity with the outcrops and contours on the rock face and became the lead climber with Perce as his back-up. These visits to the Welsh mountains were a constant source of pleasure to David who had grown to love the people, their singing, and their Celtic sense of humour. Unfortunately by 1938 the visits became less frequent and finally ceased in March 1938 when the Honourable Percy Cavendish, his friend and co-climber, changed his allegiance and took up flying as a hobby. David Green's other sporting interest was swimming. As a member of the Athletic Society he enlisted in the swimming section and found that his stamina and technique, though not suited for competitive short distance sprinting, were well adapted to long distance events. He represented Oxford's second swimming team in the half mile event and, as he grew in stature in his college, was made secretary of the Oxford Swimming Association.

When David entered Oxford University in October 1936 he had no preconceived political convictions and enrolled in the Oxford debating Society as a passive member. As a referee in political debates between Perce and Wooley the only time he felt inclined to interject and express his views was when the argument was about Nazism or Fascism. His background and first-hand knowledge of the conditions in Germany in the late twenties and up until 1931 made him a respected contributor in these debates. During his first term in Oxford he had confided in Perce and Wooley, who were aware of his Jewish ancestry, about his early life in Germany. The Honourable Percival Cavendish summed it up.

"What do ye know? It doesn't matter which sow, pardon the pun, spawns the litter, so long as the runt is a normal human being."

In private conversation Perce was inclined to be sympathetic towards Hitler but antagonistic towards Mussolini whom he regarded as a "pompous windbag full of spaghetti and shit." Hitler, in Perce's opinion, was the only bastion in the west against the Bolsheviks. According to Perce, "This fellow Churchill doesn't know what he's talking about. Hitler is a buffer between us and the Ruskies."

When the Spanish Civil War broke out he saw Franco, though a Fascist, as a defender of democracy in Spain. He could not understand why so many prominent Socialists left for Spain to support the Nationalists.

"If I had to go I'd fight on Franco's side," Perce concluded. "Mussolini's invasion of Abyssinia is typical of a bully, sending fully trained and equipped armies to fight poor defenceless natives. Typical of the pompous ass."

Wooley agreed with Perce's assertions about Mussolini but argued that Hitler was a different kettle of fish.

"I agree that Hitler has pulled Germany up by its jockstraps and built roads and revived the ailing Germany economy but I fear that he is after something more. He wants to dominate Europe and that includes us here in England."

"Balderdash," interjected Perce. "What do you think, Undertaker?"

David thought pensively for a few moments and then, with conviction, "I fully agree with Wooley. I have a feeling here," pointing to his heart, "that Hitler's talk about conquering Bolshevism is a smokescreen to take our attention away from the fact that he wants to subjugate and enslave the rest of Europe. I think that Winston Churchill is right. Britain needs to resist his every move."

Perce asked, "Would you join up and have a go at Germany after the carnage of the last war? As you're Jewish you're probably biased."

This hurt David but he replied in a firm, even tone, "Yes, I would. I would do anything to rid Europe and the world of the Nazi tyrant." As he said the words he thought fleetingly about Manfred Schmidt, his blood brother, adding quietly, "even if it means fighting against people I have known in the past."

An Officers Training Corps was established in Oxford in 1936. Wooley, a year older than David, was already in the OTC and when David came of age he joined the cadre in January 1937.

Perce was adamant and drawled, "What do ye know? I don't want to be cannon fodder for some befuddled general in the trenches of France, fighting and dying in some shithole in Flanders. You're making a big mistake fellas, mark my words!"

In October 1937 the Oxford Union arranged a debate on the motion that "Adolf Hitler presents no threat to Great Britain". The chief proposer was Sir Oswald Moseley, the responder Sigmund Fellowes, President of the Debating Society and David had been allowed a secondary question. The debate was scheduled to take place on 20th October, 1937 in the Great Hall at New College. During the summer recess Perce had been busy studying the life history of Sir Oswald Moseley. "Comes from a good family do ye know? Father was a financier in the City. Out of nothing, in October '32, he created the British Union of Fascists. He's met with dear old Adolf a few times. Sir Ossie's got some bright ideas and good men around him. He'll be worth listening to, don't ye think?"

For the debate the Great Hall was packed to overflowing. Sir Oswald Moseley, dressed in black trousers and a beige tunic with a few nondescript medals on his left chest and a black armband on his left sleeve, made an impressive entry on to the podium. He was a very tall, burly man with a black moustache and thinning black hair and had a loud, reverberating voice. His theme was simply that Adolf Hitler meant no harm and bore no ill-will against the British people, France and the Low Countries. Under Hitler Germany had become a vibrant, economically sound, and expanding nation. In order to develop his country's potential to the full Chancellor Adolf Hitler needed more room to expand. Coupled with this was the problem of German speaking enclaves within the countries which had been annexed from Germany after the Versailles Treaty in 1919. Germany simply wanted to reclaim these territories and bring the subjugated German population back into the fold. Only then would Chancellor Hitler be content that his grand strategy had been successful. Chancellor Hitler needed *lebensraum* for his people and had no designs on the sovereignty of other nations. Sir Oswald Moseley sat down amid thunderous applause.

Sigmund Fellowes' debate against the motion was not convincing. He spoke against German rearmament and supported the warnings of Sir Winston Churchill that rearmament signified aggressive intent against other countries. He pleaded that we must not imperceptibly slide into another Great War as happened in 1914 after the assassination of Archduke Ferdinand in Sarajevo. He sat down to mild applause. The further supplementary speakers added little of merit to the debate.

Sigmund Fellowes rose to his feet.

"Before asking the House to divide I will allow one supplementary question from the floor. I now call on Mr David Green to address the Chair and present a final question to Sir Oswald Moseley."

David stood up at the back of the auditorium, mouth dry and shaking nervously.

"Sir Oswald, have you ever been to Germany?"

Sir Oswald with a patient smile replied, "I have been to visit the Führer twice in the past year. I assure you that he is a genuine, pleasant, peace-loving man."

David replied, "If he is peace loving, why does he persecute ethnic, non-Aryan, minorities such as the Jews?"

The smiling guest speaker replied, "To the best of my knowledge no such oppression is occurring or has occurred in the past in Germany."

"Sir Oswald what is your precise definition of *lebensraum*?" asked David.

Sir Oswald patiently replied, "The right of Germany to expand its borders and bring back into the fold those German peoples who were annexed from greater Germany in 1918. I have already explained this..."

David, now in full flow and suffused with rage, shouted at the speaker, "Sir Oswald, I am a Jew and I was born and brought up in Munich. My family were evicted in 1931. *Lebensraum* to the Jewish people means persecution, eviction or incarceration, annexation of their property and, in some cases, death. Your beloved Hitler decreed in *Mein Kampf* that the Jewish problem will need to be resolved. Sir Oswald, are you aware that there are detention camps for Jews in Germany? *Lebensraum* means getting rid of, and persecution of, one section of the people in favour of the concept of a pure Aryan Germany. Is this an act of a pleasant, peace-loving man?"

Then, shouting to be heard above the hisses and boos, "I believe that Hitler's *lebensraum* will not be confined to his current demands across the borders of Germany. It will expand to include other countries and I have no doubt that Great Britain will not be spared."

Pandemonium erupted, followed by some clapping, a lot of booing and stamping. Sir Oswald Moseley scowled, Sigmund Fellowes vigorously banged his gavel and shouted above the din, "Division, Division."

The 'noes' won the Division by thirty-seven votes substantially endorsing the motion that Adolf Hitler presented no great threat to Great Britain. David's participation in the debate made him a few new friends but many enemies amongst the anti-Semitic element in the University. The Honourable Perce and Wooley were staunchly supportive.

"Jolly good show old chap. You showed the overbearing old bore a thing or two."

A few weeks after the Union debate Perce returned from a weekend at his ancestral home in a dejected mood. The PUW Group met at No. 10 Plato for the customary champagne sippers before dining-in.

Perce, monocled, and without his usual mischievous grin, said, "I've been to the ancestral home for a few days. Pater is extremely worried about another war between us and Germany. The poor fellow remembers the last big 'un. He was in the Grenadier Guards and a Captain at the Battle of Aix la Chapelle. Shot through the leg. Still walks with a stick and a limp. Tells me that Winston and my godfather, Lord Halifax, are convinced that we'll be at war with Germany next year. I've told you before that I don't want to waste my time with the brown jobs incarcerated in a bloody dugout in some field in Froggyland. I am going to learn to fly. So I thought that the three of us might swan off this weekend to Brize Norton where Pater knows the chief wallah, I think a group leader, called Smedley. He'll teach us to fly in a couple of days. Everything's arranged."

David and Wooley knew better than to resist. Once the Honourable Perce Cavendish made up his mind nothing short of a natural catastrophe or an accident would prevail on him to change course.

The three duly arrived at Brize Norton airfield on a Saturday morning. For the occasion Perce had purchased a leather helmet, goggles and a large white silk scarf. Group Captain Richard Smedley welcomed them in the officer's mess and took them down to the large hangar to see the 'kites'. They were all Tiger Moths. Brize Norton at that time was a pilot training centre. Perce was eager to get airborne but the group captain curbed his enthusiasm and had one of the mechanics explain all about the mechanical intricacies of a flying machine. After lunch in the officer's mess the budding aviators were individually given a trip upstairs in a Tiger Moth. Perce and Wooley were thrilled by the experience but David was not at all sure he enjoyed the flight.

The Honourable Perce drove the Lagonda back to Oxford at a frightening pace, wearing his leather helmet, flying goggles and his white scarf trailing behind in the wind, loudly singing out of tune a string of popular melodies. Perce and Wooley went to Brize Norton as often as they could and, at the end of term, the two enthusiasts embarked on a course of flying instruction which they completed in the summer recess in 1938 and by the time the college reconvened on October 7th, they were qualified pilots. Furthermore they had both enrolled as fighter pilots in the Royal Air Force and were given special dispensation to stay on at Oxford to complete their studies. True to form the Honourable Perce formed an RAF wing in university, recruiting potential pilots from the colleges for flying training.

For financial reasons, and mainly because of his innate fear of flying, David took no part and continued with his training programme with the OTC, or the brown jobs as Perce would have it, and was made a Subaltern in early January 1939. The standard OTC battle dress was a drab affair and David wondered whether it was a product of Geldman's Pusey Street factory in London. By mid-March 1939 the co-members of the PUW Club had completed their training at Biggin Hill, flying Hurricane fighters, and sat their final examinations in uniform with pilots' wings proudly displayed on their left chest. Flight Lieutenant the Honourable Percy Cavendish and Flight Lieutenant Bertram Woolford had become fully fledged officers in His Majesty's Royal Air Force. These differing military pursuits led to a partial dissolution of the PUW Group. There were a few irregular binges at No. 10 and Perce arranged a monumental thrash on completion of the examinations in June 1939. Goodbyes were said and promises of future meetings made. The Honourable Perce Cavendish summed it up.

"Wooley and I will defend the skies over Britain and it will be up to you, David, and the brown jobs to sort out the fighting on the ground."

When the results came through David had two firsts and a second. Perce managed three thirds and Wooley a first and two seconds. David's last glimpse of his two companions of the PUW Group was when they drove out of the college in full uniform in the open-topped Lagonda with its horn blaring like a lovesick bullock.

David's father and Mr David Evans MA were extremely pleased with his academic success but were displeased to hear of his intention to enlist in the Army. Daima, a pacifist, although he made an attempt to enlist with the Nationalists in Spain in 1936 and had been rejected on medical grounds, thought it all, "A bloody waste of a damn good brain." His father was further displeased that his son had changed the family name by deed poll. David spent the whole of July 1939 at his home in Pusey Street in Wapping. He tentatively renewed his acquaintance with Hannah, the Geldman niece, and took her out on a few occasions dining, strolling in Hyde Park or to a cinema. Hannah was quite attractive but extremely shy and difficult to approach.

His time at Oxford had been almost totally celibate. He met a few interested, but not interesting, girls especially after the Moseley debate. His only sexual adventure in Oxford ended in complete fiasco. Perce and Wooley persuaded him to come to the May Ball in 1939 with a promise that the Honourable Perce would find him a 'smashing bird'. When the girl arrived she turned out to be fully six inches taller than David. Phoebe, a secretary from Trinity College, was dark-haired with a long, lugubrious face and jet black eyebrows which almost met in the mid-line of her forehead. Added to this, and presumably because of her height and occupation, she had sloping, rounded shoulders. Perce had assured David that she was a man-eater. Conversation with Phoebe was almost non-existent but she showed one attribute which astounded David. She could drink champagne quicker than the Honourable Perce and apparently without much effect. They started drinking in No. 10 and the boozing continued unabated in the refreshment marquee. At around eleven o'clock Phoebe's quiet demeanour changed. She grabbed David around the shoulders and dragged her reluctant partner on to the dance-floor. David could not dance and the best he was able to manage was to stand upright and hold the undulating and gyrating Phoebe erect to prevent her from falling flat on her face and bringing him crashing down beside her.

Afterwards things became somewhat hazy. David remembered the dominant female dragging him outside the marquee and pulling him down on to the grass where she lay on top of him pushing her face into his and inserting her tongue firmly into his mouth. Her arms and legs thrashed uncoordinatedly and the octopus-like movement of her limbs, at one moment pummelled lustily into his groin and at the next moment tore at the buttons of his trousers, whilst her tongue kept forcing itself to the back of his throat. The next day David could not recall whether intercourse had actually occurred and he certainly did not remember experiencing the same, almost pleasurable, sensation as he had with Mary Loose in Pusey Street School. Something must have happened on the grass outside the marquee for when he inspected his dress trousers the following morning there were greyish-white stains on the black cloth.

In June 1939 David volunteered for the Army and passed A1 at a medical examination at the engineer depot at Hammersmith. During July he was expecting his call up papers and deliberately spent most of his time at his parents' home as he felt guilty of neglecting them. They were palpably unhappy about living in this strange country and his father was insulted by the menial and monotonous job he had to perform, day in and day out, in Geldman's factory. They were orthodox Jews and David had only attended synagogue in Oxford on three occasions in three years. He also felt guilty about the immense advantages he had acquired by going to Oxford and learning the minutiae of the social graces and meeting people from all walks of life, including his best friend the Honourable Percival Cavendish. There was no doubt that his parents were old-fashioned and socially naive and he wished they would be more outgoing. And yet, he was their only son and he loved them dearly. He had neglected them for three years and had changed the family name for his own convenience. He tried to make up for these omissions by attending synagogue regularly with his parents and in general by spending his time in the flat. These evenings at home were interminable. Light reading and listening to the radio were frowned upon and his father insisted on Bible readings most evenings. David even looked forward to the light relief offered by occasional excursions to the cinema with Hannah Geldman. The arrival of his call up papers to OCTU camp at Chester on the 21st July came as a great relief and, although he hated himself for admitting it, he was pleased and anxious to leave home and re-join the bustling mainstream of life.

Chapter Nine

The Train to Winterberg, Erica, January 1939 Parachute School, Minden, Heinz Schneider, Recruitment of Fritz Schultz

Colonel Von Bulow's Eighth Parachute Regiment was stationed in Lübbecke near Minden when Lieutenant Manfred Schmidt transferred for parachute training on the 10th January, 1939. Unpopular in the 12th Bavarian Hussars' mess, and with few friends in the regiment, he was pleased to get away from Augsburg. In September 1938 Colonel Von Bulow's battalion began training in mountaineering and skiing in anticipation that at least one parachute brigade would be utilised as ski stormtroopers. Consequently, Manfred's movement order instructed him to report to headquarters company, who were undergoing ski training for two months at Winterberg under the command of Major Joachim Haldendorf.

By the time Manfred's train arrived in Marburg it was already getting dark and there was still a two hour journey ahead of him before he reached his destination. Carrying his heavy suitcase he struggled up the last few steps leading to platform 2 of the railway station. Heavy snowfall and hard frost had disrupted the normally efficient German rail service and it was now nearly five o'clock with daylight rapidly fading from the leaden snow-filled sky. He was going to be at least three hours late reaching Winterberg. The snow covered platform was deserted. On his right-hand side was a sizeable waiting room from which voices and laughter emanated.

Manfred entered the dimly lit hut to find twenty or more soldiers sitting around a wood-burning stove, talking, drinking and laughing and when the officer entered a sergeant called them to attention and saluted. Manfred returned the salute and, as his sight became accustomed to the dim light, he saw from the flashes on their uniform that they were paratroopers.

The sergeant politely asked Manfred to sit down adding, "There is, of course, Sir, a first-class waiting room to the left of the stairway which will be more comfortable."

Manfred took the hint, realising that his presence might cramp the style of the *Fallschirmjagger* who were returning from Christmas leave.

"*Danke,* Herr *Stürmbahnführer*" and retracing his steps he trudged through the snow to the smaller first class waiting room.

Manfred entered and quickly closed the door behind him. The officers' waiting room was considerably smaller than the other, dimly lit by a spitting gaslight and heated by a central wood-burning stove. Sitting on a wooden bench near the warm stove Manfred saw a mature lady wearing a fur hat, long fur coat and thigh length boots. The only visible part of her body was her face which was full and rounded with a rosy, healthy complexion, sparkling dark brown eyes and red, rounded, smiling lips. Manfred was taken aback for a few seconds and then standing erect, clicking his heels and bowing his head, he formally introduced himself.

"*Guten abend mein* Frau*, Ich bin Oberleutnant* Manfred Schmidt."

The lady replied in a deep husky voice and still smiling, "Come and sit down by the fire. I am Frau Haldendorf, the wife of Major Haldendorf of the *Fallschirmjagger*. Perhaps you have heard of him?"

"*Ja,* Frau Haldendorf," Manfred replied.

The waiting room was quite warm and Manfred took off his heavy overcoat and sat on the bench nearest the fire opposite the fur-clad lady. They sat in silence for a few minutes.

"You're going to Winterberg for ski training no doubt. My husband, the major, is commanding the *skischule* for the next two months. The train from here will take two hours to get to Winterberg.

As we are to be companions, let's be friends. Call me Erica. What shall I call you?"

Blushing and stammering he replied, "Manfred, *bitte*, Frau Major Haldendorf."

Erica smiled and chuckled a deep throaty gurgle. Here was an innocent, inexperienced, young officer joining her husband's Company and full of hope and expectation of a bright future in the army. Her husband, when they married ten years ago, had been full of the same enthusiasm, but he was now a disgruntled major, passed over for promotion on a few occasions and destined to end his days as a Quartermaster in some remote barracks in Silesia. Furthermore the major was also getting somewhat disillusioned with Erica.

"So be it," she muttered under her breath.

The two travellers maintained a desultory conversation for about ten minutes, mainly about the weather and state of the ski slopes and Manfred's history and future plans in the Parachute Regiment.

Manfred was glad to hear the 'puff, puff' of an approaching engine and the squeal of brakes and rattle of coaches as a train drew to a shuddering halt at the platform in a hiss of steam. Erica quickly got to her feet and, pulling on her fur gloves, strode out to the platform to the single first class compartment at the front end of the train followed by Manfred, now slithering and sliding in the snow, encumbered by his own suitcase and Erica's valise. The paratroopers were also on the platform shouting and joking with each other and jostling for the best seats in the two long carriages in the corridorless train. The compartment selected by Erica was freezing cold. She sat in one corner and Manfred in the other both pulling their overcoats tightly around their bodies. Manfred had a chance to assess the woman sitting on the opposite seat. She was in her mid-thirties, had a beautiful face and inviting eyes and, as far as he could tell, under her fur coat she had a full, rounded, comfortable figure. The train started off with a sudden jolt and puffed its way laboriously out of Marburg station.

"Manfred, the journey takes nearly two hours with two short stops on the way. It is bitterly cold in here." Then with a smile, "If we are to survive the day I suggest you pull down the blinds to keep the heat in and that you sit next to me to keep each other warm."

Manfred obeyed. When he settled next to Erica he could feel her body shivering under her fur coat. Gallantly he stood up, removed his heavy overcoat and wrapped it around her knees and legs.

"*Danke* Manfred. That's much better," Erica thanked him.

Manfred felt a chill in his bones and, leaning forwards, he produced a large flask of cognac from the inner pocket of his overcoat and offered Erica a drink. She accepted and after Manfred had consumed a tot she accepted once more and then again and again until the flask was empty.

Erica's question came out of the blue and caused Manfred to blush bright red.

"Have you a young Fraulein in Munich?"

Manfred thought to say 'Yes' but did not consider his minor dalliance with Marianne Widemayer counted as a serious love affair.

He answered, "No."

Erica's next question was more devastating, "Have you ever made love to a Fraulein?"

His face became even more beetroot-like as he stammered, "No."

"In that case, young Lieutenant Manfred Schmidt, and before you learn bad habits in the Parachute Regiment, Erica Haldendorf will teach you how to make love."

Without further comment she put one gloved hand behind his neck and drew his face urgently towards her own. They kissed tenderly at first and then more fiercely as Erica's tongue started probing inside his mouth. Manfred was revelling in the sensation and yet still reluctant to fully participate in the act in view of the identity of his partner. By now, with her left hand ungloved, Erica had undone the buttons of her fur coat and her blouse to reveal a proud, firm left breast with a protruding, erect nipple. She took Manfred's right hand to her breast and then, pulling at the back of his hair, guided his mouth to her nipple. Manfred suckled the nipple with relish. He had never seen a woman's breast like this before. His mother's had been large, pendulous and sagging and not an object of beauty. Manfred suckled fiercely, much to Erica's delight and she was now writhing her legs and buttocks on the seat, sighing and whimpering. Manfred's suckling continued for two or three minutes and for his next lesson in love Erica took his right hand and placed it squarely between her open legs pushing and pulsating with her own hand to make Manfred massage the sensitive area. This action rapidly inflamed Erica's ardour. She bent down and lifted her long black skirt well above the waist and Manfred saw that she wore no underclothes and for the first time he also saw the black bushy mass of her pubic hair.

Erica explained, "When I travel to see my man I arrive prepared! Give me your hand."

Erica clamped Manfred's right hand on to her pubis where he again started kneading and pummelling. This seemed to produce joy and rapture in Erica and before long he found the moist open cleft between her legs. Manfred sensed a swelling and bursting sensation in his groin and Erica tore at his trouser buttons and buckle.

She shouted, "Stand up."

Manfred obeyed. Erica competently unhitched his buttons and, pulling his trousers down around his knees, released his erect penis. She audibly purred and taking his penis in both hands expertly flicked its tip with her long probing tongue. She then took the erection into her mouth and, using her buccinator muscles, sucked with increasing ferocity until Manfred felt that he was on the point of exploding. The lovemaking came to an abrupt end when the train reached its first stop and came to a shuddering halt causing Manfred to withdraw his penis. He pulled up the blind and let down the window letting in a rush of cool air. Outside the solitary figure of a station master wandered up and down with his lantern showing red. Manfred leant forward, legs apart, his shoulders filling the window frame and his bare buttocks protruding into the compartment.

"*Ist alles in ordnung* Herr *Bahnofmeister?*"

"*Ja* Herr *Kapitan,*" the station master replied giving Manfred a salute. The wily old man had long since learned to over-promote all military personnel who used his station in transit. Manfred was about to continue the conversation when he felt Erica's probing fingers working their way between his buttocks and grabbing his erection. He could not stand the sensation much longer and with a stifled, "*Guten nacht,* Herr *Bahnofmeister,*" he pulled back into the compartment whilst the railway official stumbled away in the gathering gloom towards the front end of the train where his red lantern light soon changed to green. As the engine started puffing and straining Manfred was coupled with Erica. The last view the startled station master had of the only occupants of the first class compartment was of a pair of black leather boots firmly entwined around the pumping buttocks of the young blond *kapitan.*

"*Wunderbar, Wunderbar,*" sighed Erica. Manfred was on his knees, his head nestling between her ample bosoms.

He was crying with relief and ecstasy, "*Danke mein Frau, danke, danke Erica.*"

They stayed in this position for ten minutes not speaking and warmed by each other's nearness, both blissfully happy and content.

"Now, my gallant Lieutenant, I will show you how to make a woman happy."

She lay flat on her back on the padded seat and guided Manfred's index and middle fingers between her legs to her clitoris. This felt like a small button to Manfred.

"Rub it gently," said Erica, and later, "More, more quickly," and later, "Do it hard now," and then she went into orgasmic convulsions shouting, "Stop, stop" and, "Yes, yes. When I say stop, don't stop but go on. Yes, yes, again and again."

Erica had orgasm after orgasm and Manfred was amazed at the power he had over this woman by merely massaging the small button between her legs. By this time Manfred was again aroused and without asking inserted his erection into Erica and, on this occasion, he derived much more pleasure from the copulation. Between orgasms she kept shouting, "*Fantastisch.*" Manfred came again with a painful explosion. Erica looked into his eyes, and in her deep throaty voice said, "That was fantastic my gallant Lieutenant."

Erica and Manfred re-arranged their dishevelled clothing and resumed their seats on opposite sides of the carriage. Shortly afterwards they drew into the second stop on the two hour journey. A drunken dishevelled sergeant from the second-class carriages appeared at the window wielding a bottle of schnapps. After a sloppy salute.

"The boys want you and Frau Haldendorf to have a drink with us, Sir."

"Thank you, Sergeant. It's very cold in here and we will be pleased to accept your offer."

The sergeant handed the bottle to Manfred, repeated his untidy salute and, almost slipping, turned on his heel and strode back to his carriage where the voices of the drunken *Fallschirmjagger* were raised in song and argument. Manfred poured a liberal tot of schnapps for Erica and also helped himself.

"What will the Herr Major say?"

"The major will not know. He will not need to know."

The chugging train continued its painfully slow progress towards Winterberg. When they were about ten minutes away, Erica asked, "Will you do me a favour? I like my man to do me from the back."

This startled Manfred.

"I cannot," he stammered. "Oh yes you can," and Erica leant across again undoing Manfred's trouser buttons and by a combination of expert fingering and verbal exhortation produced an erection. Without further ado she knelt on the opposite seat and lifted her skirt above her head. Manfred required no further encouragement. He thrust his pulsating penis into the open orifice which Erica had revealed. This time there was no finesse, just wild pumping and thudding, until his climax drove him to his knees. They managed to be fully dressed and tidied up when the train pulled into Winterberg.

Herr Major Haldendorf was on the platform to meet his wife. He held her briefly and gave her a peck on the cheek whilst Erica gave Manfred a wink over his shoulder. The revelling soldiers were picked up by a truck and the major drove Erica and Manfred to their quarters in a *Kübelwagen*. As commanding officer, the major and Erica had a *Gasthaus* to themselves. Manfred and two other officers in training were in a second *Gasthaus* while the *Fallschirmjagger* were housed in a sizeable hotel. The ski course was very exacting, ski training from dawn to dusk. It was early to bed most nights and little social contact between the officers and men. Herr Major Haldendorf was known as a strict disciplinarian and a stickler for the rules. Towards the end of the course Manfred was out on the slopes with a squad of ten men on a cross country exercise when Major Haldendorf approached.

"Lieutenant Schmidt, I will take over here. Take my vehicle back to the *Gasthaus*. I've left my map case and binoculars in my room. Please get them for me and return as soon as you can. My wife has left for Dortmund this morning and she will not be there."

When Manfred arrived at the hotel he found that the major had been mistaken. Erica was coming downstairs carrying a valise, fully dressed in her furs and long black dress and black boots. Manfred wondered if she was wearing pants. The concierge, a fat, middle-aged lady, looked on curiously as Erica beckoned with her forefinger and retraced her path upstairs. Manfred followed in her wake. In the bedroom Manfred explained, "I have come for the major's map case and binoculars."

Frau Haldendorf looked at Manfred. "So it's Frau again, Manfred. *Kommen sie hier,*" indicating the bed. "I have fifteen minutes before my train departs. I know what my gallant Lieutenant can do in a few minutes, *Nicht wahr?*"

Manfred felt his passion rising. He struggled out of his ski boots, tunic and trousers which took him half a minute and by that time Erica was lying flat on her back on the bed with her legs wide apart and her femininity inviting intrusion. Manfred leapt on the bed and entered her and their lovemaking was violent and brief. The bed protested loudly, the whole bed-frame shook and the floorboards creaked and rattled. There were shouts of *"Wunderbar, wunderbar"* from Erica and finally grunting and bellowing from Manfred as he reached his climax. They dressed rapidly and came downstairs. The whole passionate interlude had only lasted about eight minutes. The look on the concierge's face indicated that she knew exactly what had happened in the bedroom.

Manfred explained to her, "Frau Mosselman, I am here to escort Frau Major Haldendorf to the station."

The rotund Frau gave her guests a knowing look.

"Jawohl," the concierge replied.

Erica added, *"Danke, Frau Mosselman"* as she and Manfred left the *Gasthaus.* He saw Erica off from the ice-bound platform and gave her a peck on her cheek, acting proxy for the major.

"Auf Wiedersehen, Erica."

To which she replied, *"Auf Wiedersehen, mein gallant Soldat."*

With a brief wave of her hand Erica left in the train and Manfred would never see her again. She had been his first sexual encounter and, in a matter of two hours and eight minutes, had taught him nearly all he needed to know about the mysteries of sex. He would always remember and be grateful to Erica Haldendorf. Within six months Erica had moved on to pastures new. She left the dull, predictable major, and moved in with an SS colonel stationed in Dresden.

*

At the beginning of March 1939 *skischule* training at Winterberg was coming to an end. For the first time in his life Manfred had enjoyed himself in the company of the devil-may-care *Fallschirmjagger,* the skiing and cross country exercises and the camaraderie of the paratroopers after a days training. Major Haldendorf had given Manfred extra responsibilities and lately allowed him to lead the *skischule* on their expeditions, an experience he had not enjoyed with the Bavarian Hussars at Augsburg. The 12th Hussars were an ancient cavalry regiment still practising Teutonic traditions and a new young lieutenant held very little credibility in the regimental hierarchy. All new junior officers were expected to be perfectly dressed in the mess, to stand at attention at all times in the presence of a senior officer, even a captain, and to convey messages to the autocratic commanding officer only through an intermediary, usually a captain or major.

The tasks assigned to Manfred had been menial. The 12th Hussars were converted in 1936 from a cavalry into a motorcycle and bicycle regiment, although the colonel and senior officers still had their horses for ceremonial parades. Manfred was in charge of the maintenance workshops at the camp in Augsburg. The daily decisions he made were trivial; whether a motorcycle or sidecar needed a new part or whether a tired old bicycle needed replacement. He was distinctly unhappy and wrote to his father about his predicament and was exhorted by Gerhardt to, "Stick it out and better things will follow."

Manfred had been delighted when Count Erich von Bulow arranged his transfer to the Paras, recognising that von Bulow had more friends in higher places than the stuffy arrogant colonel of his Bavarian Regiment. His orders to transfer came as a breath of fresh air and his first weeks in the *skischule* with the *Fallschirmjagger* had, to date, been the happiest time of his brief military career.

Arrangements were made for the *skischule* company to return to Lübbecke during the second week of March 1939. Major Haldendorf and five paratroopers remained at Winterberg to receive the next company whilst Manfred was placed in charge of the main party with Sergeant Schneider as his second in command. Marching ahead of his company from the barracks to the railway station at Winterberg Manfred felt a surge of pride sensing that the locals were looking on with admiration and awe at the tall blond officer and his troop of bronzed, fit, soldiers parading through their small village. Nearer the railway station the troops, prompted by Manfred, broke into the *Fallschirmjaggers'* rallying song, *Rot Sheint Die Sonne*.

The two hundred and fifty kilometre, five hour journey took them through Paderborn, Bielefeld and Osnabrück arriving at the camp in

Lübbecke on the evening of the 20th March, 1939. Lübbecke was a sizeable village on a crossroads halfway along the road from Minden to Osnabrück and bisected by a second road from Herford to Bremen running north to south across a 4,900 square kilometre area of plains, grassland, fens and lakes. The barracks at Lübbecke were custom-built for a parachute division with an air-strip on the north side and accommodation for up to 2,500 men. Manfred again felt a surge of pride as he marched ahead of his company on to the main parade square at the barracks.

Sergeant Schneider dismissed the men and Manfred made his way to Colonel von Bulow's office. The colonel, wearing a broad smile, jumped to his feet when Manfred entered.

"How was the *skischule*?" shaking Manfred's hand vigorously.

"Sit down," he continued. "We've been expecting you for a day or two. The regiment is on semi-alert. I flew back from a meeting in Magdeburg yesterday. The Czechoslovakian crisis is coming to a head. The first Paras have been sent to Chemnitz. The Führer has decided that antagonism from the Czechs to our occupation of Sudeteland last October is intolerable. He's given up negotiating with Chamberlain and Daladier and I reckon he's made up his mind to attack the Czechs. Now I expect you want to know about your own training? For the time being you will be my personal aide here in this office and accompany me to conferences and into the field. Captain Hartman is my adjutant and you will work closely with him. At the same time Sergeant Schneider will continue with your training and I expect you'll have done your nine jumps by May if the weather improves and allows us to fly."

Manfred thought about the jumps. So far he was happy and proud to be in the Parachute Regiment but would he have the courage to actually jump out of a plane and rely on a few pieces of string and canvas to bring him down unharmed to earth. He hoped he would be able to see it through and not disappoint his father, the Führer and this charismatic, bubbly little paratrooper colonel.

"Thank you Herr Colonel, I wish to thank you for all you have done for me. I am proud to be a *Fallschirmjagger* and to serve under your command."

The colonel, who had never jumped from an aeroplane in his life, smiled and winked with his good eye.

"That's the spirit Manfred, well done young man."

War Diary

Colonel Erich von Bulow's prediction that Hitler would contravene the Munich Agreement with Britain and France, concluded on the 30th September, 1938, proved completely accurate. By the 15th March, 1939 Germany had annexed the greater part of Czechoslovakia and Chamberlain's policy and his cri de coeur of "Peace for our time" lay in ruins. War between Britain and Germany was now inevitable. On the 31st March, 1939 Britain concluded a defence pact with Poland pledging to declare war on Germany if Poland were attacked. On the 22nd March Hitler annexed Memel, a German speaking enclave in Lithuania. Mussolini, not to be outdone by his Nazi partner, overran Albania in April 1939 and the two dictators signed the "Pact of Steel" in Berlin in May of the same year. The scene was set for a Second World War. Hitler's main concern about an attack on Poland was the unpredictable reaction from Stalin and the Soviet Union. This was solved by negotiating a non-aggression pact between the USSR and Germany which was signed in Moscow on 23rd August, 1939 and which secretly allowed Russia to occupy the eastern one-third of Poland. All these events were loudly acclaimed by the German people who regarded them as exemplary diplomatic coups and evidence of the power and genius of the Führer and his Third Reich. The army commanders, mainly Prussian in origin, and Colonel Erich von Bulow included, were at first sceptical of Hitler as a diplomat and of his ability to conduct major military campaigns. But the Führer had reoccupied the Rheinland, annexed Austria, Czechoslovakia and Memel without bloodshed and virtually no loss of German lives. Hitler was now regarded as a genius and most Germans, military and civilian, began to believe in the invincibility of the Third Reich.

Sergeant Heinz Schneider

Twenty-three year old Sergeant Heinz Schneider had been with the *Fallschirmjager* for two and a half years and in the Army since he was eighteen years of age. A native of Darmstadt he enlisted in the *Wehrmacht* in 1935 and became a member of a Storm Company sent to Spain in 1937 under the command of Captain Kurt Student. His first experience of parachuting had been at Guernica and on returning to Germany he was posted to the First Parachute Brigade at Bielefeld and now, two years later, he was staff sergeant at Minden responsible for training recruits, including officers, for Colonel von Bulow's 8th Regiment. The sergeant, a short, muscular, well-proportioned man with blazing blue eyes and a wrinkled weather-beaten face was well adapted for his appointment. He claimed he could predict at first glance which recruit would make a paratrooper. He ruminated over his present squad and mentally singled out half a dozen who would fail to make the grade.

The officer, Lieutenant Schmidt, Schneider mused would never make it but he was unable to put his finger on his doubts about Manfred. Maybe it was his awkwardness on the ski slopes or his reserved manner or the arrogance he displayed when marching the company into the barracks. Or was it more than that. Schneider was sure that the lieutenant had made love to Frau Haldendorf on the train on the way to Winterberg. Was he jealous. No, good luck to the lieutenant. The Frau was known to be free with her favours and he felt sorry for her husband, the major. He came to realise that he was envious of the lieutenant's rank and good looks. 'Yes, the good looks may get him a woman but it won't help him jump out of an aeroplane. I'll give him hell and see how he reacts'.

Heinz Schneider was sitting on the edge of his bed smoking a cigarette before going on parade. He stood up, smoothed out his immaculately pleated tunic and trousers, adjusted his forage cap and on a cloudy, wet, March morning strode across the parade ground to meet his batch of twenty-one new recruits who were lined up in file with Lieutenant Manfred Schmidt at one end and Private Fritz Schultz at the other. He cast an expert eye over the line and made a mental note that three of them were unlikely to make the grade, no four if he was to include the haughty lieutenant. He knew about the short fat one and had been expressly instructed by the colonel himself not to push Schultz too hard but to excuse him physical duties and post him straight away to the cookhouse. Sergeant Schneider called the parade to attention and took up his position in front of the line of men.

"My name is Heinz Schneider, Sergeant Heinz Schneider. When we are on parade you call me Sir. Is that clear?" and looking at Manfred he continued, "Including you, Sir. When we are off duty you may call me Heinz or Sergeant Heinz."

Manfred felt his face redden in anger but kept his mouth shut. He was unable to get to grips with the strange informality between non-commissioned officers and other ranks in the *Fallschirmjagger* but, even so, the lower ranks did not abuse their privileges and were prompt to obey orders from their superiors.

The sergeant continued, "So you all want to be *Fallschirmjagger* and to wear the coveted wings on your tunics? Let me tell you now, and I'm a good judge, only half of you will make it. I expect you can't wait for the thrill of your first jump!"

Manfred shuddered inwardly as did the majority of the men in line.

"Let me tell you that it's not all fun. I've done eighty-seven jumps so I should know what I'm talking about. Now what's the first thing a paratrooper does when he hits the ground?" Not waiting for a reply he continued. "He walks or runs away from the point of landing to find cover. Now this could be a short distance or many miles and he will be carrying full equipment. So, gentleman, what's the first thing we must do? We must learn to march and run long distances. Today we'll go without equipment but in a week's time you will all be walking fifteen kilometres in full battle order and there will be a route march every day. So let's go for a walk. Follow me."

The squad marched six times around the parade ground and then left the barracks to walk to Lübbecke station and back again. On the return journey Fritz Schultz and another recruit began to falter. Fritz blamed his new boots which were cramping his broad, spatulate, flat feet. Sergeant Schneider took him out of ranks and sent him to the cookhouse. After Fritz had hobbled off the parade ground Sergeant Schneider again addressed the recruits before dismissing them. "That was only a short trip. Tomorrow at 6.30 you will have half an hour's physical exercise and, after breakfast, we shall leave in battle order to repeat the walk we did today. Parade dismissed."

The pattern of training for the next fortnight varied between shorter trips carrying heavy rucksacks and longer trips without equipment and, on a few occasions, the marches were interspersed with bouts of running and field firing. The size of the squad gradually dwindled and by the end of the week only fourteen of the original twenty-one were fit to turn out for training. Sergeant Schneider knew that he was pushing the men hard but his previous assessment of Manfred as a potential casualty proved incorrect. The lieutenant, despite his ungainly walk and inborn clumsiness over rough ground, was keeping up with the rest. Manfred felt that he was at least gaining Sergeant Schneider's respect at the cost to himself of a lot of pain, perseverance and physical pressure which made him face the daily training routine with dread and grim determination.

After two weeks' drilling Sergeant Schneider faced his fourteen-man squad.

"Gentleman, you are now ready to be taught how to parachute. Jumping out of a plane is easy. Any fool can do it with a push from me. Landing is where you may get injured and, in action, become a liability to your colleagues. We will now go to the gymnasium where I will show you how to land without breaking your neck, or leg, or both."

The floor of one half of the gymnasium was covered by soft spongy mattresses with a wooden structure in the middle resembling a gallows and a length of rope dangling from the centre of the high ceiling of the building. This was the jumping platform. The sergeant showed them how to do a forward roll while standing on the floor and later they repeated the manoeuvre jumping from a height of ten feet off the platform. They all managed to execute some acceptable forward rolls and there were no major injuries to the recruits apart from a few bumps and bruises. Sergeant Schneider was pleased with their progress.

"We've now mastered the forward roll from a standing position. Unfortunately, landing conditions in the field will almost never be wind- free. I will now show you how to land and hit the ground from an angle," and using the rope he swung from the gallows landing on the mattress in a perfect parachute roll.

One member of the squad severely sprained his ankle in this exercise and now there were only thirteen recruits left for the ultimate test, their first parachute jump from an aeroplane. Manfred silently dreaded the moment when he would have to face up to jumping into space.

Sergeant Schneider explained, "We are now waiting for a fine wind-free day to do our first jump. Remember gentleman, you need nine training jumps before you can wear wings on your tunic. We shall of course be jumping in battle order."

The weather in Minden throughout February and March vacillated between rainy spells, gusting winds and occasional snow flurries. Spring of 1939 was slow in appearing and Easter had come and gone before the weather became more temperate and sunny. The first 'safe' jump day was the 13th April. The squad was taken up in an old

Fokker transport plane and the grim-faced recruits sat in line along each side of the fuselage. Manfred would be the last to jump. Sergeant Schneider stood by an open hatch bellowing to make himself heard above the engine noise and rushing slipstream.

"Do as I tell you. When the red light turns green No. 1 will get up and walk to the hatch. He will attach this rope here to his parachute ripcord, face outwards, take a deep breath and dive headfirst out of the hatch. He will be pulled backwards by the slipstream and within five to seven seconds his parachute will open, and he will then go down quietly and land as I've taught you. As soon as No. 1 is out I want No. 2 to take his place and clip on. And so on until all of you are out. I'll jump last. If at any time the red light comes on unclip and return to your seats. Is that clear?"

There were muffled, murmured nervous replies. One of the recruits crossed himself and prayed silently and a few, including Manfred, lost control of their bowels. The Fokker had only been airborne for ten minutes when the green light flashed. Very quickly No. 1 disappeared and then the others, some bellowing obscenities, some shouting for protection from their deity, and some completely silent, whilst a few were helped out of the plane by a hefty push from Sergeant Schneider. Within a matter of seconds, or so it seemed, the plane was empty apart from Manfred and the sergeant standing at the hatch. Manfred clipped on as instructed and stood at the hatch ready to jump, then suddenly pulled back shouting, *"Nein, nein."*

Schneider took his elbow and guided him forward gently and when Manfred was level with the hatch he changed his tactics and shouting, "Get out, you bastard," gave Manfred a violent shove into space. Manfred felt the sergeant's hammer-blow in the middle of his back and, as he fell forwards, an even greater thud as the slipstream tore at his tunic, knocking the breath out of his body and propelling him violently backwards past the tail end of the plane. Manfred's eyes were tightly shut and his mouth wide open as he tried unsuccessfully to scream against the force of the gushing slipstream. He was conscious of the noise of the plane rapidly receding and, within seven seconds, of a resounding snap above his head which ended in a sharp jerk across his shoulders as the canopy of the parachute opened above his head. Then everything became uncannily silent and he felt his body swaying gently to and fro in space. He opened his eyes wide and over his left shoulder saw four other white parachutes descending like balls of cotton wool towards the ground. He relaxed for a few moments, breathing a sigh of relief, but then panic returned. The ground below was approaching rapidly. They had jumped from the Fokker at two thousand feet and now at two hundred feet he again closed his eyes, tensed his body, stiffened all his muscles and, forgetting all Sergeant Schneider's instruction, plunged like a javelin feet first into the ground. He landed in a patch of boggy marshland and the impact, although violent and jarring, did not cause him any harm.

For a full minute he lay crumpled on the muddy ground, entwined in parachute cords and the canopy, breathing heavily and physically exhausted. Unravelling himself from the cords he came slowly to his feet and began pulling in his canopy. Two soldiers noisily approached him with smiles on their faces.

"*Fantastiche* Herr *Oberleutnant, Nicht wahr?*"

Manfred returned their smiles and the three mud-spattered warriors hugged each other in ecstasy and relief at the success of their first jump. The collecting lorry soon came to pick them up and to recover their parachutes and in a small convoy, two lorries and an ambulance, they returned noisily to the barracks at Lübbecke. There had been no casualties. That night, under the direction of Sergeant Schneider, a party was held in the sergeants' mess to honour the 'first jumpers'. The next jump was scheduled for the following day.

The second jump went according to plan under the watchful eye of the sergeant until No. 11 went into space and, within seconds, Manfred was aware that something had gone wrong. Sergeant Schneider, his head out of the hatch, was shouting, "*Mein Gott, mein Gott,*" and, as Manfred joined him, they saw a soldier's body trailing behind the aircraft, his parachute rigging wrapped around the tail plane. In a matter of seconds, but it seemed like an eternity to the onlookers, the cords snapped one by one and finally the ragdoll figure went spinning rapidly earthwards. The second jump had been a costly affair. Apart from the paratrooper killed, recruit No. 4 had broken his ankle on landing. The third jump of eleven recruits occurred a week later. It went according to plan until it was Manfred's turn when he refused to get off the fuselage seat. Sergeant Schneider tried his powers of persuasion to get the lieutenant out of the plane, even insulting his parentage and accusing him of cowardice. But Manfred sat there stiffly resolutely refusing to budge.

"Ich habe kopfschmerzen."

Failure to jump, although allowed on two occasions, was an offence reported to the commanding officer. Manfred appeared before Colonel von Bulow the following morning. The colonel was in a benevolent mood.

"Lieutenant Schmidt, why did you not jump yesterday?"

Manfred replied, "I saw the poor chap whose parachute failed and he was killed. I feared it might happen again."

The colonel replied, "Manfred it happens to all of us," omitting to add that he had never jumped out from an aircraft in his life and continuing. "In the First Regiment they have Walter Neusel the world heavyweight boxing champion and even he failed on two occasions but now he is a sergeant instructor with over forty jumps to his credit. Your headache was the cause of your failure. Next time you go up ask the medics to give you something to settle your head pains. Promise me you won't let me or your father down next time."

Manfred stood rigidly to attention, thinking hard, and replied, "Herr Colonel, I do not want to go up again but for my father and this regiment I will do so."

For the fourth drop on the 29th April Sergeant Schneider changed the order of jumping. Manfred was to go out first. Before embarkation Manfred had a sedative injection from the medical officer and was semi-stuporous when he went to the hatch to clip on and wait for the green light. He stood erect staring straight out of the hatch at the horizon. The green light came on abruptly and Manfred simply stepped out of the side of the fuselage disobeying all instructions to dive forward. His helmeted head missed the tail end of the plane by a few centimetres. His parachute opened with a loud crack. Manfred hurtled towards the ground and, eyes closed, still in a stiff erect position, he hit a rocky outcrop with a resounding thud and a loud crack accompanied by an agonising shooting pain in his right leg. He had no doubt that his leg was broken. He lay where he had fallen, writhing in agony and bellowing loudly for help. The crash ambulance arrived quickly and Manfred was carried off the field on a stretcher with his right leg in a splint. After an agonising hour's journey over rough tracks the ambulance came to the parachute depot where Colonel von Bulow greeted Manfred:

"Hard luck, old chap. Not to worry. The medics will have you fit in no time. We'll see you back here in a few weeks."

Sergeant Schneider leaning over the stretcher, added, "Good luck, Lieutenant Schmidt, Sir."

Sergeant Schneider recognised that the injured lieutenant had foolishly shown exceptional courage and his opinion of Manfred Schmidt changed perceptibly. Due to the nature of his injury the sergeant realised that the lieutenant would probably not return to the *Fallschirmjagger* but he hoped that he would make it and that he, Sergeant Schneider, would have the opportunity to go into battle with Lieutenant Schmidt.

After preliminary first-aid treatment at the depot in Minden Manfred had to face another uncomfortable ambulance journey of some seventy kilometres to the military hospital at Hanover where he underwent a major six hour emergency operation for plating his fractured leg bones. When he awoke, around midday, two days later he was lying flat in bed with his right leg on traction through a system of pulleys and cords. At first he was completely unaware of his surroundings. He saw women in white dresses floating around the bed and in the back of his mind he saw Schneider's face leaning over him repeating the words, "Good luck, Lieutenant Schmidt, Sir" and breaking into uncontrollable laughter.

Gradually the mists in his mind cleared and the white-veiled women turned out to be military nurses. Manfred was kept on traction in bed for five weeks. His fateful last jump had taken place on the 29th April and he was not allowed out of bed until the 5th June when, using crutches to get about with his leg encased in plaster, he began a course of intensive physiotherapy to strengthen the muscles of the injured leg and to re-educate him in the art of walking. He was eventually discharged from the military hospital on the 17th August and went home to Munich for convalescence.

During his hospitalisation in Hanover he received visits from his father, Colonel von Bulow, Major Haldendorf, some of the younger lieutenants and from Sergeant Schneider. They all encouraged him to get better quickly and return to Minden as soon as possible. His father's visit disturbed him greatly. Gerhardt Schmidt had lost a lot of weight and appeared cadaverous. His jaundiced eyeballs, behind his thick-lensed glasses, stuck out of their sockets like organ stops. Gerhardt complained of stomach pains and had seen the best medical specialists in Munich who confirmed, as did the X-rays, that he had a stomach ulcer. He was on a milk diet and took antacids regularly but was unable to eat any solids and his excursions to the Hofbrauhaus and Den Berliner had stopped. Still he was hopeful that the treatment would be successful and he might soon be able to take a stein of beer and some *wurst* and enjoy a brandy or a schnapps.

The visit from Major Haldendorf brought back fond memories of Erica. The major explained with indifference that she was now living in Dresden with a colonel in the SS and that he had completely lost contact with her. When the major left Manfred spent a pleasurable hour reminiscing about the train journey from Marburg to Winterberg and the bedroom session in Frau Mosselman's *Gasthaus*, the rickety, creaky old bed, the multi-coloured duvet and the passion in the female writhing underneath his perspiring body. Such passion, such pleasure, where could she be in Dresden. His thoughts produced and erection which he placated by masturbation and afterwards, completely relaxed, he thought about his contacts with other women at the Club Erotica in Minden.

Club Erotica was a small, sleazy establishment in the Schabbelhaus area of Minden, an otherwise staid and well-ordered provincial town. The club occupied the ground floor of a three-storey building. The upper two storeys were used as rooms by prostitutes and homosexuals. Due to the presence of many large military units and depots in the Minden area prostitution was a thriving profession. On any night of the week the club hall and bars were a heaving collection of prostitutes, pimps, homosexuals and lesbians all congregated to watch the pornographic acts conducted on the four metre square stage in one corner of the club. A visit to the club was regarded as a natural follow on to a mess dinner or simply as a good laugh or a good night out on the town. Manfred was taken to the club on three occasions by fellow officers at the parachute depot. Other ranks were banned from the club and they achieved sexual gratification with the prostitutes plying their trade around Minden *Bahnhof.* On each occasion Manfred found himself in an upstairs bedroom with one of the 'girls' and paid for her favours. A short dark-eyed, black-haired prostitute called Giesela was his favourite. He recalled that one night he had taken her on three trips up to the bedroom for ten minutes of pleasure, a feat loudly acclaimed by his colleagues in the officer's mess.

More disturbingly his blond Aryan looks and paratrooper's uniform attracted one or two homosexuals and transvestites whom he encouraged for fun but, on reflection, wondered if he had not in fact derived some pleasure from physical contact with these 'peculiar' men.

Memories of Erica were still fresh in his mind and, now that he was recovering, his sexual urges were returning and asserting themselves. One of the nurses, Gerde, a tall, thin, long-legged girl with a hook nose and firm buttocks, seemed attracted to him. He was still confined to bed and Gerde helped with blanket baths and general care and seemed to be particularly assiduous in the cleanliness of his genital area. On a few occasions Gerde's administrations produced an erection which he was unable to control and which she treated glibly and laughingly by applying a cold wet compress. In mid-June, Manfred's bed was moved out to a balcony outside the main ward into the sunshine during daylight hours. Manfred insisted on sleeping in the open air on the warm June nights.

One day he pressed a note into Gerde's hand asking if she would call in to see him in the evening after duty. As requested Gerde duly appeared dressed in a plain white smock, buttoned down the front. She stood in the half light some four feet away from his bedside and deliberately started slowly unbuttoning her tunic from top to bottom to reveal her well proportioned, completely naked body. Gerde approached the bed and Manfred made a grab at her legs to pull her towards him. She resisted his attempts and slowly drew the blankets downwards to the bottom of the bed revealing his erection. Gerde gently stroked the pulsating organ and, climbing on to the bed in a crouching position across his body, guided him into her nether regions. Gerde was now in complete control. She moved her taut buttocks up and down squeezing on his erection with her pelvic muscles and very quickly brought Manfred to an explosive climax. There was no kissing or foreplay involved in the sexual act, merely a professional execution performed by the tireless Frau Gerde.

She climbed off the bed, re-buttoned her dress, took a seat at the bedside, pretended to read a book and all the time kept a watchful eye on her silent patient. Within ten minutes there were signs that Manfred was getting aroused again. The thin blanket tented over his groin and this was a stimulus for Gerde to drop her book, undo a few buttons and mount Manfred for another rapid copulation. The process was repeated once more and, as Manfred lay sated and exhausted on his bed, the red-haired nymphomaniac took her leave.

"*Guten nacht unt danke*, Herr *Oberleutnant*. I'll see you in the morning."

Throughout their sexual encounter hardly a word was spoken and both parties knew that their urgent copulating was an act designed to fulfil their inner sexual desires. As soon as Manfred was ambulant they made love standing up in a broom cupboard, on the desk in the nurse's office, and frequently in the woods in the hospital grounds. The other patients in the ward and the nursing staff were fully aware of what was going on but took a tolerant view as Gerde was providing comfort and therapy for the gallant wounded *Fallschirmjagger* Lieutenant. Comfort there may have been but there was never at any time love or tenderness in their torrid lovemaking.

War Diary

During Manfred's stay at Hanover military hospital between April and August 1939 the situation in western Europe deteriorated and war clouds were gathering. In March the bloody Spanish Civil War ended and General Franco became undisputed Fascist leader of Spain with sympathies for his compatriot dictators in Germany and Italy. The same month, after a bloodless German occupation of Czechoslovakia, Britain and France pledged support for Poland, followed in April by Hitler's renunciation of his pact with Poland and Mussolini's occupation of Albania. A month later, on May 22nd, Hitler and Mussolini signed the 'Pact of Steel' in Rome, pledging support for each other in the event of a major war in Europe. Throughout August the British Prime Minister, Neville Chamberlain and Daladier in France continued their futile attempts at appeasement but Hitler by now had made up his mind to attack Poland and risk plunging Europe into war. The war became inevitable when Hitler's envoy, von Ribbentrop, signed a non-aggression pact with the USSR and a secret codicil in the agreement allowed Russia to occupy the eastern third of Poland after Germany had attacked and crushed the Poles. On 1st September, 1939 German troops crossed the Polish border followed by a declaration of war in London and Paris on the 3rd September. The Second World War had begun.

Manfred returned to his father's flat in Munich for convalescence on the 17th August, 1939, nearly four months after his parachuting injury. He was now able to get about with a stick though he walked stiffly due to weakness in his right leg. When he arrived at No. 14 Grünewald Strasse he was shocked to see his father. Gerhardt Schmidt had become bent, wizened and shrunken with jaundiced skin and sclerotics. He complained of some pain in his stomach but the main difficulty was an increasing enlargement of his abdomen. He ate little in the way of solids and his diet was mainly broth, soups and fruit-flavoured drinks. Despite his general weakness he continued going to the Braunhaus each day to check on his files and returned home, utterly exhausted, going straight to bed.

On his first night home Gerhardt insisted on taking his son to the Hofbrauhaus to show him off and to celebrate and Willi gave them an effusive welcome. But Gerhardt was only able to drink a few sips of beer and to nibble on a piece of soft, dry bread. The celebration was over by 8 p.m. and Manfred had to half carry his father home to the flat.

On the following day Manfred insisted his father should stay in bed and he went to the Braunhaus to see Alfred Rosenberg, the senior Nazi *Gauleiter* present in the building that day. His father's illness was discussed and it was agreed that, in view of Gerhardt's exalted position in Munich and his great service to the Nazi Party, he would be taken to à Military hospital at Grafelfing. Gerhardt was admitted to the hospital on the 20th August and twelve days later the Germans attacked Poland and this was the last item of news that Gerhardt assimilated in his drugged, semi-conscious, state. He held Manfred's hand and whispered, "At last the Führer is on the march. Now we will conquer the world. Be a good soldier Manfred and fight for the Führer and Germany."

Later that day he sank into a deep coma and died at 11 a.m. on Sunday 3rd September 1939 at the very moment that Neville Chamberlain was broadcasting to the world, "Britain is now at war with Germany."

The Nazi Party arranged for Gerhardt to have a military funeral, attended by Hess, Himmler and Rosenberg with the coffin draped in a Nazi flag and a guard of honour accompanying the body to its final resting place in Grafelfing military cemetery.

For the fourteen days his father was dying in Grafelfing *Krankenhaus* Manfred had time on his hands and lived alone in the apartment. He visited his father each day but his evenings were free and he spent his nights drinking at the Hofbrauhaus or dining in Den Berliner. Willi, as always, was kind and considerately inquisitive.

After a few days he craved female companionship, his sexuality stimulated by thoughts of Erica on the train, Giesela at Club Erotica and more recently Gerde at Hanover hospital. He called on the Mayor, Herr Widemayer, to enquire if he could take Marianne out to dine. He was well received by the portly, kindly *Bürgermeister* who was genuinely sorry to hear about Gerhardt's illness and, without a second thought, agreed that his twenty-five year old daughter could accompany Manfred to the Den Berliner for dinner. They wined and dined regally and were both slightly tipsy and afterwards Marianne readily agreed to go to the Schmidt apartment for coffee and liqueurs. Manfred fumbled and hurried over preparation of the coffee, spilling most of the dark liquid from his cup on to the carpet and his hands were trembling as he poured two large cognacs. Manfred gulped down his brandy and taking the cup from Marianne pushed her back on to the couch and, crushing his body on top, pressed his tongue deep into Marianne's open protesting mouth, at the same time wildly tearing at her blouse buttons.

Fraulein Widemayer used all her strength to resist Manfred's advances but he kept her pinned to the couch while his tearing fingers exposed one of her large tumescent breasts. At first Marianne thought Manfred was having a little fun, but now she realised that he was in deadly earnest and that she had a fight on her hands to protect her virginity. She gave a tired little scream and kept repeating:

"Don't, don't, please don't," but by this time Manfred's hands were tearing away at her skirt and underclothes while his lips and teeth were tightly closed around her exposed breast nipping and sucking the turgid nipple. She felt Manfred's manhood pushing and thrusting between her legs and his hands ripping at her silk underwear. She tried clamping her thighs together but he forced them apart with his knees whilst holding her shoulders down with both hands. And then suddenly Marianne felt a searing and stabbing pain inside her lower body. She screamed aloud and Manfred placed one hand over her mouth and the other behind her buttocks whilst he remorselessly continued shoving and pushing his penis into her nether regions. After about a minute of grunting and groaning the pace of Manfred's pelvic thrusts increased in tempo until he reached a climax, gave a loud vibrating shout, and collapsed in a limpid heap on top of Marianne who was now sobbing uncontrollably.

"*Das war gut, ja?*" Manfred asked but Marianne continued to sob, the tears streaming down her face. For ten minutes there was silence in the apartment and then Manfred asked, "Shall we do it again?"

Marianne shuddered, hysterically crying through cracked lips and stammering, "*Nein, nein,*" and in between sobs, "Please take me home."

Manfred felt deflated. The thrill of seduction and rape had not measured up to his expectations. Only his climax had been satisfactory and the poor girl herself had obviously not enjoyed the experience. Still he was not sorry for her, a twenty-five year old, rather plain prude, who had never felt the joy of intercourse. Well, she now knew what it was all about. In years to come she would be grateful to him for breaking the ice. He walked her home in complete silence. At her front door he tried to peck her cheek but she pulled away and quickly ran into the house. The two were never to meet again.

It took Manfred three more days to settle up his father's affairs. Packing up the flat and leaving the keys with the new tenants downstairs he left for Lübbecke to rejoin the 8th Parachute Regiment on the 11th September, 1939. By that time the powerful German forces were well on the way to conquering Poland.

Recruitment of Fritz Schultz

During the first three months of 1939 Colonel von Bulow was actively recruiting for the 8th Regiment which was still undermanned, not in parachutists, but in support personnel. On a wet and windy Saturday in March the colonel and his driver were travelling northwards from a recruitment drive at Nuremberg. The Opel started misbehaving when they had been motoring for about an hour and finally spluttered and coughed its way into Schweinfurt where the driver declared the engine "kaput". The count took a room for the night in Hotel Kaiserhof, in the main street of the town and situated on the banks of the swollen and flooded river Main. Not bothering to change, the count, attired in his service dress, made his way to the restaurant bar and, after a few schnapps, quickly gathered a small crowd of local drinkers around him and soon had their devoted attention, tale swapping, drinking and toasting with increasing rapidity. Ever-mindful of the purpose of his travels he enquired if any of the local young men of Schweinfurt might be suitable or interested in joining his regiment.

Otto Brünner, a retired schoolmaster, was the first to speak, "Colonel von Bulow, I know of two young men who might volunteer. If you wish I will go and bring them to you."

"Yes please if you will Herr Brünner" replied the Count. Otto Brünner's favourite drinking bar was the Wildbok, only two hundred metres further down the main street and he went there most nights, but never on a Saturday when the Wildbok was frequented by a gang of hard-drinking, carousing louts, who had no respect for seniority or common courtesy and frequently became involved in drunken brawls. There were two men in their mid-twenties who, in particular, had been drunkenly offensive to the schoolmaster. He now saw a chance to fix these young renegades for good.

When Otto walked into the crowded bar at the Wildbok he saw his targets arm wrestling, surrounded by a small crowd of yelling youths encouraging the two adversaries to even greater effort. They were all well on the way to becoming very drunk and Otto seized his opportunity and edged towards the contestants.

One of the arm wrestlers was Fritz Schultz, a twenty-six year old, obese, round-faced man with heavy jowls and receding, blond hair. His face reminded Otto of a smiling bloodhound. His father owned a large bakery in Schweinfurt where Fritz worked for six days a week, starting his shift at 10 p.m. and working through the night until 10 a.m. on the following morning. Saturday was his rest day. Fritz longed for Saturday and his night out with the 'boys'. Normally placid and even-tempered he would, after six or seven steins of beer, become transformed into a bombastic, aggressive and foul-mouthed oaf, whose main ambition was to pick a fight with both friends and strangers.

The other arm wrestler was his regular drinking companion, Anton Gretzler, who drove a van for the bakery. Anton was the antithesis of Fritz, dark-haired, short, thin and wiry with a perpetual scowl on his puckered face. He also became excessively aggressive in drink and the fights that he and Fritz became involved in were nearly always instigated by Anton.

Otto Brünner summed up the situation in one glance and pushing his way to the bar through the jostling crowd asked the bartender for a schnapps. Anton glanced sideways at the schoolmaster, lost his concentration and Fritz, with a howl of delight, pushed his right arm backwards on to the counter sending a half-full stein of beer crashing to the floor. The crowd of youths around the contestants cheered loudly. Fritz had a seraphic, victorious smile on his face, whilst Anton turned to face Herr Brünner, scowling and clenching his fists, preparing himself for an attack on the insolent intruder who had lost him the arm wrestling match.

The schoolmaster smiled benignly and eyeing the two wrestlers said, "Boys, boys, all this aggression. It's a pity that you don't save your energy to fight for the Führer."

"What do you mean?" slurred Fritz.

"Germany needs good strong men like yourselves to serve in the Army," continued the schoolmaster.

Fritz, flattered and taking the bait, replied "I would join up tonight if I could find a recruiting office."

"So would I," added Anton with a leer.

"Well, your problems are solved. You can join the paratroopers tonight if you'll come down with me to Hotel Kaiserhof."

Anton was the first to speak, "Well I'm not sure I want..." interrupted by Fritz speaking with determination:

"I will sign tonight."

"If you go, I'll go too," added Anton.

Their cronies were incredulous. "I bet you won't sign, Fritzy. They won't take you. You're too fat, Fritzy."

Fritz smiled at his doubting friends and taking Herr Brünner roughly by the arm bade him lead them to the Kaiserhof. Fritz and the schoolmaster walked in front at a brisk pace followed reluctantly by Anton Gretzler and about a dozen of the young revellers from the Wildbok singing the Horstwessel song, intending not to miss the fun and to witness the signing-on ceremony. None of them believed that Fritzy, their tubby drinking companion, would go all the way and they were certain in their own minds that, in view of his obesity, he would not be a suitable candidate for the conscription.

Otto Brünner led the rowdy gang of youths into the restaurant bar at the Kaiserhof where the count was in full flight relating an anecdote about the señoritas in Madrid when he stopped short, drew himself erect, and one-eyedly reviewed the motley bunch of young men before him.

"*Mein Gott* Herr Brünner. Do all these boys wish to sign on?"

"No, only these two," replied Otto pushing Fritz and Anton forwards to the front of the mob.

Fritz felt uncomfortable at the sight of the one-armed, eye-patched, war hero whilst Anton half closed his eyes and looked into the distance. The count surveyed the two men before him. The short, wiry, mean-faced boy on the right would, if properly trained, make an excellent soldier. But what could he do with his grossly corpulent and untidy companion who kept tucking at his belt buckle and attempting to push his shirt into his waistband to cover over the bulging folds of white flesh showing around his midriff. This man would never be able to parachute and endure the rigours of day-to-day military training and yet, of the two, he would prefer having the fat one in his regiment. In contrast to the shifty-faced Gretzler, Fritz Schultz had an open, rounded, flat, Slavic face with a double chin and wide-apart, crystal-clear, blue, smiling eyes. The Count asked the usual questions about names, age, place of birth and parentage and when he found out that Fritz was a master baker, he made a snap decision to enlist him as a cook for company headquarters and the darker one, with his experience of driving, would also be of use. Count von Bulow now produced enlistment forms which were completed on the bar but left unsigned. He placed his military cap firmly in position and, calling everyone to attention, asked that Fritz and Anton should swear an oath of allegiance to the Führer. By now the room was in complete silence and the noisy rabble were overawed by the magnetic personality of the count.

Fritz repeated after the colonel, "I, Fritz Schultz, do swear an oath of allegiance to my Fatherland and to my Führer, Adolf Hitler," and then signed the enlistment form followed by Anton Gretzler.

The observing crowd clapped and cheered the two local heroes.

The count added, "This calls for a drink. Barman, a stein each for the gallant volunteers and a large schnapps for Herr Otto Brünner."

The drinking continued at the hotel bar and the party, including the count, moved back to the Wildbok where the session ended around midnight by which time Fritz had been violently sick over a table strewn with broken glass and half empty steins and then passed out under the table. Anton simply fell flat on his face on to the floor in a drunken stupor still holding an empty glass in his right hand.

On the following morning Anton called to see Fritz who was in his bedroom nursing a mammoth hangover.

"What the hell did you do to me last night you bastard? How the hell did we get home?"

Fritz's befuddled brain failed to produce a ready answer but, laughing suddenly, he said, "I think we joined the *Fallschirmjagger*."

Anton snarled, "We bloody well did. I've got a piece of paper in my pocket to prove it and so have you, Fritzy."

Fritz could not find his copy of the enlistment form. He had used it in the Wildbok toilet to clean up the messy diarrhoea from which he regularly suffered during, or after, a wild night on the booze.

Fritz added, "Don't worry, I think it's a joke the boys played on us."

A fortnight later the joke became a reality when their call up papers arrived instructing the volunteers to report for basic training at the parachute base in Minden on 22nd March, 1939. Anton Gretzler disappeared from town on the same night and Fritz was certain that he went south into the Austrian alps where he had an uncle living in Obergurgl. Fritz vacillated between wishing to go and leaving Schweinfurt and staying in the cosy protected environment he enjoyed, with a good home, a secure job and a weekly binge at the Wildbok. Uncharacteristically his father encouraged Fritz to go and see a bit of the world outside Schweinfurt. His father had no doubt that his son would be unfit for military service especially in an elite corps such as the parachute regiment. For a fortnight in March Fritz became the local hero, nightly treated and fêted by his drinking companions, and Anton Gretzler became the villain, disowned because he had deserted and run away and not kept his word to the dashing paratrooper colonel and to Adolf Hitler. Fritz's father's prediction that his son might be proclaimed unfit by the army was totally incorrect. Colonel von Bulow had arranged for the ungainly recruit to be fitted with a tailor-made uniform and to be taught basic drill. He was to be instructed in the rudiments of musketry but was not required to undertake parachute jumps. Schultz was to be attached to headquarters' mess kitchens and was to be allowed to wear soft canvas shoes to encompass his enormous flat feet. In March 1939 Fritz

Schultz went to war and was posted to the officers' cookhouse of the 8th *Fallschirmjagger* Regiment at Lübbecke.

Chapter Ten

Lieutenant David Green,
July 1939 – December 1940
Commando Training, Bronwen

A War Office directive and travel warrant reached Pusey Street by registered post on 20th July, 1939 ordering cadet officer, 2nd Lieutenant (Acting) David Green to report to No. 25 OCTU Training Camp at Chester on the 30th inst.

David was in the last week of OCTU when war was declared on Sunday 3rd September 1939, at 11 a.m. For weeks it had been evident that war between Germany, Britain and France was inevitable. Germany's unprovoked attack on Poland on the 1st September brought matters to a head and the British Government had no alternative but to honour their pledge of support if Polish neutrality was breached. The OCTU officers were ordered to attend in mess dress for a traditional Sunday curry lunch and, at 11 a.m. on the 3rd September, they stood in silence listening to Prime Minister Neville Chamberlain's faltering, emotion-laden voice crackling over the radio, "...and I have to inform you that a state of war exists between Great Britain and Germany. God Save the King."

The mess remained completely silent for thirty seconds or more, each officer lost in his private thoughts. The first to speak was Colonel Roach, a veteran of the Great War and Camp Commandant, "Well the balloon's gone up gentlemen. Let us take sherry and drink to a swift and speedy victory over the Hun."

The sherry flowed liberally and the officer cadets and permanent staff repaired noisily to the mess hall for their Sunday lunch. Conversation around the table ebbed and flowed in a cacophony of sound and dialect, "It'll all be over by Christmas," and questioningly, "What's your posting?"

David had been posted to the First Battalion the Welch Regiment. Though OCTU officers could not directly select a regiment they were given three choices in order of preference. David had opted for the First Welch primarily because of its present location in Palestine but also because his contacts with Welsh people in the past had always been harmonious and friendly.

Mobilisation of territorial army personnel proceeded at pace after Easter 1939. The First/Fifth Battalion of the Welch Regiment, mobilised in south-east Wales, were encamped for training in Haverfordwest since early June under the command of a regular officer, Colonel W. Ianto Price. Within two weeks of David's arrival the battalion moved to Portadown in Northern Ireland where they were deployed in manning local defences and for further intensive field training. David acted as an aide for the adjutant, Major J.T. (Hoot) Gibson, and also duplicated as the unit's intelligence officer. He gave lectures on the strength of German armed forces, information culled from very inadequate sources, which suggested that the German army of only forty divisions was ill-equipped with some two hundred front line tanks and a similar number of serviceable aircraft. Off-duty hours were spent sailing and fishing on Lough Neagh some twelve miles north of the battalion lines.

The First/Fifth Battalion was a peacetime territorial unit conscripted mainly from the mining valleys of the Rhondda and its conversion into an active front line regiment took several months. The First/Fifth had a mascot, a goat called Shwni, a 'Goat Major', a regimental band, a male choir and a rugby team of great experience and ability, the pride and joy of Major Hoot Gibson, the adjutant and sports officer. Twice a week the team played neighbouring battalions or Irish opposition and regularly beat them on the field and in the inevitable beer-swilling contest which followed each game.

David became an avid supporter of these matches and enjoyed drinking and singing in the company of the rugged southern Welshmen. Dining-in nights in the officers' mess were also memorable events. The regimental band played and the choir sang into the early hours of the morning, sad hymns and songs of ancient Welsh folklore and David took the trouble to learn the Welsh words for a few of the songs, *Cwm Rhondda, Calon Lan, Sospan Fach,* and the national anthem, *Hen Wlâd Fy Nhadau.*

The regimental sergeant major, Dai 'Scarper' Davies, a tough, regular north-Walian often said, "Boyos, if we is in trouble and Jerry is attacking us just give 'em a blast of *Cwm Rhondda* and the bastards will soon scarper."

During Christmas week 1939 the battalion entertained the local townsfolk and the camp became open house for the inhabitants and children of Portadown. David was home in London on leave for a week in the New Year. His father and mother were concerned for his safety but he was able to reassure them that he was very safe in Ireland and told them about the Christmas festivities. He omitted to mention that any day he might receive a posting to the Middle East to join the First Battalion which, by this time, had left Palestine and was stationed on the Egypt/Libyan border at Mersa Matruh.

*

On a dreary cold morning in late January 1940 David presented himself at the CO's office. Colonel Price and Major Gibson were seated behind a large desk, the latter sucking on a stone-cold, unlit pipe.

"Come in David and sit down. Major Gibson has been promoted to company commander with the First Battalion and will leave in three days for the Middle East. His replacement will be coming across from Brecon in about ten days. You are to hold the fort until the new adjutant arrives. There is one immediate problem. A Major Sharples of the Royal Marines is dropping in on the 20th to try and recruit men for his commando. You will arrange interviews. Don't be too helpful. We don't want to lose the best boys in the unit. He will wish to interview all NCOs and officers who speak foreign languages. Welsh of course will not count in this respect. With your university background I expect he will be very interested in having a chat with you. I'll leave all arrangements for the major's visit in your hands. Thank you for coming in," which was an indication to David that he was dismissed.

On the appointed day Major Sharples arrived in the officers' mess. David had compiled a list of eighteen officers and men whom he considered suitable for interview, selecting those soldiers and officers who had university training or had attended night school before enlisting. Precious few of the serving soldiers had any linguistic ability and most were Welsh-speaking miners and regarded English as a foreign tongue.

Major Sharples, a short stocky, pugnacious, black-haired man in his middle thirties inspected David's list and for his own reasons quickly eliminated four NCOs and three officers. The interviews lasted for two days and at the end the major shortlisted two French speaking NCOs and one German speaking lieutenant who had no wish to transfer to the Royal Marines. Only one of the NCOs, Corporal 327 Francis, professed an interest in switching to a Royal Marine Commando. On the last day, Major Sharples, who turned out to be a pleasant and humorous man, asked David to attend for his personal interview and they sat together in a quiet corner of the officers' mess.

"David, with your background and ability to speak German, Greek and Hebrew you could become a very important part of my organisation."

"Organisation?" David asked, "Surely you mean the Royal Marines?"

"Well, yes, in a way," replied the major, "but there's more to it than that. I am authorised to recruit suitable personnel for service abroad. It is required that they should be trained as commandos but will not necessarily serve with a commando unit. In fact I would prefer it if the recruit stayed with his own battalion but, if needs be, he could be mobilised for commando raids on enemy held territory and, in some instances, could remain behind the lines in an occupied country to organise resistance and sabotage. Do you follow me?" David nodded his head. "David, you are admirably suited for the Middle East theatre where your knowledge of languages will be invaluable."

David considered the major's proposition for a full minute. He realised that he was becoming bored with inactivity at Portadown and craved some action.

"Major Sharples, if Colonel Price will release me I will be pleased to sign on for commando training."

Major Sharples nodded considerately, "It is not a question of releasing you David but of arranging a temporary attachment for training with the Royal Marines. I have a special commando unit training in west Wales between March and September this year. You will be seconded to this unit for three or four months and then return here or, more likely, be transferred to the Middle East theatre to join the First Battalion. You will always be, and always remain, an officer of the First Battalion the Welch Regiment and your promotion, such as it may be, will be recommended by your commanding officer."

Major Sharples made the necessary arrangements for David and Corporal 327 Francis' secondment to the Royal Marines before he left Portadown and Colonel Price arranged a date in April for the transfer. He insisted that, on completion of training, the two men must return to the First/Fifth Battalion to instruct his own troops in commando tactics.

David spent St David's Day 1940 with the First/Fifth Battalion in Portadown. March 1st is the most important day in the yearly calendar of any Welsh regiment. There is a full dress parade and march past a visiting general, with Shwni and the Goat Major leading the companies of the line marching in close order. The officers are presented with leeks by a visiting general and tradition has it that, during the mess celebrations, the newest recruits are made to eat a raw leek standing on the mess table and downing a pint of beer. Similar ceremonies take place in the NCOs and men's messes. Every soldier or officer, in a Welsh regiment has to partake in the 'leek eating ceremony' before he can regard himself as a true member of his regiment. David, amidst laughter and cheers from his fellow officers, managed to push down most of his uncooked leek, followed by a pint of frothy Felinfoel ale, but had to ask Colonel Price's permission to be excused and raced to the officers' latrine where he was violently sick. He was then able to return to the mess and join in the festivities.

On April 4th 1940 David, accompanied by Corporal 327 Francis, left Portadown on an involved journey to the west Wales training camp. They crossed by military ferry from Belfast to Stranraer in Scotland and then travelled by London Midland Scottish railway to Crewe via Dumfries, Carlisle, Preston and Warrington. They changed at Crewe and took another LMS train into Wales passing through Oswestry, Shrewsbury, Welshpool and across the Welsh mountains to Aberystwyth. The journey reminded David of the happy days he had shared with Perce in the Snowdonia Park two years previously. At Aberystwyth there was yet another change on to a Great Western coastline train which took the men southwards towards

Carmarthen. Including delays and changes at Crewe and Aberystwyth the journey had taken thirty-six hours. They disembarked in the early morning at a single-track railway station at Llanybydder, a small village of some eight hundred Welsh speaking inhabitants nestling on the banks of the River Teifi.

Highmead Training Camp was two miles outside the village on the Cardiganshire side of the river. The officers were billeted in a grand old manor house overlooking the river and the green, fertile pastures of the Teifi valley. The Royal Marine detachment at the camp consisted of thirty men with a lieutenant in charge and it was understood that David would be subordinate to the Royal Marine officer.

The training schedule was arduous and demanding and the commandos were taught the elements of survival in a hostile terrain, forced-marching across the mountains outside Llanybydder, rock climbing and abseiling, field craft and camouflage, map reading, orienteering, river fording, wireless procedures, weaponry and unarmed combat. Most of the activities of the specialist training commando unit involved a combination of many of these procedures and spare time to visit village pubs and meet the local population was at a premium. On the rare occasions when he could get away from camp David frequented the Highmead Arms, or the Vale of Teifi, to meet and chat with the locals. He became friendly with the village boot repairer who was also an expert fisherman and taught David the rudiments of angling for trout. He also enjoyed the aftermath of every fishing expedition, which ended in the Vale or the Highmead, the locals swapping yarns and comparing their catches with particular emphasis on the enormous size of the one that got away and with increasing exaggeration as the consumed alcohol diminished their inhibitions. On one memorable weekend he led a team of Royal Marine Commandos in a tug o'war at the local sports day against the Llanybydder farmers, all built like tanks, enormously strong and weighty, and, much to everyone's surprise, the Royal Marines won hands down. The victory called for a mammoth celebration in the Black Lion which culminated in an arm-wrestling session at the bar. On this occasion the farmers' strength prevailed and honour was satisfied.

As one local commented, "We showed these army boys a thing or two tonight. Let's hope that when they meet Jerry they'll be asked to pull a tug o'war and not arm wrestling!"

On Easter Monday the Llanybydder Welcome Home Committee arranged a village 'hop' in the Mart Hall to which all Royal Marines not on duty were invited. David was ordered to attend to look after his troop and to ensure that they did not get into trouble with the locals or with the Gunners with whom the Commandos shared Highmead Camp. David did not relish the thought of wasting a night at a dance hall and for the first two hours his foreboding was fully justified, the local female talent either dancing with each other or sitting around in small groups of proverbial wallflowers, chatting noisily and ignoring the advances of the lusting soldiery.

At ten minutes to ten o'clock the whole pattern changed. A group of some twenty soldiers, Royal Marines and Gunners, slightly inebriated, gatecrashed the Mart Hall before the deadline of ten o'clock, after which admission was barred by Sergeant Ewan Phillips, the sole representative of the law in the village. In amongst the noisy newcomers were three young ladies who had been escorted into the dance by the revellers, slightly against their will, but succumbing with grace to the overwhelming insistence of their escorts.

David took a step towards the entrance expecting trouble and ready to defuse any unruly behaviour amongst the Royal Marines. And then he stopped dead in his tracks. One of the girls ushered in by the soldiers was a tall, slim, dark-haired, beautiful creature with a flashing smile, revealing white, even teeth. David walked up to the three girls, ignoring the 'keep off' glares of the soldiers.

"Have these men been bothering you ladies?"

The dark-haired girl replied with a broad grin and a mischievous wink, "Not that you'd notice Lieutenant. Nothing we couldn't handle."

With uncharacteristic boldness David blurted out, "Would you care to dance?"

Her dark, black eyes were smiling again and teasing. "Yes, thank you, General" and they both burst out laughing and took to the concrete dance floor.

David never considered himself a dancer but he reckoned he was a proper Fred Astaire that night and the smiling dark-haired beauty waltzed like a feather in his arms. Apart from one dance, the 'Paul

Jones', he monopolised his partner. She told him her name was Bronwen which in Welsh meant white breasts or, as she jokingly asserted with a flash of her white teeth, 'white tits'. The uncouth remark did not upset David's sense of propriety. He was completely enamoured by the nearness and charisma of the girl in his arms.

The strict non-conformist hierarchy in west Wales decreed that the Sabbath must be strictly observed and that all revelry must cease at five minutes to midnight on Saturday. This rule was enforced by the arm of the law in the shape of Sergeant Phillips, who appeared in uniform at ten minutes to twelve, having spent the intervening two hours with his cap off, and wearing a brown overcoat, in the back room of the Lion consuming his weekly quota of free beer and Scotch. At five minutes to twelve the three-man band struck up the last waltz, 'Who's taking you home tonight?'

David and Bronwen clung to each other like leeches and David's question of, "Who is?" was answered clearly and positively.

"You, of course, you nincompoop. I've never introduced a general to my parents before."

They were both laughing when the band struck up 'God Save the King' and David subdued his mirth with difficulty during the national anthem. They held hands as they walked uphill towards Bronwen's home. The road narrowed over a railway bridge and at that very spot, as if by some preordained arrangement, they fell into each other's arms and kissed passionately. The next two hundred yards, again uphill, took nearly half an hour and for every step there were two or three passionate embraces and kisses. Bron was as eager a participant in the passion and cuddling as David himself. Eventually they came to her house on top of the hill and with a desperate effort Bron tore herself away.

"My parents are still up waiting for me. You wouldn't believe it. I'm almost twenty and have been away nursing for nearly two years. And yet they wait up to make sure I get home safely."

Then with a barely perceptible smile in the dark doorway, "They'll want to know why it took me an hour to walk from the Mart Hall. It's barely half a mile. What will I tell them, David?"

David smiled. "Tell them that Sergeant Phillips gave us an hour's extension."

"They'll never believe that. My father's a deacon at Aberduar and if he waits up for me he may be late for service tomorrow morning. One last kiss and I'll have to go."

The last kiss lasted for nearly one minute. David could not believe that two human beings could maintain mouth to mouth contact, without taking a deep breath, for such a long time. With promises to keep in touch Bron opened the door and disappeared through the blackout curtains into the dark house.

David skipped and jumped as he walked the three miles back to Highmead Camp. He fell asleep thinking about Bron and, as he dozed fitfully, came to a firm conclusion that for the first time in his life he was in love. Bron, or to give her full name, Bronwen Elvira Thomas, was the only daughter of the headmaster of the local school. She had been strictly brought up, her father ensuring her scholastic success, whilst insisting on attendance three times a day at Aberduar Baptist Chapel on a Sunday. Bron received her secondary education at Llandysul County Grammar School and, after matriculation, enrolled as a pupil nurse at Swansea General Hospital in October 1938.

Hospital life opened up new vistas for the prim and proper girl from the backwoods. She quickly blossomed into a bubbly, gregarious and occasionally rebellious nursing trainee. Hospital rules in 1938 were forbidding and unbending but Bron, and a few colleagues, found ways of circumnavigating them without openly transgressing the strong arm of authority in the shape of Matron Annie Jones. To Bron the 'In bed by 9.30' rule was made to be broken. It spoke much of her ingenuity and natural cunning that she was never actually caught outside the nurses' home after curfew.

And then her interest in men blossomed. Up to now the male sex had been completely taboo and, according to her father, men were all filthy, lecherous beasts with only one thing in mind. She lost her virginity at a Christmas mess party in 1938. Her seducer, a married doctor with three children, was in his middle forties and an experienced womaniser. Her New Year's resolution in 1939 was celibacy but by the end of January this had gone by the board. The randy surgeon came back again and again for more and by March she was consorting regularly with him and had remote thoughts of marriage. An unwanted pregnancy brought matters to a head. Her "surgeon friend" sent her to see a colleague in Cardiff where she had a minor operation for menstrual difficulties. For a year after the abortion she conducted her sexual life with more care and discrimination. By the outbreak of the war she was rid of the attentions of the over-sexed doctor and had a steady boyfriend who was a laboratory assistant in the Haematology Department at Swansea Gen. He enlisted in March 1940 and by the time she met David she was footloose and fancy free.

The young handsome lieutenant with his dark angular face and steely-grey eyes had struck a chord somewhere in the region of her left breast where, if her anatomy was accurate, she might expect to find her heart. After the dance in the Mart Hall, as she travelled back by train to Swansea on the following day, she brooded on her new amour and decided there and then, on the platform at Carmarthen awaiting the Pembroke Dock to London express, that she wanted this man and not for sexual reasons but for an indefinable commodity loosely called love. The German attack on France on 10th May, 1940 and the subsequent invasion 'scare' put paid to any further meetings between the two lovers and they had to be content with letter writing. David, despite his academic prowess, found difficulty in baring his soul. Bron on the other hand wrote openly, lovingly and passionately never afraid to thrill David with the expressiveness of her love for him and her care and concern for his welfare. Every letter from Bron elevated his spirits and he longed and wished he could take her in his arms again.

War Diary

At 5.15 a.m. on 9th April, 1940, an hour before dawn, German forces occupied Denmark and simultaneously invaded Norway. British military experts maintained that this was a sign that Hitler doubted his ability to directly attack the French Maginot Line. The Norwegian Campaign only lasted six weeks and resulted in complete rout for the British forces who were evacuated with great difficulty from Narvik and Namsos with loss of three destroyers and severe damage to a cruiser. At dawn on May 10th Hitler unleashed his forces on the Low Countries and France. In Britain the news of the attack was released at lunchtime. Dutch, Belgian and French forces were reputedly offering stiff resistance and the defence lines held intact.

On that bright and sunny day David and Corporal Francis were helping a local farmer to harvest his potato crop. They immediately left the farm and reported to base camp and for the next ten days, although some training continued, the Royal Marine commando were on full alert in readiness for immediate deployment. On the 22nd May the Commandos were urgently recalled to their depot at Lympstone, where David stayed in the Royal Marine mess for three days and, before he left to return to Portadown, the commanding officer made him an Honorary Royal Marine and presented him with the coveted Green Beret.

David returned to his unit on the 27th May and during his absence there had been changes in command of the First/Fifth Battalion, Colonel J C Coleman replacing Colonel Ianto Price and a Major Philips taking over as Adjutant. David was promoted to captain with responsibility for unit intelligence and training.

The battle for France was at its height and news from the front line deteriorated rapidly. Early in the campaign the Germans had used airborne troops and blitzkrieg Stuka attacks to subdue Holland, followed by lightning armoured Panzer strikes through Holland and Belgium from the north and Luxembourg from the east. The Maginot Line, whose northern end only reached the Luxembourg border, was left intact. General Heinz Guderian's armoured Panzers, attacking through the Ardennes from the east, drove a wedge between the British expeditionary forces and the main French army, isolating the British in southern Belgium and forcing them to fall back to the sea at Dunkirk. Winston Churchill, who had succeeded Chamberlain as Prime Minister on the 14th May, ordered an evacuation of the British, Belgian and French troops from the port which commenced in earnest on the 24th May and continued until the morning of the 4th June, when the town capitulated. In all, three hundred and forty thousand allied troops were snatched from the beaches and returned to Britain to fight another day, described by Churchill as "a miracle of deliverance." The French armies, decimated, poorly led and dispirited fought on for eighteen days but the end was inevitable. On the 10th June Mussolini took Italy into the war invading the French Riviera. Paris fell on June 14th and the French Government formally capitulated on June 22nd, followed by the Franco Italian armistice in Rome on the 24th June 1940.

Throughout the battle for France the First/Fifth Battalion, in common with all other mobilised regiments in the United Kingdom, were on full alert. Everyone thought they would be recalled to defend the east coast of England and the south coast ports but they remained in Portadown in a state of readiness. The mood of the battalion, stuck as they were in a quiet backwater in Northern Ireland, varied between abject dejection and elation, elation because the main bulk of the British Expeditionary Force was delivered safely home and dejection because of their impotence in repelling the German invasion, expected daily from across the English Channel. Gradually the prospects of an invasion by the Germans receded and the Battalion's readiness for action lessened, but in August 1940 the air war intensified and again invasion was expected at any hour. The First/Fifth was fully mobilised and ready to move across the Irish Sea at a moment's notice. Soldiers slept in battle dress and carried their loaded weapons at all times, their trucks fuelled and loaded, ready to dash across to the mainland to fight for their lives and for the survival of Britain. The men were jumpy and edgy and even those who appeared nonchalant suffered an underlying tension and fear of the unknown struggle and possibly death which might face them. And yet, the vital call never came.

The Battle of Britain

The air battle started in July over the Channel but after August 13th the Luftwaffe concentrated its bombing attacks on military and radar installations and on airfields in the south east of England. The Battle of Britain had started. Losses in fighter planes were heavy on both sides but of more importance was the loss of pilots and by early September both these factors were causing grave concern to the British air chiefs and to the Luftwaffe. And then in an incomprehensible policy decision Field Marshal Hermann Goering ordered his bombers to carry out daylight raids on London. The target area was the London docks and Woolwich arsenal. At 5 p.m. on the evening of September 7th, wave after wave of German bombers, protected by fighters, flew up the Thames to drop their bombs and incendiaries randomly in the dock area and the attacks continued through the night until dawn on the Sunday morning. These pulverising attacks left

London dockland a blazing inferno of smashed, collapsed and crumbling masonry.

News of the air bombardment of London reached Portadown mess during a traditional Sunday curry lunch. David tried unsuccessfully to telephone Geldman's house in Hampstead but very few lines were connected through to the centre of London. David was desperately worried about his parents as they were not worldly wise and, on a Saturday, he knew that his father and mother would be at home celebrating the Sabbath as they had done ever since he could remember.

Colonel Coleman consoled him, "No news is good news."

"I know, Sir," replied David. "But our home is so near Wapping dock that I feel my parents must be in danger and the attacks are continuing."

At 8.30 a.m. on Tuesday 10th, September David sat in the adjutant's office on the telephone trying to get through to London. The commanding officer's telephone rang in the next room and an orderly sergeant called through the open door, "Telephone call for you, Captain Green. A Mr Geldman wants to speak to you."

David sprang to his feet and with a sinking heart picked up the phone.

"Hello. David here. Is that you, Hymie?"

A pause at the other end of the line and then Mr Geldman's gruff voice: "David, I have terrible news for you. Our factory was destroyed on Saturday night and burnt to the ground. I am afraid they are still looking around but they have not found your father and mother. Ella and I have moved out to Aylesbury. It's terrible in London, just terrible, terrible..." and the voice trailed into silence.

David, holding the crackling phone in one hand, was stunned, but managed to whisper into the phone, "Thank you, Hymie, thank you. I'll come over."

He then sat alone, hunched in a chair, for fully ten minutes while the devastating news sunk in. He could not believe what he had heard and Hymie must be mistaken. The ever-practical adjutant arranged compassionate leave and he was booked on a crossing to Stranraer on the night ferry from Belfast. Around midday a signal arrived in the orderly room.

"The Home Office regrets to announce that, due to enemy air action, Anna and Isaac Grünberg are missing, presumed dead."

This telegram obliterated any faint hopes that his parents might still be alive.

The interminable journey from Portadown to the centre of war-torn London took nearly forty-eight hours. The military ferry was delayed for two hours due to engine trouble, which was only partly rectified. The boat tended to yaw and hook into the huge waves and the cold north-easterly wind. The Stranraer train was late in departing and there were further delays and changes of trains at Carlisle and Crewe. The rail service in and around London was unequal to the demand put upon it and David had to disembark at Watford Station as the LMS connection into St Pancras had been discontinued. A journey by bus from Watford to Enfield took more than three hours. The roads were congested with traffic, families, cars and buses all moving away from central London. Thankfully the underground railway was still operating and David was able to slowly proceed from Enfield to Whitechapel Road, noticing as he went that, as the train approached central London, the platforms became increasingly occupied by bedding, bunks, clothing and humanity.

Dishevelled and tired he made his way down Whitechapel Road mid-morning on Wednesday 13th, September. The main street was covered with blocks of masonry and débris whilst ambulances, fire engines and police vehicles dodged around the obstacles and bomb craters. Uniformed police and ARP wardens were stationed at the end of each block of buildings controlling the traffic and herding dispirited civilians in every direction. He passed the London Hospital whose edifice was completely blackened by smoke with no intact windows visible to the passer by. Pusey Street had been cordoned off with red tape and a 'no entry' sign, guarded by a young uniformed policeman. When he saw David approach the bobby almost stood to attention and raised his right arm, his palm facing David.

"Pardon me, Captain, you can't go in there. We think there might be an unexploded bomb about one hundred yards down the road. We are waiting for the bomb disposal blokes at the moment."

"I'll take a chance," said David. "I've come all the way from Belfast. My home is down this street."

The policeman lifted the tape to let David through. "Don't tell anyone I didn't warn you."

David walked slowly down the middle of the street of his youth. The road was strewn with debris, bits of masonry, charred furniture, a slab of porcelain from a toilet, shattered fragments of glass and bundles of smouldering clothing. The whole street and front of the houses were black, covered with a fine veneer of soot and a hazy, misty cloud of smoke hung in the air above his head almost completely obliterating the sky. A few men clad in uniform scuttled around the road and houses like ferrets looking for a rabbit in its deep, dark burrow. A house on the left had lost its upper storey; the Men's Institute appeared intact but window-less; the Cat and Fiddle had lost its roof but still displayed a sign 'Open as usual', though David's trained ear could not detect any sign of life in the derelict pub. About fifty yards further down on the left he came to Geldman's factory, or more precisely, where the warehouse used to stand and where his home used to be. The factory frontage on to the road extended for fifty yards or more and the walls at each end stood proud and erect but the rest of the building had collapsed inwards leaving a huge mound of bricks, girders and machinery in a conglomerate pile on the ground. David stood silently looking at the mass of smouldering masonry. An official in a navy blue coat and tin helmet came to stand next to him.

"A big 'un hit this place. Lucky it was Saturday night and the workers 'ad gone home. Only two poor old Jews copped it. Could have been worse."

As he turned on his heel and walked back down Pusey Street, David thought, 'It could not have been worse. Those two poor old Jews were my father and mother.'

David spent the night in Whitechapel Underground. He was amazed at the cheerfulness and fortitude of the East Enders who crowded on to the station platform at dusk. Impromptu concerts and communal singing were the order of the night, *We're Going To Hang Out Our Washing On The Siegfried Line*, *Run Rabbit Run*, *Roll out the Barrel* and the *White Cliffs of Dover* were all sung to the accompaniment of an accordion and a mouth organ. Exhausted he fell asleep on the platform steps, wrapped in his overcoat and flanked by a garrulous, runny-nosed eight year old boy on one side and his obese, slightly drunken, snoring grandfather on the other.

At six o'clock in the morning the trains started rolling and woke up the whole platform. Children screamed and adults swore as they jostled for the single water pipe outlet. Taking their meagre belongings and folding their bedclothes these brave, hopeless people departed in groups and families to walk up the escalators to the outside air of Whitechapel to face another day of peril and possible death which the constant German air bombardment might bring in its wake. David departed for Watford and then retraced his journey by train northwards across England to the military ferry at Stranraer.

He arrived back at the First/Fifth headquarters mid-morning on Saturday 16th September and, completely exhausted by his journey, slept for twenty-four hours. He woke around teatime and found the officers in the mess huddled around a radio listening to reports of a massive daylight air strike on London by two hundred bombers escorted by six hundred fighters. The German air armada had been repulsed with heavy losses and fifty-six German planes, mostly bombers, were destroyed. David gave a silent prayer for those poor helpless families living in the great battered City and wondered if his sleeping companions in the Underground had survived. The Londoners' ordeal was to continue for fifty-seven consecutive nights until early November 1940.

When David came into the mess for breakfast on September 20th 1940 there were two letters in his pigeon hole. The first was from Hymie Geldman informing him that a salvage squad had found a few items amongst the warehouse rubble which might have belonged to the Grünbergs and they were now safely in his keeping in Aylesbury. The second letter was from Wooley:

My Dear David, I regret to tell you that Perce bought it in a dogfight over London on the 14th inst. He crashed his plane out at sea and his body has not been recovered. I miss him sadly. I hope you are keeping safe and well. Yours ever, Wooley.

Coming so soon after the death of his parents this was another blow for David. His morale sank and he became depressed. He now wanted to get away from the First/Fifth, to escape from beleaguered Britain, to go anywhere and have a new start and a new challenge and perhaps to repay the Germans in kind for the death of his parents and Perce.

In the last week of September, having been granted four days leave, David re-crossed the Irish Sea and took part in a simple burial ceremony of his family's remains in a quiet corner of Golders Green Jewish cemetery, attended by the local Rabbi and the Geldmans. He spent one night with the Geldmans at Aylesbury and, early on Friday morning, caught the 8.20 a.m. train from Oxford which was due to arrive in Swansea at midday. As always it was late leaving and there were delays along the line, mainly due to troop train movements and repairs to the main line. The overcrowded smoke-impregnated train finally limped into Swansea High Street Station at 4.30 p.m.

On the journey, sitting in the first class compartment, David had time to reflect on his current situation. Both his parents had been killed by Hitler's bombers. He felt an unreasonable sense of hatred for any person who could sit in an aeroplane and simply press a button to drop bombs indiscriminately on defenceless civilians. The villains dropping the bombs were German and this made him detest them more and the persecution they had wreaked on his parents, driving his family out of Germany, added fuel to the fire. They had also shot down and killed Perce, his best friend at Oxford. And then, as the train slowly trundled along outside Reading, his depression lifted at the thought that he would soon be seeing Bron. Between Reading and Swindon he debated if he should propose to her and get married, but he then thought of the uncertain future which lay ahead for both of them and decided against such action at the present time.

The old steam train laboriously pushed its way through the Severn tunnel and into Wales, through Newport and Cardiff, to finally lurch and splutter to a halt in a cloud of steam in Swansea High Street Station. After six hours in the confined compartment he was pleased to be out on the platform in the fresh air, away from an inebriated Pioneer Corps colonel who kept alternately dozing, farting and lighting his pipe, stuffed with foul-smelling wartime tobacco.

There were no cabs or buses available at the overcrowded station. David walked down High Street, past R.E. Jones, the Bush Hotel and the Castle and then to the right along St Helen's Road, proceeding towards the Rugby and Cricket Ground. Swansea General Hospital was an old Edwardian building on the right hand side at the end of St Helen's Road. Enquiries at the porter's lodge established that pupil nurse Bronwen Thomas was not in the hospital or the nurses' home. She had been called home for compassionate reasons, as her mother had been taken seriously ill.

David retraced his steps to the rail station and found that the next through train to Carmarthen would be the mail train from London to Pembroke Dock. This train got him into Carmarthen at 5.30 a.m. and, after an hour's wait, a small connecting single-line engine took him twenty miles north to Llanybydder. The journey from Carmarthen to Llanybydder took an hour and twenty minutes, the old train puffing to a halt regularly for unscheduled stops along the route. For the last five miles the track ran alongside the Teifi River and, although David subconsciously admired the beauty of the fertile valley, his thoughts were concentrated on his imminent reunion with Bron. His pulse quickened perceptibly as the train passed under the very bridge where he and Bron had kissed so passionately after the dance in May. He walked briskly from the station to the village square where a bizarre ceremony greeted his eyes.

Six men in various bits and pieces of khaki were clustered around an old Austin 8. One of the men, Emrys, had three stripes chalked on the left arm of his tunic and was called Sarge. Between them the Sarge and five other ranks wielded two shotguns, an old first war Lee-Enfield rifle with no bullets and a rusty revolver. He was witnessing a changing of the guard ceremony of the Llanybydder Local Defence Volunteers. A local dignitary, a retired naval captain, was convinced that the Germans would choose to land their airborne troops on Llanybydder mountain and these brave volunteers were manning a twenty-four hour watch in a small shepherd's hut high on the mountainside. His friend, the shoemaker, up early as usual to assess the state of the river, was in deep conversation with the group.

As David approached he looked up.

"Hello, Captain Green, what brings you back here? If you've got any spare time the river's in good condition for fishing at the moment. There's been a great late salmon run."

David explained the reason for his journey to the cobbler who confirmed that Mrs Thomas was gravely ill and they had sent for a specialist from Aberystwyth, which was common knowledge to all the villagers as was the fact that Bron's mother was dying of cancer. He took David into his home and cooked him a quick breakfast of fried bacon, egg, bread and a pot of tea. After a hearty meal David left for Bush House, only a fifteen minute walk up hill. In answer to his knocking the door was opened by a surprised Bron, sheathed in a pink woollen dressing gown, her face haggard and drawn from lack of sleep and her dark hair awry and unkempt. She fell into his arms and clung to him desperately.

David was the first to speak, "Can I help?"

"No" Bron answered tearfully. "I thought you might have been the specialist from Aberystwyth." She wiped away her tears. "Mam is dying of cancer and there's nothing anyone can do for her. We're expecting Dr Oswald Davies, a specialist from Aberystwyth. Our own doctor has been marvellous but there's little else he can do. Come in for a cup of tea."

Bron's father, the elderly schoolmaster, was hunched over the fire reading aloud from the Bible. He hardly looked up when David entered the living room and seemed completely engrossed in a private world of his own. Bron excused herself to get dressed and then returned to make a fresh pot of tea. The three sat around the oval kitchen table, sipping tea and looking vacantly into space. After about five minutes Bron turned to her father.

"Dada, the district nurse is with Mam at the moment. I'm going out with Captain Green for a breath of fresh air."

They both left the house where David had the distinct feeling the angel of death was hovering in the eaves and would pounce at any time and take Bron's mother's soul away.

Hand in hand and in complete silence they walked down to the railway bridge. Once there Bron unashamedly and in broad daylight took David's face in her hands and kissed him urgently on the mouth. He responded rapidly and again felt a surge of happiness that came to him in the presence of this ravishing, tempting Welsh beauty.

David explained that he would have to catch the eleven o'clock Great Western train back to Carmarthen to connect with the London Express. Bron gave him a sharp peck on the cheek.

"Well, my little general, that doesn't give us much time. I have to be back in the house in half an hour in case the specialist arrives. Come with me," and taking David's hand she led him over a stile and down to an embankment to the side of the railway tunnel, away from the sight of prying eyes and the road.

There she lay down on a mossy bank amongst the ferns and looking up at David said, "I didn't want our first clinch to be like this but time is against us. I told you my name meant 'White tits' so let me show you my credentials," and unbuttoning her blouse she revealed two magnificent white breasts standing out like pyramids and surmounted by two perfectly formed nipples.

David knelt beside her and fondled her breasts. Bron then took his head and guided his quivering lips to her proud nipples. David kneaded and sucked as they both enjoyed the tenderness and sensuality of the foreplay. After about a minute both partners began a series of uncoordinated movements, David lifting Bron's skirt and pawing away at her upper thighs whilst Bron tore at his trouser buttons to release his penile erection and all the while David kept his lips firmly cupped and sucking at her left nipple. Somehow, as if by chance, David found his penis was within her and his sexual ardour was heightened by the squeezing and pumping action of Bron's muscular pelvis. He reached his climax very quickly. Bron patted the back of his neck.

"There, there, my general, feeling better are we?"

This was not how David imagined it would be, but he was so overcome by his first proper sexual experience that all he could say in a croaky voice was, "Bron, Bron. I love you."

They lay still for a full minute and then David rolled off to one side and looked at Bron. She was crying in wretched anguish, her scalding hot tears cascading down her trembling cheeks.

"I'm sorry Bron I shouldn't have done that. Please forgive me, but I do love you."

Perversely she smiled through her tears. "It was my fault. I shouldn't have led you on, but I had to do it to get it out of my system. I think I love you too, David."

She then quickly re-arranged her clothing, dried her tearful face and hand in hand and in complete harmony they walked uphill to her house.

As they arrived at the door a black, chauffeur-driven Daimler pulled up outside the house and a stern-looking Dr Oswald Davies emerged carrying a Gladstone bag and adjusting the spectacles perched on top of his red, bulbous nose. Bron greeted him in Welsh and opened the door for the doctor and, turning to David, pecked him on the cheek and looked him straight in the eyes.

"You must go, my general. I promise to write in the next few days and let you know what has happened. I have to go upstairs now to attend to this pompous twerp from Aberystwyth and look after my Mam."

David walked down the village with a sad heart. He joined his boot repairer friend at the bridge over the Teifi noting that it would indeed have been a great day for fishing. The 'condition' of the river was excellent, the trout were already rising, and David thought he saw the swirl of a salmon's tail in the bridge pool. The master angler by his side confirmed that there were at least two salmon in the pool that morning and hopefully, by lunchtime, there would be two fish on the marble slab in his larder. David took his leave and boarded the GWR train, aptly misnamed the Cardigan Bay, bound for Carmarthen. As he passed under the railway bridge beneath Bush House, he clearly saw the imprint of their lovemaking couch on the mossy, fern-strewn embankment and again smelt the peculiar musty odour of Bronwen's womanly secretions.

Back in Portadown he heard nothing from Bron for ten days. When the letter came it confirmed that Bron's mother had died on the day after his visit and that Bron was now back at work in Swansea living in the nurses' quarters in Park Beck. Almost as an afterthought she added that she missed him but there was no mention of love or their lovemaking which seemed to David to have bonded them inseparably together. The letters continued at irregular intervals but in none of them could David discern Bron's innermost thoughts and feelings towards him.

Two letters arrived within two days during the second week of October 1940. The first was a buff coloured OHMS envelope with instructions for Captain David Green, First/Fifth Battalion Welch Regiment to proceed to Liverpool docks by 0900 hours on 30th October and take charge of a company of replacements for the First Battalion. The second letter was from Bron, who seemed much more cheerful and chatty and appeared to have regained her mischievousness and then, the penultimate paragraph hit David like a sledgehammer.

I have recently developed a cough and last week saw a goofy specialist here in Swansea. He says that the X-ray shows a spot on the lung and has advised bed rest and treatment for a month in the isolation hospital at Fairwood. At least I'll be near the RAF boys! There's a fighter squadron based at Fairwood. I shouldn't have told you that. Walls have ears, but who cares? I would like to see you. I've treated you

badly and want to make up. Can you come and see me? I'll
be ready and waiting in bed! Lots of Love, Bronwen. PS
Have you forgotten what Bronwen means? I'll show you when
you get here!

David was alarmed. A spot on the lung and isolation treatment meant only one thing – pulmonary tuberculosis. He was granted a week's embarkation leave and a universal train warrant to travel around Britain at will. First he went to London to see the Geldmans and to settle up his father's affairs. He was the sole beneficiary and his father's meagre fortune was deposited in Lloyds Bank in the Mile End Road. David made arrangements for most of his army pay to be sent direct to a new account at the same bank.

He then paid a visit to Abbey, Goldstein and Shattock solicitors in the Mile End Road and drew up his will with instructions that, in the event of his death, one hundred pounds was to be settled on the shoemaker in Llanybydder and a similar amount on Mr Dai Evans for use at the Angel Inn in Rotherhithe, five hundred pounds to the Geldmans to look after the family grave and the residue of his estate to Bronwen Elvira Thomas. These matters took two days and he then went west from Paddington to Swansea and managed to hire a taxi to Fairwood Isolation Hospital, a distance of some ten miles.

The isolation hospital was sighted virtually at the end of the runway of No. 11 Fighter Wing, based at Fairwood Common. Before he could be taken into Bron's isolation room he had to wear a mask and a green gown and was instructed to discreetly turn away from the patient should she inadvertently cough in his presence. Bron was sitting up in bed, dressed in a white gown, pale-faced with too much red lipstick and too much rouge on her face. She was in a bubbly, exultant mood and they held hands and gazed at each other for minutes on end. It was torture for David. Here was the girl he loved, the object of all his desires, a beneficiary of his will and yet he was not allowed to kiss her.

Bron kept urging him, "Don't take any notice of old Sister. We call her Tiger. She's good as gold. A bit frustrated but a good old sport."

But David desisted, paying more heed to medical advice than to the urgent longings within his virile body. The next day was the same with Bron taunting him and trying to arouse his passion. But again he held back. On the third day, and his last visit, he had to tell Bron of his imminent departure abroad. This news urged her into a frenzy of alternately sobbing and goading him into action.

She kept wailing, "I may never see you again. Come on, get into bed here with me. You can touch everything else as long as you don't kiss my lips."

With that she lifted her white night-gown over her head and lay stark naked on the bed. David sensed his male organ enlarging and waiting to explode through his pants. Bron's logic that he could touch anything except her lips made sense in the urgency of his sexual desire. By God she was a lovely woman with a gorgeous body. Her long slender fingers had already undone his trouser buttons and were gently and expertly massaging his erect penis. With a half-dive and a jump he was on top of Bron and pumping away like a maniac. In the middle of the sexual act the ward room door opened and within a few seconds was shut tightly again with a loud click, but this did not deter the rampant, energetic copulators. David completed his act with a flourish and had the satisfaction of hearing Bronwen moaning, "I love you" underneath his quivering body. During the height of his passion his lips had resolutely sought Bronwen's and he had been able to push his tongue inside the mask into her mouth.

Eventually the time came for the final farewell. David promised to write with his whereabouts. He suspected that he would be in the Middle East, probably Egypt, with the First Battalion but this was 'hush, hush' and a secret.

"Certainly my general," smirked Bron giving him a parody of a salute.

Before he left and through the mask he kissed Bron on the lips and once on each nipple. He turned and waved in the doorway and was gone. Bronwen started weeping uncontrollably. Sister 'Tiger' Jones eyed David up and down as he approached her office noticing the lipstick stained mask.

"Lieutenant, I hope you've been obeying instructions?" and then with a wink and a mischievous glint in her eye, "I expect what you two have been up to in there will do more good for Nurse Thomas than all the rest and medication she will be having here in the next few weeks. Good luck to you, Captain Green."

David turned towards the Sister, saluted, and made his way back to the Swansea High Street Station. In his heart he felt that he had seen

Bronwen for the last time. He was going to miss the teasing, mischievous, beautiful and loving Welsh beauty. But the exigencies of war and a turn of fate were to prove otherwise.

*

Captain David Green and forty reinforcements for the First Battalion Welch Regiment boarded the troopship *Orantes* in Liverpool docks on the 30th October 1940. Two days later the troopship left in a dense fog amidst a cacophony of fog horns and, accompanied by three other troopships and two destroyers, they proceeded southwards through St George's Channel and the Celtic sea to rendezvous with a larger convoy some fifty miles south west of the Scillies. The large convoy zigzagged its way across the turbulent Bay of Biscay and then proceeded southwards along the west coast of Africa to Cape Town. The *Orantes*, an old passenger liner converted for use as a troop carrier, had developed engine trouble after five days at sea and became the laggard of the convoy. David spent his twenty-second birthday off Cape Town waiting to enter the harbour for repairs, replenishing and re-stocking before they proceeded around the Cape of Good Hope into the Indian Ocean and then around the Horn of Africa into the Gulf of Aden and the Red Sea, to reach the Suez Canal. The voyage ended when the *Orantes* berthed at Ismalia at the northern end of the Suez Canal and the journey had taken the old ship the best part of fifty days. David and his reinforcements disembarked on the 20th December 1940 and, after a day ashore in an army transit barracks at Ismalia, were taken by lorries to Mustapha barracks in Alexandria to join the main body of the First Battalion the Welch Regiment.

The voyage from Liverpool to Alexandria was long, dreary and boring. David spent his days reading and relaxing in the sun but insisted his men had an hour's physical exercise each day. There were many spare hours for meditation and reviewing his life and ambitions. His first memories were of Aalbrücke and the kindly Joachim and Valtraut at the farm. He then recalled with a smile, Manfred, and his so called blood-brother ceremony and wondered if Manfred might be serving in the German army. He remembered Biffo and Mary Loose in Pusey Street School. Whatever became of those two. He recalled with affection Daima in Rotherhithe Grammar School. Was he still drinking and going to rugby matches. He remembered Perce and Wooley at Oxford and the tall thin girl Phoebe. God, how he missed Perce. He could not believe that he would never again see the puckered, monocled face with its impish grin. He remembered the Geldmans and their frigid niece Hannah, but most of all he recalled clearly his father and mother. He felt guilty that, since the family arrived in London, he had not been a good son and a good Jew. 'Please, God forgive me,' he thought, looking up at the full moon over the Indian Ocean, hoping to see his father's and mother's image somewhere amongst the moonbeams. Then there was Bronwen, dark eyed, beautiful, provocative and vivacious Bronwen, with an incorrigible zest for life. God how he loved her!

One night at sea after these mental reminiscences he had a vivid dream which he recalled accurately the next day. He was sitting in the cockpit of an aeroplane. The pilot had flowing blond hair, blue eyes and a fiendish grin on his face. It was his blood brother, Manfred. The co-pilot was Daima. By his side sat Biffo crouched over a machine gun and in the rear of the plane he saw Hymie Geldman, also manning a machine gun. Suddenly in front of the aeroplane appeared a British fighter with its cockpit open flown by a leather-helmeted pilot with a white silk scarf fluttering around his neck and a monocle in his left eye. The German pilot kept shouting 'Scheissen' as Biffo pressed the trigger and the British plane burst into flames and went hurtling downwards. David had a brief glimpse of the smiling British pilot plummeting earthwards in flames and winking with the non-monocled eye. Within a matter of seconds the German bomber was over London. David looked downwards and saw Geldman's factory and Pusey Street School. Manfred was now leaning out of the side window of the plane holding a large bomb which he let go with a snarl, shouting 'Kill, kill'. David watched the bomb go straight through the roof of Geldman's warehouse and wondered for a split second what Geldman was doing in the back of the plane while his warehouse was getting bombed to smithereens on the ground. Hymie shouted, 'Er weißt nicht' and with that there was a tremendous explosion and eruption of tongues of flame from the stricken building which collapsed to the ground in a heap. David glanced sideways at Manfred, who still had a fiendish grin on his face, full of hate and fury and then he woke with a start.

One of his companions in the four berth cabin said, "You had a nightmare, old boy. Go back to sleep."

David, bathed in perspiration, lay back in his bunk and fell asleep and on this occasion dreamt of Bronwen.

Chapter Eleven

The Sitzkrieg,
September 1939 – May 1940
Attack in the West, Schiphol,
May 1940

Lieutenant Manfred Schmidt arrived at Lübbecke on the 14th September, 1939, just as the 8th Regiment was preparing to leave for amphibious training on the lakes and canals around Oldenburg, some eighty kilometres to the north. Manfred was made personal aide to Colonel Count von Bulow with Heinz Schneider as his sergeant and, due to his leg injury, he was excused strenuous training and parachuting. His appointment as the colonel's aide carried the rank of captain and the colonel insisted that, despite their lack of training jumps, both Captain Manfred Schmidt and Corporal Fritz Schultz were given parachute wings. The main party completed the three and a half hour journey to Oldenburg in convoy, whilst Manfred travelled in luxury in the back of an open Mercedes staff car sitting next to Colonel von Bulow with the armed Sergeant Schneider beside the driver. They journeyed across uninhabited moorland for mile after mile relaxing in the sun and sipping cognac. The party stopped for an early lunch at an inn in Bassum where the ebullient colonel presided over the table.

They arrived in the barracks at Oldenburg in mid-afternoon and the regiment were already busy settling in. The camp was bustling with activity, a stream of lorries disgorging their loads into various buildings. The driver took them to the officers' mess where the colonel and Manfred continued their drinking session until supper time. After a few more brandies Colonel von Bulow became loquacious.

"Manfred, I must tell you that I was disappointed not to have been asked to take my regiment to the Polish campaign. The First and Second Battalions got the honour and they've done a good job. I expect we weren't asked to go as we are a ski outfit and now it seems we are to be taught to cross rivers and canals. The Polish campaign is almost at an end and it should be over in about a week. I can tell you now that Ivan has been invited to come in and take the eastern part of Poland. I heard this at a supreme commanders' meeting in Potsdam last month. I can also tell you that the plans for attack on the Western Front are well advanced and our regiment will have an important part to play in the initial strike. As my aide you will be with me at the planning conferences for the assault."

Manfred, sipping his brandy, was overjoyed as, in a matter of two weeks, he had been promoted to captain and been made personal aide to this loveable, roguish commanding officer. As Colonel von Bulow predicted, a week later Russian forces swept unopposed across the Polish border to occupy Poland as far as the eastern bank of the River Bug and crushed forever the valiant resistance of the Polish Army. Warsaw capitulated on the 17th September, 1939 and Poland was partitioned into German and Russian sectors. At Oldenburg the *Fallschirmjagger* practised amphibious crossings of the Emden to Bremen Canal and, for more extensive manoeuvres, the Vanehmoor Lakes to the south-west of Oldenburg were used. The training was intensive and was completed by early November before the onset of wintry weather in northern Germany.

On 9th October 1939 Hitler issued directive No. 6 to his military chiefs. He clearly instructed his generals to prepare for an early attack on France and the British Expeditionary Force in Belgium. The generals and *Obercommando der Wehrmacht* (OKW) ordered a strike through Belgium, Holland and neutral Luxembourg, north of the Maginot Line and led by Panzer Divisions to avoid a protracted entrenchment confrontation as had occurred in the 1914-1918 War. The attack was to take place before winter set in, but OKW was unable to produce a timetable and urged delay until the spring of 1940. Various strike plans were studied by OKW but the favourite was a modification of the Schleiffen plan, named after the general who orchestrated the attack on France and the Low Countries in 1914.

Colonel von Bulow and Manfred were ordered to a battalion commanders' conference at Spandau barracks in Berlin on 10th November, 1939. They drove along the west-east autobahn, crowded and busy with military vehicles and supply lorries moving in and out of the Nazi capital and, on the night of the 9th November, they put up in the Adlon Hotel near Brandenburg Gate in preparation for the meeting at 11 a.m. on the following day.

Security at OKW headquarters at Spandau was intense, with armed SS and *Wehrmacht* soldiers, twenty paces apart, guarding the approaches and entrances to the barracks and both the colonel and his aide had to show their military passes at frequent check points. The conference was held in a gymnasium which was packed to overflowing with senior officers of the three services, arranged in groups according to rank and status. Colonel Count von Bulow, always a popular figure at these meetings, was soon socialising with his contemporaries and with some senior *Wehrmacht* and SS officers. He introduced Manfred to two colonels from sister parachute regiments, to Colonel General Erwin Rommel and Heinz Guderian, the Panzer Division Commanders, General Freiherr von Richthofen of the *Luftwaffe* and Field Marshal Gerd von Runstedt, commander of Army Group A.

At precisely eleven o' clock General Franz Halder, chief of the general staff, called the meeting to order. The assembled company were first sworn to secrecy and the general then continued, "OKW has entrusted me with disclosing the Führer's plan for an assault in the west, Operation *Weseruebung*, which we hope to launch in the spring of 1940." Then turning to his right, referring to a map of Europe on a large board he continued, "Von Bock and Army Group B will strike into Holland and this will be mainly an airborne attack supported by three *Wehrmacht* Divisions and one Panzer Division. General Student's paratroopers and General Löhr's Tenth Air Fleet will bear the brunt of the attack as we envisage that the ground will be unsuitable for tank warfare and the Hollanders are expected to flood their fields. The main objective of the northern attack is to capture Rotterdam and its port as quickly as possible. The other two main thrusts are here and here," indicating with a pointer, "von Richenau's Sixth Army west into Belgium and northern France and von Runstedt's Army Group A south-west through Luxembourg and the Ardennes into France at Sedan. The Führer has ordered that both these major thrusts will be spearheaded by von Kleist's Panzer Divisions."

"An exact date for *Weseruebung* has not been finalised. It will not be practical to attack before Christmas and the winter will then be upon us and I expect a realistic date to be sometime in late March or early April. The information I have given you today is top secret and is only to be divulged to your senior commanders. Colonel General Guderian and Colonel General Student will now outline their proposals for the use of the Panzers and airborne forces in the forthcoming attack. Heil Hitler," saluting and leaving the podium.

Guderian, fortified by recent successful Panzer strikes and blitzkrieg actions in Poland, gave a masterly review of the use of armour in modern warfare, whilst Student expounded his concept of airborne attacks behind enemy lines to secure airfields for landing infantry and supplies. At the end of the conference the airborne officers remained behind for a further briefing from Colonel General Student who, as a member of OKW, outlined his own ideas of the role of airborne parachutists and gliders in an attack on Holland. He pinpointed Rotterdam and its airfields as key targets and a secondary drop on the airfield at Schiphol outside Amsterdam. He stressed that planning was at an early stage and further details would be released to airborne commanders in due course. Their main function at present was to return to their units and prepare the paratroopers for the forthcoming battle.

Manfred left the OKW conference with his head spinning. He had met so many important senior officers, listened to the supreme commander speak, was privy to highly secret information and, what is more, was the most junior officer present at the conference. That night Colonel von Bulow took Manfred on a tour of Küfurstendam which, he explained, 'was his happy hunting ground'. They drank and ate to excess and returned to the Adlon just before daybreak. There was only time for an hour's sleep and a bath before they were again speeding westwards out of Berlin to return to Lübbecke. The three hundred kilometre journey took eight hours and for most of the way the two officers slept in the back of the staff car. As they left Hanover, the colonel turned to Manfred with his characteristic lopsided smile.

"So it's going to be Holland. I don't imagine the Hollanders will put up much of a fight. I expect we'll all land in the tulip fields and come up smelling of roses," at which he laughed outright. Manfred forced a stifled laugh, uneasy at the thought of landing anywhere, especially by parachute, even if the natives were assumed to be fairly friendly.

War Diary

Since their experience of blockade in the First World War the German Navy were very conscious of their inability to gain access to the high seas and the Royal Navy were again in command of the straits between the Shetlands and Norway. Soon after the fall of Poland Admiral Erich Raeder sent a memo to Hitler proposing occupation of Norwegian ports to allow Germany ready access to the North Sea. Hitler was sympathetic but was preoccupied with launching Exercise Weseruebung.

The picture radically changed on the 30th November when Russia invaded Finland and Britain and France mobilised an expeditionary force to go to assist the Finns. To reach Finland they had to cross Norway and Sweden and Raeder was quick to point out to the Führer that their presence in Scandinavia might cut off supplies of Swedish ore, essential for the maintenance of the German war effort. Raeder now proposed an urgent seaborne invasion across the Skagerrack to occupy southern Norway combined with airborne landings at Trondheim and Oslo. The Admiral's concern about an Allied invasion of Norway was further strengthened by a secret visit by Quisling, the Norwegian traitor and Nazi sympathiser, who predicted a British landing at Stavanger. Admiral Raedar hurriedly arranged a conference at his naval headquarters in Bremerhaven for the 13th December. Raeder's Kriegsmarine *were to be the main spearhead of the attack, supported by one parachute regiment and two mountain regiments.*

On the 13th December Colonel von Bulow and Manfred attended Admiral Raeder's briefing at the *Kriegsmarine* Depot in Bremerhaven. When they arrived around ten o'clock the place was in chaos and the conference was delayed. Reports were coming in of a major naval action four hundred miles off the coast of Argentina between a German pocket battleship, the *Graf Spee*, and three British cruisers. First reports intimated that all three British cruisers were immobilised and the *Graf Spee* was safely inside Uruguayan territorial waters and entering the port of Montevideo for urgent repairs before re-joining the battle to finish off the British ships. Admiral Raeder and his staff were on constant alert and the military visitors were encouraged to stay in the naval base as observers. At first there was an air of jubilation, fortified by reports from the ship's Captain, Hans Langsdorf, and eager anticipation at the imminent departure of the *Graf Spee* to rejoin battle. But on the second day niggling doubts began to pervade the naval control centre. Colonel von Bulow sensed that Admiral Raeder's earlier optimism was rapidly fading and his intuition was confirmed on the evening of the 15th December when the haughty, crusty Admiral requested all military personnel to leave.

On the return journey to Lübbecke Colonel von Bulow commented to Manfred, "There'll be some bad news from Montevideo tomorrow, mark my words. The *'Spee* has been badly hit and will be a sitting duck for the British navy."

The colonel's prophetic words were confirmed on the following day when Goebbels announced that the *Graf Spee* had been scuttled in the River Plate estuary some three miles off shore and that Captain Langsdorf, in true naval fashion, had gone down with his ship. Goebbel's statement, however, was not strictly true. Hans Langsdorf stayed ashore when the ship left harbour and committed suicide by shooting himself in the Riverside Hotel in Montevideo on 18th December 1939.

The Sitzkrieg

Colonel von Bulow's Eighth Parachute Regiment remained in a state of permanent alertness over Christmas 1939 and well into 1940. All leave was cancelled and the *Fallschirmjagger* remained in barracks at Lübbecke where the officers, by constant exhortation, fortified the troops' morale in preparation for the hard battle to come. Manfred again renewed his acquaintance with the Club Erotica and Giesela and over Christmas he frequented the club most nights, drinking and fornicating to excess.

On one of the evenings in the Erotica Manfred was teased by an effeminate blond-haired youth wielding a silver cigarette holder in one hand and making improper suggestions which, in the past, Manfred had thought amusing but, in his drunken state, he was flattered, excited and sexually aroused. He felt he wanted to find out more about the young man and his unconventional habits and accompanied Henshen to an upstairs room prepared to enjoy himself and let events take their course. In the bedroom the two men removed their jackets and embraced, Henshen's delicate long nailed fingers probing and massaging Manfred's groin and producing an erection within a minute. Manfred was guided backwards and made to lie flat on his back on the bed and Henshen leant over him and delicately and professionally performed an oral sex act. Manfred reached his climax with his penis still engulfed within Henshen's avaricious mouth. As soon as the act was over Henshen demanded money for his services. On reflection the next day Manfred felt remorse, but his misgivings were tinged with guilt. He had actually enjoyed a sexual act with a blatant homosexual. To Manfred there was no love involved and he equated his encounter with Henshen with those with the other prostitutes at Club Erotica.

On the 13th January, 1940 an order came from OKW: 'Due to inclement weather all units are to stand down' and in late January Manfred took a company for a week's ski-training at Winterberg. No Erica on this occasion. How he missed female company or, more correctly, the sexual comfort that a female could provide. He made do with a plump, middle-aged, bovine *hausfrau*, who made the beds and was available for about ten minutes each morning. The fecund, large breasted Frau, though a submissive partner, derived no pleasure from the sex act. At the end of the week Manfred showed his thanks by giving her a generous tip for 'services rendered'.

On 1st March, 1940 Colonel von Bulow, accompanied by Manfred, left Lübbecke to attend a military group conference at Panzer headquarters in Potsdam. General Fedor von Bock, commander of the Army Group B, presided and sitting on his left was an elderly monocled, moustached officer, a relic of the First World War and a Prussian of noble descent. General Nikolas von Falkenhorst was appointed by Hitler to plan a strike to the north, a combined air and seaborne invasion of southern Norway. Von Bock outlined the plans for Army Group B's attack on Holland. He envisaged a right hook from Steinfurt across Holland, south of Apeldoorn and then south again along the coast to Antwerp.

He continued, "Our main objective is Rotterdam, one hundred and twenty kilometres from Steinfurt and by the time we get there General

Student's airborne divisions will have taken the bridges around the city. There will also be an airborne assault around the Hague and to the north at Amsterdam to protect our right flank. For the first fifty kilometres our advance should be rapid on firm ground and we will be able to use armoured vehicles. Beyond Apeldoorn the Hollanders are certain to flood the land and we'll have to walk or swim."

A slight nervous titter from the floor.

"The engineers will supply all units involved in the attack with inflatable boats and, as the ground is so flat, bicycles and motor cycles. You will now divide into two groups – those involved in Operation Nord will attend General Falkenhorst's briefing and Army Group B will be briefed by my Field Commanders and by General Student. Good luck in this enterprise."

Colonel von Bulow looked at Manfred, "You had better go to old Falkenhorst's briefing. I'll stay here and see what Student has to say."

The vague, doddery, archetypal Prussian general was clearly out of his depth in his concept of the use of airborne troops and of the number of *Fallschirmjagger* needed to ensure success of Operation Nord. Luckily Student was present for the first part of the meeting and it was agreed that three parachute companies were needed for deployment, one each at Trondheim, Narvik and Oslo. Student also stressed that mountain troops might be of greater value in the north and that the paratroopers sent to Norway should be selected from his ski battalions. Von Falkenhorst deployed a mountain regiment to Narvik, Trondheim and Namsos and a company of airborne troops to take the airfields at Trondheim, Narvik and Oslo and the Eighth Regiment was to supply a company for an assault on Stavanger.

When Manfred met the colonel later at their hotel, the old rascal was already on his fifth brandy and very amiable and verbose.

"They've given the Eighth Regiment the airfield at Amsterdam. The other Regiments are involved in landings around the Hague and Rotterdam. Our instructions are to capture and hold the military airfield at Schiphol and to wait arrival of our ground troops. Tell me about the Nord assault. Kurt Student told me that one of my companies would be involved."

Manfred explained the proposed plan for the Norwegian attack and the Eighth's involvement in a drop on Stavanger.

"Mad, mad," said the colonel, "breaking up a crack unit like ours just to take an airfield in Norway. Manfred, it's such a very large country. When we take it we will need a few thousand men to keep out the British. A mad enterprise led by a defective old war horse. Our Leader should be concentrating on the job in hand and using all our forces in *Weseruebung*. But still, orders are orders. Let's have another cognac."

Manfred thought the colonel's reference to von Falkenhorst as a 'doddery old duffer' and 'a defective old war horse' were rather unkind considering that the colonel himself was around the same age as the general and cast in the same mould and regarded in his own regiment as a loveable, but rather ineffectual, eccentric.

Von Bulow's predictions proved to be prophetically true. Germany did indeed conquer the land mass of Norway but it took a garrison of some sixty thousand men to defend the country and to subdue Norwegian resistance forces. On the same day as the Potsdam conference Hitler's directive to initiate Exercise *Weseruebung* in mid-April was announced. No. 2 Company of the Eighth Regiment selected for Operation Nord, were taken to Winterberg for ten days intensive ski training whilst the other four companies stayed on at Lübbecke for more amphibious training with an engineer battalion from Minden. An air of expectancy pervaded the camp. Everyone knew that an attack on the west was imminent. No one knew when, but it had to be soon. Sergeant Schneider predicted with a laugh that it was certain to be on the 4th May, his birthday. His guess was not far out of line. Operation *Weseruebung* was launched on the 10th May, 1940.

"Manfred, are you looking forward to your first battle?" asked the colonel one evening after dinner in the officers' mess.

Manfred thought about the older man's question and replied, "I don't know what to expect. I think I will be nervous. I'm very frightened of jumping, but I know I have excellent and brave men with me and I'm sure we'll do well."

Colonel von Bulow took a long sip of his vintage cognac, rolled the fluid around inside his mouth and, licking the underside of his moustache, continued, "I remember my first action at Verdun in the winter of 1916. We were in trenches about three hundred metres away from the French line. Just before dawn our major gave the order to charge and off we went like a hoard of startled rabbits, sprinting towards the French trenches. The major was hit within thirty metres and I stopped to look at him. His eyes were glazed but he managed to speak in a croaky voice, 'leave me here Erich, get out there and spike the Froggies'. I got to my feet and started forwards again. The din was unbelievable – shells bursting and bullets whizzing around our ears. Men, comrades, lay in crumpled heaps on the ground, in shell holes or impaled on our own barbed wire. The whole muddy rain-sodden field was littered with shell holes and the stench of decomposed bodies, both ours and theirs, spread like a thick blanket on the ground. I charged forward through the smoke and must have 'run' another hundred metres when I met a group of our own soldiers retreating. A sergeant shouted, 'Get back, Sir, they're only forty metres behind'. I had sudden thoughts of glory, of making a stand there in the middle of the battlefield, to sacrifice my life for the Kaiser and for the Fatherland. But as the last one of our retreating lads passed me he suddenly fell flat on his face shot through the back of his head. I didn't need any further encouragement and turned and sprinted back to our line. I was the only officer left behind in our trench, a green lieutenant in my first battle. I suddenly felt important and brave. 'Fix bayonets,' I shouted, 'Fix bayonets and charge.' We went over the top again and this time in amongst the Frenchies. The *Poilu* is as brave a man as any but when they saw cold steel they turned and ran back to their own lines. After the battle I could feel blood running down my face and a jagged piece of shrapnel sticking out the corner of my eye. To this day, on occasion, I can still smell my own blood and in the background the foetid stench of dead and decaying horses and humans blown out of their shallow graves by the shelling. It was the same outside Guernica in 1937 but the fighting was closer, more hand to hand. I lost my left arm in that battle. I don't know why I've told you all this but it must be the effect of the Rémy Martin."

Colonel von Bulow lapsed into silence and Manfred spoke softly and wistfully.

"I hope I shall be able to do my duty to the Führer and my regiment when the time comes."

There was a long uneasy pause between the two men, each wrapped in his own thoughts. The colonel was the first to speak.

"You know that I am not required to jump because of this," indicating his empty left sleeve. "And, as my aide, you will stay with me. As soon as the airfield is clear we will fly in and join the rest of the battalion. I think it's important that we arrive in full dress uniform on the first transport plane into Schiphol."

Manfred felt easier in his mind. At least he was not expected to parachute on to an airfield and by the time the first plane landed the airstrip should be secure. But to fly to war in full dress uniform was another matter. He thought the colonel had gone mad. They would look like two cock pheasants and would be sitting ducks for any armed Dutch infantry, or snipers, in the vicinity. But he still felt safer with Colonel von Bulow at his side. The 'old man' was regarded as a lucky mascot by the men of the Eighth *Fallschirmjagger*.

Norwegian War Diary

Major Haldendorf and his second company left for Wilhelmshaven on the 2nd April, 1940. On the 9th they successfully dropped and captured the airfield at Sala near Stavanger. Casualties were light, although Major Haldendorf suffered serious injuries from which he subsequently died. The airfield was held for three days until relief mountain troops and heavy supplies were flown in and the port was made secure by the Germans on the 12th April.

Elsewhere the invasion was held up by Norwegian resistance. Narvik was taken by a seaborne invasion involving seven German destroyers who sank two Norwegian battleships in the fjord. Trondheim was easily taken, but a naval and air bombardment at Bergen resulted in the sinking of the German cruisers, Köenigsberg and the Karlsruhe was torpedoed off Kristiansand. Within thirty-six hours the ports of Narvik, Trondheim, Bergen and Stavanger along the western seaboard of southern Norway were captured by the Germans. Their assault on Oslo was held up in the fjord by an artillery fort at Oskarborg, where Norwegian batteries sank the Bleucher and damaged the Leutzow and the Emden. Oslo was finally occupied on the 18th April when German airborne forces captured an undefended airfield at Fornebu and the Norwegian King and his Government fled the capital.

On the 12th and 13th April British naval forces, led by the battleship Warspite, attacked and sank seven German destroyers in Narvik Fjord. British land forces were slow in arriving in Norway. On the 20th April a brigade landed at Andalsnes and a second at

Namsos. The brigade at Andalsnes moved inland but were defeated by the Germans at Lillehammer on April 21st and evacuated on April 30th. On May 2nd all Anglo-French forces were evacuated from Namsos and southern Norway was now firmly in German hands. There was still a force of two thousand men around Narvik in northern Norway and on May 28th they drove General Edouard Dietl's six thousand mountain ski troops out of Narvik only to be evacuated themselves two days later. King Haakon and his advisors were evacuated to London from Tromso on the cruiser Devonshire *on the 7th June and spent the next five years in exile. The battle for Norway, Nord* Weseruebung, *proved yet again that the armies of the Third Reich were unconquerable. As a result of the naval battles, however, Germany lost ten out of twenty destroyers and three out of eight cruisers and two battle cruisers and a pocket battleship were so severely damaged as to be virtually valueless as a fighting force. Grand Admiral Raeder's dreams of German sea conquest during the Second World War were shattered in April 1940 in the fjords and ports of Norway.*

On 12th April, 1940 Colonel von Bulow addressed his regiment on the main parade ground at the parachute barracks in Lübbecke. Standing on a podium, flanked by Manfred on one side and the second in command, Major Hans Werner on the other, he spoke in a high-pitched voice which penetrated clearly through the cold, thin, early morning air.

"*Fallschirmjagger* of the Eighth Regiment. I have to announce that yesterday our gallant comrades of No. 2 Company, led by Major Haldendorf, captured the airfield at Sala and are attacking the town of Stavanger in Norway."

The *Fallschirmjagger* responded with loud cheers and thunderous applause lasting for nearly a minute.

"Our casualties are light. Major Haldendorf has been injured but his condition is not serious. I can also tell you that our airborne colleagues from the Third Regiment have taken Trondheim and in Norway our troops have captured all their first day objectives. The Navy landed troops in Narvik and Bergen and both these towns are in our hands. There is still some fighting around Oslo and they have called in a reserve paratrooper company from the Fifth to sort things out. I am pleased to give you this news. Three cheers for Major Haldendorf and our Second Company. Hip hip... Hip hip..."

There were three deafening 'hoorahs' from the eight hundred men on parade and then, like a tidal wave, the paratroopers sang in unison, *Rot Sheint Die Sonne.* It was a very moving moment which brought tears to the colonel's good eye as the manly voices of his paratroopers rose through the misty early morning air. Colonel von Bulow later confided in Manfred:

"I have only twice felt like this before. Once was in the trenches in the Somme on Christmas Day in 1917 when there was an agreed truce between us and the Tommies and we sang carols, *Silent Night,* I recall and the other time, in 1937, in Catalonia when, with a setting sun as a backdrop, Franco's soldiers, victorious in battle that day, came back from the front singing *Ave Maria.*" The colonel was silent for a few moments and then dabbing his eye with his handkerchief continued, "Manfred, it will be our Leader's birthday on the 20th April and you and Major Werner will arrange a grand parade and march past. I will get Brigadier General Fromm from Minden to take the salute. Major Werner will rehearse the march past and you, Manfred, will look after the singing. I want my men to sing again before we go into battle." Each day for the following week the *Fallschirmjagger* of the Eighth Regiment rehearsed the march past and Manfred conducted them in singing national and Party songs on the parade ground.

20th April, 1940 was a bright sunny day. The Führer's birthday was traditionally celebrated by a grand parade and march past either in Nuremberg or Berlin and all military units in Germany and its occupied territories celebrated his birthday by parading at 11 am, reiterating an oath of total allegiance to Adolf Hitler. Events in Norway had unsettled the Führer who had vacillated between supreme elation and utter depression and at one stage he threatened to call off his grand birthday parade in Berlin. Hitler was impatient to get 'this business in Norway over and done with so that I can press forward with the attack in the west'.

Colonel von Bulow's parade at Lübbecke was a great success. In bright sunshine the Eighth Regiment marched on to the parade ground singing *Wir Fahren Nach England.* The oath to Hitler was recited by Brigadier General Fromm and the whole parade stood at attention and gave a Nazi salute chanting *"Sieg Heil".* The general then inspected the five companies on parade and, before they marched off, they sang the German national anthem *Deutschland Uber Alles*. As they marched eight hundred male voices were raised in song, *Rot Sheint Die Sonne*, the paratroopers' war-cry. The saluting party returned to the officers' mess for an elaborate lunch. Brigadier General Fromm was full of praise for the Eighth Regiment.

"I hope," he commented, "the Englanders know what's coming. Your men, Colonel von Bulow, are in excellent spirits and ready to go, as has been shown in Stavanger. I wish the Eighth Parachute regiment all the best of luck in the forthcoming encounter."

A toast was drunk to Colonel von Bulow and the Eighth Parachute Regiment. As was customary on these occasions the cooks were ordered to enter the mess hall at the end of the meal. The sergeant *Chef de Cuisine* led his four white-tuniced assistants to stand at the back of the main table and accept a schnapps from the commanding officer. On cue the sergeant chef and his staff downed their schnapps with military precision and an obvious wealth of practice. Manfred was amused when he recognised one of the chefs, the short squat man with bulging eyes, ill-fitting uniform, corporal's stripes and paratrooper's wings on the left side of his tunic. It was the same man who had defaulted from the recruitment squad after the first day's training and had been excused training jumps. During the past eleven months Fritz Schultz had been promoted and permanently attached to headquarters company as a cook.

Colonel von Bulow insisted, "And a damned good cook he is! Let him have his eagles so that he feels at home and one of us. If this makes him happy in his work so be it."

And so it transpired. Corporal Schultz was extremely happy in the officers' kitchens with easy access to cognac and schnapps in the mess and a kind and benevolent sergeant in charge. He was even more happy when, on two occasions, he had been home to Schweinfurt on leave to show off his winged eagles and chevrons at the Wildbok and the Hotel Kaiserhof.

When Manfred retired to bed on the night of the grand parade he began to have niggling doubts about Colonel Erich von Bulow. He noticed that whenever the colonel spoke about the Führer he referred to him as 'The Leader'. Only today on parade he has sworn an oath to his Leader and not to '*Die* Führer' and, in the mess after the parade, he had toasted the Leader. Manfred knew that a Prussian element in the *Wehrmacht* were opposed to Adolf Hitler, objecting to his ruthless disregard of seniority and tradition. Some senior commanders mistrusted the demagogue who had risen from the rank of corporal and Manfred wondered if Colonel von Bulow might have been one of the insurgents who secretly opposed Hitler in 1939 and in the events which culminated in the attack on Poland in September of that year.

At that time many notable military figures were conspiring to depose Hitler and to prevent an escalation of events which ultimately led to the outbreak of World War II. Prominent among these conspirators were General von Beck, Chief of General Staff, General von Witzleben, Commander in Berlin, General Hoepner, Divisional Panzer Commander in Munich and Admiral Canaris, Senior Intelligence Officer of the *Oberkommando der Wehrmacht*. It was known at the time that these military leaders commanded a large volume of support among senior officers of the three services. But the success of Hitler's political tactics in Czechoslovakia and his blitzkrieg attacks on Poland and Norway crushed an impending revolt. General Beck was dismissed and replaced by General von Brauchitsch who had originally been sympathetic towards a military coup but, after the Polish victory, had a change of heart and became one of Hitler's staunchest supporters.

Satisfied that the situation in Norway was well under control, Hitler issued a directive to OKW to implement Operation *Weseruebung*, the attack in the West. All units were ordered to move to their battle stations. Colonel von Bulow's regiment were to fly from Bückeburg to their drop at Schiphol, a distance of two hundred and seventy-five kilometres and about one and a half flying hours. The Eighth Parachute Regiment, less a company still active in Stavanger, arrived in convoy at Bückeburg air station on the 3rd May led by Colonel von Bulow and Manfred in a radio-equipped command *Kübelwagen*.

The regiment was housed in three large empty hangars and the paratroopers were equipped for battle in their beige camouflage smocks, trousers and helmets, cradling their MP40 sub-machine guns. The large aerodrome at Bückeburg was strewn with hundreds of Junkers JU-52 aircraft and DFS-230 gliders nestling under camouflage netting, leaving two runways clear of vehicles and planes.

There were two other parachute regiments at Bückeburg, the Second and the Fourth, and they were destined to be dropped around the Hague. Major Hans Werner had produced a papier-mâché replica of the 'drop zone' at Schiphol and every day the *Fallschirmjagger,* in sections, were taken through the routine of their drop and the objectives they were expected to achieve on the first day of fighting on the ground. The paratroopers were excitedly confident and eager to go as they waited, day after day, for the signal to jump off the blocks.

The colonel kept repeating that on this momentous occasion he and his adjutant would jump with the first wave. Manfred shuddered at the thought. Sergeant Schneider, hovering around the back of the group with a rueful smile on his face, commented, "That'll be the day! I can't wait to see the old man and his blond aide actually jumping from a JU-52."

The days passed slowly occupied by briefings, eating, sleeping, playing cards and the inevitable singing of popular songs.

On the 9th May the order came that Operation *Weseruebung* was to start before dawn the following day. The troop-carrying Junkers destined for Rotterdam and the Hague drops were to go first, one and a half hours before daybreak. The Eighth Regiment was one of the last to become airborne, about one hour before daybreak. On the evening of the 9th in each hangar the Padre conducted a church service asking for God's blessing on the enterprise. The elation of the preceding days evaporated rapidly and the men became sombre, cocooned in their own thoughts and worried about the battle they would enjoin on the morrow, a battle from which they knew that some, if not most of them, would never return. Hymns were sung with feeling as if communication with God at this late hour conferred some protection and hopefully immunity from the ultimate fate that might await them on a Dutch airfield at dawn.

Colonel von Bulow, moving around giving encouragement and placating fears, stayed with his *Fallschirmjagger* until the battalion settled down for the night. Accompanied by Manfred he repaired to the *Luftwaffe* mess where the mood was one of quiet optimism tinged with solemnity. Amidst a chorus of 'Good luck' and 'Give them a good bashing' the colonel and Manfred went to bed at midnight.

Manfred was woken from a fitful sleep by an orderly at one o'clock.

"Colonel von Bulow wishes to see you immediately in his quarter, Sir."

Manfred put on his heavy overcoat and found his commanding officer sitting up in bed, brandy glass in one hand and blindfolded by a black silk scarf. The colonel sensed his entry into the room.

"Manfred I cannot fly with my boys tomorrow. About an hour ago I developed a terrible headache with flashes of light in my eye. I have been sick and I feel giddy. I thought this brandy might settle me down." The colonel took another huge gulp of cognac. "You'll have to see the men off. Major Werner will take command in the field and the adjutant will go in with the boys. Go and see them off and keep me informed. Tell Major Werner that I want regular bulletins and tell him that once the airfield is secure and safe I will be the first officer to land. Turn the light off please on your way out and ask the orderly to bring me another bottle of Rémy."

Manfred returned to his cramped quarters and lay on his bed for a while but could not sleep. Reveille for the paratroopers was at 2.30 a.m. He dressed and put on his field-grey overcoat over his camouflage smock glancing at his parachute pack hanging on the back of the door and thinking, 'On this drop you will not be needed. Thank God.'

He emerged into the cool night air and walked around the airfield where, even at this hour, aircraft mechanics under the dim light of hooded torches were busily huddled over the aeroplanes.

Other shrouded figures walked around in the darkness but no one exchanged a word and the mechanics spoke in whispers conscious of the importance of tuning the JU-52 engines for peak performance on the following day. Manfred walked the perimeter only speaking to return a verbal salute from an alert sentry. On his trek around the airfield he estimated that there were about ninety JU-52s of Löhrs Fifth Air Fleet parked ready for take off. On the following day they would fly into the jaws of death. How many, he wondered, would escape unscathed.

At 3 a.m. Manfred reached the Eighth Regiment hangars and heard stifled conversation from inside the building. At the entrance he found Major Hans Werner, propped against the hangar wall and inhaling deeply from a cigarette. In the dim light from the hatchway Manfred saw a circle of white cigarette stubs, some lengthy, others short, strewn around the major's boots, an indication that he had been in this position for a long time.

"*Guten morgen* Herr *Major.*"

"*Guten morgen Manfred,*" the major replied.

Manfred addressed the faint outline of his second in command, "Hans, I have been instructed by Colonel von Bulow that you are to command the attack on Schiphol. The colonel is unfortunately severely incapacitated and unable to fly today or to come and see the regiment off." Hans Werner nodded his assent. "Unfortunately I have to remain with the colonel and the adjutant will take my place. Colonel von Bulow wishes you the very best of luck and is sorry he cannot be with you. He wants regular reports from you and insists that on the first flight into Schiphol, when you have secured the airfield, he and I will be on the plane."

Then extending his hand he squeezed Major Werner's elbow, "Good luck, Hans."

They entered the hangar together. The *Fallschirmjagger* were already fully clothed, alert and making minor adjustments to their weapons and webbing, talking together in low voices, their grim faces pale and mask-like in the dim glow of kerosene lamplight. Major Werner and Manfred walked amongst them encouraging, joking and occasionally smiling, and the process was repeated in the other two hangars allocated to the regiment. At 3.30 a.m. the noise of revving aircraft engines reached their ears as the pilots moved and jockeyed their planes to the end of the runway. The first planes in position were beginning to load with paratroopers from the Second and Fourth Battalions and within ten minutes the JU-52s taxied into the darkness and took off at intervals of about forty seconds. The roar of aircraft engines was now constant and above the din Manfred stood on a packing case in the hangar and shouted at the top of his voice:

"Colonel von Bulow wishes you all luck and God speed. Hit the target and clear the airfield. Do this for Colonel von Bulow and the Führer."

It was now time for the troops to enplane. This they did in single file and in an orderly fashion with Sergeant Schneider fussing around them like a hen with a brood of chicks. An occasional joke or a verbal comment was heard above the noise of the revving engines but, in the main, the *Fallschirmjagger* were silent, determined and grim faced. Major Werner's plane took off first followed quickly by the others at regular intervals, thirty JUs in all carrying five hundred and forty into battle. Sergeant Schneider, on the last plane to leave, turned to face Manfred in the dim light at the hatch and saluted.

Manfred returning the salute shouted, "Good luck, Sergeant Schneider. Give them one for me."

The sergeant smiled broadly.

"We'll miss you, Sir. But don't worry we'll have the airfield clear for you by tomorrow."

Manfred stood there transfixed, ashamed that he felt so pleased to be missing this flight and that he could, without any qualms, send his men into a fight from which many would not return. He was still standing in the same spot as the last JU-troop carrier noisily taxied to the runway, increased its revs and raced westwards into the dark sky and a sudden hush descended on Bückeburg airfield. With a sigh, Manfred turned on his heels and walked to the mess where he was able to report to his sleepy, befuddled colonel that the regiment was safely off the ground and on their way to Schiphol.

"*Sehr gut,*" came the reply from under the bedclothes.

Manfred had a mug of strong black coffee in the mess, shared with three bleary-eyed *Luftwaffe* officers and again walked outside as dawn was breaking. The sky in the east became perceptibly lighter and again the noise of revving JU-52s split the silence as they taxied towards the second runway to take off, each aeroplane towing three or four gliders. The first plane took off in semi-darkness but by the time the last Junker left the ground the sun was peeping over the horizon. Manfred was amazed to see the dull grey aeroplanes towing three grey-bellied DFS-230 gliders into the air and slowly disappearing into the misty western horizon. He thought that his parachute troops were brave, but the destiny of the twelve men sitting in each of the flimsy balsa-wood gliders lay in the hands and skill of their pilots. As if to reinforce the dangers of gliding, two of the gliders' tow ropes became entangled and both gliders crashed into the ground at the end of the runway. Seven men crawled out of the carnage alive leaving fourteen of their comrades dead, or trapped, amongst the twisted wreckage of their balsa-wood machines.

About an hour after sunrise empty JU-52s returned. A few of the planes were slightly damaged and one crashed on landing but, of ninety planes despatched into battle, eighty-seven returned safely. The air crews gave glowing reports of accurate drops and glider landings on selected targets. They had encountered a fair amount of anti-aircraft fire around Rotterdam and the Hague but the Schiphol strike reported only minimal activity from ground defences.

Manfred hastened to the colonel's quarters with news of a successful drop. The colonel had to be shaken awake and when given the news merely readjusted his blindfold, fell back on the pillows yawning and, within a matter of seconds, was snoring loudly and soundly asleep. The first wireless report from Major Werner came through mid-morning.

"Successful landing. Casualties light. Re-grouping and advancing towards airfield. Glider troops overshot target and landed five kilometres to west. Engaging the enemy and hope to take airfield before nightfall. Enemy resistance light, mainly small arms. Dykes and water courses restricting our advance. Send inflatable boats."

On his own initiative Manfred requested a plane load of dinghies to be dropped to the advancing paratroopers. At lunchtime he accompanied the colonel's orderly into his bedroom. Colonel von Bulow, his blindfold removed, sat upright in bed taking a bowl of broth, black bread and cheese. He immediately questioned Manfred:

"How are we doing?"

Manfred read out Major Werner's report and described his actions in response to his request for inflatable boats.

"Well done, Manfred. I knew I could rely on you. We are now reaping the benefit of all that amphibious training. I thought the Hollanders would flood their dykes. We should have thought of sending the boats in with the first wave. My headache is nearly gone. I'll get up this evening and spend an hour or two in the command room."

The message that came through at teatime was not expected. It originated from Abwehr headquarters, Oslo.

'Regret to inform you that as a result of his serious wounds Major Haldendorf died in Oslo Military Hospital, at 10 a.m. today, 10th May, 1940.'

Manfred felt genuinely sorry for the major, cuckolded by his wife, denied promotion and now dying in a remote hospital away from the Fatherland. Colonel von Bulow took the news very well. He praised the major for his loyalty to the *Fallschirmjagger* and to himself adding, "He was a good, if unimaginative, man. He was a solid, dependable officer. Yet he knew what we are all here for and that death may be the ultimate penalty we have to pay for serving our country."

'No mention,' thought Manfred, 'of loyalty to the Führer.'

Colonel von Bulow was in the wireless room at Bückeburg headquarters when Major Werner's second report came in at 11 p.m. 'Pinned down within sight of airfield. Dutch forces resisting. Mainly small arms. Four fighter planes destroyed on runway at Schiphol, one by our machine guns and the rest by Stukas. Casualties still light. One paratrooper killed and three wounded. Digging in for the night.'

When the colonel heard this news he went berserk.

"What's the fool doing? He must press on and attack. Surprise is the key to success in airborne landings. They must take casualties to reach the objective. I wish I were there. I'd get them to move forward,' and then, still fuming, he clutched his forehead announcing that his headache had returned and he retired to his quarters. Manfred walked with him and the colonel asked one question that did not require an answer:

"Why in God's name have they not made contact with the glider troops?"

Once in his quarters the colonel poured himself a large cognac, put on his blindfold and, fully clothed, slumped down on the bed, fully clothed, where he remained all through the following day. Werner's reports during the day were not encouraging. Resistance around the airfield was escalating and Dutch reinforcements had arrived in numbers. Contact had not been made with the glider troops in the west. Casualties were mounting and the Dutch had started shelling Werner's positions along the dykes to the south and west of the airfield. Colonel von Bulow remained in his darkened bedroom receiving the reports with a nod and a grunt and an occasional, "*Mein Gott.*"

On the 12th some progress was reported and Dutch resistance seemed to be weakening. A section of forty glider engineer troops had fought their way from the west to reinforce Major Werner's paratroop battalion. With improvement in the reports from Schiphol, Colonel von Bulow's headaches vanished and he again assumed command in the control centre on the evening of the 13th May and was full of optimism, stating with confidence that he expected better news in the morning. By 10 a.m. on the 14th May the Dutch forces at Schiphol had withdrawn and about a hundred soldiers surrendered under a white flag. Werner reported that his paratroopers had occupied the eastern half of the airfield and were mopping up small pockets of resistance. Sporadic shelling continued, but there were signs that Dutch resolve was weakening and that the Eighth Regiment might be in full control of the airfield by the 15th. This report from Werner completely transformed the colonel who became self-assertive and impish once more, declaring to all and sundry that he had predicted victory. "All along, Major Werner and my paras had my full confidence."

The news from other sectors in Holland was also encouraging. Von Bock's forces had penetrated deeply in the south and were only forty kilometres from Rotterdam and the Hague, which were invested by Student's airborne forces. The Dutch appeared to be on the point of surrender and at 2 p.m. on the 14th May Major Werner reported, 'Paras now in complete control of Schiphol and digging in around the perimeter. Sporadic small arms fire and occasional shelling. Glider engineers clearing the runway. Safe to land tomorrow. The Eighth Regiment awaits its commanding officer'.

Colonel von Bulow's sense of high drama did not forsake him and with an expansive gesture of his right arm and pointing westwards he announced, "Captain Schmidt, now is the time for us to go to war."

The colonel insisted that they should fly to Schiphol dressed in full mess regalia. The colonel's uniform was light blue with red lapel tabs, a silver regimental badge on the right breast and the Iron Cross on the left breast pocket which also secured a gold pin holding his empty left sleeve. Manfred's mess kit was dark blue with silver wings on his left chest. The colonel insisted on wearing dress caps and not a dull, dirty-brown parachute helmet.

The Junker JU-52 supply plane left at 6 a.m. and flew the two officers directly to Schiphol, landing on the runway without incident at 7.30 am. The plane taxied to the main airfield buildings, the hatch opened and Colonel von Bulow descended to the ground with Manfred standing at the hatch behind him. All around the airfield perimeter groups of Eighth Regiment *Fallschirmjagger* cheered loudly at the sight of their commanding officer in his resplendent outfit.

Sergeant Schneider came sprinting across from a dugout as the colonel and Manfred started walking towards the main building where Major Werner waited to receive them, when a hissing, whistling noise of increasing intensity became apparent. Sergeant Schneider, some two hundred metres distant from the party shouted, "Down, down" and flung himself earthwards as the loud thundering crash of an exploding mortar bomb shattered the silent morning air. Colonel von Bulow, a First World War veteran, reacted quickly and flung himself flat on his face, but Manfred was slower and as he leapt forwards, a piece of shrapnel hit him on the side of the head. His unconscious body crashed sideways on to the ground. It took the medical orderlies about two minutes to get to the stricken captain. Clamping a dressing on the side of his bleeding scalp they manhandled the semi-conscious officer into the command building and down a flight of stairs into an underground first aid post. A medical officer got to work at once, staunching the blood flow and suturing the six inch laceration on the right side of Manfred's temple. He awoke on the operating table and in his semi-conscious state recognised Colonel von Bulow and Major Werner.

He then lapsed into unconsciousness again finally waking up four hours later with little recollection of the incident. The mortar bomb had been discharged from behind a granary some two kilometres to the west of the airport at the intersection of a slow flowing river and two canals. The bomb killed the JU-52 pilot and injured a *Luftwaffe* corporal as well as Manfred. Colonel von Bulow escaped unscathed. His only comment was, "We should have worn our helmets. Let this be a lesson to us," and then he laughed loudly.

War Diary

At about 2 p.m. on the 14th May Stuka bombers attacked Rotterdam, flattening the town centre and killing eight hundred civilians. This unprovoked blitzkrieg attack on a defenceless city served to strengthen the will of the Dutch forces to resist. By the 14th May they had been on the point of capitulation and asking for an armistice. The Dutch defenders, having evacuated Schiphol airfield, were not strong enough to mount a counter attack but were positioned in the moat-protected granary and were able to accurately zero their mortars on the western end of the runway and airfield buildings. Their nagging accuracy and intermittent bombardment prevented aircraft landing and kept the German paratroops pinned in their fox holes.

After a fitful restless night Manfred woke in the medical centre at 8 a.m. on the following morning with a splitting headache. He managed to get out of bed unaided and, unsteady on his feet, inspected himself in the bathroom mirror. His head was heavily bandaged with some blood-staining of the linen tapes. He felt a little giddy and very thirsty and suddenly developed an intense hatred for the enemy who had caused him the indignity of being shot down in front of his battalion.

He dressed in his parachute smock and gingerly placed the round metal helmet over the bandages. By this time an orderly was protesting that he should lie down and when the medical officer appeared he was also insistent that Manfred was not fit to walk about. The sudden appearance of Sergeant Schneider came to his rescue.

"What's happening, Schneider?"

The sergeant looked pleased to see Manfred on his feet.

"There are three or four mortars hidden behind a large granary about two thousand metres to the west. They're lobbing their shells at will and stopping our planes landing. We have no artillery on the ground as yet and we can't get at them as the building is between a deep river and a canal and the ground between is flat as a pancake."

Manfred turned to his sergeant.

"Did the inflatable boats arrive safely?"

The sergeant replied, "Affirmative."

"Right Schneider, get me a squad of twenty of our men and six boats. We'll have a go at the granary. I haven't had a chance to have a look around as yet. Where's Colonel von Bulow?"

"The colonel and Major Werner are in an underground bunker in the next building. Major Werner has cracked a bit and is under sedation. The colonel is fine but staying with the major," the sergeant replied.

Manfred drank some hot coffee and went to the flat roof of the two-storey central building. Scanning eastwards with his binoculars he saw for miles over the flat surface of the ground, dotted here and there with stricken JU-52s and gliders, tails up in the air, leaning sideways like drunken crucifixes. On the airfield itself both runways were clear, though pock-marked with craters and at the sides there were four crashed JU-52s, one being salvaged and pulled off a runway by the engineers. At the western end of the runway he distinctly saw the granary some two thousand five hundred metres distant and shrouded in dust and smoke, with rows of shattered windows on each side of the gaping central hatches.

Manfred knew that somewhere high in the granary there was a 'spotter' guiding the mortars on to their targets. The mortars were firing from behind the main building and, even as he watched, he saw a canister shooting upwards in a lazy parabola followed, after four seconds, by a faint thud and twenty seconds later the whistling noise of a descending mortar bomb which landed with a vibrating bang on some waste ground behind the central building causing Manfred and Sergeant Schneider to duck involuntarily behind the parapet. Manfred studied the ground between the granary and the end of the runway. It was flat and featureless with only two or three clumps of bushes which might be useful for concealment. The granary itself was placed inside the S-bend of a deep, slow-flowing river some fifty metres wide, and between the granary and the west bank of the river Manfred saw freshly dug emplacements indicating that the Dutch were prepared to defend themselves against any attempt at a river crossing from the airfield.

Manfred turned again to the eastwards end of the airfield. With his first scan he had seen a group of small houses some four hundred metres to the south of the runway and reasoned that buildings in this area were usually aggregated near lock gates. A second look at the houses revealed the faint outline of a canal bank running straight as an arrow from east to west leading from the lock gates to approach the S-bend in the river. He followed the outline of the waterway and at one point, beyond the granary, the canal was within fifty metres of the river bank. Manfred checked twice on the nearness of the two waterways and, having formulated a plan, turned to speak to Sergeant Schneider at his shoulder.

"Sergeant Schneider. I think we can take the granary. Have a look. You see that clump of trees between us and the river bend? I want a diversionary squad to make for the trees carrying a couple of inflatable boats. I know the granary is out of range for our light mortars but they could let off a few rounds. In the meantime you and I and an assault section will make our way to the lock gates at the eastern end of the runway in amongst the four houses you can see to your left. We will paddle down the canal, protected by the banks, and reach this point," indicating with his finger, "about a mile beyond the river bend. I reckon we'll have to carry the boats some fifty metres across land to get into the river and then a quick row and a charge up the river bank should bring us in behind the enemy mortars. While we're in the canal and crossing the river our light mortars will keep a constant barrage on the Dutchmen dug in in front of the granary to keep their heads down. Right, Schneider, get our mortars out to their position. You and I will take the main party to the lock gates."

The diversionary mortar section positioned itself in a sheltered copse between the airfield and the S-bend of the river. Manfred's twenty-man assault team made their way to the lock gates with five inflatable boats and launched themselves into the canal for a two-mile row in line astern towards the west. The tall sides of the canal bank shielded the attackers from the defending Dutch gunners. After thirty minutes rowing in complete silence Manfred and his assault platoon could hear the German mortar bombs exploding well short of the granary. They proceeded unscathed and undetected to a point in the canal some four hundred metres west of the granary. At this spot the paratroopers left the cover of the canal bank and crawled undetected some fifty metres across open ground to reach the south bank of the river, dragging the inflatable dinghies behind them. The re-inflated dinghies were pushed away from the river bank and paddled across to reach the other side. Manfred and his twenty men were now in position, under cover, in an orchard on the northern bank of the river.

Sergeant Schneider and four *Fallschirmjagger* were sent to the left side of the orchard whilst Manfred and six men advanced down the middle ground and six paras moved cautiously down the river bank and established an avenue of retreat to the four boats, which were moored under the bank, guarded by the remaining two paratroopers. All the while there was an intermittent thud of mortar fire from the Dutch soldiers about three hundred metres to their front and the faintest snapping noise of their own smaller mortars in the far distance, whilst from the front of the granary recurrent fusillades of small arms fire indicated that the diversionary feint by the engineers was producing a reaction from the Dutchmen. Manfred, perspiring freely, drew a deep breath and felt a trickle of warm blood running down from under his bandage and, as he tugged at his collar, his fingers were covered in blood from the re-opened wound on his right temple.

He looked towards Sergeant Schneider.

"Right Schneider, go now," and the sergeant and his section jumped over the bank, crawled across open ground to reach the left side of the orchard. When Schneider's group were nearing the end of their run Manfred took his own section at a steady pace across the same open ground to reach the middle of the back of the apple orchard. The third section followed and acted as cover, cautiously advancing towards the granary along a muddy towpath.

The Dutch, typically methodical, had planted their apple trees in orderly rows from east to west. At the end of one of the rows some three hundred metres distant Manfred saw a sand-bagged emplacement and two helmeted Dutch soldiers carrying mortar bombs into a dugout. Looking to his left Manfred indicated to Schneider that he had sighted the enemy. Within a minute Schneider returned the signal indicating that he too had found a mortar emplacement at the end of one of the apple-tree avenues. By moving two rows to the left the sections became invisible from the gun emplacements and simultaneously the German attackers raced down selected paths towards their targets. Half-way down Manfred heard a loud crack and a bang from his front at about two o'clock and realised that there was a third mortar battery nearer the river bank. Still running he pointed with his right hand whispering, *"Rechts, rechts,"* at which command three of the paratroopers veered off to the right.

Manfred and Sergeant Schneider's sections reached the mortar emplacements at the same time, hurling hand grenades into the bunkers and firing their MP 40 SMGs from the hip. Both emplacements and their occupants were eliminated in half a minute, but the attack on the third bunker had come to a halt. The Dutch soldiers, alerted by the furious fusillade of machine pistols and grenades to their left, faced their rear and managed to kill two and injure one of the attacking *Fallschirmjagger*. The section cautiously advancing along the river towpath was still some hundred and fifty metres away and not within sight of the right-hand bunker.

Manfred leant against the parapet of the captured bunker panting heavily with blood dripping from the side of his head on to his tunic and on to the sandbags. Sergeant Schneider's section arrived in a rush and took up position behind the sand-bagged parapet. The mortar emplacement near the riverbank, not visible from where they were standing, was still resisting fiercely and Manfred turned to his sergeant.

"The firing is coming from forty metres to the right. Take the men here and outflank them. Leave Sempler with me. We'll go into the granary and get the spotter. Right, Sergeant, go."

Schneider and his section took off through the apple trees in a curving run to the right, followed almost immediately by Manfred and *Fallschirmjagger* Sempler who ran straight for the back door and into the granary. They crashed through the open door into a dimly lit room where the air was thick with fine, white dust generated by the constant reverberations of mortar fire. A wooden ladder led straight up to the ceiling to the next level and, as Manfred peered cautiously upwards through the open hatch, he saw the ladder stairway leading to the third floor above his head. Sempler and Manfred stood together quietly and perfectly still. They heard the explosion of grenades, shouting and small arms fire from outside the back door and the constant staccato small arms fire of the Dutch defenders in front of the building. Manfred took another look up the wooden staircase, in two minds as to whether he should go up to flush out the spotter.

The dilemma was quickly resolved. On the third level he saw a large olive-green rump and black jackboots of a Dutchman descending backwards through the floor hatch. He gently pulled Sempler backwards into a darkened recess behind the ladder and, touching his lips with his forefinger, cautioned the paratrooper to remain silent. Half a minute later they heard heavy footsteps on the floorboards above their heads and then the black jackboots started down the ladder followed by the rounded posterior of the Dutchman. Manfred stepped forward two paces and, pointing his SMG upwards, fired from the hip unleashing a stream of bullets at the unmissable target.

The Dutchman screamed and lost his footing on the ladder as the bullets from below tore through his genitalia and buttocks. For about ten seconds he clung to the lintel of the hatch and then came crashing down to hit the granary floor with a thud, where he lay in a heap amidst his own blood, urine and faeces. He was conscious when he landed on the floor. His binoculars were still slung around his neck and his blood-covered hands clutched desperately at his crotch in an attempt to tear the bullets out of his mutilated nether regions. His pleading eyes looked up at Manfred who stood over him with his SMG pointing at the Dutch officer's forehead.

"*Schweinehund, Schweinehund,*" screamed the Dutch officer with venom in his voice. Manfred squeezed the trigger releasing a further stream of bullets which blew away the top of the officer's skull, spattering blood, brain and bone over the floor and walls of the granary.

Sergeant Schneider came crashing through the doorway.

"All three mortar emplacements secured, Sir."

"Good," answered Manfred. "Now we must clear up the ground between us and the river bend. Post five men on each side between the building and the river banks to prevent anyone escaping and the rest of us can occupy a window each on the floors above and fire down on the backs of the Dutchmen. I think they'll give in quickly enough. What do you think, Heinz?"

For the first time Manfred had used the sergeant's Christian name and Schneider suddenly felt self-conscious and awkward.

"*Jawohl mein Kapitan,*" he stammered and turned on his heel to carry out Manfred's instructions.

The combined power of the paratroopers' SMG fire from eight windows of the granary, soon produced the desired effect. At first the gallant Dutch infantry turned to face the enemy at the rear but, within a few minutes, their officer, a young blond lieutenant, ordered them to lay down their arms. The lieutenant and sixteen infantry men, some injured, were captured in the action and three Dutchman lay dead in the trenches, together with the spotter officer on the floor of the granary and all eighteen Dutch engineers in the mortar pits behind the building.

Manfred's assault group had suffered two paratroopers killed and four injured, one of whom died the next day from his wounds. Manfred and his assault group returned in triumph across the river at the apex of the S-bend to waiting trucks. They were transported to the administrative buildings where Colonel von Bulow and Major Werner were present to greet them.

"Well done, Captain Schmidt, I have already been through to Bückeburg and supplies and reinforcements will arrive later today. Thanks to your initiative we have captured our objective and tomorrow we can remuster and make a move to take Amsterdam. Are you all right, Manfred?"

Manfred was swaying on his feet and before anyone could support him he fell forwards in a dead faint. For the second time in twenty-four hours he woke up on a bed in the cellar of the main building. His head had been redressed but already blood was seeping through and staining the white bandages. Manfred felt weak, extremely tired and washed out and was given some hot broth and brandy. Together with twelve other paratroopers injured in the battle for Schiphol airfield and the granary he was evacuated by plane to the Military Hospital at Bückeburg. On the following day under general anaesthesia he was subjected to an operation for debridement and re-suturing of his head wound.

War Diary

Hitler's five week blitzkrieg campaign in the west had again paid dividends. His generals came to regard him as a military genius and his success far exceeded even the wildest dreams of the Wehrmacht *Commanders. Holland was overcome in five days, aided at the end by blitzkrieg tactics and bombing Rotterdam into submission on the 14th May. Despite gloomy predictions before the invasion of Holland the Panzer divisions were able to operate for up to one hundred and twenty kilometres inside Dutch territory. The airborne drops on airfields around the Hague and at Schiphol were not immediately successful but, by the end of the first day, airborne forces had captured four important bridges south of Rotterdam near Nieuire Maas and further south over the Meuse at Dordrecht and Moedijk. Over these bridges von Bock's forces and General George von Kuechler's Eighteenth Army were able to turn northwards and attack Rotterdam, forcing an entry into Fortress Holland from the south. Hitler, impatient at the delayed advance of Kuechler's forces, ordered Field Marshal Goering's* Luftwaffe *to bomb Rotterdam into submission. This was achieved with deadly efficiency and the Dutch surrendered and lay down their arms at 11 a.m. on the 15th May.*

When Colonel von Bulow heard about the Dutch surrender he ordered the Eighth Parachute Regiment into Amsterdam and formally accept surrender of the city. On the appointed day the regiment was conveyed in lorries to the outskirts of the city and then marched into the centre behind a hastily conscripted parachute engineer military band, with Colonel Count Erich von Bulow at the head of the column riding in an open-topped *Kübelwagen*. The Mayor of Amsterdam formally surrendered the city to Colonel von Bulow in the Marktplatz at 3 p.m. on 17th May, 1940.

War Diary

Von Runstedt's Army Group A's central assault into Belgium was going as planned. Near Liege, Fort Eben Emael, at the junction of the Meuse and Albert Canal, was taken on the second day by glider-borne troops, opening up the cities of Brussels and Antwerp, which were defended by the British Expeditionary Force and Belgian and French forces, dug in along the Dyle and Meuse rivers and outnumbering the Germans by thirty-six to twenty divisions. Von Richenau's Sixth Army and General Hoepner's Third Panzer Division were held up in their advance on the Dyle line between Antwerp and Namur. On the 13th May General Halder, Chief of Army General Staff, ordered a German coup de gras, a lightning breakthrough across the Meuse south of Namur and a swing westwards towards the Channel ports. The German attack started before dawn on the 14th May led by Rommel, Guderian and von Kleist's panzers. Resistance from the French to the massive armoured thrust was negligible and the panzers were let loose to rampage across southern France relatively unopposed.

A mighty phalanx of the seven armoured brigades pushed westwards between the French and British defence lines, north of Paris and the Seine to reach the coast at Abbeville on the 20th May. The BEF, the Belgian Army and three French Armies were trapped in a pincers movement between von Kleist's panzers on the southern flank and von Runstedt's forces in Belgium and, slowly, the German pincers closed. By the 24th May Guderian's panzers, advancing northwards along the coast from Abbeville, captured Boulogne, invested Calais and reached the port of Gwelines some twenty miles from Dunkirk. The Allied forces were trapped in a triangular area based on Dunkirk, with its apex some seventy miles inland at Valenciennes. A personal order from Hitler on the 24th May stopped Guderian's Panzers for two days to re-group and re-arm in preparation for a final assault on the British-dominated bridgehead. The two day respite proved vital for survival of the British forces around Dunkirk for on the 26th May Operation Dynamo, evacuation of the BEF, commenced and continued day and night until the 4th June by which time three hundred and thirty-eight thousand two hundred and twenty-six British and Allied troops had been brought safely home, snatched off the beaches by an armada of small vessels and Royal Navy ships. King Baudoin the

Third of the Belgians surrendered his forces unconditionally to the Germans on the morning of May 28th and Dunkirk fell to German panzer forces on the 4th June, 1940.

Whilst these major battles were raging, Manfred lay in a hospital bed in Bückeburg. The festering wound on the side of his head bled and throbbed constantly and he had an irritating headache and a high temperature for most of the time. After a week the headache faded and the granulating wound became easier, though it still ached incessantly after dressings were re-applied. Company by company the Eighth Regiment flew back from Schiphol and Amsterdam to Bückeburg and were joined by the company from Stavanger on the 29th May. Major Haldendorf's body was brought home in a supply plane for burial at the Paratroopers' Cemetery at Hildescheim. On the 30th May Colonel von Bulow returned from Schiphol to take command and reform the Eighth Paras at their base camp at Lübbecke where they would be in reserve for the continuing battle in France. The war in the west was not finished but, by now, everyone realised that capitulation of the Belgians and separation of the main British and French forces heralded defeat for France and another lightning conquest for the Führer's invincible armies.

The colonel called on Manfred on his way back from the Hildescheim funeral on the 13th June.

"How goes it Manfred?" Without waiting for a reply he continued, "You missed some fun in Amsterdam! After you were evacuated I was asked to accept surrender of the city. So on the 17th we marched into the city and the Mayor signed the surrender document in the Marktplatz. For three days I was the undisputed boss in Amsterdam. You would have loved it," chuckling, "We had our headquarters in the *Rathaus* and dined and wined in comfort. And then that arrogant devil von Bock arrived and took over. We went back to Schiphol where von Bock's Third Engineer Regiment had already taken over the airfield. There was nothing more to do in Schiphol so we've been flying back section by section and should be at full battalion strength again in about four days time. I've just been to Major Haldendorf's funeral at Hildescheim. A brave man. I'm going to nominate him for a posthumous Iron Cross. You too, Manfred. I saw your attack on the granary from the roof of the command building. I'm going to nominate two others for decorations, Sergeant

Schneider and Corporal Ritter, for his gallantry at Stavanger. Do you approve?"

"Yes," Manfred replied, "I am in full agreement with your nominations. I might add Sempler's name to the list. He acted very bravely inside the granary."

The colonel re-adjusted his eye patch.

"We mustn't be too greedy. If I can get five decorations for the Eighth I'll be satisfied." Then, looking at Manfred, "You don't look too good. Are they treating you all right?"

Manfred felt tired, an accumulation of blood loss and analgesia for pain and replied in a tired voice, *"Ja, danke Colonel."*

The old war horse, not completely satisfied, turned to a nurse hovering in the corner of the room.

"My dear Sister, please look after this young officer. He's my right hand man, or in my case my left hand man! He captured Amsterdam on his own and will get an Iron Cross for his bravery. So be nice to him."

Then turning towards Manfred once more he flashed a broad smile and a wink with his good eye and strode out of the ward with a parting gesture, *"Auf Wiedersehen Kapitan Schmidt."*

On the following day Sergeant Schneider came to see Manfred and each day a member of the unit appeared and brought gifts. He was amused one day when the obese corporal cook turned up with a large *Strudel mit Zanah*, freshly cooked, and ready for consumption. Corporal Schultz was visiting a colleague from the cookhouse, recently admitted with salmonella poisoning. The visitors kept him up to date with the war news.

On the 5th June, the same day as Dunkirk was taken, the Germans launched a massive offensive over a four hundred mile front in the Somme. The result of this unequal battle was predictable. Against one hundred and fifty-three Wehrmacht *and ten Panzer Divisions the French could only muster sixty-five divisions and very rapidly weight in numbers and superior battle tactics overcame the demoralised and badly led French forces. Paris was declared an open city and occupied on June 10th and on the same day Mussolini attacked France in the south but, even with a superiority of some twenty-five divisions, he was unable to dislodge the French forces in the Côte d'Azure. On 25th June at Versailles an Armistice between France and Germany*

*was signed by General Charles Huntziger and General Keitel in the
same wagon-lit used for the 1914-18 Armistice. Two days later the
Franco-Italian Armistice was signed in Rome. Operation
Weseruebung, the battle for France, was over after six weeks of
fighting. The French, humiliated and demoralised, threw the towel
into the ring without much of a fight. Hitler's armies and his Axis
partners now occupied Belgium, Holland, one half of Poland, France,
most of Scandinavia and the Balkans and, Britain apart, were the
undisputed masters of western Europe.*

One night, as he lay in his bed, Manfred felt a sudden flush of
patriotism. He regretted that his poor old Papi had not survived to see
these glorious days of victory and conquest by the Third Reich. He
reminded himself that the architect of these famous victories was
Adolf Hitler, his God, his Leader, his Führer. These thoughts, as
they often did, aroused him sexually and produced an erection. At the
hospital only male orderlies were on duty at night. The plain-looking
sister in charge during the day would do nicely, but he had to be
content with masturbation to relieve his sexual frustration.

On the day following the Franco-Italian armistice Manfred and two
other officer casualties were sitting outside the ward in the warm
midday sun enjoying an alfresco lunch, liberally complimented with
schnapps and beer, when Colonel von Bulow burst through the door.
The colonel drew up a chair, helped himself to a schnapps and asked
the other officers to leave the table, as he wished to speak to Manfred
alone. His voice quivered with suppressed excitement.

"I have excellent news for you Manfred. Kurt Student has agreed
to accept my citations. You are to get an Iron Cross First Class.
Major Haldendorf will get the same, posthumously, and I will receive
a clasp to my own Iron Cross. Sergeant Schneider, Corporal Ritter
and Paratrooper Sempler are each getting an Order of the German
Cross. So the Eighth have done well with six decorations. The
Second and Third Regiments, who landed in the Hague and
Rotterdam, only received two apiece." Wiping his perspiring
forehead with a table napkin he continued, "Now our Leader has
ordered a grand parade in Paris on the 4th July to show the flag to the
Frenchies. He will take the salute and afterwards personally present
Crosses to the officers. Every Regiment engaged in Operation
Weseruebung will provide a forty man section for the march past.

Sergeant Schneider will lead our section and Major Werner will be in command. You will be with me on the saluting base. Do you feel up to it?"

Manfred replied with alacrity, "Of course, Herr Colonel, I must be there to receive my Iron Cross from the Führer."

The colonel beamed. "That's the spirit. We'll leave for Paris in my car in three days time. I've cleared your discharge from here with the surgeon major. He's a bit doubtful about letting you go but I pushed him into it."

He gave Manfred a one-eyed wink and continued, "My driver will pick you up in my staff car at 8 a.m. Best mess dress will be worn" and then, looking at Manfred's head bandages, "Get the medics to give you clean bandages. I want the Leader to see one of his gallant wounded officers on parade. I am sure he will notice you amongst the crowd. Let's have another schnapps to celebrate. It'll be champagne all the way to Paris!"

Chapter Twelve

The Grand Parade, 4th July, 1940
Paris, July 1940 – January 1941
The Wooing of Lise Frank

A black open-topped Mercedes staff car, pennant flying, left Lübbecke barracks at 9 a.m. on the 28th of June en route for Paris. Sergeant Schneider occupied the front seat next to the driver and Colonel von Bulow, Manfred and Major Werner sat in the rear seats all bedecked in their No. 1 uniforms and displaying their medals. It was a gloriously sunny day. The sleek limousine had its roof open and the colonel had ordered a liberal supply of liquor and a food hamper for their comfort during the four hundred mile journey. They moved steadily westwards through Bielefeld, Dortmund and Cologne and then followed the River Rhine southwards through Bonn to Koblenz. The colonel was in a gay mood, talking incessantly, reminiscing about various paramours in the towns they passed through and saluting the waving and cheering crowds they encountered on the way. A holiday mood pervaded the whole of Germany and celebrating Germans savoured their rapid victory in the west and the conquest and subjugation of France.

Proceeding westwards from Koblenz along the River Mosel the party had a long leisurely lunch at a small inn at Zoll, the patron pleased to provide a meal and unlimited wine for the colonel and his gallant paratroopers. The drunken party then made their way carefully westwards along the Mosel passing through Bernkastel to reach Trier in the early evening. Trier was a marshalling point for von Kleist's armoured divisions before their push westwards into Luxembourg and their break through in the Ardennes. The roadsides near Trier showed evidence of the mighty concentration of armour which had accumulated prior to the thrust westwards. A few tanks and lorries lay by the roadside, not casualties of war but of mechanical failure, and engineering battalions were busy retrieving vehicles. Trier was packed with German military units and manpower. The colonel's staff car now became one of many vehicles moving in and out of the town and parked outside the larger hotels, much to the displeasure of Colonel von Bulow who directed the driver to push forwards towards Luxembourg.

The road from Trier to Luxembourg was busy and cluttered with military vehicles of all description. Progress was slow and the congestion became worse as they approached the city. Darkness was approaching and the colonel, now in an irritable mood, ordered his driver to circumnavigate Luxembourg. By nightfall they reached an inn in the small village of Steinfort where they put up for the night. Colonel von Bulow, sullenly drunk and remorseful, claiming a headache, went straight to his room to be followed shortly by the rest of the party.

The colonel woke the next morning in high spirits, eager to restart and get to Paris as soon as possible. They drove from Steinfort through Arlon and Bosillion and crossed the Meuse into France at Sedan. The roadsides were again littered with broken down vehicles and tanks and progress was slow. The bridges over the Meuse at Sedan were intact and the colonel was unable to resist the temptation of glorifying the occasion by reference to the fact that these were the very bridges that carried the conquering Panzer Divisions into French territory, which called for a toast and the first schnapps of the day was downed on a bridge south of Sedan. The staff car then proceeded south westwards through the Ardennes, emerging from a thickly forested area at Attigny, and followed the Canal Des Ardennes westwards to Neufchateau. The colonel enthused over the achievements of von Kleist, Guderian and Rommel in negotiating the impenetrable forest and pushing three Panzer divisions and a mechanised convoy, extending a hundred miles back into Luxembourg, deep into France. The first evidence of French resistance to this Panzer juggernaut was seen between Attigny and Neufchateau, where dozens of French tanks and mechanised lorries littered the roadsides and the open fields on each side of the road. The colonel again felt a sense of occasion and raised his glass in a toast to the three generals and their gallant Panzer troops. By the time they reached Soissons the car-load were again in a festive mood.

They dined sumptuously at Hotel Château Geran in Soissons and, after lunch, the party fell asleep, leaving the driver, the only sober member, to continue southwards to Paris. The journey was interrupted at various German check points along the road until they reached St Denis on the northern outskirts of Paris where the stoppage became permanent and a military police lieutenant insisted on searching the car.

The long stop woke the colonel who quickly summed up the situation and, standing erect, started berating the luckless lieutenant. The sight of the diminutive eye-patched, one armed, medal-bedecked colonel quickly unnerved the lieutenant who rapidly gave orders to raise the barriers and let the colonel's car through, explaining to Colonel von Bulow that the Führer was expected and that he was under strict orders to let no one into Paris unless authorised by *Reichsleiter* Martin Bormann.

Colonel von Bulow replied haughtily, "I fully understand Herr Lieutenant. You are only doing your duty and I shall commend you to our Leader when I meet him. Carry on Lieutenant," returning the officer's Nazi salute. The rumpus woke Manfred and Major Werner and, as the staff car drove onwards, the three had a good laugh at the expense of the unfortunate military police officer.

They drove into Paris in style, approaching the city from the north west, up Avenue Grand Armée, around Arc de Triomphe and down Champs Elysées to Hotel George V. For a defeated city Paris seemed little affected by the holocaust which led to the downfall of France. The French were out in the streets, some cheering the passing cars and others turning their backs on the unwanted Germans. The noisy street cafés were crowded with customers, mainly French men and elegantly dressed women, but with a smattering of uniformed officers and other ranks of the Third Reich. The city had an air of a place that war had by-passed, which virtually happened, as Paris was declared an open city by the retreating French.

The driver pulled up outside the main entrance to the George V Hotel. The foyer was crowded with German officers of all ranks, talking, jostling, intermingling and drinking with a few gaudily dressed French ladies interspersed amongst the milling throng. Not for the first time Manfred witnessed the colonel's technique of

persuasion. He approached a black-coated manager, clicked his heels
in traditional Prussian manner and, fixing his beady blue eye on the
Frenchman, said:

"I am Colonel Count Erich von Bulow, Commander of the Eighth
Parachute Regiment. My adjutant has booked two rooms here, one
for me and one to be shared by my second in command and my aide
Captain Manfred Schmidt. Captain Schmidt and I are personal guests
of the Führer. We are all tired after a long journey from Minden.
We wish to go to our rooms now."

The manager replied in broken, halting German, "But, Sir, I have
no room left in the hotel and I did not receive a cable. I am afraid..."

The colonel did not allow him to get any further. "You're afraid!
I should think you are. You'll be more afraid when the Leader hears
that you have turned me away. You'll end up in a great deal of
trouble and I will personally make sure that you are booted out of your
job. Come, gentlemen, we don't want to stay in this flea pit," and,
turning on his heel, giving Manfred a wink, the colonel started
walking away from the reception desk.

"Wait Sir, I think I can find you two rooms on the first floor.
They have been reserved by the SS but no one has arrived as yet.
You may have them."

The colonel turned to face the fawning manager with a broad
smile.

"Thank you, my good man. Your kindness towards us will not go
unrewarded."

They were shown to their rooms by a panting, elderly, red-faced
porter. The colonel had a suite and Manfred and Major Werner
shared a large room next door communicating by a side door with the
colonel's lounge. Both rooms had balconies overlooking George V
Avenue. Colonel von Bulow tipped the gasping old porter with a
bottle of schnapps.

"The poor old devil," he mused. "He must have been a *poilu* in
the first war. Gassed at Verdun or the Somme no doubt."

The Grand Parade

Major Werner and Sergeant Schneider rehearsed all day and every
day for the march past of a forty-man section of the Eighth Regiment
on the Grand Parade, scheduled for 4th July 1940. The marchers

were encamped in temporary tented barracks in the Bois de Boulogne. Manfred and his colonel had ample time to explore and savour the sites and continental lifestyle of the sophisticated Parisians. They drank coffee and cognac on streetside cafés on the Champs Elysées, they dined in style at Romans and Maxims, they went to late night shows at the Moulin Rouge and the Folies Bergère, they visited a French brothel in Quay d'Orsay, they climbed the steps to Sacre Coeur, they visited Notre Dame and the Louvre and spent an afternoon at the Eiffel Tower.

On the eve of the Grand Parade they were summoned to Elysée Palace on Rue de St Honoré for a briefing by Field Marshal Goering. The Field Marshal, in a happy and jubilant mood, informed them of the order of the parade and of the seating arrangements for the officers on the saluting base. Each Regiment involved in the campaign in the west provided a section of marchers, led by an officer, and each Regiment had two seats on the saluting stage. Adolf Hitler would take the salute at Rond Pont des Champs Elysées and the officers would be arranged, according to rank and seniority, on the platforms behind and to each side of the Führer. The parade was timed to arrive at the saluting base at 10.30 a.m. precisely and would last for an hour. The two hundred officers on the saluting base and the section commanders would be entertained to a grand lunch at Café de Roma at 12.30 p.m. The Führer, at his own request, would then present Iron Crosses to his officers at the Tour de Eiffel at 3 p.m. At the conclusion of the briefing the officers were invited to a champagne reception and musical entertainment by the massed bands of the Second, Third and Sixth Field Engineer Regiments who would be leading the parade on the following day.

It was a gloriously sunny and warm day on 4th July, 1940. Colonel von Bulow and Manfred took their appointed seats at 9 a.m. and watched with interest as a cavalcade of high ranking officers arrived in their staff cars. The saluting dais filled up rapidly and by 9.30 a.m. all seats were taken. Manfred glanced left and right and mused on the important personages gathered on the platform at Rond Pont Marcel Dessault. Seated on the saluting platform itself he saw Field Marshal Goering, Himmler, Ribbentrop, Speer, Goebbels and Generals Jodl, Halder, Brauchitsch, Richenau and von Runstedt of the *Wehrmacht*, von Kleist, Guderian and Rommel of the Panzers, General Student of the Paratroopers, Generals von Richthofen and

Hugo Spurrle of the *Luftwaffe* and Admirals Doenitz and Raeder of the *Kriegsmarine*.

At precisely 9.45 a.m. the Führer's entourage arrived in a fleet of cars with black uniformed SS motorcycle outriders. Hitler, Rudolf Hess and Martin Bormann sat in the open saloon car. The Führer advanced towards the saluting base and, when some twenty paces away, stopped short. The French spectators on the far side of the Champs Elysées watched with awe as the whole platform of distinguished military officers rose in salute chanting, '*Zieg Heil, Zieg Heil, Zieg Heil*'. Hitler moved on to the platform shaking hands in turn with Nazi officials and the *Wehrmacht* officers nearest to him. His face was rigid and impassive, his ego inflated by the momentous occasion and by the first display of German military power in the heart of vanquished France. What the Kaiser had failed to do in four years of bitter fighting in 1914 he, Adolf Hitler, had achieved in a six week blitzkrieg war. He had always hated the punitive French terms of the 1918 Versailles Armistice and this had now been redressed. Now the victorious troops of the Third Reich were going to march through the centre of Paris, through the very heart of France, with an awesome show of strength which would, forever, quench the French thirst for fighting Germany, their traditional enemy.

Adolf Hitler, proudly standing on the saluting base, awaited the approach of his gallant soldiers, sailors and airmen. At five minutes to ten the sound of massed bands of the *Wehrmacht* and *Luftwaffe* heralded arrival of the parade. All eyes looked left up the Champs Elysées as the military units marched in step down the avenue with the Arc de Triomphe silhouetted in the background. The first marching troops were a company of Leibstandarte, Hitler's own regiment, followed by a cadre of Waffen SS Troops in black uniforms.

As each unit passed the saluting base, seated members of the regiment rose and saluted their brethren. Himmler returned the salute to his SS Stormtroopers, Admirals Raeder, Doenitz and Canaris, acknowledged the *Kriegsmarine*, Goering, von Richthofen and Spurrle and others returned the salute to the *Luftwaffe*. And still the cavalcade pounded endlessly past the erect, stern-faced Führer. The armoured divisions were led by three tanks followed by a company of *Panzerjager* on foot. Most of the stand rose to acknowledge the debt the army owed to the armoured divisions and their commanders Hoth, von Kleist, Guderian and Rommel. General Student took the salute for the *Fallschirmjagger* and Colonel von Bulow and Manfred proudly acknowledged the Eighth Regiment as it marched past the saluting base.

As the various units passed, Colonel von Bulow made derogatory remarks; the *Liebstandarte* were, "ass wipers" and the SS, "ignorant butchers" and some of the *Wehrmacht* and horse drawn artillery units bringing up the rear were "fairies" and "buck passers", mainly in reference to his dislike of their commanding officers.

When the last unit had disappeared into the Tuileries Gardens the band on the podium played *Deutschland Uber Alles*, Hitler turned to salute the galaxy of officers on the platform and was whisked away in his black limousine to lunch at Elysée Palace, whilst the military commanders and officers on parade were entertained to a champagne reception and buffet lunch at Café de Roma in the Champs Elysées.

By three o'clock the officers due to receive their Iron Crosses were on parade at the foot of the Eiffel Tower. Manfred was nervous and edgy, worried because his wound had started to bleed at this most inconvenient moment and that the blood-stained bandage might offend the Führer. Colonel von Bulow was, as usual, full of bonhomie, walking up and down the assembled rank of officers, joking and shaking hands and generally entertaining the would-be recipients of battle honours. There were eighty-four officers to be decorated. The Führer and his entourage, Goering, Hess, Himmler and Generals von Brauchitsch and Jodl arrived punctually at five minutes to three. Hitler progressed down the line of officers pinning crosses on each one's left chest and saying a few words as he performed the ceremony. He was in an amicable mood, smiling occasionally and shaking each officer firmly by the hand. When he came to Colonel von Bulow he smiled, pinned a clasp on his chest and said:

"You old rascal, thank God you're still around to fight for me and for the Reich."

The colonel beamed. "My honour, Sir, to fight for my Leader and my country."

Further down the line he confronted Manfred, shaking in his shoes and towering head and shoulders above the Führer who looked at the encrusted blood-patch on Manfred's bandaged forehead, pinned an Iron Cross firmly on his tunic and said, *"Danke, Hauptmann Schmidt,* you have been wounded in a good cause. Your dear father would be proud of you today. I am proud of all the young men who have fought so valiantly to secure this glorious victory for the Fatherland. I hope you will recover soon. I want young officers like you back in action. There is still much work to be done by my gallant armies."

As Hitler shook his hand Manfred stammered, *"Danke, mein Führer."*

The medal ceremony over the decorated officers and their comrades returned to Café de Roma for a champagne party which lasted well into the early hours of the morning of the 5th July.

On the following morning at eight o'clock, suffering from a hangover and a blinding headache, Manfred was aroused by a dispatch rider from Elysée Palace and ordered to attend *Reichsleiter* Martin Bormann's office at eleven o'clock. When Colonel von Bulow, breakfasting in his room, heard about the message he commented, "I wonder what that cunning bastard Bormann wants with you, Manfred? Watch out for him, he's devious and underhanded. I expect the Leader wants to speak to you again. After all he knew your dear old father well."

As ordered, Manfred punctually reported to Martin Bormann's office where the *Reichsleiter* sat behind a large mahogany desk flanked by two swastika banners with a large portrait of Adolf Hitler on the wall behind his back. He kept writing for a full minute, then stood upright and returned Manfred's Nazi salute. Bormann was a short, tubby, balding man in his late thirties with square shoulders and a pugnacious, ugly, pock-marked face. He studied Manfred from top to toe for a few seconds.

"Captain Schmidt are you to be trusted?"

Manfred replied, "Yes, Herr *Reichsleiter*."

Bormann sat down and picked up the sheet of paper on which he had been writing.

"Gut, gut, das ist gut. The Führer has asked me to speak to you. The Führer thinks you can be of service to himself and to Germany." He paused. "We know that in Germany at present and in the *Wehrmacht* in particular there are those whose ambition is to depose the Führer and take command of the army. I have in my hand a list of suspects and the Führer wishes you to stay in Paris as liaison officer to our *Gauleiter*, who will be officially named tomorrow. Your position in the *Gauleiter*'s department will allow you to meet and mingle with various high ranking officers who will, from time to time, visit the city. You will be able to arrange their entertainment and you must

make yourself available to satisfy all their needs and wishes. In close contact with these senior *Wehrmacht* officers you will listen to their conversation and if you hear anything that might seem derogatory to the Führer you will report to me, verbally and personally, and to no one else. Is that clear?"

"*Jawohl* Herr *Reichsleiter,*" Manfred stammered as Bormann handed him a list of twenty names written in copper plate handwriting on a sheet of Hitler's personal stationery and Bormann continued.

"Read it now and memorise all the names."

With shaking hands Manfred read the names on Bormann's list of potential traitors which was headed by Admiral Wilhelm Canaris, head of Abwehr Intelligence, General Ludwig von Beck, former Chief of Staff of the *Wehrmacht*. Count Helmut von Moltke and Count Albrecht Bernstorff came next, followed by Field Marshal von Blomberg, General Karl von Stulpnagel, and Colonel Klaus von Stauffenberg. Manfred was dumfounded by the next five names on the list, General Franz Halder, General Walter von Brauchitsch, Generals Erich Hoepner and General von Kluge and, most alarmingly of all, Colonel Count Erich von Bulow, followed by a dozen or so lesser-ranked names. Manfred read and re-read the list twice committing the names to memory.

"Have you finished, Herr *Kapitan* Schmidt?" the *Reichsleiter* enquired as Manfred looked up quickly, handing the sheet of paper back to Bormann.

"*Ja* Herr *Reichsleiter.*"

Martin Bormann took the incriminating sheet and set it alight, brushing the ashes into a waste paper bin. He looked at Manfred.

"I repeat, the names you have memorised are only suspect. If you find anything out you are to report to me. An order will be issued tomorrow that you are to be temporarily attached as liaison officer to *Wehrmacht* headquarters at Place de l'Opéra where General Stulpnagel will be your commanding officer. That is all. Heil Hitler."

Manfred saluted and took his leave.

Colonel von Bulow was inquisitive about Manfred's visit to the *Reichsleiter's* office.

"What did the cunning fox have to say to you?"

Manfred explained that, by order of the Führer, he was to be attached temporarily to the *Wehrmacht* in Paris. The colonel, far from being dismayed, was enthusiastic about the proposal adding, "It will do you good, Manfred, to spend a month or two convalescing in Paris, enjoying the food and wine and sampling the women. I want you back with me in a few weeks and definitely before we go into action again. The next drop will be in England. There's a briefing conference in Dortmund in three days time. Major Werner and I will return to Lübbecke tomorrow. Don't drink all the champagne in Paris and keep some for me. I intend coming back again for a few parties and for a night at Madame Claudette's salon."

When Colonel von Bulow and Major Werner left to return to Lübbecke in time for the Dortmund conference Manfred commandeered the colonel's suite at George V for his own use. He had little idea as to what his new post entailed. He surmised that General Stulpnagel, the newly appointed military governor of Paris, would be busy establishing his own headquarters at the Grand Hotel l'Opéra and that intrusion from a liaison captain would not be welcome at this stage. He also realised that in his attachment to General Stulpnagel's office he was expected to spy on his superior officer and report only to *Reichsleiter* Bormann.

By mid-July, in the aftermath of the western campaign, there were still some twelve thousand German troops encamped in small units all over the city, but mainly in the St Cloud area. The German army was responsible for manning road blocks and policing the main railway stations in and around Paris. By July 20th most of the front line troops were withdrawn, the paratroopers to airfields on the west coast of France, the *Kriegsmarine* and *Wehrmacht* assault units to the channel ports and the Panzer divisions to Germany for replenishing and refitting. The job of policing the captured city was left to second line troops of the *Wehrmacht*, liberally supported by small SS Units to control and oversee their actions.

The German conquerors were amazed at the rapidity with which the Parisian population adapted to their new landlords. The unwelcome visitors, the dreaded *Boche*, were reluctantly assimilated into the social structure of cosmopolitan Paris and, within a few days of the occupation, buses and trams started running and cafés and restaurants along the main boulevards bustled with activity, as the Parisians resumed their favourite pastime of eating and drinking at the kerbside and watching the world go by.

There was no shortage of food. The citizens of Paris, expecting a lengthy siege, had accumulated stocks of food and drink which now came flooding back to the market place. Black marketeers thrived and were soon trading their wares with the occupying forces in return for chocolate, cigarettes and coffee. The brothels never closed, catering for the needs of the French and conquerors alike.

By the middle of July the centre of Paris had almost returned to normality but, due to lack of fuel, cars and taxis were rarely seen on the streets and horse drawn carriages and drays made their appearance for conveying the public to and from work. The attitude of the Parisians towards the *Wehrmacht* also changed rapidly. Surly at first, their Gallic temperament surfaced and the subjugated citizens were soon mixing readily and chatting amicably with their German masters.

The only troops feared and dreaded by the French were the *Liebstandarte*, the Waffen SS, and the Gestapo, arrogant unbending soldiers in their black uniforms with silver epaulettes, commanding immediate obedience and servility. The French attitude was simple: 'The *Boche* has arrived and is here to stay. We have to get on with living and put up with our unwelcome visitors.' Very few Frenchmen in Paris in July 1940 felt shame and degradation at the loss of their main city and the fall of France. *Egalité* and *Fraternité* were still within their grasp but *Liberté* was denied them and this would continue through the dark and gloomy years of occupation which lay ahead.

War Diary

By mid-July 1940 Hitler and the German High Command were in a quandary. A rapid conquest of France and the overwhelming supremacy of German armed forces left them without a plan for an invasion of Britain. Hitler and his advisors assumed that with the fall of France, Great Britain would ask for an armistice very quickly, but this was not happening. The German Navy, mauled and severely depleted in the Norwegian campaign, was unable to gain control of the English Channel to allow Hitler's armies to undertake a seaborne invasion. Plans, code-named Operation Sealion, were hastily prepared which involved airborne landings on a massive scale supported by a seaborne invasion once an air corridor above the English channel had been secured by Goering's Luftwaffe.

The key to success was air supremacy and Field Marshal Goering presented his battle plan to Hitler at an OKW conference in Berlin on July 6th 1940. Goering's Luftwaffe Units were concentrated in three great armadas, one in Norway and two in northern France, Luftflotten II stationed in Holland and Belgium under Field Marshal Kesselring, Luftflotten III under Field Marshal Spurrle in northern France and the Norwegian Luftflotten IV under the command of General Stumpff. Goering had at his disposal nine hundred and fifty fighters, mainly Messerschmitt ME-110, two thousand bombers and three hundred and sixteen Stuka divebombers.

The Royal Air Force, in contrast, had around eight hundred Spitfires and Hurricanes and a small bomber force. Goering's plan was basically very simple. He intended to lure the RAF into aerial combat over the Channel and, by a process of attrition, wear them down so that his air fleets could convey ground troops and paratroopers to a final assault on the island fortress. Throughout July and the first week of August aerial skirmishing went on over the Channel and four destroyers and twenty merchant ships were sunk. The Luftwaffe lost over three hundred planes at the cost of one hundred and forty-eight to the RAF.

On August 13th Operation Eagle was launched by Goering. The first bomber attacks were on airfields and railway installations and were successful in the south of England although the Germans lost seventy-five planes to the RAF's thirty-four. General Stumpff's Luftflotten V, based in Scandinavia, received a severe mauling off Tyneside on August 15th and were effectively eliminated as a fighting force. On August 17th heavy losses amongst the Stukas forced Goering to withdraw these bombers from his attack force. After a five day respite, due to bad weather, the battle recommenced on August 24th and the Luftwaffe now concentrated its bombing on sector command stations and the fighter airfields in southern England. Each day between 25th August and 6th September repeated raids by five hundred bombers at a time became the norm.

During this period the RAF lost four hundred and sixty-six planes and two hundred and twenty pilots were killed or wounded. Unbeknown to the Germans the RAF was on its knees and persistence of these daylight attacks on the airfields would have eventually brought victory to the Luftwaffe. And then, on September 7th, Goering switched his attack to massive raids on London and the gallant RAF *fighter pilots were reprieved. Night raids continued unabated for a week and the RAF retaliated with minor scale raids on Berlin on the 24th, 28th and 29th August, which did little damage to the city but demoralised the population and dented their confidence in Hermann Goering's ability to protect them from aerial bombardment.*

Meanwhile, Goering, considerably impressed by the questionable success of his night bombing of London, exposed all his air power in daylight assaults on the battered city. On Sunday 15th September eight hundred planes, two hundred bombers and six hundred fighters, converged on the city at midday followed by a similar wave two hours later. The RAF claimed to have shot down a hundred and thirty-five planes in the battles over the sea off the coast of East Anglia. The rout of this German air armada led Goering to cancel all further daylight attacks though the night bombing of London and other British cities continued well into the spring of 1941. Goering's Operation Eagle had failed in its intention to bring Britain to its knees and begging for mercy. On the contrary it had strengthened resolve of the British to stand firm and defend their island fortress.

When Goering's plan failed, Hitler postponed an invasion of Britain which would have to wait until another time. He had his eyes to the east and the conquest of Russia became his first priority and, on the 17th September 1940, Operation Sealion was called off indefinitely. An attack on Russia, Operation Barbarossa, became the planning priority of OKW and the German High Command. On 27th September 1940 Germany signed a Tripartite Pact bringing Japan into the Axis Alliance and in October Rumania was coerced to join the Alliance, which allowed Germany ready access to Rumanian oil. Russia also had designs in the Balkans and Stalin's objections to German diplomacy prompted Hitler's Directive No. 21: "Operation Barbarossa. German armed forces must be prepared to crush Soviet Russia before the invasion of England. Preparations to be completed by 15th May, 1941". The die was cast. Hitler was about to embark on an attack doomed to failure which would, in the end, lead to destruction and demolition of the Third Reich.

Manfred reported to General Stulpnagel's headquarters at the Grand Hotel l'Opéra at 10 a.m. on the 7th July, 1940. The hotel's main entrance in Rue Scribe opened into a capacious vestibule leading into a rectangular open-air courtyard and flanked on each side by elegant entertainment salons and dining rooms. The General's office and apartments were on the first floor overlooking Place de l'Opéra whilst the two floors above were used as dormitories for his officers and staff. Manfred arrived early for his appointment and had to wait in a queue in the vestibule for nearly an hour. The General was obviously very busy and a steady stream of high-ranking officers were called to his presence before Manfred was asked to enter. General Franz Stulpnagel, holding a dossier in his hand, rose to greet the paratroop captain. The elegantly dressed, tall, aristocratic, good looking Prussian with slicked-back, black hair greying at the temples, and a well trimmed grey moustache, eyed Manfred and spoke with a soft, cultured accent.

"Captain Schmidt, welcome to my headquarters. You come with impeccable references from Berlin and from my friend Count Erich von Bulow. I have here in my hand a pass signed by our Leader authorising you to enter any military or civilian unit in France. You must be one of our Leader's blue-eyed boys. Would you like some French coffee?"

Manfred nodded and accepted, *"Jawohl,* Herr *General."*

Stulpnagel continued, "The purpose of my command is to maintain peace and order in occupied France. To achieve this I have been allocated fifty thousand troops, mainly second liners, with a sprinkling of first class units."

An orderly arrived with a tray and both officers waited whilst he poured two cups of black steaming coffee. The general continued, "Your function here in Paris will be to act as my liaison and entertainment officer. From time to time important visitors will arrive in Paris and you will look after them. For the time being you should keep your suite at the George V Hotel which has been commandeered as an officers' mess. You will take the visitors sightseeing and wherever they wish to go and look after their entertainment whilst they are my guests in Paris. Spare no expense. I shall not be here all the time. My deputy, when I'm away, will be Colonel Hans Göerdler. You will report to his office every day. I have instructed the motor section to release a *Kübelwagen* for your exclusive use and you can select a driver from the ranks of the mechanised battalion at my headquarters. For the next few weeks you will visit the commanders of all units in Paris and see if they need entertainment for their senior officers. This will include the *Liebstandarte* SS, the

Waffen SS and the Gestapo who are setting up their headquarters at the Triomphe end of Avenue Foch. I want you to especially befriend the SS and Gestapo and see if you can learn anything from them. If you do, report back to me and to no one else. Are you ready for some food? Let's go downstairs to the Café de la Paix for lunch."

After a quick meal of cold meat, cheese and bread Manfred travelled back to the George V Hotel in his newly acquired *Kübelwagen* with Hans Reminger at the wheel. He was deep in thought.

'What an intriguing scenario. Within a few days I have been ordered by Martin Bormann to keep an eye on some senior *Wehrmacht* officers and in particular General Stulpnagel and, by my new boss, to spy on the SS and the Gestapo. Evidently there is no love lost between the regular army and the SS officer corps. Furthermore General Stulpnagel refers to Hitler as the Leader and not as the Führer and is friendly with Colonel von Bulow and Admiral Canaris, two of the names high on the list of suspect plotters against the Third Reich.'

Manfred felt a tingle run down his spine as he contemplated that he might eventually become a very important pawn in the chess battle between the *Wehrmacht* on the one side and the Gestapo and the SS on the other.

July was a quiet month for Manfred. Each day he called at Göerdler's office around noon, made a few visits to local units and was only once called upon to exercise his position as liaison officer when he had to spend two miserable days looking after a frosty old artillery colonel whose interests, outside the army, were old churches and art galleries. Manfred had to suffer two visits to the Louvre and during one of these the colonel spent an hour looking at the empty frame which once held the Mona Lisa and all the while he kept prattling on about art and artists. Manfred was considerably relieved when his dull, uninteresting charge took his leave to return to his unit in Calais. General Stulpnagel was away from his office for long periods, usually at the Channel ports where French stevedores and dock workers were sabotaging German invasion equipment accumulating in Boulogne, Calais and Le Havre for the final push across the Channel.

His evenings were completely free and he took to dining alone in local restaurants, ending up more often than not in some sordid attic with a prostitute, a casual pick-up from the dimly lit streets, or the bars and cafés. Many of these chance encounters ended in fiasco. Manfred was frequently unable to initiate or maintain an erection and, in his eagerness to penetrate, he suffered from premature ejaculation. He soon realised that his ability to perform satisfactorily was directly related to his sobriety. And yet, night after night, drawn like a moth to a flame, he drank to excess and compromised his ability to have satisfactory intercourse. He always paid handsomely for the prostitute's time and favours.

On the 20th July, using his pass signed by the Führer, Manfred interviewed the colonel of the Waffen SS billeted in a barracks on Avenue Victor Hugo. The colonel made it clear to Manfred that his visit was only granted because of the Führer's pass and that there was nothing that Manfred had to offer which would, in any shape or form, be of use to the officers of the Waffen SS. Similarly a few days later at Gestapo headquarters in Avenue Foch, near the Arc de Triomphe, he was received with haughty indifference and curtly dismissed by the Gestapo commandant. His third visit on the 27th July to an SS *Liebstandarte* battalion, billeted also in the Avenue Foch, was a different kettle of fish. Colonel Otto Kaltenburger, the commandant, received him with open arms.

"Captain Schmidt, I am pleased to welcome you to my barracks. I noticed you receiving your Iron Cross from the Führer at the Eiffel Tower and I could see that the Führer was interested in you. I am glad that your wound is healing and that you no longer have to wear your head bandages. You made a good impression on me at the ceremony and you were the only man on parade who showed the scars of battle."

The squat, sallow-faced, balding colonel fixed his dark-brown, beady, eyes on Manfred. "Now what can I do for you?"

"Well, Sir," Manfred replied, "I am here to offer you help in entertaining senior officers of the SS who might be visiting your unit. I am empowered by the military commander to look after all their needs, cultural and social and to this end I have a suite of rooms at the George V Hotel."

Colonel Kaltenburger smiled lopsidedly and asked, "How many VIPs have you looked after so far?"

Manfred replied, "Only one, Sir, and he was a crusty old artillery colonel who only wanted to look at churches and art galleries."

A sinister sly smile again returned to the colonel's face.

"I don't think you'll have many customers in the next few weeks. Most of the top brass are either with their units in the Channel ports or in Potsdam, or Berlin, at planning conferences for Operation Sealion. They'll be busy until we put England out of its misery and then you will have your hands full." The colonel closed his eyes and then looked upwards towards the ornate ceiling, thinking hard for a few moments.

"The SS are hard men in battle. We do however know how to enjoy ourselves off duty. I have a birthday party on the 3rd August and will be celebrating with my officers at the Hotel Wagram. I invite you to come along and see how we relax and enjoy ourselves. Wear your best mess kit. The SS will entertain the entertainer!" He gave a short, high-pitched, snorting laugh. "I am looking forward to my birthday."

On the following day Manfred reported as usual to Colonel Göerdler.

"Colonel Kaltenburger was friendly towards you? He's a shifty old fox, not very brainy, but ruthless. Be careful Manfred but by all means go to his birthday party and enjoy yourself. See if you can learn anything from the *Liebstandarte*."

*

Hotel Wagram was a crumbling, rather dilapidated building, with bedrooms and narrow balconies overlooking Avenue Wagram and a small, confined, dimly lit main entrance in Rue Brey. The SS had commandeered the whole hotel, including its thirty bedrooms, for Colonel Kaltenburger's birthday party. Hans Reminger dropped Manfred at the entrance in the narrow side street and then drove away to park the *Kübelwagen* on the main avenue. Manfred entered the foyer and met a handsome, young, blond SS lieutenant at the foot of the stairs. The young man was evidently very nervous.

"Is this your first party with Colonel Kaltenburger, Sir?" Manfred replied in the affirmative and the blond adonis continued, "I only arrived in Paris this week. The other officers tell me that the colonel's parties are *fantastiche*. I'll take you upstairs to the dining room."

They ascended the staircase together, the younger officer tugging at his collar and patting his slicked-back blond hair. At the top of the stairway a group of six ladies of the night sat silently upright in high backed chairs staring fixedly at the ceiling. Two were smoking cigarettes. The young Lieutenant, still adjusting his epaulettes, stood aside and allowed Manfred to enter the dining room through a large oak-panelled door.

In the smoke-filled room there were fourteen SS officers bedecked in their black mess uniform with silver epaulettes, chatting noisily and sipping champagne. In the centre of the room there was a long table, laden with food and drink and, at the head, Colonel Kaltenburger holding a tumbler of champagne in one hand and a cigarette holder in the other, legs apart, was engrossed in conversation with two young Lieutenants.

"Welcome to the party, Captain Schmidt," he said, as he walked forwards to greet his guest, shaking him by the hand and then, holding on, he led Manfred around the room to be introduced to the other officers.

The introductions were polite and formal. The colonel kept hold of Manfred's hand and led him to the table thrusting a glass of champagne into his left hand. They clinked glasses and Manfred proposed a toast to the colonel's health, wishing him a happy birthday. Colonel Kaltenburger smiled in acknowledgement and let go of Manfred's hand returning to the end of the room to continue conversation with the two young officers who looked at their colonel with adulation.

Manfred circulated and continued drinking and chatting amiably with the SS officers but thinking what a dull, boorish, uncouth bunch of men were gathered in the dining room. They all drank rapidly and steadily and, on Colonel Kaltenburger's invitation, descended on the food like a swarm of vultures. There was no finesse in their table manners. A major had hold of a whole leg of gammon and was steadily gnawing his way through the meat down to the bone, fat and saliva dripping on to his uniform, laughing all the time and alternating mouthfuls of meat with gulps of champagne. The tempo of the banquet and the drinking increased and within half an hour most of the food had been devoured and the table was littered with empty champagne bottles, half-eaten chicken carcasses, pie crusts and squashed sausages.

At a signal from Colonel Kaltenburger the party quietened and a coarse-faced, stocky captain, an ex-sergeant, took over as master of ceremonies. Hermann, the MC, proposed a formal toast to the SS colonel but once this was over proceeded to entertain the party with uncouth, blasphemous stories, received with gusto and hilarity by his colleagues. Manfred was shocked into disbelief. The man was an obvious pervert but was readily accepted by his colleagues who urged him on to further obscenities and ridicule. They applauded, cheered, broke into ribald songs, threw their empty champagne glasses on to the floor and generally began to work themselves into a frenzy of excitement. Manfred noticed that Colonel Kaltenburger was now sitting on a chair with one young officer on each side-arm and the colonel's arms and hands resting nonchalantly on their thighs.

The drunken, blabbering, perspiring Hermann suddenly gave a shout, "Now is the time, bring in the first Fraulein."

His ugly pock-marked face was suffused with erotic anticipation and he wore a frenzied, leering grin as he undid his tunic and loosened his trousers. Two of the officers pulled the tablecloth and the bottles and crockery on to the floor and cleared the table to make room for the first prostitute to lie on her back whilst the bellowing rampant Hermann, pulling his pants down to his knees, without ceremony, mounted the voluptuous woman and began pounding frantically between her thighs. The SS officers formed a semi-circle around the copulating couple, urging their hero to greater feats of endeavour, whilst Manfred stood aside, excited and slightly disgusted by the pornographic exhibition. Colonel Kaltenburger pushed his way to the table, a leather thong in his hand, and began whipping Hermann's exposed buttocks in time to his copulatory thrusts. Hermann reached his climax in about a minute with an explosive roar and withdrew his penis, wiping it clean on the edge of the tablecloth and returning it into his trousers. Two of the officers took it in turn to have intercourse with the impassive and servile whore. Manfred noticed that Colonel Kaltenburger, though an avid watcher of the proceedings, showed no inclination to join in the physical ritual.

After the third officer had completed fornicating Manfred was invited by Hermann to take his pleasure but he declined politely. The used prostitute was then allowed to dress and leave the dining room and Hermann brought in another two of the ladies in waiting. They were instructed to partake in lesbian activities at one end of the table, cheered on by the officers. Colonel Kaltenburger, by now, was lying at the other end of the dining table, his two young attending officers draped on each side kissing him and fondling his breasts and genital area. The colonel was soon in a state of ecstasy. He beckoned Manfred to join them but, though he felt a slight compulsion to do so, he restrained himself and turned his attention back to the gyrating lesbians who had aroused his sexual desires. The lesbian act ended with faked orgasms from each of the participants and with loud applause and cheering from the onlookers.

Hermann now ordered all six prostitutes to be admitted dressed only in their black silk stockings and suspender belts. At this point Colonel Kaltenburger approached Manfred.

"I shall be in Room 48 if you want to see me and the boys. If I don't see you call around the office tomorrow lunchtime."

Together with his two blond aides he disappeared upstairs.

Before the prostitutes entered the glass-strewn dining hall Hermann had arranged seven chairs in a circle announcing that they would now play his version of 'musical chairs'. Seven officers sat one on each chair and the six naked prostitutes were made to circle around the seated officers to the accompaniment of music from Hermann's mouth organ. When the music stopped the officers grabbed the nearest female and sat her on his lap. Manfred was in luck at the first interruption, pulling a buxom dark-haired girl on to his lap. His penis was already semi-erect and the experienced whore, undulating her perineal muscles, soon produced an urgently painful tumescence. Then the mouth organ started to play again and the woman tore free from his grasp to be replaced by another when the music stopped, a thin, fair-haired prostitute whose bones dug painfully into his thighs. The organ music restarted and he looked sideways at his companions who were undergoing the same discomfiture and desires. And then one of the officers to his right lost self-control and, unbuttoning his trousers, released his erect penis, which was the cue for all six to follow suit. When the mouth organ stopped playing the next time the prostitutes descended on the seated officers and, sitting astride, guided the erections in between their legs.

Manfred had the well-proportioned dark-haired girl on his lap and she was soon working her pelvis up and down on his manhood. He felt he would burst as the other officers one by one reached their climax with an explosion and Manfred was deemed the winner as he delayed his ejaculation longer than any of the other five men. Hermann declared, with a raucous shout, that the prize for the winner was free entry into the second round. Manfred survived this round but made sure that he was the first to arrive at a fake climax and, on this occasion, he had the thin bony-hard whore on his lap. Her breath smelt of garlic and cheap wine and he was glad to be out of the contest at an early stage.

Musical chairs continued for another hour and the SS officers gradually began to wilt. Hermann himself joined in the last two rounds, playing a mouth organ whilst seated and having the advantage of being able to stop the music when one of the prostitutes he fancied was directly opposite. Later a few mattresses were laid in the corner of the room and the assembled company, still dressed in their black tunics, breeches and jackboots, lay around drinking and smoking with the naked prostitutes in their midst, cajoling and urging each other to further feats of sexual endeavour. Only a few managed to rise to the occasion and disappeared upstairs where Manfred followed to room 50 for a brief sexual interlude with his favourite black-eyed girl.

As he lay with his companion on the bed he heard excited voices and shouting from next door where Colonel Kaltenburger and the two homosexual officers were actively engaged in perverted lovemaking. When Manfred left the SS party at 3.30 a.m. there were still four officers and three whores on the mattresses in the dining hall, all sound asleep and snoring. Hermann, the coarse master of ceremonies, snored loudest of all.

On the following day Manfred, filled with trepidation, called at Colonel Kaltenburger's office. The colonel was, however, in a light-hearted mood.

"What did you think of the party? Did you have a good time?" He asked with a knowing wink.

"*Wunderbar mein* Colonel," lied Manfred.

The colonel continued, "There will be another party next month. Our SS parties are famous. Everyone wants to come to them. I'll make sure you are invited."

Manfred thought that he would, if possible, try and avoid a repeat public performance of Hermann's version of musical chairs. Colonel Kaltenburger walked to stand in front of the Führer's portrait and posturing, with his arms placed on his hips, looked Manfred straight in the eye.

"Have you read *Mein Kampf*, Captain Schmidt?"

"Yes, on many occasions," Manfred replied.

The colonel continued, "You will be aware that the Führer believes the Jews are responsible for the present state of Germany and their greed and avarice has been the main reason for our slow recovery after the Great War. The Führer has decided that French resistance leaders, Romanies and Jews are to be ruthlessly pursued and deported from France to be incarcerated in Germany. The SS and Gestapo have the honour of conducting this purge, which should be a function of the military governor, but Stulpnagel is not strong-willed enough and he won't pursue the matter to its ultimate conclusion. The SS however will do so."

"Now, Captain Schmidt, you are ideally situated in George V Hotel. I will appoint one of my junior officers to join you there and you could both infiltrate the cafés and night-clubs dressed in civilian clothing and pose as two young German officers sympathetic to the French. Get to know the local padrons, pimps and prostitutes. Be generous with gifts of cigarettes, wine and cognac and sleep with the girls. You may learn something of interest and may be able to find the safe houses and Jewish establishments in our area. Will you do this for the SS and for your Führer?"

Manfred thought for a long minute replying, "Colonel Kaltenburger, I will be pleased to be of service to my Führer. I will have to explain my mission to General Stulpnagel but without reference to yourself. My general will expect me to continue entertaining his visitors as and when they arrive in Paris. I think that the task that you have outlined for me will be both interesting and productive."

Otto Kaltenburger beamed with pleasure. "That's settled! Now I want to make a presentation to you. Come with me."

Colonel Kaltenburger kitted Manfred out in a SS captain's uniform to be worn at functions in the SS barracks and on duty, so that the parachute officer would feel "at home" in the company of his SS compatriots. Manfred studied his profile in the mirror. He was tall and handsome and his new black outfit would look even better with the blue parachute emblem and his Iron Cross on the right breast pocket of his tunic. The only thing that marred his appearance was the vivid red, partially encrusted scar on the right side of his forehead and a bald patch of skin on his scalp above the scar where new blond hairlets were already sprouting from the shaven area. In any event, the peaked black cap camouflaged most of his disfigurement. As

Manfred took his leave of the SS colonel, promising to report back each week, he revelled in his triplicity as agent for the SS, Martin Bormann and the military commandant of Paris.

Contrary to his expectations General Stulpnagel and Colonel Hans Göerdler approved of his plans to do some spying for the SS, but Manfred did not reveal his remit to seek out Jewish enclaves and strongholds in Paris. The kindly military governor came to Manfred's aid in late July when a cable arrived from Colonel von Bulow ordering Manfred to return to his parachute headquarters at Lübbecke, where the regiment were preparing for the cross-Channel airborne assault on England. General Stulpnagel countermanded this order pointing out, "At the Führer's behest Captain Schmidt is carrying out duties in Paris of extreme military importance."

He was accordingly allowed to stay on for a further four months, officially as liaison officer to the military commander, but living in the lap of luxury at George V and acting as an independent agent responsible to three masters at one and the same time.

By mid-August 1940 Manfred Schmidt was firmly established in his resident suite at Hotel George V and his daily routine was also formalised. His personal valet woke him at precisely 10 a.m. with a cup of black coffee, and, after a hot bath, breakfast was brought to his bedroom. He then dressed, donning the appropriate uniform for his daily visits either to Colonel Kaltenburger's SS headquarters or Colonel Hans Göerdler's office at Grand Hotel l'Opéra. He usually lunched in the mess and returned to his hotel by 3.30 p.m. when he dismissed his driver, undressed and had a two hour siesta. At around 4.30 or 5 p.m. he showered, dressed in French civilian clothing, consumed a few cognacs and smoked a cigar before his SS companion arrived to pick him up to go out for a night's entertainment. The young officers ordered by Colonel Kaltenburger to accompany him varied in rank and compatibility. Some were stiff and monosyllabic, just doing their duty but others were outgoing, gregarious and evidently pleased to have a night out on the town at the *Abwehr's* expense.

Manfred had no doubt that Kaltenburger's officers were present to spy on him and report back the next day to headquarters with full details of the events of the previous night. Manfred took the staid and uncompromising officers to an upmarket restaurant and a night-club. The fun-loving ones were entertained to drinks at a kerbside café, a meal at a cheap bistro and a visit to a brothel or a back-street strip club. Manfred made sure that his companions had plenty to eat and drink and, if they so desired, had a good time with the night-club dancers or the slinky prostitutes present in abundance at night on the Paris back-streets. The jubilant, inebriated, pair returned at around 4 a.m. to the George V for a nightcap before his officer companion was driven back to the SS barracks and Manfred went to bed for a dreamless, exhausted sleep.

As the weeks went by Manfred noticed a change in the attitude of the French clientele of the bistros and cafés they frequented. At first they were openly antagonistic, turning their backs on the newcomers, or downing their drinks and leaving the premises. Some, usually older men who might have served in the First World War, openly spat on the floor when the Germans entered. Manfred insisted on correctness and politeness, all the while striving to give the impression that, though they were the conquerors, he and his friends were openly sympathetic to France and abhorred the predicament of the French nation. By subtlety he managed to win the confidence of some of the waiters and patrons and their new found allegiance was cemented with liberal doses of wine and absinthe.

The prostitutes proved to be invaluable in breaking the ice. Plying their trade in and around the night-spots the professional ladies, touting for business, often approached the two men. After all, a man was a man, whatever his nationality and, provided he had money, he was fair game. By an unwritten law of whoreland the girls of the night worked singly, or in pairs, and it was in the bistro or in the bedroom afterwards that Manfred and his companions hoped to pick up information which might prove valuable to their superiors. The information they did manage to accumulate proved singularly unrewarding. Colonel Kaltenburger was getting impatient and General Stulpnagel expressed his misgivings at the lack of results from the enterprise. Manfred, completely captivated by his debauched lifestyle, urged the two to allow him to continue with his programme, promising results in the near future. The breakthrough came in early October when Manfred met a part-time prostitute at Bistro Cervoise. By this time the Führer had called off his proposed invasion of Britain and the pressure was off for Manfred to return to his parent regiment. Lise Frank, an unemployed Jewish school teacher, became Manfred's lover and mistress.

244

War Diary

On the night of the 25th, August 1940 British bombers attacked Berlin and the assaults were repeated again on the 28th and 29th August. This shattering news, released by Goebbels' propaganda department, shook the Germans to the core. Goebbels ranted and raved. 'How could the cowardly British attack a defenceless city like Berlin, causing damage to houses and killing innocent German citizens?' The propaganda minister was outraged and Hitler became maniacal in his desire for revenge. All Germany wondered why Berlin's impregnable air defences were not able to repel the British. Goering lost face and credibility which caused him to make a fatal decision to switch the Luftwaffe offensive from the British airfields to the city of London. Churchill had calculated that these raids on Berlin might sting the Germans into reprisal attacks and he was prepared to sacrifice London and, if need be, the citizens of London, in order to take the heat off the airfields and radar stations on the south coast which were gradually being rendered unusable by repeated bombing.

Churchill's plan was successful. Hitler wanted revenge and Goering was persuaded to, 'bomb the city of London off the face of the earth'. On September 7th massed German formations of von Manstein's, and Spurrle's Luftflotten, bombarded London and the attacks continued throughout the night. London was then subjected to daily air raids, culminating in the largest German daylight raid on September 15th when fifty-six enemy planes were destroyed before they could reach their target. The RAF lost twenty-six fighters in the battle and, after this resounding defeat in the air, Goering called off his daylight bombers and the city of London was subjected to months of night bombing. On September 17th, due to the lack of success of the Luftwaffe, Hitler cancelled Operation Sealion and turned his eyes eastwards towards the vast might of the USSR.

*

General Stulpnagel's staff car left Paris, bound for Calais and Boulogne, on the 16th August 1940. Manfred and Major Shöneheim, the general's aide, accomapnied by the general on a fact finding tour following reports of sabotage in the docks at the Channel ports. The open tourer, protected by two armed motorcyclist and sidecar outriders, made rapid progress westwards through Chantilly, Compiegne, and Amiens and reached Arras by lunchtime. The general commented on the tranquillity and loveliness of the French countryside and the absence of evidence of recent heavy fighting, apart from an occasional burnt-out lorry at the roadside or shell-blasted, scarred buildings in some of the villages.

As they approached Arras the road traffic became heavier and the occupants of the car became aware of a periodic throb of aircraft engines, planes making flights from, and to, a large military airfield outside town. They lunched in the town square at Hotel Cambrai. Between Arras and Bethune movement became considerably slower, the road cluttered with slowly moving lorries carrying supplies and landing craft westwards. About five kilometres north of Arras the general ordered his driver to turn off the road to General Spurrle's headquarters.

Security at the airbase was intense but the general's pennant and his credentials of office allowed him through the barriers. Field Marshal Goering was paying a flying visit to the airbase and was resting in the officers' mess after a prolonged lunch break. Goering was dressed in a light-blue airforce uniform and was in a confident, almost arrogant, mood. The flabby, overweight, round-faced and slightly inebriated field marshal gave his visitors a summary of the air battle to date.

"The preliminary skirmishes in July over the English Channel were very successful and we sank at least ten British destroyers and many more merchant ships, probably twenty. My plan now is to destroy their airfields and yesterday and today General Spurrle's air fleet has been attacking airfields in the south of England. We have already rendered five of these unusable to the enemy. Tomorrow, gentleman, will be our big day. The combined might of the *Luftwaffe* will attack British airfields; General Spurrle from here, Field Marshal Kesselring from the Netherlands and General Stumpff from Norway and Denmark. In all some one thousand three hundred bombers and a thousand fighters will combine to erase the British airforce from the face of the earth. If you are in Calais tomorrow you will see General Spurrle's airfleet flying into battle, a magnificent sight I assure you."

Goering rose unsteadily to his feet and, holding a long white cigarette holder in his left hand and a large tumbler of cognac in his right, toasted the Third Air Fleet and its commander General Spurrle. He then sat down heavily in a large armchair and became sombre, almost melancholic, and on the point of crying.

"Of course, this has not been achieved without loss. We have already lost over three hundred aircraft and, worst of all, over two hundred air crew. But the spirit of the *Luftwaffe* is excellent and they will see us through."

He then gulped down the rest of his brandy, his head gently fell forwards and within thirty seconds he was soundly asleep and snoring loudly. General Spurrle ushered his visitors out of the mess and they took their leave. The airfield was strewn with planes of every description, ME 110s, JU-88s, Heinkels and Dorniers, some revving up, one or two taking off and others coming in to land on the bumpy runway.

Once they were in the staff car and driving westwards towards St Omer and Calais, General Stulpnagel commented, "The Field Marshal is under great strain at present. He feels acutely for those young fliers who have not returned form their missions. It reminds him of his younger days as a fighter pilot in the Great War. He's a very sensitive man."

They drove in silence for the greater part of the rest of the journey to Calais.

Calais was bursting at the seams with military and *Luftwaffe* personnel. General Stulpnagel managed to find beds for Manfred, Major Shöneheim and the driver in a *Kriegsmarine* officers' billet in the docks whilst he himself put up in the senior officers' hotel. Manfred was awoken half an hour before dawn on 17th August by the roar of heavy bombers flying overhead in the dark, followed at daybreak by another squadron of bombers and the high-pitched whine of Messerschmitt ME 110s. He made his way to the harbour wall, looking westwards, and, as the sun's rays lit up the white-capped waves, he saw a flotilla of some eighty bombers, flying low to avoid radar detection, with buzzing Messerschmitt formations higher in the sky in attendance on their slower and bomb-heavy sister planes. Dover was not visible and an early morning haze shrouded the English coast.

Within fifteen minutes the distant muffled thuds of landing bombs were heard, whilst high in the sky out at sea the observers saw Messerschmitts, Spitfires and Hurricanes in deadly combat in a cloudless sky. Within half an hour of daybreak returning bombers flew low over Calais on their way back to Arras and the inland airfields. Some were limping and shuddering as they stuttered along but the majority made the return journey to refuel, reload with bombs and cross again for further bombing sorties on the English airfields. The procession of planes flying westwards continued unabated throughout the day. General Spurrle's *Luftflotten* flew four hundred bomber and five hundred and fifty fighter sorties on August 17th. General Stulpnagel and his aide joined Manfred at around 9.30 a.m. and all three stayed at their observation post in Calais Harbour throughout the day 'watching history being made', as the general succinctly observed. The purpose of their visit was forgotten in the excitement of the intense drama unfolding before their eyes.

On the following day, 18th August, 1940 the raids were repeated on a watered-down scale. Manfred observed that the flights of Stuka dive bombers had been drastically reduced. Most of the German plane casualties had been the slow flying Stukas and Heinkels and after the 17th August these planes were withdrawn from air combat missions. On the 19th August General Stulpnagel and his entourage got to Boulogne Harbour, where the bulk of German landing craft and small boats were concentrated for the impending seaborne invasion of England.

The *Kriegsmarine* colonel in charge of the amphibious operation in Boulogne was not over-enthusiastic about the chances of success. There were not enough custom-built landing craft and the small ships were either too old, or had been sabotaged by the French, before the Germans acquired them. At sea they would be sitting ducks for the British Royal Navy. The colonel estimated that from his section in Boulogne he could probably transport some one thousand five hundred men with some measure of safety across the Channel and only half this number from Calais. He was accordingly more than hopeful that Field Marshal Goering's bombing sorties would bring Britain to its knees and lead to peace overtures from Churchill and the British Government. In the event, failure of Goering's massive air assault on Britain and the resilience of the British people, led Hitler, on September 15th, to postpone indefinitely his plans for an invasion of the British Isles. Instead he turned his eyes eastwards towards Russia and ordered OKW and the General Staff to prepare detailed plans for an attack on the Soviet Union.

*

At a briefing in General Stulpnagel's headquarters, Manfred was advised that Colonel von Bulow would be paying a visit to Paris as the general's guest. Manfred met the colonel off the train at Gare du Nord on the morning of October 10th. The brilliant sunny summer had lapsed into a cold, drizzly and misty autumn. Manfred drove the colonel in his *Kübelwagen* through the wet Parisian streets to meet General Stulpnagel at his headquarters. Von Bulow and Stulpnagel were old friends and spent two hours closeted together whilst Manfred and Hans Göerdler drank innumerable cups of coffee in the ante-room. Manfred then took Colonel von Bulow to his suite at George V for a rest and change of uniform before they embarked on a sightseeing tour of Paris.

They had not gone much further than a few blocks away from the hotel when the colonel, asserting that he had seen most of Paris in the past, asked to be taken for a quiet lunch. Manfred acquiesced and took him to Maison Catherine at Abbesses, where they sat at a secluded corner table at the back of the dining room. After a few aperitifs von Bulow relaxed and a mischievous twinkle appeared in his bright blue eye.

"Manfred, General Stulpnagel is very pleased with your work here. The General and I go back a long way to the Military Academy in Berlin in 1932. He's a good honest man and the right choice for *Gauleiter* of Paris." As always von Bulow's comments were not strictly accurate but Manfred let it pass. "We have spent some time discussing your future. I have difficulties at the regiment at present. Major Werner is cracking up under the strain and Major Haldendorf's replacement from the Second Paras has not proved a success. I want you to come back to the Eighth and take over No. 2 Company. You will, of course, automatically be promoted. The general agrees with my plan but has made a good case for keeping you here for a few more weeks."

The colonel smiled wistfully and tugged at his moustache.

"I wouldn't mind a holiday here in Paris. I hope you are making the best use of the opportunities that come your way. As you know, I asked for your return in July when the airborne attack on England was imminent. The Eighth were given dropping zones around Southampton and Portsmouth, in the territory of Eleventh Fighter command, but fat old Goering lost us the chance of a quick victory with his useless bombardment tactics. The Leader should have listened to General Milch who urged him to cross the water immediately on the heels of the departing Tommies. If we had gone across during the last week in June we would now be sitting in London drinking their filthy warm beer. *Nicht wahr?*"

Manfred smiled and nodded and after another liberal helping of pastis the colonel continued.

"Our Leader got it wrong and General Stulpnagel agrees with me. Hitler called off the planned invasion about three weeks ago on the 15th September. This week the Rumanians have been coerced into joining us and we shall have oil supplies from Ploesti. But this move will put a great strain on our relationship with Uncle Joe. Mark my words. Our Leader is about to make another big mistake and I have no doubt that before long we shall be plunged into a campaign in the east. Look what happened to Napoleon Bonaparte. There are many senior *Wehrmacht* officers who feel as I do. We think that Hitler has gone off the rails and that further military action should be directed by the high command and not be in the hands of a semi-demented corporal."

The colonel stopped speaking abruptly. He searched Manfred's face for a reaction, for an indication of where his loyalties lay. Manfred clutched his glass in both hands and looked down at the table, deep in thought. He was now sure that his colonel and General Stulpnagel were opposed to the glorious leader of the Third Reich. The Führer had maybe mismanaged the proposed attack on England and General Gerhardt Milch might have made the correct decision, but he could not contemplate the thought that his idol, his Führer, would not succeed in subjugating the barbarian armies of the Soviet Union. Was not the *Wehrmacht* the best army in the world. He did not foresee that Germany, with its mighty army, could fail to conquer Russia. Inside he was seething with anger at the thought that von Bulow and Stulpnagel had doubts about Hitler's ability to conduct yet another successful campaign in the east and that they wanted Hitler ousted from his position as undisputed leader of Nazi Germany. Outwardly he remained calm and looked up at his superior officer.

"Colonel von Bulow. I respect your opinions about the Führer but I cannot join with you in active opposition of the future conduct of the war in Europe. Look what the Führer has done! Since '38 we have overcome Austria, Czechoslovakia, Poland, Norway, Denmark and France and now Rumania is our ally. We have enough *lebensraum* and I am sure that the Führer will call a halt to any further campaigns, apart, of course, from the conquest of Britain, which will have to wait until the spring of next year."

The colonel nodded. "Very well, very well, Manfred. We shall not speak of this matter again until you have seen the error of your thinking... I am in Paris to enjoy myself and not to talk politics. What are the plans for tonight?"

Manfred, glad to be clear of the political minefield, outlined plans for his commanding officer's week's stay in Paris.

"Tonight General Stulpnagel and his staff are entertaining you at a formal dinner at La Petite Chaise in St Germain des Pres. Two other dinners are planned at General Stulpnagel's headquarters and the *Wehrmacht* barracks during the week and for the rest of the time I shall be looking after you. After all, that is my duty at present. I'll make sure we'll have a good time, Sir."

"Excellent, excellent," beamed the exultant Count. "Let's get started."

Colonel von Bulow's week in Paris was a mixture of official banquets, small dinner parties, drinks in the bistros and night-clubs along the boulevards and visits to Madame Clementine's brothel for senior officers established at No. 32 Rue Clement Moro, about five minutes walk from George V. In his usual carefree manner the colonel enjoyed all the activities and, with his exuberant outward personality, became the dominant entertainer at all the functions. On the 17th October an exhausted Manfred took his commanding officer to the Gare du Nord to catch his train to Minden. On the platform they shook hands and the colonel thanked Manfred for his company and entertainment during his week's stay in Paris.

Leaning out of the window before the train departed, he called, "Remember Manfred I want you back in the unit in charge of No. 2 Company as soon as possible. At the moment future plans for my *Fallschirmjagger* are uncertain but if the Leader moves eastwards we'll be involved. I want you with me when that happens. *Auf Wiedersehen*, Herr *Hauptmann* Schmidt," and with that the train pulled away from the platform.

During the week following Colonel von Bulow's visit SS Colonel Kaltenburger quizzed Manfred on a few occasions about the Count. Manfred was careful to ensure that none of his replies gave the slightest hint that von Bulow or the military governor were in any way implicated in a *Wehrmacht* plot to depose the Führer. Kaltenburger was naturally dismayed that his SS observation officers were not allowed to attend the entertainment functions for the Count. His manner towards Manfred became abrupt and brusque. He wanted results quickly, 'or else...' Manfred wondered what the 'or else...' meant. He felt lonely and alone in his predicament. He could not trust Kaltenburger and now he could not confide in Stulpnagel or von Bulow. He wondered where he could turn for advice. If only his father were still alive. *"C'est la guerre"* as the French, so expressively, put it.

The Wooing Of Lise Frank

By late September 1940 Manfred was sexually disenchanted with the robot-like performances of the prostitutes in Madame Clementine's brothel. He wanted more danger and passion in his sexual adventures and found that the prostitutes north of the Champs Elysées offered better prospects and gave better value for money. One dark, wet evening in late October Manfred and his SS shadow were in a window seat of Bistro Cervoise, enjoying an aperitif before their evening meal. In the warm summer evenings the prostitutes plying their trade in Rue de Colisée were spaced at regular intervals along the pavements using Hotel Colisée to entertain their clients. But on this cold, wet, blustery night they congregated outside the bistro sheltering in its shadowy doorway, dimly illuminated by gas light from the restaurant window. Paris was an 'open' city and there were no black-out regulations in force in 1940. Manfred, sipping his apéritif, and studying the menu, debating between the *moules* and the *huîtres*, caught sight of a commotion in the street in front of the bistro.

Three regular prostitutes were attacking a diminutive girl dressed in a shiny black raincoat and wearing a red beret. The prostitutes were encircling the unfortunate girl as she ducked and weaved attempting to avoid their fists and flailing handbags. The girl in the black raincoat suddenly broke loose from the mêlée, crashed into the bistro, dripping wet, shaking and holding her hands to her face, where a sizeable bruise was appearing under her right eye. Two of the prostitutes followed her into the café and a further scuffle started inside the doorway. Manfred sprang to his feet and, grabbing the girl's wet sleeve, pulled her to sit down at his table, turning on her assailants and ordering them to leave her alone. By this time the patron had arrived on the scene and was ushering the two harlots out of the doorway to return to their 'beat' in the rain-sodden street.

Manfred had a good look at the black-haired waif sitting at his table, shaking and crying uncontrollably, tears running in rivulets down her powdered cheeks. She had a plain oval face with a prominent nose, dark hair and jet black eyes starkly offset by her flaming red beret. Her full lips were outlined by ruby red, smudged lipstick which, when she opened her mouth to thank him, revealed even, white teeth. She looked startled and uncomfortable at the turn of events and tried to get up to leave but Manfred held her arm firmly, ordered a cup of coffee and a cognac and sat back to examine his prize in greater detail. His first impression that she was a girl was incorrect. She was a fully grown twenty year old female with tense turgid breasts pushing out her rain-soaked coat and, as Manfred imagined, a well proportioned body underneath. Manfred was smitten. What a gorgeous creature!

The hot coffee and cognac arrived and she gulped greedily at both in turn. She accepted Manfred's handkerchief to wipe and tidy her face but refused to take off her wet raincoat.

"What is your name?" asked Manfred.

"My name is Lise," the girl whispered in a trembling voice.

"Have you had a fight with your friends outside?" Manfred enquired.

"No, they are no friends of mine," Lise replied.

Manfred ordered three *plâts du jour* and a bottle of wine for the table. Lise refused the wine, adding that she would not be able to pay for her meal. Manfred assured her that the meal would be paid for and asked, "What would a beautiful young lady be doing out on the streets on a filthy wet night like this?"

Lise did not answer and greedily guzzled down her food and mopped up the sauce remnants with chunks of stale bread. She was obviously starving and when asked if she would like more Lise nodded and a second plateful of *coq au vin* was brought to the table. Manfred's SS companion was getting fidgety and wanted to move on but Manfred was completely enamoured by the waif-like, dark-faced woman with flashing white teeth.

After twenty minutes Lise got up to leave and Manfred, sensing she was petrified at the thought of going outside alone to face the aggressive whores, also rose, put on his raincoat and guided Lise through the doorway leaving the bewildered SS lieutenant sitting at the table. Holding her elbow Manfred gently chaperoned his cringing companion through the avenue of spitting and blaspheming whores.

"I hope you like Jewish meat," one of the prostitutes shouted from a dark doorway, as the couple passed out of the arc of gaslight.

Once clear of Rue de Colisée the girl broke free from Manfred's grasp and with a shout of *"Merci"* disappeared rapidly down a darkened side street. Manfred, tempted to run after her, stood his ground and shouted after the red-bereted, black-coated, figure.

"Lise, Lise, I want to see you again. Come to the bistro tomorrow night."

He walked back to the restaurant where a prostitute emerged from the doorway and approached him.

"That little Jewish bitch is trying to muscle in on our beat. We've kicked her out a few times. You don't want to bother with her *mon Capitan*. She's kosher. Now if you want a good time I've got a new method we could try. Only fifty francs. What do you say?"

Manfred thanked her politely and returned to his meal in the bistro. For the rest of the evening he was unable to get Lise out of his mind and, though he spent four hours in Cherche La Femme night-club, he was not tempted to take any of the voluptuous hostesses to the upstairs bedroom. Back at George V, and before he went to bed, he analysed his feelings and came to the conclusion that he was in love with a wonderful, diminutive Jewish woman called Lise. He briefly thought of the consequences of a liaison with one of Hitler's hated *Juden* but rationalised the situation by promising himself that it would only be a 'fling' and that, through Lise, he might be able to learn more about the local Jewish community.

'That should please Colonel Kaltenburger,' he thought as he fell into a deep dreamless sleep.

During the next week Manfred concocted excuses to be at Bistro Cervoise each night, despite protests from various SS companions who wanted a change, but Lise did not appear. A loquacious prostitute chided him.

"You've scared her off, *mon Capitan*. Little Madam *beret rouge* has not been around here since you walked her down the road."

He was now getting desperate to see Lise again. Some nights he walked up and down Rue Colisée hoping to see her and then on the eighth night he caught sight of a red beret in an arc of lamplight down one of the side streets. He raced down the road but the tiny figure had disappeared into a tall terraced house. He waited in the dark for an hour but Lise did not reappear. And then, as if by magic, on the ninth evening she walked into the Cervoise, picked up a chair and sat at Manfred's table. His SS companion ogled her speculatively but Manfred's stony stare soon doused any amorous feelings the officer might have been generating.

"Lise, my name is Manfred and this is Heinz Moltke. Please join us. What will you have to eat?"

Lise was starving and ate hungrily but again refused any wine or liquor. At the end of the meal Manfred announced that he intended escorting Lise to her home and would return in a few minutes to join his SS companion. He took Lise by the hand, led her out of the bistro and through the fog-bound November night, to her home at 29 Rue de Ponthieu. Lise's attic room was on the fourth floor of a large terraced house, dimly lit inside and approached by climbing four flights of stone steps. Lise was obviously used to the climb and led Manfred by the hand until they reached the door to her bed-sitting room.

During the walk, and whilst ascending the stairs, Manfred made plans for Lise's seduction. He envisaged a delay on the doorstep but, once inside the room, he intended forcing himself on her, so great was the urgency and intensity of the desire welling within him. Lise found difficulty in fitting the latch key into the lock. Manfred helped by striking a match which illuminated the door and Lise's white, drawn face and red beret. Scratched on the door, etched into the fading varnish, were the simple letters L. Frank.

Manfred's urgent desire for sex quickly overcame his racial prejudices. Inside the cold room he tried to scoop her into his arms but she pushed him away and then with deliberation began to undress – her black raincoat first, and then a woollen cardigan and her thin calico dress. Underneath her chemise she was naked and Manfred had noticed this trait in the other prostitutes with whom he had shared a bed in the past few months. Lise retreated to the divan bed and lay flat on her back, pulled the chemise up to her shoulders to reveal her pointing pyramidal breasts and, beckoning with her finger, invited Manfred to join her. He was already fully aroused and it only took him ten seconds to undo his trouser belt and lie on top of the inviting female. Copulation was urgent and all over in half a minute. He rolled off the unresponsive body underneath and looked at her face. Lise had been silently weeping and still had the red beret stuck firmly on top of her head. Manfred began to dress.

"*Danke, mein* Fraulein. How much is it for your services?"

Lise turned her face to the wall and began sobbing uncontrollably. Manfred had not had this experience with any other prostitute and the woman looked so small, girlish and vulnerable. A primeval instinct made him sit on the edge of the bed and he cradled Lise in his arms, her head on his shoulder, and rocked her gently to and fro. This feeling of tenderness was a new and pleasurable experience for Manfred and he remained rocking Lise gently until they both fell asleep. After a few minutes Manfred was awaken by movement of the firm warm body in his arms and he felt Lise's lips and tongue kissing and licking his neck. Her hands started moving purposefully towards his groin and before long she had released his erect penis from within his trousers. The next ten minutes were sheer bliss for Manfred. He lay on his back and Lise did all the work, expertly and gently. They both reached their climax at the same time, and, on this occasion, the energetic girl above him was smiling contentedly beneath her flaming red beret. Lise jumped off the divan, wrapped a blanket around her body and went to the corner of the cold room to reheat some coffee on a small gas ring.

"*Très bon, mon Capitan.*"

They sat together on the divan holding mugs of steaming coffee and Manfred asked, "Why did you do that, Lise? Why the second time?"

Her face wrinkled in thought as she replied, "You were kind to me at the restaurant a week ago. I wanted to repay you in the only way I can but I did not think I would enjoy it so much. It was wonderful, Manfred." Drawing the blanket tightly around her naked body she continued, "I'm alone in Paris. My parents and I lived in Chantilly.

They are both dead. My father was a lawyer. I came to Paris to see some life but then your people came and it all changed. I am a qualified teacher but there are no jobs here for Jews. Two months ago I started on the streets to make some money. The rent for this room is two hundred francs a week and I'm afraid I haven't been very successful in my business. We're starving and I have to go out on the streets to earn some money. You saw the fight outside the Cervoise. That happened because the girls thought I was pushing in on their beat. I wasn't really. I only wanted a coffee and something to eat."

She blurted out her story rapidly in French and Manfred found difficulty in following her words. He took some notes out of his tunic pocket but Lise refused them. They made love again, tenderly and passionately and, as dawn was breaking, Manfred left the house and walked back to George V with a sprightly step, full of the joys of spring, despite the dark, dismal November morning.

He had arranged to meet Lise again at the bistro the following evening. His eyes lit up and his heart missed a beat when he saw the small figure in black and wearing a red beret coming through the swing doors. Lise came straight to the table, sat down and ate a hearty meal before she and Manfred left to spend the night together in the attic room of 29 Rue de Ponthieu. On the second night together Manfred made a proposition – he would pay the rent and bring in food and drink provided Lise kept herself off the streets and reserved her sexual favours exclusively for himself. Lise readily agreed.

Within ten days of their meeting Manfred was spending most nights and sometimes afternoons with Lise in their attic love nest. He showered her with food and wine and gave her a weekly allowance of four hundred francs. They joked and laughed together and Manfred took Lise out to eat most evenings to local bistros and cafés but never to the upmarket restaurants where he might come across *Wehrmacht* and SS officers dining out for the night. There were times when he was unable to see his beloved Lise, when he had to entertain visiting officers at Maxims, Les Deux Magots or the Folies Bergère. At such times he was impatient for the VIPs to depart so that he could get back to his love nest and his black-eyed, red-bereted Parisian mistress.

On 28th October, 1940 Manfred was present in General Stulpnagel's headquarters when a high priority message was received that Mussolini had ordered his troops in Albania to attack Greece. Hitler and Mussolini were attending an Axis conference in Florence on that day and Mussolini announced the attack as soon as Hitler and his entourage arrived by train. The Führer was apparently furious that Mussolini had embarked on a military adventure without prior consultation.

General Stulpnagel, announcing the news, commented, "Our Italian allies will be no match for the Greeks, especially in the mountainous terrain of southern Albania. I predict that Il Duce will be in trouble very soon."

They were prophetic words and by the middle of November the Greeks had driven the Italians back across the Albanian border and, when winter set in, Greek and Cretan forces were holding a line in the Petrus Mountains and had occupied the southern third of Albania, where they remained locked in defensive positions throughout the harsh winter months of December 1940 and January and February 1941.

The SS Raid on 29 Rue de Ponthieu

Rue de Ponthieu was a short street some three hundred metres in length in the Jewish quarter of arrondissement 8. Apart from a kosher *boulangerie* and a *pâtisserie*, the street accommodated sixty large four-storey, stone-built houses each divided internally into flats and apartments. No. 29 was no exception and housed ten Jewish families and had an attic and two basement single room flats, the latter entered by stone steps leading down from street level. During his visit Manfred had noted the Jewish names carved, or scratched, on the door panels at each landing. The attic rooms were occupied by Lise, two elderly Jews and one plump middle-aged lady, who was 'on the game' and had frequent male visitors after nightfall. Manfred hardly ever met any of the inhabitants of the other apartments but as far as he could tell the basement flats were unoccupied.

Manfred quizzed Lise about the other occupants of the house, only to be told that they were, 'Good, honest, law abiding French Jews'. From the lack of activity in the house, especially after dark, he concluded that most of the residents were elderly and infirm and that they went to bed early to conserve heat and light. During the day Lise looked after the residents' shopping and cooked meals on her gas ring for them, a stew for the Harbergs on the second floor, or broth for the Rothschilds in apartment 3. She generously shared the food Manfred brought her between the families and the visits from her German 'amour' were regarded by the residents as a blessing in disguise.

In early December Manfred was summoned to Colonel Kaltenburger's office at the SS barracks in Avenue Foch. The colonel was in a pernickety mood.

"I hear you're seeing a lot of your French tart? Who is it? Is it safe for you to be seeing her?"

Manfred replied, "Yes, Herr Colonel I am working on a lead. She lives in a Jewish quarter and I think, given time, I might be able to find out a thing or two about the residents in that area."

"*Gut,*" the colonel replied, "but I want results soon. The SS are wasting a lot of money keeping you in the lap of luxury and my officers who accompany you for entertainment tell me that, most nights, you disappear and leave them on their own. This is not good enough and must stop. I want a written report from you next week with details about this woman and what you have learnt so far. Is that clear?"

Manfred indicated that it was perfectly clear, saluted and left the barracks in deep thought, perturbed that his liaison with Lise might lead to a confrontation with the SS colonel. The following week Manfred produced a brief report which the colonel accepted 'for the time being', reiterating that he wanted results quickly.

On a rare sunny afternoon in late November Manfred stood on the small balcony outside the attic room, smoking a cigar and idly looking out over Rue de Ponthieu. He was at peace with the world having just finished an hour's lovemaking session with Lise, who lay dozing naked and spread-eagled on the divan couch with her red beret stuck at an awry angle on her head. From above he saw black-hatted, elderly men shuffling up and down the street singly, or in pairs, chatting amicably and carrying groceries and provisions. It was early evening and the *boulangerie* and *pâtisserie* across the street were busy. There was a young Frenchman standing outside the *boulangerie*, looking furtively right and left, soon joined by three other young men. At a given signal three of the Frenchmen quickly crossed the road and disappeared from view entering No. 29 and going down the steps to the basement. After about half a minute the fourth young man crossed the street and took up a position outside the front door of the building.

Lise stirred and Manfred returned to sit on the edge of the divan.

"I thought you told me that there was no one in the basement flat, Lise?"

She replied, "Two new families are going to move in soon and the workmen are there decorating."

This answer satisfied Manfred. When he left the house he saw a young muscular man whittling away at a stick and sitting on the window sill at the top of the steps leading down to the basement. A few nights later, walking towards 29 Rue de Ponthieu with Lise, he saw, some fifty metres ahead, two figures scuttling across the road and running down the basement steps.

"Your new tenants have moved in Lise?"

"I expect so," she replied in a faltering voice.

When Manfred left Lise's flat just before dawn he saw a brief flash of match light in one of the basement windows. He walked pensively up the Rue de Ponthieu and was now certain that the basement flat was occupied by a group of young men, probably four or five, not in keeping with the age range of the rest of the residents of the building. Manfred reported his observations to Hans Göerdler on the following day.

Göerdler asked, "Have you told Kaltenburger about this? I think you should know that he has asked the Gestapo to keep an eye on you since you started this dangerous liaison. If you are positive that these men in the basement are up to mischief you should tell Kaltenburger immediately. In that way you can save your skin. Go and see him now."

In Kaltenburger's office Manfred was greeted with stony silence. He outlined his suspicions about the occupants of the basement of 29 Rue de Ponthieu and Colonel Kaltenburger responded.

"We have information from other sources about the same building. You are to continue to entertain your Jewish tart until I order you to stop. Don't go near the basement. My men will look into the matter and deal with it."

Manfred found difficulty in continuing lovemaking with Lise knowing that her house was under surveillance. Colonel Göerdler had mentioned the Gestapo and he now became aware of an odd-looking man sitting in a recess in the Cervoise, or of a shadowy figure in a doorway in Rue de Colisée, near Lise's house. He soon became certain that these were Gestapo agents on his trail. Meanwhile Lise seemed blissfully unaware that her apartment was under surveillance.

On a few occasions Manfred suggested a move to a large apartment in another area in Paris, but Lise would not hear of it.

"I am happy here with my own people. I have you to myself. I love this attic room, our own attic. Why should I move?"

Manfred could not argue with her, but now that the Gestapo and SS were involved he feared for Lise's safety. He wished he could tell her more, to warn her about the Gestapo and SS, but he knew that to do so would mean the end of his military career, imprisonment, or worse.

Manfred was awoken by the insistent ringing of his bedside telephone at 3 a.m. on 24th December, 1940. Colonel Kaltenburger's adjutant was on the line.

"You are to report to this headquarters in thirty minutes. We have sent a car to pick you up. It should be at George V in about ten minutes."

Manfred dressed quickly in his black SS uniform wondering what it was all about, but dreading the thought that it might involve Lise. Perhaps she had been taken in for interrogation. When he arrived the SS barracks was already bustling with dark-uniformed, armed men running around and a convoy of eight lorries with doused headlights and engines revving standing in the courtyard. Colonel Kaltenburger was brief and to the point.

"Our target this morning is 29 Rue de Ponthieu. All persons in the building are to be brought here for interrogation. No one is to be spared. We have rehearsed these raids many times and today we'll do it for real. I've invited Captain Schmidt along to see the SS in action. We need to be in position in Rue de Ponthieu an hour before dawn at precisely 5.45 a.m. Heil Hitler."

The SS company assigned to the raid performed its duties with ruthless efficiency. Soldiers were taken to each end of the short street and lorries used to block the exits from Rue de Ponthieu. Armed soldiers silently crept down the dark, silent street from each end, guns at the ready, forming cordons fifty metres on each side of No. 29. Manfred took up his position behind one of the lorries blocking the street exit. A strike force of twelve SS engineers, wielding sledgehammers, and twenty soldiers moved slowly down to the main entrance as dawn was breaking. Three piercing blasts of a whistle from Colonel Kaltenburger initiated the assault and the engineers smashed through the main door and the basement door followed by the stormtroopers.

From within the house shouts of, *"Raus, raus,"* the smashing of wood and the rumble of jackboots on the stone floors split the quiet morning air. Within a minute four scantily dressed men were ushered up the basement steps and made to stand, hands high, against a wall covered by three SS troopers pointing their loaded guns at the captives. Manfred prayed that these would be the only arrests but within another minute a pathetic stream of bewildered, elderly men and women came out of the main door, scantily dressed in night-clothes, shivering in the cold morning frost. They were made to stand against the wall prodded by the rifle butts of the soldiers.

It took fifteen minutes for all the occupants of No. 29 to join their co-residents lined up against the street wall. Many of the arrested Jews were infirm and had to be helped by their relatives and neighbours down the stairway, receiving no assistance from the Germans who were continually shouting *"Raus, raus"* or "Filthy Juden".

Lise was the last to be brought out of the house helping an old Jew to negotiate the steps. She wore her black raincoat over her night-clothes and her red beret was firmly stuck on her head as she walked proud, erect and defiant to stand with her neighbours against the wall, next to the four young men from the basement. The last German to emerge from No. 29 was Captain Hermann who, pointing his *Schmeitzer* in the air, let off half a dozen rounds and then there was complete silence. Hermann's shots were a signal for the lorries to move in and pick up the captives, twelve to each lorry, with armed guards sitting at the tailboards.

As the small convoy proceeded out of Rue de Ponthieu Manfred moved into a doorway but could not avoid Lise's scornful look as the lorries passed by at snail's pace. He half-heartedly raised his right hand to wave but then let his head bend forward and stared miserably at the rutted, muddy tyre tracks on the road. He felt a pang of anguish. Lise had been torn away from him and he had done nothing to prevent her leaving. When he raised his head again, in the hope of a further glimpse of his lover, the lorry was gone, turning right into Rue de Colisée and, gathering speed, racing into the Champs Elysée.

It was all over by seven o'clock in the morning and the raiding party returned to the SS barracks where a hearty breakfast had been prepared for the gallant soldiers to celebrate a successful raid. Colonel Kaltenburger was in an expansive mood and even proposed a toast to the two plain clothes men in their company, two agents of the Gestapo, involved in the raid. Manfred did not feel much like celebrating but showed a brave face and pretended he had enjoyed the morning's raid. Inside he was heartbroken. When Manfred politely asked Colonel Kaltenburger what would happen to the captives he was told:

"The older Jews will be interrogated here, registered, and returned to their homes in a few days. The four young men and the girl and the fat prostitute have been taken to Gestapo headquarters for interrogation. The Gestapo are fairly certain that we have captured a nest of Jewish resistance fighters. I am sure that with their methods of interrogation they will find out all there is to know. Drink up, Captain Schmidt. With your help we have carried out our first successful raid and rid Paris of a dangerous group of killers."

Manfred returned to George V with a heavy heart. He had no stomach for this type of activity and, in the bargain, he had lost his first real love. He now craved to be away from Paris, away from the George V and away from 29 Rue de Ponthieu. His wishes were granted in the New Year of 1941 when he was promoted major and returned to take command of No. 2 Company of the Eighth Parachute Regiment. Manfred never saw Lise again. Together with her plump companion and the four young Jews she was shot in Orly prison on the 10th February, 1941. Lise wore her black shiny overcoat and red beret for the execution.

Chapter Thirteen

The Long Train Journey, Lübbecke to Athens, April – May 1941

Major Manfred Schmidt, pleased to be away from Paris with its bitter-sweet memories, rejoined the Eighth Regiment at Lübbecke on the 18th January, 1941. After the Christmas Eve raid on 29 Rue de Ponthieu he moved into General Stulpnagel's headquarters at Place de l'Opéra. His majority was celebrated on New Year's Eve in headquarters mess and he only ventured out once for a farewell dinner at Café de Deux Magots with the general and Colonel Gördeler. When alone at nights he lay awake worrying and wondering about poor Lise and thinking about the 'treatment' the Gestapo might be administering to her. He travelled by train from Paris to Minden and was picked up at the station by Heinz Schneider, now promoted to *Feldwebel* of No. 2 Company. Schneider was overjoyed to see him.

"Welcome back to the regiment, Sir. We've all missed you. I expect the dames in Paris will also miss you!"

"Thank you, *Feldwebel* Schneider. It's nice to be back again. Don't worry about the French ladies. They are capable of looking after themselves," and they both burst out laughing.

Colonel Count Erich von Bulow was in the mess to greet Manfred. Standing at the bar with his new aide, a Captain Schwarzkopf, he was surrounded by 8th Regiment officers. Captain Schwarzkopf belied his surname and had a mop of golden yellow hair. After a quick lunch Colonel von Bulow ushered Manfred into his office, and, without preliminaries, his face split by a grin and his right eye twinkling, he opened the conversation.

"Come and sit down, Major Schmidt. I'm very glad you're back with us. Major Hellsdorp needed little persuasion to transfer back to the Second Regiment. He leaves at the end of the week and No. 2 Company will then be yours with Schneider as your *Feldwebel*. Good news, isn't it?" Manfred agreed.

"Well now, Manfred, I expect you've heard rumours in Paris about our famous Leader's next escapade. Well, it's now official. We're going to attack Russia in May. I personally think this is madness and that we'll start something we will be unable to finish. But High Command agree with dear old Adolf and the campaign called Barbarossa – what a name – they think it will frighten the backward Bolsheviks – is planned to start any day after the 15th of May. I don't know any further details but I have no doubt that our airborne divisions will be heavily involved in the action. All we can do now is to keep the paras fit and ready to go. They can't do any jumping but there's plenty of snow about for extensive ski training. Who knows? We might find plenty of snow on the Russian steppes and we are, after all, a designated mountain ski regiment. So take a few days to settle in and get to know your men. Then, it's back to work in the field. You'll need to get fit again after your Paris duties! By the way, how's my old friend General Stulpnagel and that nice chap Colonel Göerdler? I wouldn't mind their posting, but I don't think I would last for much longer than a few weeks in Paris!"

Manfred thought differently. He was certain that the fun-loving, hard drinking, womanising, one-armed, one-eyed colonel would last the pace in Paris with flying colours.

Briefing for Operation Barbarossa: 14th February, 1941

General Franz Halder, Chief of General Staff, outlined the airborne forces' contribution to Operation Barbarossa at the 23rd Infantry Divisional headquarters at Potsdam on the 14th February, 1941. Colonel von Bulow, his aide, Captain Schwarzkopf and Manfred flew from Bückeburg for the briefing on the 13th arriving in good time to settle in the mess and attend the pre-conference dinner. Flanked by two tall, handsome Aryan officers the diminutive colonel soon became the centre of attention at the dinner and at the meeting on the following day.

Halder chaired the conference supported by a glum-looking *Reichsmarschall* Goering who, throughout the meeting, stared idly into space fidgeting with either his monocle and gold bracelets or his ivory cigarette holder. General Student and General Löhr, Commander of the Third Air Fleet, represented the airborne forces on the podium. General Halder, a tall aristocratic Prussian with a crew cut and wearing a pince-nez, opened the proceedings.

"The Führer has requested me to personally thank our gallant airborne forces for their exceptional bravery in the campaign in Poland and on the Western Front. As chief of the general staff I am here to outline your participation in our next campaign which will be our last battle in Europe. Operation Barbarossa, our attack on Soviet Russia, is well forward in planning. I will give you an outline of the grand strategy for the offensive and Generals Löhr and Student will supply more detail of the demands that will be made on the airborne forces."

A large map of eastern Poland and Russia was then unveiled on the wall behind the general who continued, "We are facing the Soviet armies along a thousand mile front from the Baltic to the Black Sea. My generals have planned assaults along the whole front, but there will be three main, major offensives led, as on the Western Front, by our Panzer Divisions. The terrain in western Russia is eminently suitable for tank warfare and our superiority in this department will allow us to advance rapidly across the Russian steppes and overcome weaker Russian armour. The tactics will be as before, lightning blitzkrieg Panzer attacks followed by mechanised infantry for consolidation. There are no major mountain ranges between us and our objectives and the only area to be avoided will be the three hundred and fifty square mile marshland in north-western Ukraine, the Pripet Marshes, which will be circumnavigated by our advancing forces."

The general paused to take a few sips of water, readjusted his pince-nez, turned again towards the map of the Soviet Union and continued, "The disposition of our forces will be as follows. Army Group North, commanded by Field Marshal von Leeb, will strike from east Prussia across Lithuania, Latvia and Estonia and make for Leningrad where they will join up with the Finnish army. By order of the Führer Leningrad is to be razed to the ground. A section of von Leeb's army will also strike south towards Minsk. Army Group

Centre commanded by Field Marshal Fedor von Bock will strike towards Moscow, taking Smolensk and Minsk on the way. Field Marshal von Runstedt will command Army Group South striking into the Ukraine and Caucasus and capturing the vital oilfields. Their targets will be Kiev, the Crimea, Rostov and Stalingrad on the Don. Once our three key objectives have been secured the USSR will collapse and our victorious forces will have concluded their last and greatest battle.

"My advisors tell me that the quality of Russian armaments are inferior to ours and that their armies, though numerically superior, will be no match for the German fighting soldier. The general command has estimated that if we start our attack in May we should all be eating our Christmas dinner in Moscow. I might add that apart from these three major offensives other lesser thrusts will be undertaken by our Rumanian allies in the south with the specific objective of capturing Odessa in the Crimea. We have some one hundred and eighty divisions available for this massive onslaught. We believe that the Russians can muster about two hundred divisions and most of these will be inferior to us in morale and in fighting capability." Halder stopped and looked across at Goering, "Herr *Reichsmarschall*, have you anything to add?"

Goering looked up with a start, as if he had not been listening to Halder's briefing, and, not bothering to stand up, continued fidgeting with his coat buttons and commented, "No thank you, Herr General. You have covered everything," and then as an afterthought, "I can assure you that the *Luftwaffe* is fully prepared and you will not find us wanting when the battle starts."

The fat *Reichsmarschall's* comments were received in stony silence by the assembled officers. His *Luftwaffe* had not overcome the Royal Air Force and his bombers had failed, and were continuing to fail, to crush the spirit of the indomitable British nation. He had also failed to prevent the RAF bombing Berlin. Was there any reason to believe that he would not fail again in the forthcoming campaign in Russia.

General Kurt Student was next to speak and rose to tumultuous, spontaneous applause.

"The chief of general staff has outlined the broad strategic plan for Operation Barbarossa. The question is, where do the airborne troops fit into the plan? All of the nine regiments will be deployed, two in the north, three in the centre and three in the south and the Eighth

Regiment and one glider regiment will be kept in reserve. I will contact each regiment by written order which will reach you by February 22nd. You will need to plan transportation for your regiments to a start-off point in east Prussia and Poland by the last week in April, or, at the latest, the first week in May. All regiments will proceed east by rail. The planes and supplies for your attacks will be flown in separately to your jumping-off airfields. The airborne forces in this assault will act as support troops for the main armoured and infantry thrusts. This will be achieved by our paratroopers and glider pilots being available to the commanders in the field for drops behind enemy lines or for establishing bridgeheads across rivers, to be held for twenty-four or forty-eight hours. Our armoured columns will be able to cross unimpeded and keep up pressure on the retreating enemy. As our troops continue to advance the distance from our airfields in Poland and Rumania will become greater and we shall have to capture, or establish, airstrips on Russian territory.

"It may also happen that wintry weather may hold up our advance and if this happens Colonel von Bulow's Eighth Ski Regiment will be used to support the forward troops as will all the airborne forces if ordered by high command. I can assure General Halder, OKW and the high command that my airborne forces are ready to strike.

"Let us now return to our barracks and prepare for the mammoth task ahead. I will issue further instructions to all commanding officers within fourteen days. God bless this enterprise, our Fatherland and our Führer. Heil Hitler."

The conference erupted. The *Fallschirmjagger* officers sang chorus after chorus of *Rot Sheint Die Sonne* much to the discomfiture of General Halder and *Reichsmarschall* Goering, who were made to stand on the podium for a full twenty minutes longer than they expected. Colonel von Bulow was in his element rushing around greeting old comrades and excessively proud of the fact that he and his beloved Eighth Regiment had been selectively mentioned by General Kurt Student. He was so ecstatic that he spoke of nothing else on the two hour flight back to Bückeburg.

"What d'you think, eh, Manfred? The good old Eighth Regiment was the only one mentioned by Kurt Student and that fat old *Reichsmarschall* didn't like it at all. His damned *Luftwaffe* had better not let us down this time. I want to dine in the Kremlin on Christmas day."

*

There was heavy snowfall in northern Germany during February and March, ideal for ski training and forced marches, but impossible for parachute drops and for this Manfred was very thankful. Manfred's No. 2 Company led by *Feldwebel* Schneider performed remarkably well in the exercises. Morale in the regiment was at a high level and the men were informed early of their destination and duties in the next German offensive.

On one of his rare off-duty days Manfred again took to visiting his favourite club in Minden and spent many a happy night with Giesela at Club Erotica. Now and again he spared a thought for Lise and wondered if she had been released by the Gestapo and had returned to her flat in Ponthieu Street. During March the Eighth had two visits from General Student who was impressed with the state of preparedness and high morale of the unit. Manfred and the adjutant made detailed plans for the transfer of the regiment and its equipment from Lübbecke to Plozeazno some eighty miles south east of Warsaw, a train journey of nine to ten days.

On March 20th Major Hofmeister, one of Colonel General Guderian's field commanders, came to Lübbecke for three days to discuss the possible need for parachute drops in the early days of the Russian campaign. Guderian's Panzers were a spearhead of Army Group Centre in the drive towards Moscow. Colonel von Bulow and the company commanders studied detailed maps and Major Hofmeister pinpointed the areas where bridgeheads might have to be established and held by airborne forces in advance of the oncoming Panzers. Army Group Centre planned to attack from Sedlice to strike eastwards and take Brest Litovsk, Pinsk and onwards to Minsk where they would join forces with von Leeb's Fifth Army moving southwards. A drop might be needed at Pinsk but the bridges across the River Nyoman at Minsk, a distance of three hundred miles from the start, needed to be taken and held. This would probably be the first drop for Colonel von Bulow's regiment.

Major Hofmeister estimated it would take ten to twenty days for the Panzers to reach Minsk and, assuming that the start date was May

15th, Guderian's Panzers should be knocking on the door of Minsk between 4th and 6th June. To be fully prepared the Eighth Regiment should be in position in Plozeazno by the 2nd or 3rd May allowing them three weeks preparation. After taking Minsk the next objective, some two hundred miles east, was Smolensk where the Dneiper bridges were the target. The major estimated it might take the Panzers a further twenty to twenty-four days to reach Smolensk. Once Smolensk was secured German armour would only be two hundred and fifty miles from Moscow, a hard slog, but they should be in the Kremlin by mid-October.

After Major Hofmeister had departed Colonel von Bulow commented, "So it's to be Minsk. Manfred, you will make a scale model of the area and terrain around Minsk and pinpoint the bridges which we will need to take so that we can brief the section leaders on their objectives. It is important that we make a successful first drop in Russia."

Manfred and Major Werner spent the following weeks drawing up plans for the attack on the Minsk bridges. Their deliberations were restricted by lack of knowledge of the strength and disposition of the enemy and lack of accurate maps. Colonel von Bulow kept a fatherly eye on developments and frequently wandered about the map room with a glazed look in his eye, murmuring, "Minsk, Minsk", under his breath. Meanwhile the whole regiment at Lübbecke was packing its bags and equipment in preparation for a move to eastern Poland.

All the arrangements and planning were shattered on the evening of 22nd April when a cable was received from General Student's headquarters in Berlin marked 'TOP SECRET URGENT' which read, 'Commanding Officer and two senior company commanders to report to Gatow HQ immediately. Take first plane available. Signed, Kurt Student, GOC Airborne Forces'.

Colonel von Bulow was shaken by the cable.

"Something big has come up. Kurt Student doesn't panic easily. Manfred, I want you and Major Werner to come with me to Berlin. Get a flight from Bückeburg tonight if possible. Don't let those *Luftwaffe* transport boys put you off. If Kurt wants us in Gatow urgently there will be a very good reason for it."

The three officers flew from Bückeburg in a Dornier air transport at 6 a.m. on the 23rd April, taking three hours to complete the three hundred and forty mile journey and arriving at General Student's headquarters at 10 am. General Löhr and twenty-four senior officers from the other airborne regiments were present and four more were expected within the hour.

General Student, agitated, and casually dressed in shirt sleeves, received them at his command centre at 11 a.m. The general looked tired and drawn and obviously lacked sleep and, uncharacteristically, was chain-smoking from a packet of cheap cigarettes. Dispensing with introductions and formalities he began, "Gentlemen, German intervention in Yugoslavia and Greece to help our Italian allies has been instrumental in bringing the war in Greece to a rapid conclusion. The Führer has ordered our airborne division to undertake a landing in the Aegean theatre as a preliminary to moving across to North Africa to join forces with Rommel. The long term objective of the attack will be to capture the Suez Canal." He paused and relit a new cigarette. "I am honoured to be chosen to command the largest airborne invasion in world history. The attack which I am planning will involve all my parachute battalions, four storm glider battalions and three mountain regiments."

He paused again and the excited murmuring amongst his audience indicated their amazement at the enormity of the assault.

"I know that you have all been hard at work on Barbarossa but you will now have to change your plans. The war in Greece is almost over and another week should see us in Athens. All my regiments will move to Athens immediately. A few companies will be flown but most of you will have to travel by rail. General Löhr's gliders and supplies will take precedence in aircraft space. Gentlemen, today is the 23rd April. All my nine regiments will be on the ground in Athens by the 6th or 7th of May. This will give us fourteen days to get there. Now I know you're wondering what the target will be. I will not divulge this today. You will be told when we meet again in Athens. Now, gentlemen, return to your headquarters and start moving south, tomorrow if possible. There will be no difficulty with rail travel. The Führer has empowered you to requisition any rail stock you need and all lines in Germany will be cleared for our troop movements, which carry highest priority. The *Luftwaffe* will have transport planes available to fly out our heavier equipment. The *Fallschirmjagger* will travel in light battle order only carrying sidearms, ammunition and personal essentials. Gentlemen, speed is essential. I wish you safe journeys and don't forget that the honour of the airborne division is in the hands of each and every *Fallschirmjagger* under your command. God speed. Heil Hitler."

Emerging into the warm spring sunshine the bemused airborne officers were plagued with unanswered questions. Where would the drop occur. Would they be able to get their regiments to Athens by rail in the stipulated time. Most of the officers considered that Cyprus or Crete would be obvious targets, probably the former. Colonel von Bulow had no doubts in his own mind.

"The only logical target is the Suez Canal. We shall occupy the canal zone and press on the enemy from the east whilst Rommel and his Panzers attack Cairo and Alexandria from the west. There is no point in occupying an island which is two hundred miles away from our troops in North Africa, Mark my words, we shall be dropped on the Suez Canal. Not in the canal I hope!" his eye twinkling and smiling, "I'm told it's a filthy sewer and full of the most horrible diseases known to man."

Within an hour of the briefing party's return from Berlin Colonel von Bulow ordered a general muster on the parade ground and announced that the Eighth Parachute Regiment was moving southwards to the Mediterranean within forty-eight hours. All leave was cancelled and the men were to prepare their equipment and arms for a long rail journey to the sun. He was unable to divulge their destination at present but they would be given further instructions by their company commanders. He ended by saying that the purpose of the move was to meet up with other airborne regiments for a massive invasion that would strike at the heart of the enemy.

For the following two days Manfred hardly slept for more than an hour at a time. Major Werner was responsible for preparing the men and their personal equipment and Manfred was deputised to organise movement of the regiment from Lübbecke to Athens. As soon as the colonel's parade ended Manfred, his driver and *Feldwebel* Schneider drove at speed to the military rail depot at Osnabrück where they spent twelve hours with a transport major arranging trains and carriages for the long journey across Europe to the Balkans.

The logistic problem of moving twelve hundred men and their equipment by rail was considerable. Manfred estimated he would need twenty-two carriages for the officers and men, three wagons to carry their light equipment and two kitchen wagons for feeding the regiment en route. The transport major agreed and suggested three assemblies with one kitchen wagon attached to the end of each train and, realising the urgency of the situation, he agreed that he would have the rolling stock available to start out from Osnabrück at first light on the 27th April. The eventual destination of the troop trains was not divulged to the transport manager. With a knowing smile he concluded that the regiment was moving to the eastern front in Poland.

The following four hours was spent on the telephone arranging clearance of the lines for the troop transporters from Minden to the Polish border. Later that day Manfred called on the *Luftwaffe* commander at Bückeburg where, again, arrangements were made for transport planes to be available on the 27th and 28th to fly the regiment's heavier equipment to Kielce in Poland from where they would be re-routed south to Athens. He also commandeered a fleet of *Luftwaffe* lorries and trucks to move the regiment out of Lübbecke to the rail terminal at Minden.

By 6 a.m. on the morning of April 28th the Eighth Parachute Battalion were mustered in companies in the shunting yard at Minden railway station. Three troop trains arrived at hourly intervals and loading started at 8 a.m. By 11 a.m. the Eighth Battalion were on their way eastwards, travelling through Hanover, Magdeburg and Dresden, which they reached by nightfall. Movement across Germany was rapid and top priority status, granted to the trains by the Führer's order, ensured clearance of the railways of any but essential goods trains. The rail convoy stopped overnight at Dresden where the paratroopers were given a hot meal cooked in their own rail kitchen. Sergeant Fritz Schultz, in charge of the officers' kitchens, prepared a sumptuous meal, under difficult conditions, for Colonel von Bulow and his regimental staff.

Thereafter, on the following day, progress was much slower as the train crawled across Czechoslovakia. It took nearly a whole day to reach Prague and, after a night's stay, a further twelve hours before they passed through Bruno and across the border to Budapest in Hungary. The days and nights came and went in a confused clutter. The snail-paced rail convoy proceeded southwards crossing the Hungaro-Rumanian border at Szeged travelling further south to Timisara, where progress was considerably delayed in crossing the Retezat Mountains to reach Craiova in southern Rumania. Seven days had passed before the troop train crossed the Danube into Bulgaria at Oryakhevo reaching Sofia before nightfall.

The paratroopers were exhausted by the humdrum, tedious journey and Colonel von Bulow ordered a twenty-four hour halt in Sofia. After replenishing their stores and water supplies and resting in the marshalling yards the convoy continued southwards to cross the Graeco-Bulgarian border at Kalata and into Thessaloniki on the ninth day. It took two more days to move from northern Greece to Athens in the south, mainly due to inadequacies of the Greek railways and the ravages of the recent fighting which had disrupted many of the railway lines. The slow-moving train convoy finally ground to a complete halt at Corisa, some one hundred and fifty miles north of Athens on May 9th.

The paratroopers were pleased to be off the cramped and confined rail carriages and spent a morning sunning themselves and cleaning up. They were eventually picked up in a fleet of lorries and driven in convoy to their tented base camp at Tatöi, an airfield some twenty kilometres outside Athens. The long journey of two thousand five hundred miles had taken the Eighth Parachute Regiment thirteen days to complete and was achieved without mishap, injury, or loss of life. The colonel congratulated Manfred on the excellent arrangements for the long and arduous trek and he was fully aware that, after they crossed the German border into Czechoslovakia, the whole venture was in the lap of the gods and the uncooperative officials of the Czechoslovakian, Rumanian and Bulgarian railways.

The Railway Marshalling Yard at Sofia

The twelve-hour stop in the marshalling yards at Sofia gave the Eighth Regiment a chance to stretch their limbs, bathe, have a hearty meal and generally clean up the railway compartments in which they had been imprisoned for nine days. The marshalling yards, a mile square, were a morass of criss-crossing railway lines and storage sheds enclosed in a high barbed wire fence and illuminated at night by electric lights, radiating from the top of forty foot pylons placed at intervals around the perimeter fence and patrolled day and night by sullen, flat-faced, fully armed Bulgarian soldiers.

The *Fallschirmjagger*, glad to be in the open air and away from the stuffy, sweat-laden atmosphere of the train compartments, slept on ground sheets around and underneath the rolling stock. A full moon partially illuminated the area with its phosphorescent beams as

Manfred began his tour of inspection before turning in himself for a good night's sleep in the officers' wagon-lits. He felt at peace with the world as he quietly acknowledged the greetings and goodnight wishes from his men, lying like logs in neat rows, virtually and metaphorically sleepers in the marshalling yard.

Manfred walked slowly towards the wire fence and saw the guards moving around silently outside, nervously fingering the triggers on their weapons. He wondered what they would do if the *Fallschirmjagger* decided to attack. Probably they would turn and run away in disorder. They surely could not expect to contain over a thousand fully armed paratroopers in this barbed wire enclosure. And then he thought their presence might be to prevent the citizens of Sofia from attacking the Germans. Rumour had it that Bulgaria, a fiercely proud and aggressive nation, was an unwilling partner of the Tripartite Pact and most of the population resented the intrusion of German troops into their country. He mused on these thoughts as he silently and quietly continued walking along inside the perimeter wire moving from the brighter light cast from the pylons into the more dimly lit areas of the marshalling yard, illuminated only by the shadowy light of a full moon.

When he had been walking for about ten minutes he came alongside a low two-storey, balconied, administration building which he entered through a half-open, heavy oak door hanging on its hinges. Once inside he entered a passageway running the whole length of the building, illuminated at each end by a single naked electric bulb. He turned to his right along the corridor, ascended a flight of wooden steps and found himself on an unlit balcony running the whole length of the first floor. Manfred approached the parapet of the balcony and looked over the marshalling yards, dimly lit by the moonbeams. He saw the shadowy outlines of the parked engines and carriages and the indistinct forms of his sleeping paratroopers, an occasional flaring match indicating that a few were smoking and conversing in stifled whispers. The night was perfectly still and silent. He ambled slowly along the balcony in semi-darkness, pausing from time to time to lean over the parapet and scan the bivouac area.

Suddenly, and without warning, he felt a jab in the small of his back and a high-pitched voice urging *"Hande Hoch"*. He raised his hands above his head, prompted by the urgent prodding from a gun muzzle. He smelt the earthiness and dried sweat of the unseen soldier behind him. Manfred stood perfectly still, hands held high, whilst the urgent prodding of the gun in his back became less insistent as if the holder of the weapon was unsure as to what to do next and was probably more frightened than Manfred himself. He turned slowly to face his adversary and to his surprise looked into the dark frightened eyes of a female in uniform with badges of rank on her lapels. He slowly lowered his hands as the uniformed lady hesitantly depressed the point of her gun.

Manfred took stock of the situation. The female under-officer was about five feet tall, had short jackbooted legs with baggy trousers and a blousy khaki tunic topped by a peaked cap with a red band, jammed on top of her straggly jet-black hair. She cowered with fright and started to shake. Manfred smelt fear oozing from every pore of the peasant officer which excited him and aroused him sexually.

He now took charge of the situation.

"*Guten abend, mein gnädige* Fraulein," he spoke with a welcoming smile.

Manfred noticed that in her left hand the woman soldier held a crushed cigarette and he surmised that she must have retreated into an alcove to have a smoke.

"Smoking on duty my beautiful young lady? That will never do!"

The Bulgarian woman's face was blank and uncomprehending. Continuing to smile amicably Manfred produced a packet of cigarettes from his tunic pocket and offered it to the frightened Bulgar. She snatched the packet, "*Danke danke,*" extracted one cigarette and, placing it between her lips, attempted unsuccessfully to strike an old, battered, flint lighter. She failed and her fear suddenly evaporated. She burst out laughing. Manfred joined her with a chuckle and moved closer. The Bulgarian woman looked him straight in the eye with an intense, inviting stare.

Manfred felt the excitement and electricity of the moment, felt his own sexual arousal, smelt the soldier's halitosis and the musty odour of female secretions within the baggy uniform and, without further ado, lunged at the woman, clutching her around the waist and pulling her fiercely to his own body. The officer dropped her gun and Manfred's cigarette packet and for the next minute there was a fiendish skirmish whilst they tore at each other's tunic buttons and belts and liberated their lower torsos from the encumbrance of clothing. Manfred attempted penetration standing up but was not successful. He picked the woman up in his arms and, turning her around, draped her over the balcony inserting his manhood into her while he clutched at her muscular, heaving buttocks. Their lovemaking was frenetic and short lived. Manfred reached his climax very quickly. He stepped backwards to look at her ample white buttocks silhouetted above the red-striped breeches hanging like deflated balloons above her black jackboots.

The sated Bulgarian officer smiled as she readjusted her clothing. Her hair was awry and her cap had fallen on to the ground below the balcony during their feverish copulation. Manfred picked up her rifle and cigarette packet and handed them back to her and then helped her light a cigarette, turning his face sideways to avoid her malodorous breath. The whole interlude had only taken seven minutes. He walked down the stairs and as he passed beneath the balcony picked up her cap and threw it to the Bulgarian officer, now puffing contentedly on her cigarette and murmuring, *"Danke, danke"*, at the slowly disappearing figure of the first German she had ever encountered. *'Danke, bitte, ja, nein, Hande hoch'*, were the complete extent of her German vocabulary. Manfred wondered, as he walked away, if her *'Danke'* was a tribute to his sexual prowess. He hoped so, but it could have been her way of saying thank you for the cigarettes.

The travel-weary Eighth Battalion reached their tented accommodation on the periphery of Tatöi airfield at midday on the 11th May. The airfield was jam-packed with Junkers 88s and Dornier 70 transport planes and about three hundred gliders. The flat, arid ground around the airfield accommodated two other battalions and one regiment of mountain troops. The whole area, some two square miles, was busy with troops and airmen moving around in marching groups or driving about in lorries. Colonel von Bulow's comment on arrival was typical of the old fighter.

"I've never seen such an accumulation of military personnel. The milk of the German army may be at the Eastern Front, but the cream is here in Athens, preparing for our strike against Suez. I hear that there are more of us at Eleusis, Mycene, Argos, Atalaöi and Malaöi. What a formidable force! We should take the canal in a few days."

He then declared his intention of calling on all his regimental friends after a few hours' rest. For the following three days Manfred and the colonel spent their time being driven around by *Feldwebel* Schneider to various headquarters in the vicinity where he was always made welcome and his opinion, as a senior statesman of the *Fallschirmjagger*, was highly respected. Manfred was amazed at the enthusiasm and optimism of the airborne officers. Not all the officers they met agreed with Colonel von Bulow's assessment of the target for this great air strike but most conceded and bowed to his seniority and acknowledged reputation as a thinking military strategist. The parting salvo from most of his compatriots was, "Wait and see. All will be revealed on the 15th". On the 15th May, 1941 all senior officers were to attend General Kurt Student's military briefing at the Hotel Bretagne in Athens.

Chapter Fourteen

Captain David Green's Trip to Athens Crete Before the Invasion April – May 1941

In December 1940 reinforcements for the First Battalion Welch Regiment were in transit at Mustapha barracks, Alexandria. Captain David Green, in charge of his detachment, was finishing off his breakfast when a mess sergeant appeared at his elbow.

"The two IC wants you in his office, Sir."

"Thank you, Sergeant Price," David replied as he got to his feet and marched smartly across to the CO's office where he found Major Gibson sitting behind a desk, closely studying a memo.

"David, come and sit down. You're a very important person. There's some *punkahwallah* in room twenty-nine at Shepherds Hotel in Cairo who wants to see you urgently. It's all hush, hush. I've cleared the arrangements with the old man. You're to get up to Cairo tomorrow. Your rail pass has been processed. Make sure you use the first class coach and not the second or third, which are always packed with thieving natives. Daddy Duncan suggests you take some spare kit and stay on in Cairo for a couple of nights. Be back here for the mess party and carol concert on Christmas Eve. Any questions?"

"Yes," answered David. "Whom am I to report to in Shepherds Hotel?"

The major winked and tapped the side of his nose.

"I told you, old chap. Its all hush, hush. You'll find out soon enough when you get there. Now, off you go."

Shepherds was an old Victorian, colonial-style, hotel in the centre of Cairo overlooking the Nile. The hotel had a large entrance vestibule ventilated by six rotating ceiling fans. David pushed his way through the motley, multi-uniformed, mixed crowd of men and women in the foyer to reach the stairs and climb up to the second floor. Room twenty-nine was at the very end of the corridor and David noticed that the doors of rooms twenty-seven and twenty-eight were boarded.

He knocked and entered and to his surprise was confronted by a stockily built, bottle-blonde, bespectacled sergeant sitting behind a desk, with large filing cabinets carpeting the walls and a view of the dirty brown Nile over a balcony balustrade. Three feluccas meandered to and fro on the river, their stark white sails standing out brightly in the scorching noonday sun. The sergeant sprang to attention.

"Captain Green reporting, Sergeant."

She inspected a file and nodded. "Follow me, please, Sir," and walked ahead through a communicating door into rooms twenty-eight and twenty-seven.

These rooms were blacked out with heavy damask curtains and illuminated by four exposed light bulbs hanging from the ceiling. The presence of candles stuck in jam pots and tin cans served as a reminder of the unpredictability of Cairo's electricity supply. Of the men in room twenty-seven David immediately recognised Colonel Sharples who looked bronzed and healthy and stood in front of a large map of the eastern Mediterranean pinned on a wall. Sitting on two chairs in front of the map were a tall, angular, red-headed guards' captain and a short, wiry, dark-eyed Black Watch lieutenant.

David saluted and stood to attention. Colonel Sharples indicated an empty chair.

"Please sit down, David. Let me introduce you to Captain Bertrand Osborne of the Grenadier Guards and Lieutenant Andrew McQuiddy of the Black Watch. From now on its Christian names only. Mine's Henry. So it will be Henry, David, Bertie and Andrew. Now you must be wondering what its all about?" The three listeners nodded their interest and Henry continued, "I am not authorised to reveal my information sources. I will confirm that the directives we receive in this office come from the highest authority. The purpose of this exercise is to look into the feasibility of sending small commando groups behind enemy lines to harass the Boche and activate local resistance. You're all commando-trained. As you know the Italian spaghetti merchant has taken on Greece. They've been at it since mid-November and the truth of the matter is the Greeks have got Musso by the short and curlies. The Ities are held up in southern Albania. We've sent troops and planes to Greece but they're managing very well on their own. Intelligence reports this week suggest that Adolf may soon join in to bail out Mussolini. If this happens mainland Greece may be lost. The question is, where will Adolf strike next?"

Colonel Sharples turned to the wall map and using his pointer continued, "The ultimate aim of the Germans is to capture the Suez Canal. Musso's boys in Libya haven't a hope in hell of doing this on their own. If Hitler takes Greece we have to guess where he will move next. My guess is that it will be Cyprus, which is strategically placed in the eastern Med," indicating with his pointer, "for a further thrust across the sea to Lebanon and then down through Palestine and the Sinai to take the canal from the east."

Henry paused to take a sip of iced lemonade.

"The other two islands we must consider are Rhodes and Crete. Rhodes is too far from the Canal to be a serious possibility. It could be used but Hitler won't want to provoke the Turks. Now let's have a look at Crete," again using the pointer to delineate the island. "The only trouble with Crete is that it is virtually a mass of high mountains. There are some flat areas on the north and south shorelines but, by and large, landing on Crete will be difficult. So the odds on bet is Cyprus." Colonel Sharples paused to look at his audience. "Any questions so far?"

There were none. He continued, "My proposal is that each of you is allocated an island to study in detail. You all speak Greek and will need to recruit commando teams. You will be my field operators. So who goes where?"

The drawling, supercilious grenadier officer was first to speak.

"I want Cyprus please, Henry."

Lieutenant McQuiddy, demurring to David's senior rank, suggested he should look after Rhodes. David stood and took a closer look at the map.

"Well, Sir, it looks as if I'm stuck with Crete."

Colonel Sharples audibly purred, "Excellent! The way you sorted things out is exactly the way I planned it. Rhodes can go ahead in about three weeks. Andrew will gather ten or so commandos and we'll get him off to Rhodes by late January at the latest. In the meantime return to your regiments. I will arrange matters with your commanding officers to release you for special duties as required. We will meet again in January after Christmas and the New Year binges. In January, Andrew will be assigned to this unit permanently until he leaves for Rhodes. Bertie and David will report here once a week in the New Year. Any questions?"

There were none. Colonel Henry Sharples licked his lips.

"Forward planning is thirsty work. Let's go down to the bar and have a few cold beers. Thank you for your attention, gentlemen."

David stayed on in Cairo for two nights savouring the atmosphere and delights of the ancient city. He returned to Mustapha barracks in time for the Christmas celebrations. The regimental band played dance music and someone had enticed a few nurses and ATS officers to join in the celebrations. David felt lonely and homesick and longed for the company of his beloved Bron. During the first week of January 1941, the battalion commander confirmed David's secondment to Commando Group 14. By mid-January the First Welch were scheduled to move to Mersa Matruh in preparation for another move to Crete on February 10th for garrison duties at Khania.

When the First Welch left Mustapha David transferred his billet to the engineers' officers' mess in Qhira and daily attended 14 Group offices in rooms twenty-seven, twenty-eight and twenty-nine Shepherds, where he functioned as an aide to Colonel Sharples. Lieutenant Andrew McQuiddy and his ten-man commando departed for Rhodes during the last week of January and David assisted with their last minute basic training. Towards the end of February Captain Bertrand Osborne and his commandos were despatched to Cyprus and room twenty-nine Shepherds became a quiet backwater, the colonel at work in one office and David sharing the ops room with ATS Sergeant Nancy Willoughby. Messages, some coded, and all secret were received throughout the day at her desk, usually delivered by hand from some unidentified source in the bowels of the hotel.

David spent most of his time planning his own operation on Crete. The longer he studied the terrain the more convinced he became that the Germans would be foolish to attempt a seaborne landing on the inhospitable northern coastline and British naval superiority in the Aegean would deny passage to an invading armada. Proximity of the massive mountain range to the shoreline almost precluded an airborne assault but parachutists and gliders might get a toe-hold on, and around, the airfields at Maleme and Heraklion. German air supremacy over the island might allow an airborne assault but, all in all, Crete did not appear to be Hitler's main target after the conquest of Greece.

In the Balkan theatre Mussolini's armies were held up in the freezing Petrus mountains in southern Albania and the Italians in Libya were under pressure from Wavell's victorious armies west of Benghazi. A disquieting message was received in Cairo on the 15th February, 1942. Erwin Rommel, a Panzer general, had arrived in Tripoli and German armoured vehicles were being unloaded in the docks. Decoded messages from the Balkans reported heavy concentration of German forces in southern Rumania at Craiova on the Bulgarian border. Colonel Sharples interpreted this accumulation of armour as a possible threat to Greece and when, on the last day of February 1942, the Germans moved into Bulgaria, Hitler's intentions became abundantly clear. Greece was the next target on the Führer's plan of action.

Urged by London, Colonel Sharples now redirected David's non-existent commandos to mainland Greece and urgent formation of a team became priority for Section 14. The colonel admitted to David that he had used up all available Royal Marine personnel for the Rhodes and Cyprus expeditions. He had no one to offer but expected an experienced Royal Marine commando sergeant to arrive from the UK with the next draft into Alexandria.

David scoured the local camps and units looking for suitable men, looking for dependable soldiers who would fit the bill and with whom he could live in close proximity for weeks or months on end. He set high standards and, not unsurprisingly, failed to come up with any recruits in the short time available. Colonel Sharples understood his dilemma.

"It's your show, David. You must go in with men you can trust in a tight spot. Keep trying. I'm also looking around and between us we should be able to collect a few likely lads in the next couple of weeks."

Events overtook Colonel Sharples' best laid plans. On 15th March, David was called into the colonel's office and introduced to a civilian in his mid-thirties with prematurely greying hair.

"This is Tim Gammon. Just flown down from Camp Meiol, our training centre near Haifa. Tim is an expert on radio-communications. He is off to Athens to see what's going on. Everything seems to be in a hell of a mess there. You will go with him. Your official position will be an aide on General Wavell's staff. Sniff around and see what's going on and stick to Tim like glue. He'll show you the ropes. Tim will be in civvies but you will be in uniform. You'll be sailing on the 20th, so get to know each other over the next few days. Off you go."

David was impressed with the clarity and decisiveness of the colonel's briefing. The orders were issued clearly with no prevarication and no 'ifs' or 'buts'. Sitting with Tim in a quiet corner of Shepherds bar, with a glass of iced lager in his hand, David asked a question, as if thinking aloud.

"I wonder who's the top man in our organisation?"

"No need to know. Don't want to know. In any case I'm not in your group. I'm Special Operations Executive and attached for special duties."

Tim sat brooding, sucking the stem of his pipe for a full minute and then spoke in a subdued, 'hush, hush' voice.

"Rumour has it that Colonel H has connections in very high places. He's certainly got more power to act than the SOE top brass. He was a decoding officer at the Admiralty in 1939 and, though its pure speculation, most SOE operatives think that Colonel H has direct access to Winnie and the Cabinet. Anyway it will do us no good to probe too much. So let's drop it. My round. Same again?"

David nodded, "Yes, please," and watched as the older, grey-haired man made his way to the bar. 'A curious customer,' David thought. 'Not a man you can get to know easily.'

Tim's expertise was in wireless telegraphy and in his baggage he carried four transmitters and two heavy duty batteries. The heavy equipment was equally divided between the two men and the batteries and sets, packed in waterproof sheets, were carried in large haversacks. David travelled 'light' only carrying a Sten gun slung over one shoulder and a small pack of personal equipment. They sailed for Athens aboard a destroyer at dusk on 20th March. At the dockside in Alexandria, Colonel Sharples took David aside.

"Now, keep your eyes and ears open. Don't trust anyone. Not even Tim. Listen to what is said. Don't let on that you understand German or Greek. Stay mum. Don't keep any notes and remember that officially you are an aide on Wavell's staff. You are to report back to me and no one else. Is that clear? Good luck, David."

And, with a formal salute, the colonel turned on his heel and marched from the dockside to join Sergeant Willoughby in the waiting staff car.

The destroyer crossed the Aegean at speed and docked at dawn in Piraeus harbour on the following day. The harbour was crammed with ships of all description, naval frigates, motor torpedo boats, merchantmen, colliers and troop carriers unloading men and supplies on to the dockside, where convoys of three-ton lorries moved in and out of the pyramids of war material taking on loads of supplies and ammunition. The whole undertaking was supervised by a harassed, red-faced Royal Army Service Corps major. After a brief altercation with the sweating major, who resented being addressed by a mere civilian, Tim was directed to an ambulance truck and installed in the back amidst a plethora of medical supplies and stretchers, in the company of a Royal Army Medical Corps corporal, who seemed very suspicious of Tim, but was courteous and pleasant towards the Welch regiment captain. Within an hour, after a bumpy gear-crunching journey, the ambulance reached Hotel Bretagne, headquarters of the British Military Mission and seat of the Greek Government. Alexandros Koryzis, the Greek Prime Minister and Constantinos Manidiakis, the Public Security Chief, had their offices in the hotel. The British commander, Major General T.G. Heywood and his Chief of Staff, Colonel Salisbury-Jones, occupied the ground floor.

Tim Gammon's arrival caused quite a stir. Two men in semi-military attire, but no badges of rank, rushed to meet him and amidst much back-slapping and hilarity Tim and his equipment were whisked away into the hotel foyer leaving David standing in the hot sun, unsure about his next move. He was about to ascend the steps to the main entrance when a young uniformed Scots Guards captain came rushing out to meet him. Captain Peter de Bouvier, tall, blond, bronzed and hatless greeted David.

"Welcome to the mad house. I'm Colonel Salisbury-Jones' adjutant. You'll bunk with me in room fifty-nine. I'll take you up there to freshen up and then you can say hello to the commanding officer."

David took to the fresh-faced, enthusiastic young Guards officer. At six o'clock he was taken in to the commanding officer's quarters and introduced to Colonel Salisbury-Jones, a Coldstream Guards officer.

"I'm not sure why they sent you here, Captain Green. I have no work for you at the moment. Hang around the operations room for a few days and acclimatise. We'll then see if there's anything I can offer you. Captain de Bouvier, Peter, will look after you. I'm dining with the Greek Prime Minister tonight. I'll see you around during the next few days."

In September 1940 Hotel Bretagne had been converted into a military and civil headquarters in the centre of Athens. Since commencement of hostilities with Italy the hotel had become the seat of the Greek Government and residence for the Prime Minister, who occupied the whole of the second floor. The large ballroom on the first floor had been converted into an assembly chamber for meetings of the Greek Government and War Cabinet. The bedrooms on the third floor of the hotel were reserved for members of the Government and their advisers. The police chief, Constantinos Manidiakis, had a suite of offices and living quarters on the same floor. The British military mission requisitioned the ground floor where they shared quarters with the Greek commanders and their staff. The large dining room acted as operations centre and British and Greek staff officers had set up trestle tables and desks with telephones and four radio transmitters. Colonel Salisbury-Jones and his staff officers had their offices and quarters in the kitchens near the dining room. The top floor of Hotel Bretagne was occupied by a very mixed bunch of British and Greek 'experts' and boffins, most dressed in civilian clothes, but some in pseudo-military attire with no insignia to denote their rank or regiment of origin.

It took four days for David to discover that Tim Gammon and his transmitters were billeted on the upper fifth floor of the vast hotel complex. The operations room, day and night, was a hive of activity, telephones ringing, messages received and transmitted, impromptu conferences and briefings and men with clipboards scurrying to and fro. Similarly, the main corridors of the first floor were never empty. David frequently met Alexandros Koryzis in the Government offices corridor, always surrounded by black-suited bodyguards and officials and invariably accompanied by Colonel Manidiakis, the Chief of Police.

Nearly a week went by before he accidentally bumped into Tim Gammon on the second floor corridor. He was accompanied by an unsavoury looking, plump, Greek civilian.

"How's it going, David?"

"Everything's fine," David lied, adding, "Where are you billeted, Tim?"

"Top of the house," he replied with a faint grin and, as he hurried away, "I'll take you up there in a few days time."

"I'll look forward to that," David shouted at Tim's rapidly disappearing back. David's unproductive first week at the Bretagne was spent hanging around the operations and orderly rooms and wandering rather aimlessly, clipboard under his left armpit, along the myriad corridors of the vast hotel.

Late one evening Captain de Bouvier approached David in the orderly room. "After you've finished your cocoa the colonel will see you in his office."

David gulped down the remainder of his hot drink and marched smartly into Colonel Salisbury-Jones' office. The colonel, sitting behind his desk reading a late report from Alexandria, looked up.

"Captain Green, I have a job for you. The general and I are concerned about the activities of the civvy blokes on the fifth floor. We think there's some cloak and dagger stuff going on behind our backs and that these chaps are hand-in-glove with some of the unsavoury elements amongst the Greeks, including that police chappie Manidiakis. I believe you came ashore with one of the Brits, a fellow called Gammon? General Heywood will be obliged if you could somehow find out what's happening on the fifth floor."

The colonel paused, re-arranged the papers on his desk and resumed.

"We also have a problem at the dockside. Poor old Major Bush is rushed off his feet and his inventory of arrivals is often incomplete and completely inaccurate. The Aussies and New Zealanders in particular give false returns in order to disembark quickly. At the moment we reckon there are some forty-seven thousand British and

Anzac troops in Greece. Major Bush has also been lax in informing us of the arrival of the civilian irregulars. I particularly wish to know about these chaps. You will park yourself on the dockside at Piraeus and keep an accurate daily check on disembarking personnel. Don't bother with equipment. Major Bush seems to have this part of the inventory under control. I'll inform the major you are acting under my direction. He won't like it, but he can lump it. There's a small taverna, the Ariadne, at the dockside. Put up there and rest between arrivals. Report to me here twice a week."

"Thank you, Sir," David replied, glad to have an opportunity to be of some use and pleased to get away from Hotel Bretagne with its strange atmosphere of intrigue, plotting and counter-plotting.

On the following day, David was driven to Hotel Ariadne in a staff car. He selected a room on the first floor with a balcony overlooking Pireaus harbour, but unfortunately directly above a busy and frequently noisy hotel bar. Having deposited his kit in the bedroom he reported to Major Bush who was not well pleased to have a line regiment captain interfering in his domain. But the directive came from Colonel Salisbury-Jones at headquarters and he had to comply, like it or not. For the next fortnight, David and the RASC major worked together in symbiotic disharmony. As the days went by Major Bush gradually relinquished the task of personnel inventories to David, whilst he continued to keep a record of equipment and war materials which arrived in ever-increasing abundance during the last fortnight of March.

War Diary

Towards the end of March, 1941, the puppet government in Yugoslavia signed a pact with Nazi Germany and Italy. This event rang alarm bells amongst the Greek politicians in Hotel Bretagne. On March 26th, Peter II, the Prince Regent, led a popular uprising, which overthrew the Axis-dominated Yugoslavian junta. Koryzis' Government were now convinced that Germany would invade Yugoslavia to help Mussolini and that subsequently there would be fighting on Greek soil.

David was sitting sunning himself on his balcony at the taverna when he heard news of a Yugoslavian uprising and it came from an unexpected source. Peering over the balcony he saw a short, muscular man, clutching a tankard of beer, sitting at a table on the pavement below. A crown and one pip on his shoulder indicated that the newcomer was a lieutenant-colonel and a large bush hat on the table, and his voice, identified him as unmistakably Australian. David hastened downstairs to speak to the new arrival and saluted.

"Could you please repeat that bit of news for me, Sir?"

Lieutenant-Colonel Richard Maclean, commander of the First Australian Commando Force, squinted from under his wide-brimmed hat and with a lop-sided grin said, "Cut out the crap," indicating David's salute. "Grab a chair and join me in a beer."

As instructed David drew up a chair and without invitation the Australian colonel proceeded with his life story, only interrupting his narrative to order more beer and to belch loudly from time to time.

Lieutenant-Colonel Richard Maclean – 'call me Dickie' – was born in 1909 on a large sheep farm about twenty miles south of Perth in western Australia. He was the youngest of four brothers and, at the age of sixteen, ran away from home to enlist in the Regular Army as a band boy. He rose steadily through the ranks and was commissioned in 1932, attaining the rank of captain by 1938. Stimulated by the guerrillas in the Spanish Civil War, the Australian Army formed a commando company and Dickie became its company commander. By 1940, the commando was expanded to battalion strength and Lieutenant-Colonel Richard Maclean became commanding officer of the first and only Australian commando. Colonel Dickie Maclean and his battalion left Australia in November 1940 and arrived in Egypt on Christmas Eve. The colonel expected his unit to be thrown into the desert war on arrival but for two months they had remained idle in a transit camp in Ismalia.

In early March a company of his commando were ordered to Greece for 'special' duties. Dickie, not wishing to be left out of any action, took command of this company leaving his second in command in charge at Ismalia. The sea voyage had been a disaster. A leaky old collier, the *Hesperus*, conveying the company across the Mediterranean, repeatedly broke down with engine trouble. The ship limped into Heraklion harbour on Crete, where his troops and all their equipment were disembarked and held themselves ready for a further seaborne move to Athens.

Dickie himself, impatient as usual, took an opportunity of crossing to Athens on a destroyer, leaving a staff captain and an experienced sergeant in charge of the men and equipment on the dockside at Heraklion, under instruction to follow their commander to Piraeus at the first possible opportunity. For ten days, Dickie had called at Hotel Bretagne but the British commanders had no knowledge of the impending arrival of his commando. He had been to General Maitland-Wilson's Anzac headquarters at Korditsa where he was assured that his company would be valuable reinforcement to the Australian troops holding the Alikmon line. And now he came daily to the harbour at Piraeus to await arrival of his men. The news from Yugoslavia continued to be disturbing but Dickie reckoned that the German advance into Greece might take weeks and the lads from 'down under' would hold them long enough to allow his commando battalion to get at them and smash the German army to pieces.

"In the meantime, while we wait, it's bottoms up, you Pommie bastard." David responded by getting two more beers, followed by baked fish and olives. David rapidly grew to like the aggressive, rough-and-ready Australian colonel. Their sessions at Bar Ariadne became a welcome daily break. The Aussie, full of anxiety in the morning, pacing up and down on the quayside, mellowed after a few lagers at lunchtime and sat at his favourite table at the Ariadne for hours, talking, chain-smoking and drinking, before staggering off to his billet for a night's sleep.

Twice a week David drove to Hotel Bretagne headquarters to report to Colonel Salisbury-Jones. Dickie accompanied him on April 2nd, and, refusing to be fobbed off by Peter de Bouvier, insisted on seeing the headquarters commander. Colonel Salisbury-Jones received Dickie in his office standing behind his desk and towering over the shorter, blustering Australian officer.

"How can I help you, Lieutenant-Colonel Maclean?"

Dickie removed his bush hat, wiped his sweaty brow, took a deep breath and spoke rapidly.

"My company has been stuck on the dockside in Heraklion for the best part of two weeks. They were due to arrive here on 22nd of March. I've been trying to get information of their whereabouts, but no one seems to know or care what's happened to them." And in a loud voice, almost shouting, "I want to know where they are and when they'll arrive and I want to know today."

Colonel Salisbury-Jones looked at Dickie with a wan, quizzical smile.

"I appreciate your concern for your men, Colonel. Things are a little chaotic here at present. As your men have not arrived we'll have a look at last week's movement orders out of Heraklion," and turning towards Captain de Bouvier, "Peter, please get me copies of last week's movement orders." Then he addressed Dickie. "Please take a seat while we sort this one out."

Dickie slumped into an easy chair in a corner of the office while the senior officer thumbed through a pile of buff yellow-coloured papers.

"Ah, here we are. SS *Hesperus* left Heraklion at 0400 hours on the 22nd, so they should have made it here by the 24th. As you are aware, Colonel, there is no record of their arrival." Dickie snorted and the colonel looked up sharply and perused the files. "Yes, here we are, *Hesperus* re-docked at Heraklion on 27th at 1315. Troops disembarked. Ballast problems." The colonel continued to leaf through the yellow pages. "And this is the last entry dated yesterday, the 1st of April, 'First Australian Commando Company left Heraklion 0500 hours. Destination Pireaus'. We've had two communications from Heraklion today and no reference to the *Hesperus*. Your boys, Colonel Maclean, are at sea and should arrive here tonight or, at the latest, tomorrow morning."

Dickie thanked the colonel and was about to salute and leave the office when Salisbury-Jones, as an afterthought, added, "By the way, Colonel Maclean, I think you should be told the up-to-date situation. German troops are moving up to the Yugoslav border and we believe that an attack is imminent. We also have information of German troop concentrations, some half a million men, on the Graeco-Bulgarian border. Greece will shortly be subjected to attacks from two directions. It may be that our forces will be unable to repel the Germans and we may have to evacuate. Think about it Colonel Maclean. Your boys may be better off if they don't make it to Piraeus."

Colonel Maclean's face reddened and his anger welled to the surface. He was indignant at the thought that the Pommie colonel was half-suggesting that his commando were trying to avoid a fight. He placed his bush hat firmly on his head and glowering at his superior officer said, "My commando is prepared and ready to go. When they arrive we'll show you how to deal with the Germans."

"That's the spirit," replied the colonel saluting to dismiss the truculent Australian commando officer.

Whilst Dickie was creating havoc in headquarters David took an opportunity to stroll around Constitution Square. As he approached the steps to the hotel foyer he met Tim Gammon and two Greek officers, coming from the opposite direction, laden with boxes containing wine, beer and spirits. "Hello, Tim, having a party?"

Tim Gammon looked abashed and slightly defensive. "Well, yes, David. Old Pendlebury has been here for a few days and is leaving tomorrow. We're throwing a party to see him off. Care to come along? We'll be on the hotel roof garden. Kick off at around eight."

David accepted the invitation and asked if he might bring an Australian colonel with him.

"Why not?" said Tim. "The more the merrier."

On the return journey to Piraeus Colonel Richard Maclean was in a foul mood. In his estimation everyone was a 'bastard' especially the Pommies. He blasphemed about the lack of organisation at Heraklion, and the questionable sea-worthiness of the *Hesperus* and the lack of initiative of his own staff captain. It took quite a few pints of lager at bar Ariadne to dispel his black mood. David's news that they were invited to an informal party at the Bretagne that night revived him.

"David, we'll drink the bastards dry."

Professor John Pendlebury's leaving party on the roof-top garden started with a bang at 8.30 p.m. Most of those present, a mixture of British and Greek civilians, were dressed in an array of nondescript clothing, faded drill shirts, baggy black trousers, tamoshanters and black berets. David and Dickie were in uniform. Most of the guests were Greek and seemingly unable to speak English and David, whilst mingling with the loquacious crowd, ensured that they thought he was unable to understand their language. The wine, ouzo and beer flowed freely.

Pendlebury, the guest of honour, was toasted on several occasions in both languages. He was a tall, thin, round-shouldered man with greying hair, an imperious aquiline nose and a glass eye. Tim informed David that Pendlebury was a 'big man' in Crete, a renowned archaeologist and revered by the Cretans. David spoke to him briefly and in turn was introduced to Peter Smith, Monty Woodhouse, Michael Forrester and Peter Ferman. Dickie Maclean withdrew into his shell and stood drinking feverishly near the balustrade overlooking Constitution Square. None of the British personnel were forthcoming with information on their movements and posting. They were only interested in circulating amongst themselves and breaking up into groups of two or three for whispered conversations in the darker corners of the roof garden.

The Greeks, however, let themselves go and, as their blood alcohol rose, so their spirits soared and they danced, laughed and sang together to the plaintive sound of a bazouki. *In vino veritas.* The Greek tongues were wagging and David discovered without difficulty that his British civilian compatriots were engaged in clandestine activities and the letters SOE were repeated at frequent intervals.

The noisy party came to an abrupt halt when the visibly inebriated Dickie started squaring up to Peter Smith.

"Call me a convict would you, you Pommie bastard? I've a good mind to knock your block off."

Before Smith could reply a smiling, drunken Greek stepped between the two adversaries and was sent spinning to the ground by a blow to the side of his head from Dickie. The incensed Greeks now piled in on Dickie and pulled him to the floor where a scuffle developed and he was submerged in a sea of flailing arms and legs. One of the Greeks on the fringe produced a knife and circled around the writhing mass looking for an opportunity to stab Dickie. David reacted quickly and instinctively. With a kick he sent the knife flying from the Greek's hand and then crashed his knee violently into the assailant's crotch. The man collapsed to the floor with a howl of anguish which drew the attention of his compatriots. They all turned on David and began to close in on him. At that moment Professor Pendlebury stepped in front of the advancing Greeks and, in a high-pitched squeal, shouted in Greek, "Stop. Stop."

The Greeks stopped in their tracks in response to the command of the revered professor. By now, Dickie was on his feet and shouting, "Come on you Greek bastards. Come on and have a go."

David stepped up to his friend and, placing an arm around his shoulder, led him away from the party, down the stairs, through the hotel foyer and out into Constitution Square. Once in the cool fresh air they both burst out laughing.

"What a shower. What a bunch of gutless bastards!" cried Dickie and David couldn't help but agree.

They returned to Piraeus in a happy mood and continued drinking at Bar Ariadne until midnight. On the following day, April 3rd, David informed Colonel Salisbury-Jones that the occupants of the fifth floor of Hotel Bretagne were secret agents, most working for the SOE and directed from Cairo. From the colonel's lack of interest David concluded that he already knew the nature of the clandestine operations in which the fifth floor tenants of Hotel Bretagne were involved.

War Diary

On 6th April, 1949, Field Marshal von Brauschitsch's twenty-nine divisions were released on Yugoslavia and simultaneously Greece was invaded from Bulgaria by General von Kleist's Panzer armies. From the day of the first strike until the surrender of Greece twenty-two days later, on 28th April, German superiority in the field was supreme. Allied forces, some fifty-three thousand in number, retreated rapidly to the south coast of mainland Greece and the port of Piraeus again became a lifeline, not for sustaining military action, but for evacuating troops from a defeated country. During the campaign in Greece over two thousand British and Dominion soldiers were killed or wounded and fourteen thousand taken prisoner. Most of the evacuated troops, some twenty-seven thousand, were taken to Crete. Of more importance to the war effort in the Middle East was the loss of equipment suffered on the Greek mainland. Two hundred and nine aircraft were shot down and over a hundred tanks and three hundred heavy lorries were destroyed, or abandoned, during the campaign. The loss of men and material had a profound effect on General Sir Archibald Wavell's capacity to contain Rommel's renewed offensive in Libya.

The German offensive in Greece was only four days old when the British Commander ordered preparations for evacuating his forces. On April 10th David was instructed by Colonel Salisbury-Jones to make available enough shipping to evacuate twenty thousand men from Piraeus. No further reinforcements were to be landed and troopships were re-routed to Crete. Cargo ships were retained in harbour after discharging their loads and, in some instances, dumped their cargoes at sea, returning empty to Pireaus. Evacuation of non-essential personnel and civilian embassy staff commenced on 11th April. By this time, Colonel Richard Maclean, despairing of the arrival of his commando troop, left for the Alikmon line to see for himself the battle between the Aussies and the advancing Germans.

The lightly defended Alikmon line held the German advance at Mount Olympus for five days and then the floodgates opened and German Panzers and infantry raced southwards to the coast. On the 9th of April von Kleist's 2nd Panzer Division captured Salonika, accepting surrender of the 2nd Greek army. The rest of the Greek Army and the Cretan V Division were surrounded in Albania and surrendered to the Italians. By the 20th April British and Dominion forces had reached the south coast of mainland Greece and the military evacuation started in earnest.

The evacuation route was from Piraeus and south coast ports to Crete and troops were instructed to dump their weapons at sea. No heavy equipment was ferried to Crete. David and Major Bush were continually employed in supervising the evacuation and kept a record of the ship's name, maritime complement, number of troops boarded and intended destination. By and large the evacuation proceeded without incident. British units amongst the evacuees were orderly and well-behaved but the Anzacs refused to accept regimentation with equanimity. Their unit commanders tended to be domineering and incapable of accepting a queue on a 'first come first off' principle. The Anzacs were masters at queue jumping and this led to a great deal of acrimony between British and Dominion infantry. If only Dickie Maclean were around to sort out his petulant countrymen.

On the 18th April, 1941, the Greek Prime Minister, Alexandros Koryzis, overwhelmed by events, shot himself at Hotel Bretagne. There were daily requests from the Bretagne for special boats to evacuate important personnel from Piraeus and from the smaller ports around Athens and Cape Sunion. The royal household left by Sunderland flying boat from Phaleron to Alexandria on the 22nd April, followed next day by the King of the Hellenes and Colonel Blunt, the British Military attaché. On the 24th April, the motor-steam yacht, Kalanthe, sailed south with the main group of

SOE operatives. Each day David made a hazardous journey to Hotel Bretagne to pick up officers and men for evacuation. On the 25th April he found the hotel almost deserted. Tim Gammon was still at work, standing by his radio transmitter.

"Get out, David, there's no one left here now. I'll look after myself. Good luck."

David said his goodbyes and best wishes and drove back to the Ariadne for his last night on Greek soil. Standing at the bar, large as life, and holding on firmly to a mug of ouzo was Dickie. He had been involved in the bitter battle at Mount Olympus and had escaped unscathed, making his getaway southwards with an Australian rearguard party. The Ariadne had been cleaned out of lager and wine by the departing soldiery and David and Dickie celebrated their reunion with ouzo. Before dawn on April 26th, nursing a mammoth hangover, David toured the dockside and made certain that all military personnel had embarked on the last two ships to leave Piraeus. He then collected Dickie from bed and together with a mixed party of forty infantrymen and airmen they boarded a one and a half thousand ton collier, the *Julia*, which sailed out of Piraeus harbour about half an hour before first light. The *Julia* was the last scheduled ship to leave harbour before the arrival of von Kleist's Panzers at tea-time on the 26th April, 1941.

*

The crossing from Piraeus to Soudha Bay in Crete took forty hours. Within one hour of clearing the harbour the *Julia* was attacked by a Stuka dive bomber on dawn patrol. The bombs missed the old tub by one hundred yards and during the attack Colonel Maclean lay flat on the deck and emptied a magazine from his Sten gun in the general direction of the screeching aeroplane, oblivious of the fact that the maximum killing distance of a Sten gun was forty yards and his chances of hitting a moving target at four hundred feet was infinitesimal. Still, he felt better after the attack and warned his comrades on the ship and *Luftwaffe* pilots in the air.

"If the bastards come again I'll get one of the buggers."

The Stukas did come again, twice, but both attacks were abortive and the bombs landed wide of the *Julia*, though the detonations shook the old ship to its keel. *Julia's* hold was thick with black coal-dust and grime and the black-faced evacuees stayed on deck where they presented an inviting and sitting target for marauding fighters.

In view of increasing German air activity, the Greek captain took his ship into a sheltered cove off the island of Cytheria, where they hove to for the rest of the day and, exhausted, the party fell asleep. The *Julia* steamed out of Cytheria at sunset and after an uneventful crossing reached Soudha in Crete at 0600 hours on the morning of 28th April, 1941.

During the crossing Dickie Maclean was strangely subdued. He spoke for a few minutes about his parents' farm in Perth and his ambition of one day owning his own sheep farm in Australia. He expressed his concern about his commando company left on the dockside at Heraklion on 20th March and wondered if they were still there. He spoke tenderly of his wife and two children left in their terraced house in Sydney. And then, uncharacteristically and for the first time they had been together, he asked David about his life and military training.

A cool night breeze swept across *Julia's* deck as the returning warriors lay with their legs covered with tarpaulins, blankets and overcoats. Everyone spoke in whispers and there was little light banter or laughter amongst the troops. The eerie silence was broken occasionally by a deep sigh, or a snore, from the shrouded bodies lying on deck. The scratch of a match on emery paper and a sudden blaze of light, illuminating a tired face drawing on a cigarette, broke through the pitch black darkness from time to time.

David sat upright, his spine wedged against a bulwark and Dickie, smoking a cigarette, sat beside him. David sensed a serene peace descending on the ship as he outlined his career, omitting nothing, to the attentive commando colonel sitting by his side.

Dickie responded, "So you've had some commando training, David. Well done. It will be useful if we get into a tight corner."

Quite what the commando colonel meant by a tight corner David could not comprehend.

The *Julia*, rolling slightly from side to side, sailed silently and proudly across the jet black Aegean. As dawn was breaking over her starboard bow they were within sight of Crete and half an hour later the tired, battered, old collier was threading its way through a galaxy of ships, some moored and some sunken, dotting the sheltered harbour at Soudha. The *Julia* had made it and David and Dickie landed safely on the island of Crete.

Crete Before the Invasion: May 1941

As dawn was breaking on 28th April 1941 the old collier approached a jetty at Soudha with David and Dickie standing on its prow. They could just see the massive bulk of the White Mountain in the background and it seemed at one stage as if the *Julia* might sail straight into the base of the rock. Apart from the chugging of boat engines and an occasional cough from the forbidding darkness an eerie silence prevailed in the harbour.

By the time they landed on the dock, weak, early morning sunrays were filtering through the hazy, smoky air over the harbour and David saw the vast outlines of a beached cruiser, *The Duke of York*, listing heavily to port. Behind him in the eight kilometre long bay of Soudha there were thirty or more ships of various tonnage, some standing proudly in the water and others identified only by masts and rigging showing above the oil-covered sea. They walked to the end of the jetty where a New Zealand captain wrote down their details on a clipboard and, looking at Dickie, said:

"I think, Sir, you and your party should move inland as quickly as possible. We get regular dawn raids from Jerry. I'm expecting the Stukas to show up any minute. So keep your heads down!"

The colonel thanked the New Zealander and, taking charge of the small bedraggled party, strode purposefully towards the dockside buildings and then along a dusty road towards the olive trees and brush on the sharply rising escarpments at the base of the towering White Mountain. They had barely gone half a mile up the road when a squadron of Stukas came out of the haze to the north and, one at a time, plummeted screeching and wailing towards earth releasing their bombs at the last moment and pulling out abruptly from the dive to turn and fly out to sea.

There were three waves of Stuka attacks that morning. The hapless, stranded *Duke of York* appeared to be a prime target, although some of the bombs were dropped on the dockside buildings and surrounding olive groves. Messerschmitt fighters, accompanying the Stukas, strafed the roads leading away from Soudha docks and the unopposed raid was over in half an hour. Colonel Maclean quickly moved the party deeper into the olive groves away from the dockside area.

During the previous three days remnants of General Freyberg's New Zealand division, evacuated from Rafina in southern Greece, had arrived in Soudha and were now bivouacked in the olive groves around Dssiklakia. The enterprising New Zealanders had constructed makeshift tents from ground sheets and overcoats. Food was scarce but, despite their heavy losses in Greece and the shame of a hasty evacuation, morale was excellent. The New Zealand officers had no information about the position of Australian and British troops on Crete. Colonel Maclean was hell-bent on getting to his commando unit in Heraklion but there was no transport available. The mixed band of soldiers and airmen had no alternative but to make camp amongst the New Zealanders and, during the cold night they sat shivering with teeth chattering as David and Dickie discussed their future strategy. Top priority was to get to Heraklion, one hundred and forty kilometres to the east. Dickie announced that the next day he would start walking to rejoin his unit but David had a better idea.

"The First Welch, my battalion, are in Khania about ten miles east of here. We could walk there and get a lift to Heraklion."

Dickie said, "Let's go now" but common sense prevailed and they left at first light on the following day before the daily hate bombing.

The First Welch Regiment had been a garrison battalion in Khania since mid-February. When David and Dickie arrived they were greeted as long lost friends and ushered to the officers' mess for a hot bath, change of clothing, a few drinks and a substantial meal. Later the commanding officer, Daddy Duncan, took them aside.

"So you want to get to Heraklion, Colonel Maclean? As you are aware this place is in chaos. My men are manning the beach defences here in Khania. We've got about two thousand New Zealanders in and around Maleme and Kastelli. You have seen another couple of thousand Anzacs camped around Soudha. I believe the Australians have been evacuated mainly to Rethymno and Heraklion and the main British force is in Heraklion. Dotted amongst the divisions are Greek battalions of varying strength and capability. Getting you to Heraklion won't be easy. Petrol is scarce. Tomorrow I'm sending my two IC to Chappell's headquarters in a fifteen hundredweight. He'll get you there if anyone can." Then looking at David, "Communication between Heraklion and Cairo is easy, so you could find out your next move from your HQ in Cairo."

That night David and Dickie were entertained in the officers' mess. Colonel Richard Maclean was a star, entertaining his fellow officers with jokes and anecdotes well into the early hours. His references to the 'Pommie bastards' brought forth peals of laughter. It was not until the next day that a sober Dickie realised that a 'Pommie bastard' was not an insult to the Welsh but referred to an Englishman of unspecified parentage.

Major 'Hoot' Gibson drove the two officers to Heraklion, a distance of about a hundred and forty kilometres, but, due to roadblocks and traffic, progress was slow and they did not arrive at Brigadier Chappell's headquarters until early evening. The brigadier greeted them with news that Lieutenant General Freyberg, who had arrived the previous day on the destroyer *Ajax*, had been made commander in chief of all forces on Crete. He had no news of the location of Colonel Maclean's commandos but there were so many unidentified units, or parts of units, all over the place that they could be anywhere.

The brigadier suggested, "Try the docks area first. That would be my advice."

David was given permission to dictate a message to Colonel Sharples asking for instructions and then saying their goodbyes to Major Gibson, David and Dickie left brigade headquarters and walked along the dockside which was littered and almost completely strangled with the paraphernalia of war. Heraklion harbour was bombed daily by the Germans but the concentration of bombardment was not as heavy as the Soudha attacks. David and Colonel Maclean threaded their way down the dockside where ships of all sizes and shapes were anchored, many showing the effects of damage suffered at sea from aerial bombardment. As they passed a battered, blackened ship sitting low in the water and holed at the water line a shout came from amongst some crates piled high against the retaining sea wall:

"Colonel Maclean, here, Sir!"

Dickie Maclean stopped in half-stride and spun around to his left to face a curly headed, red-faced, bronzed Australian sergeant wearing only a pair of shorts with his stripes held onto his left upper arm by an elastic band. As the colonel approached the sergeant crammed his bush hat on his head, slung a loaded machine-pistol over his left shoulder, jumped down to the dockside from the crate on which he had been sitting and saluted with his right hand whilst concealing a lighted cigarette behind his back, cupped in the palm of his left hand.

"Sergeant Hawkins, where is Captain Tucker and the rest of the boys?"

The sergeant had three commandos with him, all stripped to the waist, positioned around and guarding a pile of equipment stacked under a dirty brown tarpaulin.

"Captain Tucker left here yesterday with most of the company, leaving me and three of the lads on guard. Apart from this three-tonner the rest of the company's stuff is hidden outside town. We ran into trouble..."

The sergeant stammered and, looking at David, he stopped in mid-sentence, eyeing his colonel and visually asking if he should continue. Colonel Maclean, half turning to David, said, "Sergeant, this is Captain David Green from some bloody Welsh regiment. He's a commando and one of us. Carry on, Hawkins."

The sergeant continued, "After you left, Sir, we got back on that old tub behind you," the sergeant indicated the battered and immobilised *Hesperus* sitting low in the water, "and, after a night at sea, we were back here again on the dock with more engine trouble. About a week later they got her going again and we had another go at getting across to you in Greece. This time she lasted two days at sea and then a bastard Stuka plonked a bomb in her side. We lost five men in that attack. The old *Hesperus* again brought the company and equipment back to the dock. The next day, that'll be five days ago, a British colonel ordered us off the dockside but Captain Tucker refused to budge. Three days ago the colonel came back and ordered us to remove all the lorries and equipment to a bivouac area outside the port. Captain Tucker had no choice. We left some small arms and ammunition and one truck here under guard and the rest of the convoy went to a vehicle laager. The place was already overcrowded. The major in charge turned us away so Captain Tucker took us about ten miles to the east and found a farmhouse near a place called Piskopiano, where the lorries and stuff have been stored away in a barn. I can take you there. I came back the next day and we've been guarding our kit here waiting for you to come. Glad to see you, Sir."

The sergeant grinned broadly, "The Pommie bastards tried to push us off the dock but we've dug in" and then looking at David he blushed, "Begging your pardon, Captain Green."

David smiled and Dickie Maclean laughed, "He's not a Pommie, Hawkins. He's one of us. Where is Captain Tucker now, Sergeant?"

"Brigadier Hargest came around yesterday and took the company in battle order off to Rethymno. Only nine commandos are left in this area – myself and the three lads here and Corporal Anderson with four boys at the farmhouse in Piskopiano."

Colonel Maclean took David aside to the back of one of the three-ton lorries parked nearby.

"David, I am not sure what's going on. Colonel Campbell apparently commands the Australian Brigade at Rethymno. I knew him well in Australia. He's not a commando but I expect he has something special lined up for my boys. I must get up to Rethymno straight away. Will you sort things out here and go and have a look at the equipment in that farmhouse, wherever it is? Take Hawkins and the boys from here with you. Stay put at the farmhouse but come into Chappell's headquarters everyday. I'll get a message to you and tell you where we can rendezvous. Don't let anyone take the stores away from you. They belong to my company and I want to keep them. You'll find Hawkins is a good man to back you up if there's any trouble."

For another hour Colonel Maclean busied himself with instructions to Sergeant Hawkins and commandeered a fifteen hundredweight lorry and an RASC driver to take him up to Rethymno. David stood around in the background until the colonel had left and then settled down to get to know Sergeant Hawkins and the three Aussie commandos. They bunked at the dockside overnight whilst David slept on the floor in Brigadier Chappell's orderly room.

Early next morning, after the dawn raid, David and Sergeant Hawkins made a full reconnaissance of the dockside, inspecting each building and the lighthouse tower at the western end of the harbour entrance. From the tower David could see the general configuration of the port itself and, a mile distant to the east, the runway of the military airfield. The view of the airfield was partially obscured by the sheds along a high wall on the eastern side of the harbour entrance. He pointed out to Sergeant Hawkins the exact spot where mortars might be positioned to be effective in bombardment of both the harbour and the airfield.

By the time they returned to the trucks Sergeant Hawkins' commandos had already packed the guns and equipment into the back of a three-tonner and they set off on the thirty kilometre drive to Piskopiano. David, sitting beside the driver, kept a sharp eye on the terrain between Heraklion and the hillside retreat. Travelling eastwards the land on the right hand side of the road was flat and thick with orange and olive groves leading up to hilly escarpments covered with scrubland and rocks. About eight kilometres outside Heraklion a steep escarpment almost three hundred foot high, running from north to south, made an excellent observation point and came down to within two kilometres of the road, opposite the fishing village of Gournes. Between Gournes and Hersonisos the flat ground on the right receded as the ever-present Dikti mountain range encroached northwards towards the shore line.

At Hersonisos Sergeant Hawkins directed the three-tonner southwards on to a dusty, uneven road which, after one kilometre, began to rise sharply as it started to ascend the Pirgia foothills to reach the hamlet of Piskopiano. The loaded truck had to struggle hard for the next two kilometres up a mountain track leading south-west from the village in the direction of Kastelli, seemingly going straight into the belly of the main mountain in the Pirgia range. The lorry swung to the right off the dirt track along a rutted, shrub-covered path which brought them into an open yard with a small farmhouse situated at its northern end, whilst the westward side had two large outhouses on the banks of a dried-out river bed.

Corporal Anderson was already in the middle of the yard when the truck arrived. He greeted his sergeant with a smile and a pat on the back and looked a little suspiciously at David. By now the welcoming party had increased to three, the corporal explaining that one commando was acting as a lookout near the road junction and the other was out foraging for lunch. The corporal had been having tea with the Cretan farmer when the truck arrived and Sergeant Hawkins suggested that they should go to the farm to meet the owner adding, "The old man speaks no English."

Spiros Constantinos was a typical middle-aged Cretan, of medium height, dark-eyed with black crinkly hair, an aquiline nose and a broad black moustache covering his upper lip. When David entered the dark, sparsely furnished, earthen-floored living room, Spiros was sitting behind a solid wooden table clutching a cup of tea, whilst his wife, dressed completely in black, hovered attentively in the background. He rose to his feet and shook hands with a firm friendly grip. David immediately warmed to this proud-looking farmer and exchanged greetings in Greek. Sergeant Hawkins took off his hat scratched his forehead and looked at David.

"You speak the lingo?"

"Just a little," David replied with a smile. Spiros was overjoyed to meet someone with whom he could converse. He asked David to sit at the table and spoke to his wife ordering her to prepare some food for the British officer and his Australian friend. In no time some black bread, goat's cheese and olives were produced for the guests and washed down with cups of stringent tea. Spiros explained that the farm was his inheritance and that it had been owned by the Constantinos family for over three hundred years. Sadly he only had two unmarried daughters so the farm would eventually have to be sold. The main crops of the farm came from the olive groves but he also had a herd of thirty goats and some twenty sheep on the lower reaches of the Pirgias and a few chickens in the outhouses. His elder daughter, Antia, was out looking after the goats at present and the younger daughter, Stephia, was at the back of the house washing and preparing an evening meal.

The conversation in Greek was incomprehensible to Sergeant Hawkins who stood up abruptly.

"Thanks, Spiros, for the food and char," and went outside to the yard to chat with his boys.

David told Spiros about the fighting in Greece and the older man became quite agitated, seeming to vehemently resent the German attack on his country. Spiros asserted that the Italians, though cowardly, were basically men of honour, but the Germans were different. They had annihilated the Fifth Cretan Division in southern Albania and some eight thousand gallant Cretans had been killed or captured.

"Do you think the Germans will come to Crete?" asked Spiros.

David explained that he could not answer the question. Eyes flashing and banging the table with his fist the excited Cretan shouted, "I hope they will come, I would wish to fight them."

David prayed silently that the Germans would not come to Crete. If they did they would certainly disrupt and destroy the lifestyle and livelihood of proud, but simple, Cretan peasants like Spiros.

During the following two days David and Sergeant Hawkins made a complete inventory of the equipment stored in the farmyard sheds. All the items were well greased and packed in waterproof sheets. Together with supplies brought from the dockside Colonel Maclean's commando at Piskopiano had a command vehicle, three fifteen hundredweight trucks, four Bedford three-tonners and a water carrier, all neatly parked in the farmyard. Inside the shed the other supplies were stacked in orderly fashion, thirty-five Lee Enfield 303s, twenty-five Sten guns, four six inch mortars, twelve landmines, five crates of hand grenades and thousands of rounds of ammunition for the rifles and Stens. In another part of the storage shed there was a plentiful supply of tinned meats, sugar, beans, fruit, chocolate and sweets. A large hamper contained water bottles, two pairs of binoculars, rubber and latex tubing and a plentiful supply of webbing and straps together with spare shirts, shorts, underclothes and plimsolls.

David called on Spiros at the farmhouse once or twice a day. The Cretan was intensely nationalistic and impressed David with his patriotism and high opinion of the fighting qualities of the Cretan soldier. David asked the question as to what would happen if the British and Australian soldiers left Crete and the Germans came. Spiros' reply was a fierce:

"We will fight them and drive them out of Crete. We, the Cretan people, will make a civilian army and go into the mountains and fight the Germans from there. They'll never get us out of our mountains. Look at the Diktis."

On the second day David met Spiros' eldest daughter Antia, a plain, dumpy and extremely shy woman but the younger daughter Stephia, though plain of face, had dark brown flashing, inviting eyes, a curvaceous body and a vivacity which seemed ready to bubble to the surface at the least provocation. Corporal Anderson was apparently smitten by her youthful exuberance and spent much of his day working in the fields and tending the goats with Stephia as his consort.

Two days later David and Sergeant Hawkins drove back to Brigadier Chappell's headquarters in Heraklion. During the journey, with the sea on the right hand side of the vehicle, David noted that they crossed four bridges over dried river beds running south to north across the plain of Heraklion and its myriad of windmills. At brigade headquarters there was a message from Colonel Sharples.

"Take a good look at the nest. Come back to Cairo to collect the chickens."

There was no news from Rethymno about Colonel Maclean and his commando company. On the way back to Piskopiano David conceived the idea of sequestering some of the supplies in the farmhouse and finding a hideout to conceal the equipment for possible future use by resistance fighters. By now Sergeant Hawkins was getting distinctly unhappy and asked permission to take one of the lorries to Rethymno the next day. Permission was granted and David also wished to know what had happened to his friend, Colonel Dickie Maclean. Sergeant Hawkins and two commandos left for Rethymno early the following morning and David took the opportunity to carry out a reconnaissance of the olive groves and farm pastures in the surrounding areas.

Spiros' farm was triangular in shape. The apex of the triangle nestled between two almost vertical rocky outcrops, about one kilometre from the farm house, from which emerged a small dry river bed which bisected the triangle from its apex to its base. On each side of the dried out rivulet olive trees were planted in a seemingly haphazard fashion. In between the trees and covering the low hills on each side of the triangle was thick scrubland, ideal grazing for Spiros' sheep and goats. David walked southwards along the edge of the dry stream until he reached the apex of the funnel where the river track ended under a sheer rock face, its front worn smooth by a waterfall which David surmised must be active during the rainy season. From ground level he could not see where the water emerged from the rock.

Within five minutes David had scaled the rock face to reach a flat plateau about thirty metres long and twenty metres wide. A portion of the plateau at the waterfall end was smooth and surrounded by a rocky balustrade where obviously rainwater collected in winter months. The rest of the plateau was carpeted with fine moss, scrub, thistle and cacti. The dry stream emerged from a vertical cleft, almost six foot high and four foot wide, in the rock face of the main escarpment and the edges of the exit were concealed by overgrown shrub and fern. David pushed his way through the cleft in the rock face to find himself in a large cavern extending about thirty yards into the rock with a series of ledges along the side walls. The interior of the cavern was dark, cool, and eerily quiet apart from a regular plop of water falling from the forty foot high ceiling into a water-filled hollow in the floor.

David emerged into the blazing midday sun and, standing on the ledge, looked northwards towards Piskopiano and the sea. He had a clear view of Spiros' olive grove and the roof of the farm outhouses and beyond the farm he saw the tip of the church spire at Piskopiano and, in the far distance, the hazy blue ribbon of the seashore around Hersonisos. Directly westwards from the rocky plateau on the other side of the dried out stream there was another sheer cliff with a flat ledge in the rock face. The cave would make an excellent hideout and storage site if he ever needed to have an operational base in Crete.

Sergeant Hawkins and his driver returned from Rethymno on the following day with the disastrous news that Colonel Maclean had been killed in action and that Captain Tucker and all but two of the company of the eighty-four commandos had been taken prisoner by the Germans. Major General Freyberg and other high-ranking officers of the New Zealand and Australian Expeditionary Force had been ferried on HMS *Ajax* to Rethymno from Corinth, arriving on the 26th April. They brought news that two kayaks carrying two generals and many other senior officers had been forced to land on Poros. The captain of the *Ajax* proposed they should make a dash for Poros under the cover of darkness and land a rescue party on the island. Colonel Maclean, Captain Tucker and eighty-four commandos left on the *Ajax* on a rescue mission on the 1st May and landed without difficulty, but the Germans were waiting, having been alerted by one of the kayak captains and having brought in a battalion of paratroopers.

Colonel Maclean was killed early in the action and, after a brief, but fierce battle, Captain Tucker was forced to surrender with seventy-three commandos still standing. The high-ranking Anzac officers were all captured and taken into captivity. Two Australian commandos, who brought back the news of the abortive action, managed to escape by commandeering a kayak at gunpoint and eventually making their way back to Soudha bay.

Sergeant Hawkins had informed the adjutant at Rethymno that he had a corporal and nine commandos at Piskopiano in his charge and in addition lorries, rifles, ammunition and general stores. He asked what should be done with his small but well-equipped unit. The adjutant ordered that the lorries and men should be brought to Rethymno but that the supplies were superfluous to his needs and, if the British commander in Heraklion did not want them, Sergeant Hawkins was to destroy the whole lot.

David withdrew from the party that had gathered around the sergeant and sat on a stone slab near the edge of the watercourse thinking, 'The Nazis have done it again. First it was my father and mother, then my poor old pal Perce and now, Dickie Maclean. I have a score to settle with the Germans.'

At that moment David formulated a plan to transfer the moveable goods to the waterfall cave for storage and then to evacuate the farm, sending the lorries to Rethymno and keeping one fifteen-hundredweight truck for himself to reconnoitre the surrounding district. He returned to sit with the quiet, dispirited and sorrowful commando group who had lost their comrades and their charismatic commanding officer in a futile action on a dusty island in the Aegean.

One evening after supper at the farmhouse, where David had experienced traditional Cretan hospitality, Spiros requested, "Would it be possible for one of the soldiers to look after my sheep and goats for two days? I am going to a wedding at Kastelli with my wife and two daughters. The celebration will last two days."

David put this proposal to Sergeant Hawkins and it was agreed that Corporal Anderson would look after the animals. After the meal David and Sergeant Hawkins took a stroll around the farmyard in the bright light of a full moon. The sergeant was puffing contentedly on a cigarette.

"Captain Green, Sir, I have been thinking. You've got contacts with HQ at Heraklion. Could you take the supplies to Brigadier Chappell's quartermaster to see if they want them? If they don't then could I leave it to you to destroy the lot? I'll leave Corporal Anderson with you. He's one of the company's explosive experts. I'm going to move across to Rethymno at first light and take two three-tonners and a fifteen hundredweight with me and most of the men. If I leave Corporal Anderson and two drivers for the other three-tonners, you will have a fifteen hundredweight to yourself. Once the supplies are off-loaded, or destroyed, I want the drivers to report to me in Colonel Campbell's headquarters at Rethymno."

"Good thinking, Sergeant," David replied.

At first light the sergeant in a fifteen hundredweight led the three-tonners in convoy out of the farmhouse and westwards to

Rethymno, closely followed by Spiros in Cretan costume, sitting on a donkey, attended by his female pedestrian entourage. After breakfast David instructed the corporal and his two commandos to start loading the three-tonners. In the fifteen hundredweight he drove westwards to Brigadier Chappell's headquarters in Heraklion where he made certain that there were no further messages from Cairo or Rethymno. Brigadier Chappell's adjutant was helpful:

"I don't think that headquarters need any supplies at present. Transport yes, but rifles and bully beef no. I suggest you try the vehicle laager on the outskirts of town."

David drove to the vehicle bivouac, but so crowded was the area with broken down or damaged lorries that he was unable to find a senior officer. Exasperated he drove out of the gates of the laager and, as he was near the airport, he decided to recce the area.

The long runway of Heraklion airport ran along the seashore. The control tower and main buildings were at the westward end of the runway which offered shelter and hangars for aeroplanes on the ground. Opposite the control tower and a mile or so away were two conical mounds, shaped like female breasts, nicknamed 'the Two Charlies', and, from this vantage point, David had a clear view of the whole runway and hangar buildings and, about a mile to the west, the warehouses of the east dock of Heraklion harbour. Behind these pimple-like mounds of rock the ground was hollowed out and the basin had been planted with orange trees. In amongst the trees at the very base of the mounds David saw the red roofs of about a dozen chicken coops. He descended the hillock and, jumping into his vehicle, made good speed to get back to the farmhouse by mid-morning and by that time he had made up his mind to transfer the arms, ammunition and supplies to the hideaway in the cave at the head of the olive grove.

*

Corporal Jim Anderson hailed from a farming community near Adelaide. A renegade throughout his youth and at school, he grew up into a short, squat, muscular, abrasive man, an area middle-weight boxing champion and a tearaway brawler and drunkard in his home town saloons. His family and the local townsfolk were relieved when he volunteered for the army and enlisted in the commandos. The strict disciplinary regime of commando training had not completely eradicated his resentment of authority but he learnt to knuckle under and obey his superiors and became a reliable soldier. He was promoted corporal in charge of the company mortar section before the unit left Australia.

David approached the tough, stocky corporal as he was walking around the lorries inspecting their loads.

"Corporal Anderson, I've been to Heraklion this morning and Chappell's HQ don't want our guns and supplies. I know Sergeant Hawkins told you to scuttle the lot if they're not needed but I have a better idea. There's a cave at the top end of the olive grove where we could hide the stuff. It's all wrapped up in waterproof canvas and all the rifles and bullets are greased so the kit should keep dry and in good working order. What do you think?"

The corporal screwed up his forehead in concentration for fully half a minute.

"It's a shame to chuck it all away Sir, but who's going to use it?"

David replied, "I don't really know. Corporal, but it might come in handy for our own troops, or for the Cretans, if Jerry does attempt to take Crete."

"Right Sir. Let's do it. We won't be able to get the mortars into the cave so they'll stay in the lorries. I want to go up to the top of the grove in any case to get the goats in."

For the rest of the day and the following morning David, Corporal Anderson and the two Aussie drivers worked hard to move their supplies into the cave. David had rigged two thirty foot ropes from the edge of the plateau to the ground and these were used to haul up the larger crates and ammunition boxes. By careful manipulation the two drivers managed to get the lorries into the grove some fifty yards distant from the cave and the men manhandled the supplies for the rest of the way. As each item of equipment, or supply crate, arrived in the cave David stowed them on the ledges at the sides, away from the watercourse and clear of the floor. After ten hours of hard graft the transfer of supplies was complete. David took care to conceal the cave entrance with branches and brushwood, unhitched the ropes and ordered the men to erase the lorries' tyre tracks in the powdered earth. By the evening of the second day all that remained in the yard of the farmhouse were two three-tonners, loaded with mortars and one fifteen hundredweight truck. Spiros' outhouses were cleared of all evidence of military presence and occupation. From now on David and the soldiers would sleep, eat and rest in the vehicles in the farmyard.

Spiros and his family returned from the wedding in Kastelli in good spirits. Jim Anderson was particularly pleased to see Stephia and David explained that Sergeant Hawkins' party had already left and that the rest would also be leaving within a few days. This news saddened Stephia and she clung on to her corporal with increasing tenacity. It was obvious to all that, despite language difficulties, a strong bond had developed between the dark-eyed Cretan woman and the swarthy, muscle-bound, tenacious little Australian corporal. On the 10th May David took his small convoy and the mortars to Heraklion. He first reported to Brigadier Chappell's headquarters but there were no messages from Cairo and none expected from Rethymno. David then drove his vehicles into the olive groves at the base of the breast-like mounds which protected the westward end of the Heraklion airfield. Leaving the two drivers he took Corporal Anderson up the steep incline to the top of one of the hillocks where they had a clear view of the runway and command buildings. Corporal Anderson needed no explanations. His eyes lit up as he glanced over his shoulder at the three vehicles parked in the hollowed out olive grove.

David asked simply, "Where would you put the mortars?"

Pointing with his index finger the corporal replied, "Down there, Sir, near the chicken sheds."

They came down the hill and inspected the coops. A generous smattering of fowl excreta on the floor indicated that they had recently been occupied but that the birds had flown or, more probably, had been devoured by the soldiers and airmen of Heraklion garrison.

Corporal Anderson and the two drivers got to work immediately. The floorboards in two of the sheds were removed and they dug a circular hole, some three yards in diameter, in the hardened earth into which the base plates of the mortars were firmly entrenched. The mortars themselves were fixed on to the plates and the floorboards replaced around them, the mortars sticking up through the floor like smokeless chimneys. The mortar shells and ignition caps were laid carefully under the floorboards and after the corporal had made some quick calculations he set the mortars at an angle.

"I'm fixing one to hit the buildings and the other on the end of the runway. The distance from here to the target is about one thousand two hundred yards. They may need adjusting but we'll only know that when we fire the first one. We'll need a spotter on that hill that looks like a tit."

"Thank you, Corporal," said David. "Let's hope we never need to use them."

David took the sweat-sodden men, covered in smelly chicken manure, down to the harbour for a bathe and a swim and then the two three-tonners were driven away to Rethymno. Corporal Anderson stayed with David and his parting words to one of the drivers were:

"Tell Sergeant Hawkins that I'm staying on for a bit with Captain Green. Tell him that I haven't got rid of the mortars yet."

He omitted to add, he also wanted to be around the farm in Stephia's company.

On the 11th May David took Corporal Anderson in the fifteen hundredweight truck in a southerly direction across the Dikti mountain range to the south coast of Crete. The road was narrow, windy and practically deserted, with precipitous drops on the left hand side for most of the journey. They motored through the mountain villages of Pandeleimon, Kastelli, Aghios Paresyevi, Tavayia, Hondros and finally reached the sea at Keratokombou a distance of thirty-eight kilometres but, due to the tortuous mountain roads, the journey took nearly four hours. David estimated that on foot the hike would take the best part of a day. On the outward and homeward journeys they received hospitality from Cretan villagers who were pleased to share their food and wine with the Allied soldiers.

On the following day David left the farm at an early hour and drove himself in the fifteen hundredweight truck into Heraklion. He checked for messages at Brigadier Chappell's headquarters and then set out to drive the hundred and forty kilometre journey to the Welch regimental headquarters at Khania. He made a diversion at Rethymno and searched for Sergeant Hawkins but the whole area was crowded and teeming with soldiers and vehicles. He soon gave up and continued on his way.

On arrival he reported to Colonel Duncan's headquarters in the middle of the town. As usual Colonel Daddy Duncan was clear and precise in his assessment of the situation.

"General Freyberg's Creforce headquarters is in a quarry near here. They have been warned that Jerry has his eyes on Crete and that a seaborne landing is to be expected on the 17th May, in five days time. I don't think the Germans will come by sea as we still have naval superiority. Jerry commands the air and I expect an airborne landing, possibly in the Heraklion area, although they might go for Maleme airfield as well. At the moment the Welch are facing the sea, dug in, defending the beaches and possible landing sites. The New Zealanders are further west and cover Maleme and Kastelli and, as you already know, the Aussies are mainly camped around Rethymno with the British and Greeks in Heraklion. We've got the best part of thirty thousand troops on the ground and should be able to stop Adolf's boys in their tracks."

The colonel paused to relight his pipe.

"General Freyberg has got a lot on his plate at the moment. He is being plagued by half a dozen local chieftains demanding arms and ammunition and hanging around his HQ. He's sending them around to me tomorrow so I would be obliged if you could stay around for a couple of days and look after them. I know you speak their language and that would be useful."

Major Gibson interjected, "It may be, Sir, that it would be better if David did not disclose his ability to speak Greek. In that way, by listening, he might learn something about what's going on with these wallahs."

David and Colonel Duncan were in agreement with the major.

The Cretan party arrived earlier than expected. The officers were still sitting at breakfast when an orderly sergeant announced that a group of six strange looking men had arrived outside the mess and were disembarking from a three-tonner.

"I think they're locals, sir."

The colonel and David left the mess to greet the arrivals. In the warm early morning sun outside the mess steps were six middle-aged, medium-sized Cretans standing proudly erect with their right hands clutching ivory-handled daggers tucked into their multi-coloured cummerbunds. They were dressed in traditional Cretan clothing, black, intricately woven, cloth caps called *kepis*, short embroidered cutaway jackets, flamboyant coloured waistcoats and wide legged crap-catcher breeches tucked into their calf length boots. Each one had a flowing dark moustache and piercing deep brown eyes. David thought they looked like a circus troupe but the arrogance of their stance and demeanour convinced him that this was a group of men who meant business.

Colonel Duncan introduced his officers and greeted the visitors.

"Good morning gentlemen and welcome to my headquarters. This is Captain Green who will look after you," nodding towards David.

David responded with a few faltering salutations in Greek at which a Cretan, who had parked himself in front of his compatriots, remarked, "Ah, so you speak Greek?"

David responded by rolling his eyes and shrugging his shoulders, an indication to the guests that he did not understand. Colonel Duncan invited his visitors into the mess for breakfast. Three of the Cretans were headmen of their own particular region in western Crete. The other three were their aides, one of whom spoke English poorly and acted as interpreter for the group. The three Cretan *kapitans* were Georgou Papadakis, Georgou Halkiadakis, from Rethymno and Georgou Psychoundakis and David had the task of showing the party around the Khania defences.

Ignorant of the fact that David could understand their conversation the three *kapitans* spoke freely amongst themselves and it soon became evident that they did not trust each other and that each coveted the position of Senior *Kapitan* in western Crete. They also had heated arguments about control of the whole of Crete and the names of Manoli Bandouvas and Satanas frequently cropped up in conversation. The eastern Cretan *kapitans* were regarded as a big threat, as they seemed to have protection from the British and were the favourites of the resistance agent, Pendlebury, whose base was at Knossos outside Heraklion. The reason for their presence in Khania was clearly to establish contact with Freyberg's headquarters and, more importantly, to get guns and ammunition for their resistance fighters.

When David enquired through the interpreter as to how many rifles were needed Papadakis replied insolently, "Two thousand at least."

David had grave doubts as to whether any of these *kapitans* commanded more than two hundred men. Papadakis was the dominant figure of the three, an arrogant bully and an outrageous liar. David spent two days with the Cretan party and showed them the defence positions of the Welch Regiment in Khania and took them to the New Zealanders at Maleme and the Greek and New Zealand troops at Kastelli Kissamou. The *kapitans* showed little interest in troop dispositions and spent their time bickering and arguing amongst themselves. When it became evident that they were not to succeed in obtaining arms from the military at Khania they departed quickly and without ceremony, riding out of the First Welch barracks on their mules and making towards the vastness of the White Mountains.

When his guests had thankfully departed David was ordered to report to General Freyberg's Creforce headquarters. The general, holder of the Victoria Cross, was a large, homely man with sagging jowls. He received David in his command post where he and Brigadier Hargest were studying a detailed map of Soudha Bay. As David entered and saluted, the general looked up.

"Captain Green, what did you make of the Cretan *kapitans*?"

David replied that he thought they were devious and untrustworthy and that they should not be given arms and ammunition at this stage. The general nodded.

"Just as I thought. I believe they went back to the hills yesterday, but I expect we'll see them again. Call at Intelligence and give your report. Brigadier Chappell is having trouble with a similar bunch in Heraklion. When you've finished with Intelligence here push on to Chappell's headquarters. Thank you, Captain Green."

David was dismissed. Army intelligence was located in Fernleaf House a large white building set back in the cliffs and with an uninterrupted and commanding view of Soudha Bay. The downstairs rooms were festooned with maps, wireless transmitters, trestle tables and desks and a mixture of personnel, some in military uniform but most in brown denims, sat around singly, or in discussion groups, all apparently hard at work. A uniformed captain approached David.

"Captain Green. We've been expecting you. You're the chap who's been looking after Papadakis and his mob for a couple of days. Let me get a few of the lads together and we'll hear your report."

The captain shouted, "Pirie, Wilkinson, Fielding here at the double."

A group gathered around the captain's trestle table and David repeated his observations on the Cretan *kapitans* and particularly on their untrustworthiness. David's report confirmed their own assessment of the *kapitans*. The group broke up and the captain asked David to sit beside him.

"Thank you for taking those Cretans off our hands. I can tell you there's been a big panic here. The old man insists that Jerry will be coming in by sea on the 17th or 18th but we have a sound source of information which points strongly to an airborne attack on the 17th and we're having one hell of a time trying to change the general's mind. I don't know if our message has got through to Heraklion. As you are leaving tomorrow I wish you to take a verbal message to Brigadier Chappell. Tell him it's from British Army Intelligence Fernleaf House, source Ultra. Tell him to expect an airborne attack on the 17th or 18th. You may find Peter Ferman and Pendlebury in Heraklion. Give Peter the same message but don't pass it on to Pendlebury."

David indicated that he understood the captain, took his leave and drove back to the Welch battalion barracks to prepare himself for the return journey to Heraklion on the following day.

As dawn broke on the 16th May the undulating drone of the shufti Dornier was heard over Soudha Bay, followed precisely fifteen minutes later by the screech of Stuka dive bombers attacking shipping in the harbour. David lay in bed, fully awake, listening to the distant thud of exploding bombs. The early morning bombardment had become a routine occurrence in Khania. The bombers usually concentrated their attention on Soudha Harbour and the storage depots around Maleme airfield. Lying in bed David wondered if today the bombardment might be a prelude to an airborne assault. After fifteen minutes the bombing stopped, the engine noises receded into the misty north and peace once again descended on Soudha Bay. David took his leave of Colonel Duncan and his fellow officers over breakfast and in his refuelled fifteen hundredweight started on the return journey to Heraklion, a journey which took nearly ten hours due to the numerous road blocks, traffic congestion and troop movements, all using the coastal road. Again he had half an idea to contact Sergeant Hawkins but the sheer volume of men and vehicles, guns and supplies on the road outside Rethymno banished the thought from his head. On arrival he immediately reported to Brigadier Chappell's headquarters and spoke to the second in command, a full colonel in the Black Watch.

The colonel nodded his agreement to David's message from British Army Intelligence and added, "We've been aware of these reports for a couple of days, but the Brigadier and I are still of the opinion that they'll come in by sea." He added, "All available men are on standby at dawn tomorrow. I expect you to report here at 0400 hours for stand to."

David went to bed early to be awakened at 3 a.m. by a batman brandishing a steaming mug of tea. In the darkness before dawn the headquarters' staff and all available men made their way to the shoreline. At daybreak the shufti Dornier made its solitary sweep, followed by one wave of Stukas and five minutes of bombing. As dawn broke thousands of eyes stared out to sea through the lifting mist but the Germans did not come and the defenders of Heraklion stood down at midday. Apart from the daily hate raid there were no incidents for three days until the morning of the 20th May when the exhausted defence garrison witnessed the approach of the German armada, not from the sea as expected, but from the air.

Chapter Fifteen

Hotel Grande Bretagne, Athens
15th May, 1941
German Assault on Crete,
20th May – 2nd June, 1941

At 6 a.m. on the morning of the 15th May 1941 General Kurt Student was roused from a deep sleep by Willi, his personal valet, who brought to his bedside a steaming mug of black ersatz coffee. Willi knew that punctuality was the general's phobia and he also knew that to be a minute late would incur great displeasure from his master. Whilst shaving the general allowed himself a moment of adulation and self-indulgence. In the mirror he saw a rugged, sun-tanned face with deep-set blue eyes surmounted by a shock of wiry grey hair. His jowls were a little heavy and his muscular stocky frame was encased in a thin layer of fat, but he was not grossly overweight and for a fifty-five year old soldier he was in excellent health and physical trim.

On this morning he had every reason to be pleased with himself. As general commanding the German airborne parachute division, he had been selected to plan Operation Merkur, the German airborne invasion of Crete. His *Fallschirmjagger* were to lead the attack supported by General Löhr's glider battalions and the *Luftwaffe*, under the command of General Freiherr Wolfram von Richthofen. General Student had respect for General Löhr, a solid but unimaginative commander, but he could not readily take to General Richthofen who was arrogant, self-opinionated and domineering, mainly due to his aristocratic background and the fame which his family name commanded in the Reich.

Student himself came from a middle class family in Bavaria and had worked hard to progress up the military ladder. He reflected that his rise to the top was greatly enhanced by his attachment, as a captain, to the Condor Legion in the Spanish Civil War and a rapid increase in parachute manpower in the German army prior to 1939. He felt elated and justly proud that today he would be the supreme commander of the greatest airborne invasion in the history of modern warfare. He dressed carefully in his resplendent light blue uniform and inspected his profile meticulously in the full-length mirror.

He entered the mess where his aide, Major Wilhelm Gunter, was already seated at the table together with three junior officers. Major Gunter and the others were in battle dress and, on Student's entry, they rose in unison and gave a Nazi salute, which Student returned with a perfunctory flick of his right arm. The general seated himself at the top end of the table and exchanged normal pleasantries with his officers. They breakfasted on coffee, fresh orange juice, cold salami, hard boiled eggs and bread and honey. By 6.45 a.m. the general was ready to leave and made this obvious to Major Gunter by repeatedly examining his pocket watch.

The general's staff car arrived at the main entrance, a sleek, black eight-litre Mercedes saloon displaying a parachute regimental pennant and swastika on each side of the bonnet. The meeting was planned for 8 a.m. at Hotel Bretagne. A further glance at his watch confirmed that they were in good time and the journey from Student's villa on Cape Sunion to Constitution Square in the middle of Athens, a matter of twenty-five kilometres, should only take about thirty-five minutes. Being a punctilious man he wanted to walk into the crowded conference room at exactly one minute to eight o'clock.

General Student's driver was an old comrade wounded in the parachute drop at Rotterdam in May 1940. Hans Friedler had recovered from his wounds but was considered unfit for active service and the general had taken him back to the regiment as his personal bodyguard and driver. Hans was devoted to his master and always carried a loaded *Schmeitzer* sub-machine gun slung over one shoulder or lying on the seat beside him in the Mercedes. They drove along the coast road from Cape Sunion towards Athens. In the early days, after capitulation on the 28th April, this road had been completely blocked by the paraphernalia of war. General Student ordered his Engineer Parachute Battalion to sort out the mess and within two days the road was passable and by now progress was easy and uninterrupted. General Student relaxed and leaned backwards into the plush comfort of the car's leather seats.

The sun was already well above the horizon, its rays warm and inviting and the scenery on the seaward side of the car was magnificent. Kurt Student felt at peace with the world and, half-turning towards Gunter with a brief smile, said, "Wilhelm, this is a great day for all of us. A great day for me and a great day for my *Fallschirmjagger*. I think it'll be a day to remember for the rest of our lives."

"*Jawohl*, Herr General," Gunter replied.

No further words were spoken until they were near the centre of Athens. Leaning backwards in the comfortable leather seat with the sun's rays on his face and his cap held in his hands General Student closed his eyes and mused on the events which had led up to his present position. Born in 1888, the son of an army sergeant, he had grown up in a succession of army quarters in Germany and the Rheinland. From the beginning he was destined for an army career and, at the age of twenty-six, found himself in the trenches in the Somme and, by the end of the Great War, he had attained the rank of sergeant. He remained in the *Wehrmacht* after the Armistice but promotion was slow in post-war Germany. He was commissioned in 1930 and, as a lieutenant and later captain, commanded a German platoon in the battles of the Spanish Civil War.

His unit was initially seconded to defend the airfields of *Luftwaffe* Force Condor and this unit received secret orders to investigate the feasibility of parachuting troops into action. Kurt Student implemented these instructions and four successful drops were made during 1937. Student's platoon was under command of the *Luftwaffe*, in the same way as the High Command regarded the *Kriegsmarine* as a branch of the German army. Experiments with parachute drops were expensive in manpower and when Student returned to Germany in 1937 he spent the summer months perfecting the harness and technique of parachuting.

In late 1937 the first parachute regiment was mobilised and Colonel Kurt Student became its commanding officer. Six further regiments were formed during 1938 and by the outbreak of war, in 1939, Kurt Student was promoted to brigadier general in command of a *Fallschirmjagger* division. During the blitzkrieg war on the Western

Front, in May 1940, four of his regiments were successfully deployed, three around Rotterdam and the fourth south of Amsterdam. After the fall of France an extra two storm regiments were conscripted and Student's command became completely independent of the airforce and a branch of the *Wehrmacht*.

War Diary

On the 25th October, 1940, General Student met Hitler at Berchtesgaden. At that meeting General Halder suggested that control of the eastern Mediterranean might be dependent on capture of Crete by an airborne landing but Hitler favoured Malta. At an Axis meeting in Florence earlier in October 1940 it was agreed by Hitler and Mussolini that the eastern Mediterranean would be an Italian sphere of influence but a division of German airborne troops would be available for an attack on Crete or Malta. General Student was appointed commander of the Cretan airborne operation and started planning for an air assault late in November 1940. On the 5th December Hitler announced his plans for the invasion of Russia. At that stage only the German high command were privy to the decision but were given instructions to alert their senior commanders. Kurt Student was informed that the invasion of Russia, Operation Barbarossa, would start on the 15th May, 1941 and that his airborne divisions would be extensively employed in the early phases of attack.

In November Italian troops moved southwards into northern Greece. They met with fierce resistance and were eventually repulsed and held in stalemate by the Greeks during the harsh winter of 1940-41. Since October 1940 German troops had been stationed in Rumania, who had become a member of the Tripartite Pact, and Student deployed two of his Fallschirmjagger Divisions to Rumania in preparation for Barbarossa. In February 1941 the German forces in Rumania moved southwards into Bulgaria. In early April, to help his Italian allies in northern Greece, Hitler unleashed his forces simultaneously into Yugoslavia and Greece and, after a venomous blitzkrieg attack on Belgrade, subjugated Yugoslavia in three weeks. This victory gave the German armies open access to Greece via Albania in the north-west and via Bulgaria in the north-east. The Wehrmacht *undertook both these offensives and Student's forces were kept in reserve.*

As a result of German involvement in Yugoslavia and Greece, and much to Hitler's displeasure, Operation Barbarossa had to be postponed for six weeks. On 21st April, the day after Hitler's birthday. Hermann Goering entertained the Führer and Student at his estate in Monischkirchen, situated to the south of Vienna. At this meeting Student proposed that Crete and then Cyprus would be used as stepping stones to the Suez Canal, the eventual prize and goal of Rommel's troops in north Africa. Hitler still favoured Malta but, persuaded by Student, acquiesced to an airborne attack on Crete.

Führer's directive No. 28 issued on the 25th April authorised the occupation by Germany of the Greek island of Crete. Operation Merkur was re-born.

The day after this meeting in Monischkirchen Student flew into Templehof airport in Berlin to organise the transfer of his *Fallschirmjagger* regiments to Greece in preparation for the airborne invasion. This involved the transfer of ten thousand paratroopers and their equipment through northern Germany, through Austria, Hungary, Rumania, Bulgaria and then Salonica to their camps in southern Greece. With typical Teutonic efficiency the troop movements of two thousand miles, or more, were achieved within the time schedule and by the second week in May eight *Fallschirmjagger* regiments were bivouacked on five airfields around Athens. This concentration of airborne power was now at his disposal and the briefing of his troops at Hotel Bretagne in an hour's time would be the culmination of his endeavours and ambitions for the past six months. This indeed was to be his finest hour. Kurt Student was about to impose his will and personality on the greatest airborne invasion ever undertaken in the history of modern warfare.

General Student sat up with a start. His embroidered cap had fallen to the floor and, in the state between sleep and awakening, he was uncertain what had brought him back to consciousness. It might have been the jar of a bumpy section of the road or, more likely, the insistent tugging of the left sleeve of his tunic. Major Wilhelm Gunter was trying to waken his commanding general, at the same time admiring his commander's composure, being able to slip off to sleep on such a momentous occasion.

"What time is it Willi?"

"We are very early Herr General.   It's not yet 7.30," Major Gunter replied.

Student checked his own timepiece, ran his fingers through his bristly grey hair, and placed his cap firmly on his head.   Looking out to his right side he saw the Parthenon glistening white in the early morning sunlight.   Tapping Hans' shoulder he ordered the driver to take the next turning right and proceed towards the base of the Parthenon as he felt that, on this day of destiny, a private communion with the ancient Greek gods might not go amiss.   Hans did as commanded and very quickly became entangled in the narrow meandering streets of the Plaka.   The large Mercedes almost filled the narrow roadway and Hans could only proceed at snail-pace.   About two hundred metres into the Plaka, and directly ahead of the limousine, there was a dray carrying melons to the market and about a dozen men surrounding the cart urging the donkey forwards, tugging, pushing, shouting and swearing and completely blocking the lane. Hans had to stop the car and the general and Willi were faintly amused at first but, within a minute or so, became concerned as more men appeared to join the crowd around the marooned donkey cart.

Hans hooted the klaxon which made a deafening noise in the narrow street.   The startled donkey reared on his hind legs, tilting the cart sideways, spilling its contents on to the road and the filth-strewn gutters on each side.   This incensed the Greeks who turned their attention to the German car.   Shouting obscenities and surrounding the Mercedes they started banging the roof and kicking the sides of the vehicle.   Using their combined strength they rocked the car from side to side in an attempt to overturn the vehicle.

The general took his Mauser pistol from its holster and only then realised that the gun was not loaded.   The Greeks outside were now banging on the thick plate glass windows and in a matter of time would have broken through.   Wilhelm Gunter had no sidearms and reacting quickly, threw his body in front of the general to protect him. Hans also reacted quickly and picking up his *Schmeitzer* machine gun he opened the sunshine roof a few centimetres, thrust the nozzle of the gun through the aperture and fired into the air.   The volume of noise and reverberation in the enclosed alley was deafening but Hans' action produced the desired result.   The men disappeared rapidly into doorways and alleys and the donkey took fright and bolted down the Plaka, pulling the empty cart behind.   Hans now drove the Mercedes rapidly down the lanes squelching its wheels through the watermelons and vegetables and intermittently tooting the horn until the car emerged into a deserted square at the base of the Parthenon.

Major Gunter apologised for flinging himself as a shield in front of his general. Student acknowledged the apology and, retrieving his cap from the floor of the car, placed it firmly on his head. He ordered Hans out of the car with his *Schmeitzer* and then let himself and Major Gunter out of the back seat. They stood in the middle of square, a group of three with the ever-alert Hans fingering his sub-machine gun and the two German officers admiring their private view of the Parthenon, emblazoned in the early morning sun. They stood in silence for nearly three minutes and, returning to the car, they drove away along a main road back towards Constitution Square.

The general half-turned towards Major Gunter.

"Willi, you may wonder why I got out of the car in the square? It was to show the local people that German officers and soldiers are never intimidated by local insurrection. I could order our paras into this area on a shooting spree. This I will not do. This incident in the Plaka is to be forgotten and never spoken of again" and, looking at his watch, "We will now be in perfect time for the meeting at Hotel Bretagne."

At six minutes to eight the general's black Mercedes made its way sedately down St George's Avenue into Constitution Square. On each side of the avenue Student's beloved *Fallschirmjagger* were posted, twenty paces apart, presenting arms as the car made its way into the main square. Similarly around the whole of the square there were paratroopers in battle order and across the empty expanse the front facade of the hotel was festooned with Nazi banners. In front of the main entrance were two rows of paratroopers from the First Regiment commanded by Captain Burkhardt, who had won a Knight's Cross for gallantry in the campaign in Holland in 1940.

Hans opened the rear door of the Mercedes and General Student and Major Gunter emerged and walked up to the guard commander. The general inspected the guard, chatting amiably with the captain, and at two minutes to eight walked through the main entrance of the Hotel. The conference room was on the first floor and in peace-time was used as a ballroom. Three hundred men were present for the briefing as the general had decreed that all senior officers and senior NCOs of the *Fallschirmjagger* were to attend.

At one minute to eight General Kurt Student made his entrance into the conference room and, with deliberate steps, walked on to the podium, stood at attention and raised his right arm in salute. The officers and men in the room responded with Nazi salutes and 'Heil Hitler' intonations. The audience remained standing and, as if by order, started clapping the general, the applause lasting for a full minute.

General Kurt Student surveyed his audience. In the front row he saw General Löhr, commander of the Fourth Air Fleet, General Sussman, commanding the First Parachute Brigade, Captain Gericke, Captain Heydte, Captain Burkhardt, a senior naval officer and three aides and a sizeable contingent of senior *Luftwaffe* officers headed by General Freiherr Wolfram von Richthofen the only officer, apart from himself, in full dress uniform.

'Trust him,' thought Student. 'Always a showman.'

For some inexplicable reason he recalled that von Richthofen was the architect of the blitzkrieg attacks in Guernica in Spain in 1937 and more recently the murderous attacks on Belgrade during the Yugoslavian campaign. He concluded that he did not like the pompous *Luftwaffe* general. On the right wing of the front row sat the charismatic Colonel von Bulow, unmistakable with his black eye-patch and empty left tunic sleeve and next to him his blond, handsome adjutant, Major Manfred Schmidt.

On the wall behind the general was a dust sheet which, when removed, revealed a large map of Crete. Student began, "Fellow officers and comrades of the *Fallschirmjagger* division. I am commanded by the Führer to carry out an invasion of Crete and to implement Operation Merkur. Comrades, I welcome you to this conference. You might have thought that when we came down to these parts last week we would be on holiday," loud laughter from the audience, "but we are here on very serious business. The parachute divisions and General Löhr's glider division with protection from the *Luftwaffe* and Navy have been assigned the task of invading and capturing the island of Crete."

Pointing at the map he continued, "Crete lies some two hundred and forty kilometres to the south of Athens. To look at it you would think that the island is one long mass of high mountains, coloured brown for those who can't read maps," more laughter from the audience, "and seemingly not at all suitable for airborne landings. We can achieve landings on the north side of the island at four points, Khania, Maleme, Rethymno and Heraklion. Of great importance are the airfields at Maleme and Heraklion. It is vital that we secure these airfields on the first day so that General Löhr's transport planes can fly in supplies and reserve manpower. The whole operation is within the range of General Freiherr von Richthofen's fighter planes and we shall have continuous protection from the air. The Navy will also play its part in ferrying some troops, but mainly supplies, to the ports in Soudha Bay and Heraklion.

"This plan was conceived by our leader Adolf Hitler and directive 28 gives me the power and authority to conduct the invasion. The Führer regards the occupation of Crete as a stepping stone to an eventual airborne landing and capture of the Suez Canal. We shall then join up with General Rommel and his gallant forces in North Africa. Details of the airborne invasion will now be presented to you by my operations staff. Make no mistake, this is the greatest airborne invasion in the history of modern warfare and we, in the airborne division, have been given the honour to strike at the heart of the enemy and conquer Crete for the Fatherland."

Tumultuous applause.

General Student asked, "Any questions?"

A voice from the back of the auditorium, "When do we go?"

General Student replied, "You will be informed of the date two days before invasion but it will be this month."

Luftwaffe General von Richthofen got to his feet, "I can foresee difficulty with fighter cover due to the distances involved and fuel consumption of the planes which will probably only give us ten to fifteen minutes over the target in Crete."

General Student replied, "My dear General von Richthofen I am sure that our glorious *Luftwaffe* will surmount all difficulties and provide the troops on the ground with the high standard of air cover we have come to expect from the best airforce in the world."

'That should placate the bastard,' thought General Student, and continued, "I will now hand you over to my staff officers for further information and details of the operation." There was loud applause and clapping as General Student descended from the podium and joined the audience, choosing deliberately to sit next to General Freiherr von Richthofen.

The next officer to take his stand on the podium was Major Reinhardt, General Student's intelligence officer.

"General reconnaissance has revealed that the island appears to be lifeless. There are some five thousand British garrison troops on Crete, mainly second rank soldiers. Four hundred men are located in Heraklion and there are no troops at Rethymno. Nearly all the Australian and New Zealand forces evacuated from Greece returned to North Africa. There are a few Greek troops on the island and, as you already know, ten thousand Cretan soldiers were killed or captured in the battle in southern Albania."

Major Reinhardt concluded that all the signs indicated that the Cretan population would welcome the German invading forces with open arms.

Captain Burkhardt outlined the plans for the airborne invasion. The Parachute Storm Regiment would drop on the airport at Maleme. The Third Regiment and Engineer Battalions would drop on Khania and attack Soudha from the east. The Second Regiment would drop on Rethymno. The First Regiment's target would be the airport and docks at Heraklion. One of General Löhr's glider regiments would be flown to Maleme where the Fifth Mountain Division would land to secure the airfield. Other staff officers made contributions but the one sobering problem that remained was a lack of special high octane gas necessary for fuelling the transport planes of General Löhr's air fleet. General Student's planned invasion on the 17th May would have to be postponed until the fuel for the aircraft became available.

The general resumed his position on the podium and with a traditional Nazi salute left the auditorium amongst tumultuous applause from the assembled airborne troops. He was escorted to the Mercedes by Captain Gericke and, together with Major Gunter, was driven back to divisional headquarters at Cape Sunion. Kurt Student was pleased with his morning's work.

As they drove towards his headquarters the general became somewhat subdued and felt tired and anxious. He was sure that Operation Merkur would be a success, as the troops were in fine fettle and ready for action. His only concern was the date on which he could unleash his airborne armies. Hitler's directive 28 ordered an attack on Crete between 14th and 17th May. Clearly these dates were impractical. On the 18th May 1941 all airborne personnel in southern Greece were alerted to be in readiness for an impending invasion. On the 19th May all senior commanders were given a further final briefing on Operation Merkur. Student's concern about fuel supplies for the aircraft were allayed when a tanker, the *Rodine*, arrived in Piraeus with sufficient high octane gas to fuel the whole operation. The operation was delayed from the 17th May to the morning of the 20th May. On that morning the whole might of Germany's airborne forces was unleashed on Crete. Operation Merkur, the German invasion of Crete, had become a reality.

War Diary

General Student's claim that the German invasion of Crete would be the largest airborne assault in history was not an idle boast. In fact it remains a military miracle that he was able to concentrate his large air armada in and around Athens in the time available to him between the 23rd April and the 17th May. The organisation required to move this massive army of men and planes speaks volumes for German ingenuity and the extraordinary capability of the German war machine in the early months of 1941. All this was achieved whilst, at the same time, Hitler's plans for an invasion of Russia were in full swing and there were many counter demands for manpower and equipment from the Eastern Front.

Within twenty-two days the airborne planners were able to gather their forces together in Greece and to mount a massive invasion of Crete. Control of the air was a vital factor and this was provided by General Freiherr von Richthofen's Eight Air Corps of one hundred and eighty Messerschmitts, based at Argos and Malaöi. General Löhr's Fourth Air Fleet of one hundred and twenty Dorniers, forty Heinkels and two hundred and thirty Junkers JU-87 based at Eleusis and Tatöi provided transport for troops and equipment for the battle and Student's airborne forces had available five hundred Junkers JU52's and two hundred and thirty gliders for the attack. Three of Student's paratroop regiments, the Second, the Fifth and the Sixth, were used as foot infantry in Yugoslavia, Albania and northern Greece and they arrived in Athens on the 29th April relatively intact, having suffered few casualties. The other six regiments, including Colonel von Bulow's Eighth, had moved from Germany across Europe and the Balkans to reach the start line as had the four battalions, of Meindl's Storm Regiment and three battalions of General Ringl's Mountain

Regiment. By the 17th May General Student had at his disposal a total of twenty-two thousand men and sufficient planes and gliders to ferry them to their targets.

German estimates of the strength of defenders on Crete were grossly inadequate. By the 20th May there were forty-two thousand British and Dominion troops in Crete, half of which were second line infantry and the number included fourteen thousand battle-weary troops from the campaign in Greece. In addition there were some nine thousand poorly trained Greek soldiers together with some three thousand Cretan irregulars.

Student's strategic plan was simple and involved early capture of airfields at Maleme, Rethymno and Heraklion by parachute drops, supported by glider landings, to allow the main bulk of his forces to be flown in as reinforcements and a further airborne assault to secure harbour facilities for troops to be brought in by sea. All the while air supremacy was vitally important and was provided by von Richthofen's air corps of Messerschmitt fighters who could fly to Crete and back without re-fuelling, but only had a maximum of fifteen to twenty minutes' flying time over the target.

Student planned that his Glider Storm Regiment of some one thousand nine hundred men, commanded by Colonel Mendl and Captain Ramcke, would take Maleme, the Second Regiment, some fifteen hundred strong, under Colonel Stürm would be dropped at Rethymno, Colonel Herdich's Third Regiment of two thousand men would land at Khania and Colonel Braüer's First Regiment of two thousand five hundred men would take the port and airfield at Heraklion. The Eighth Battalion and a mountain regiment were in reserve at Tatöi to be used as necessary and as the battle developed.

At dawn on the 20th May, 1941 the attack on Crete commenced. On the second day, after a fierce battle with the New Zealanders, Major Ramcke's Storm Regiment gained control over Maleme airfield and for the rest of the campaign fourteen thousand reinforcements were flown in by General Löhr's air fleet. After fierce fighting in all sectors the Germans advanced eastwards towards Heraklion and on the 24th May the allied forces started evacuating Crete, which finally fell to the Germans on the 2nd June, 1941. The cost in lives to the British and Greek forces was heavy, one thousand seven hundred and fifty men killed and the same number wounded. The Royal Navy in the sea battles around Crete lost one thousand eight hundred sailors. Twelve thousand two hundred British and Dominion forces were made prisoners of war. But the loss in men to the German airborne divisions was horrendous; three thousand nine hundred and eighty-six paratroopers, five hundred and eighty mountain troops and three hundred and twelve air crew killed and two thousand five hundred and ninety-four wounded and, added to this, three hundred and sixty Junkers transport planes were lost.

When the battle was over Hitler decorated Student with a Knight's Cross upon his Iron Cross and all the survivors of the Battle of Crete received Iron Crosses. But Hitler regarded the battle as a "victorious catastrophe" and decreed that never again would airborne forces be used in any major capacity in future campaigns. The remnants of the shattered regiments were collected together and later, in 1941, were sent to fight as foot soldiers on the Eastern Front where many died or were captured on the frozen wastes of the Russian steppes.

*

After General Student's conference on the 15th May and the announcement that Crete was the target, urgent preparations went ahead for the forthcoming battle and the *Fallschirmjagger* were kept on constant alert. The paratroopers spent their days on short route marches, cleaning and checking their guns and equipment, attending lectures by medical officers in the emergency treatment of wounded, writing last letters home, making wills and, for the religiously inclined, attending daily church parades. For the officers and company commanders these were days for urgent tactical conferences. Major General Süssmann, the general commanding the Second Parachute Brigade and Colonel von Trettner, Student's operations officer, held daily conferences at 8 a.m. in their headquarters in Eleusis, attended by all regimental and company commanders. Prior to the commencement of the campaign, General Student had appointed Colonel Herdich regimental commander of the Third Brigade, much to Colonel von Bulow's displeasure. The old war-horse had little respect for Colonel Herdich whom he regarded as a 'pumped up little sergeant promoted too rapidly by General Student and certainly too young and inexperienced to be a brigadier.'

Manfred realised that the wily old colonel must have had his one good eye on the position himself but was too crafty to disclose his objections at the Süssmann conferences. In fact his military experience was frequently called upon at the early morning meetings and this pleased the colonel immensely. Colonel Herdich, a tall, dark-haired, good-looking man with a quiet soft voice, had been rapidly promoted by General Student after the Rotterdam airborne assault, where he had shown exceptional courage and leadership, to his present position where he was out of his depth in the broader tactical concepts of airborne warfare.

Colonel von Bulow took full advantage of his younger superior officer's indecision and tended to take over afternoon briefings at regimental headquarters. Soon after Student's conference Colonel von Bulow had completely dismissed his previously incorrect prediction of a Suez landing and was now committed to a Cretan invasion. So much so, that he proposed to Colonel Herdich that his battalion, the Eighth, should come off the reserve list and be awarded the Heraklion drop. Colonel Herdich objected but such was the force of von Bulow's argument that he agreed, only to have the order countermanded by General Student later in the day.

Student observed, "Well now, Herdich, the old brigand will never lie down. He wants to be in the thick of it all the time. The plan of campaign remains as outlined on the 15th. Colonel von Trettner will be at your briefing tomorrow to sort this out."

On the following day, in the presence of senior officers from Division, von Bulow backed down with grace and dignity and it was ordained that the Eighth Regiment remained in reserve for the Cretan assault. At this briefing Colonel von Trettner also announced that due to lack of essential fuel supplies Operation Merkur was postponed until the 20th May. The massed airborne armada now only had four days to finalise their preparations for the invasion of Crete. During this time Colonel von Bulow's mood changed from one of elation to gathering depression. He started drinking heavily and on the 19th May took to his bed in the officers quarters at Tatöi complaining of vicious headaches affecting the sight of his one good eye. Manfred was assigned control of the Battalion and Major Derpa took over the Second Company. Manfred recalled the same sequence of events happening on the eve of the battalion's airdrop at Schiphol during the Western Front Campaign. His duties now were to attend the daily conferences and report back to the darkened room each evening where the Colonel rested in bed, reeking of brandy, and frequently not responding to Manfred's verbal reports.

At 3 a.m. on the 20th May loading of the gliders and aeroplanes commenced. The airborne soldiers shuffled slowly in the dark along pre-arranged, tape-marked lines whispering and speaking in hushed voices. At 5 a.m. the night air was split by the roar of aircraft engines as the Dorniers, already on the runway, started off towing four or five gliders behind them and disappearing into the blackness to the east. Major Koch and Captain Ramcke's First Storm Regiment, bound for Maleme, were first paratroopers to get away. Dawn had just broken when Captain Gericke's Fourth Battalion started off but within five minutes it was obvious to Manfred that a delay had occurred as the twinkling lights of airborne planes stopped appearing in the receding darkness to the east.

Dawn broke quickly and the cause of the delay became evident. A Dornier, towing four gliders, missed its markers and became entangled with another plane taking off. The runway was littered with broken gliders and bodies and the two Dorniers were firmly interlocked together. Engineers were feverishly pulling the planes off the runway whilst ambulances carried the injured and dead stormtroopers away from the scene of the accident.

After an interminable delay Captain Gericke's troops took to the air, also bound for Maleme but, by now, nearly an hour late. Whilst the carnage on the runway was being cleared Captain van der Hydte's Seventh Battalion were seated in their Dornier 17s, dry-mouthed and sweating in the rapidly increasing heat of the blazing morning sun. Bound for Heraklion they were three and a half hours late leaving Tatöi and did not reach their target until 11.30 am, where they dropped into the waiting arms of the defenders on the ground.

The situation on Tatöi airfield became even more confused as empty carrier planes from the first attack on Maleme started returning at around 7.30 a.m. These planes, short of fuel, were diverted to other airfields and many did not make it and were forced to crash land in the sea or on the fields on Cape Sunion. Major Heilmann's Ninth Battalion took off at 1.30 p.m. for a drop on the small airfield at Rethymno and by midday Tatöi airfield was clear to receive incoming planes.

During the whole morning, in fact since midnight of the previous evening, Manfred had been watching the departing planes from the control tower. First reports from returning pilots indicated that, both at Maleme and Heraklion, anti-aircraft fire was light, but the descending gliders were severely mauled by small arms' fire from the ground where many were seen to crash on landing. Manfred reported to his ailing colonel that the air armada was on its way to Crete and that resistance on the island seemed light. The confused, drunken colonel showed little interest, merely holding his bandaged head and moaning pitifully with only the top of his thinning, grey hair showing outside the bedclothes. The colonel's manservant, Willi, complained that his master had not eaten a thing for two whole days but the empty brandy bottles in the corner of the room testified that he otherwise had an adequate fluid intake. Manfred took his leave and went to the Eighth Regiment camp outside the perimeter where Major Werner and his men were sensibly resting in the shade of their tents with their equipment ready to hand and there they remained in animated suspension for forty-eight hours.

On the third day of the battle, Maleme airport was secured by Captain Ramcke's stormtroops and a steady flow of Dorniers and Heinkels were able to land with replacement manpower and equipment to consolidate the bridgehead. Progress at Heraklion airfield was slower and on two occasions during this period the Eighth were alerted to prepare for a drop. On the 22nd May Colonel von Trettner appeared and ordered a Company of the Eighth Battalion to combine with the Eighth Mountain Regiment to form a *Schiffsstaffel*, an accumulation of ill-assorted boats, for a seaborne invasion of Crete. Manfred volunteered his Second Company for the *Schiffsstaffel* but, after consultation with Colonel von Bulow, Captain Schwarzkopf and No. 3 Company were delegated. The colonel insisted that Manfred should stay with him at headquarters.

"I'm getting stronger every day and will be able to resume command in a few days time. I want you with me here. Major Werner will make any drops ordered by HQ and when our boys have secured Heraklion we shall both be on the first plane to land at the airfield, just as we did in Schiphol."

Manfred touched the side of his head delicately, a reminder of that eventful landing on the Dutch airfield. On the night of the 23rd May Manfred saw the *Schiffsstaffel* leave Piraeus harbour. The convoy was an accumulation of small caiques and motor boats escorted on their two hundred mile sea voyage to Heraklion by a single Italian destroyer, the *Saggitario*. Captain Schwartzkopf was full of enthusiasm for the assault, unconscious of the fact that eventually only one caique, containing some forty men, reached Heraklion safely. The rest were decimated by the Royal Navy off the island of Santorini when the *Saggitario* fled and left the *Schiffsstaffel* defenceless and floundering at sea. Some of the boats managed to make land on the small islands around Santorini but the majority of the soldiers drowned, including Captain Schwarzkopf and all but thirteen of the Third Company.

At sunset on the evening of the 23rd May, Colonel von Trettner arrived at the command post in Tatöi airfield demanding to see Colonel von Bulow. Manfred attempted to stall his visit but von Trettner was insistent and was ushered into the colonel's darkened bedroom.

"Colonel von Bulow," Trettner began. "I have bad news for you."

The small masked head on the pillow moved sideways and von Bulow lifted the corner of his blindfold with his right fingertip.

"Von Trettner, can't you see I am sick?"

"I am sorry for that Herr Colonel," Trettner replied, "but General Student ordered me to speak to you personally."

Von Bulow groaned and tried sitting up in bed but fell backwards on to his pillow.

"Colonel von Bulow, it's about your company that sailed on the *Schiffsstaffel* yesterday, I'm afraid they did not get further than Santorini. The whole flotilla has been sunk and we fear there will be few survivors."

Colonel von Bulow's shoulders started shaking and his head fell forwards on his chest.

"My boys, my poor boys," he sobbed as Colonel von Trettner continued.

"General Student has ordered a drop of your reserve parachute battalion into Heraklion tomorrow at dawn. Maleme airfield is safely in our hands and reinforcements have been flown in, but Maleme is one hundred and forty kilometres from Heraklion and there is fierce fighting at Khania and Rethymno between the two towns. Your battalion is to drop east of Heraklion to join up with Van der Hydte and Captain Burkhardt's battalions which are held up some ten kilometres east of the airport. The *schwerpunkt* is Heraklion airfield. We must take it within the next forty-eight hours or the whole enterprise may be in jeopardy."

Colonel von Bulow sat up in bed.

"As you see Herr Colonel I cannot take part in the assault. Major Schmidt is my deputy and I want him here. Major Werner will lead my *Fallschirmjagger* into battle. I will try and get up in the morning to see my boys off. Please discuss further details with Major Werner and Major Schmidt."

With a weary sigh the tired old man sank back on his pillows, re-adjusted his blindfold and was soon fast asleep. Major von Trettner and Manfred turned and left the prostrate figure in the darkened room with Willi hovering and fussing in the background.

The total strength of the remainder of the Eighth Parachute Regiment at Tatöi was six hundred and fifty and it was agreed that Major Werner was to command the troops on the ground. The drop zone was identified at Elea, a lowland region covered with olive groves and mostly held by German forces. Once on the ground the Eighth were to strike north to secure the coastal road to Heraklion at Hanikohlini where Captain van der Hydte's Seventh Regiment were surrounded in an olive grove. The Eighth would then link up with the Seventh and advance westwards along the coast road to the airfield at Heraklion.

Despite heavy losses in his carrier fleet General Löhr's operational officer assured the planners that a mixed fleet of Heinkels, Dorniers and Junker JU-82s were available, at short notice, for the proposed operation. He stressed that continuous supply of men and material to Maleme airfield still held highest priority with his commander and that, to date, they had flown in seven thousand reinforcements, adding that the attack force should approach Crete well out to sea from the east and come in with the sun on their backs for the drop. The *Luftwaffe* colonel added that during the past two days anti-aircraft fire over Heraklion had intensified and all planes flying to Crete should avoid this area. At this point Colonel Herdich asked to speak to von Trettner in private. They retired to a side office.

"Colonel von Trettner, I want to go on this drop in the morning. By tomorrow all my brigade will be in Crete in the Heraklion/Rethymno area and that is the place I should be. May I respectfully suggest that you make Colonel von Bulow temporary brigade commander here in Eleusis," and then he added, with uncharacteristic venom, "After all, the one-eyed renegade and his pretty boy Schmidt has had his eye on my job since the beginning."

Colonel von Trettner thought about the proposal for about a minute and, knowing General Student's philosophy on the place for senior commanders in battle, agreed, there and then, that Colonel Herdich would drop on the following morning with the Eighth Battalion and take over control of the land battle for the capture of Heraklion airfield.

Back at Tatöi Manfred's report to Colonel von Bulow produced a dramatic effect on the tired, ailing officer. He whisked away his head bandage, called on Willi to come and shave him and ordered his best mess uniform to be laid out. He was shaky on his feet but insisted on dressing and ordered Manfred to parade the six hundred and fifty men getting ready for the drop. Once assembled outside the command post at Tatöi the colonel addressed them from the mess steps.

"Fellow *Fallschirmjagger* and comrades. Later today Major Werner will lead you into battle. Your target is the airfield at Heraklion. I know that my Eighth Battalion is equal to this task. I regret I cannot jump with you but I can assure you that, as at Schiphol, Major Schmidt and I will be on the first plane to land on the airfield. I wish you God speed and just to please your wicked old colonel please sing our regimental song before you leave."

The experience of six hundred and fifty lusty male voices singing *Rot Sheint Die Sonne* in the dark, still, moonless night sent a shiver down Manfred's spine. Led by Major Werner and *Feldwebel* Schneider the Eighth marched silently past their Commander towards waiting trucks that took them to Eleusis and the planes that would fly them into battle, maybe to their deaths, on a hot, sun-drenched, arid island to the south.

Manfred was amazed at the sudden change in Colonel Count Erich von Bulow. After the speech to his departing *Fallschirmjagger* he retired to his room and was not seen again until he walked into the officers' mess for breakfast, full of the joys of spring, sitting erect at the table, alert, attentive and eating a hearty meal. Arranging a piece of bread and honey neatly with his good right hand he looked across at Manfred, by now weary and tired after forty-eight hours with little sleep.

"Tell me Major Schmidt, how many men of the Eight Regiment are left at Tatöi and Eleusis?"

Manfred shook himself awake and after a few seconds pause, answered, "Sir, there are some eighty men here, mainly HQ company and cooks and probably around twenty non-combatants at Eleusis."

"Hum, hum," the colonel thought aloud. "Tell you what we'll do. We'll transfer our Eighth regiment lads to Eleusis and set up a mess at brigade headquarters. Is that damn good cook Schultz still around?"

Manfred answered in the affirmative and the colonel continued, "Schultz will set up a kitchen in Eleusis. If we can't be of much use in this battle we can at least eat well while I'm in command of the Brigade."

He then paused, took a firm bite of a honeyed bread slice, and, leaving a few goblets of opalescent honey on his bristly moustache, assumed a more serious mien.

"Any news of the drop yet, Manfred?"

Manfred, angered that the colonel had not made this his first question and that he was more pre-occupied with his own temporary promotion to brigade commander rather than the welfare of the Eighth Regiment, replied testily, "No, Sir. The first Stukas from the drop should be back within the hour. They can fly faster than the Heinkels and Dorniers."

And so it transpired. The first plane to return from the mission was a Junker JU-88. The pilot brought good news of a perfect drop in perfect conditions and seemingly little resistance from the defenders on the ground. Later arrivals confirmed that resistance was light but one Junker pilot thought some of the Heinkels had overshot the dropping zone and had released their paratroopers four or five kilometres west of Elea. Later reports confirmed that there had been a miss-drop by the Heinkels and Colonel Herdich and one hundred and twenty *Fallschirmjagger* were killed or massacred by Cretan partisans, as a result of the miscalculation.

At his new headquarters in Eleusis Colonel von Bulow assumed the mantle of an archetypal Prussian officer, standing ramrod stiff, with a steady, searching gaze and a forbidding frown on his forehead. He certainly knew how to assert his authority on the junior officers who stood around cringing and fawning. The colonel looked around the room, eyeing each officer in turn, and then announced:

"Gentlemen, I am your new brigadier. I expect the same loyalty from you as you gave Colonel Herdich. This place is like a pigsty. Tidy it up. Let me have any reports from the regiments as they come in, day or night. Is that clear? Good," and turning on his heel he strode purposefully out of the operations room giving Manfred a wink as he walked past.

Back in the car he chuckled, "That showed them who's the boss around here. They've had it too easy with dozy old Herdich. He doesn't know his arse from his elbow," and then turning to the driver, "Make for General Student's headquarters. It's about time we called to see how they're managing the battle."

Manfred was completely taken aback by the insolence of his commanding officer and yet he had so many endearing qualities which inspired such loyalty in others that he felt this was a man he could follow, and lay down his life for, if he was ordered to do so.

When Colonel von Bulow burst into the operations room at Hotel Bretagne all eyes turned towards him and the grim-faced staff officers looked up from their maps with a mixture of disbelief and amusement. He was soon surrounded by a bunch of comrades back-slapping and eagerly asking questions about his health and whereabouts. He was about to reply when the talking in the room stopped suddenly and General Student, accompanied by Brigadier Schlemm and Colonel von Trettner, walked towards the main battle chart on the wall. General Student spotted von Bulow.

"Glad to have you aboard, Colonel von Bulow. I hear your battalion has landed safely on target H. You're in time for today's briefing."

Colonel von Bulow palpably grew in stature as he was ushered by his fellow officers to the front of the men surrounding the tactical wall-chart. The arrival of von Bulow at command headquarters coincided with an improvement in the fortunes of the German airborne forces fighting on the ground in Crete and Student came to regard him as a lucky mascot. The colonel revelled in the adoration of his fellow officers and Manfred basked in the glow of the respect and idolatry which was bestowed on his regimental colonel.

During that day at headquarters Manfred learnt that the battle plans had gone seriously astray on the 20th May. Apart from the stormtroopers drop at Maleme, the other planned assaults at Khania, Rethymno and Heraklion had been, for various reasons, delayed and the defenders had prior warning of their impending arrival. The descending paratroopers, under their canvas canopies, were sitting targets for the defenders on the ground. One thousand five hundred and forty-seven German airborne soldiers were killed on May 20th. The carnage continued on the 21st May and late that evening General Student was almost forced to abandon the invasion. On the 22nd May the position became more stable. Progress was made at Maleme and from the 24th onwards regular supply flights were possible into the captured airfield. By the end of the campaign nearly fourteen thousand men were landed on this airfield from Dornier, Heinkel and Junker troop-carriers. A state of stalemate existed at Rethymno and Heraklion. Heraklion was invested from the west by three parachute battalions under the command of Majors Schultz, Walther and Weidemann whilst to the east the decimated battalions of Captain Burkhardt and Freiherr van der Hydte were pinned down some twelve kilometres away from the airfield.

General Student's conference on the 24th was not unduly prolonged. He had committed his last paratroop reserve to join battle and could now only sit and wait. Overnight reports indicated that his forces at Maleme were advancing steadily despite fierce resistance from New Zealand and Maori Battalions. At Khania the fighting was extremely heavy and little progress was made against stubborn resistance both from British and Australian units. At Rethymno both sides had gone to ground but Major Kroh's Fourth Battalion, surrounded in an olive factory, was still holding out under severe pressure from the Australians. The main problem was around Heraklion where no progress had been made. On the 21st May the Greek forces in Heraklion surrendered to Major Schultz but the German troops were driven out by the Yorks and Lancs Regiment and were now entrenched four kilometres south of the city. Burkhardt's battalion, reduced to two hundred and thirty men, was engaged by the Black Watch ten kilometres east of the airfield and van der Hydte's battalion, also reduced to two hundred and fifty paras, was surrounded about four kilometres further east. The morning drop of the Eighth Regiment brought crucial reinforcements for Burkhardt's group. Unfortunately about one hundred and twenty paratroopers dropped in the wrong zone and landed in the territory held by the Black Watch. The remaining three hundred and fifty fresh paratroopers were expected to strike north and cut the coast road between Heraklion and

Malia and join forces with Burkhardt and, if possible, van der Hydte's decimated battalion.

After a night's rest at Eleusis Colonel von Bulow and Manfred again returned to divisional headquarters early on the morning of the 26th May. At the 11 a.m. conference General Student looked drawn and haggard. There was little to add from the day before but reports arrived of heavy fighting at Galatas where a Maori battalion was surrounded and annihilated. At Heraklion the newly dropped Eighth Regiment had secured the coastal road and were making steady progress towards Burkhardt's beleaguered unit.

The general then continued, "Maleme is safely in our hands and our transport planes have free access to this airfield. The British do not have an air presence in the battle zone and we can fly to Crete unimpeded. We must congratulate General von Richthofen and General Löhr on the excellent air cover and transportation we have received during this campaign. The enemy is weakening and on the retreat but there are still a few major battles ahead. As you will be aware I have always held that the right place for a commander during a battle is in the field with his troops. Colonel Trettner and I are flying out to Maleme later today. The 6 p.m. conference this evening will be taken by Brigadier Schlemm and Colonel von Bulow will act as his deputy. That is all," and with a salute he turned on his heel and left the operations room.

Later that day, at 3 p.m., a Heinkel 111 flew out of Tatöi airfield carrying General Student and Colonel von Trettner, chaperoned by six Messerschmitt fighters. As the planes took to the air Colonel von Bulow turned to Manfred.

"There goes the best general in the German army. I am now certain of our victory in Crete. Manfred, my friend, our next flight will be to Heraklion when our lads have made the airfield secure."

As he spoke he had the lean hungry look of a hunter in his eye as he gazed skywards and southwards in the general direction of the island of Crete.

Colonel von Bulow requisitioned accommodation at Hotel Bretagne and Sergeant Fritz Schultz and a team of chefs from Eleusis were transported to the grand kitchens of the most prestigious hotel in Athens. The colonel was behaving like a dog with two tails, completely transformed from the ailing, sickly man of forty-eight hours previously into an alert and energetic dynamo, up at dawn to receive early despatches, vociferous in the conferences with Brigadier Schlemm, visiting the wounded in the Red Cross hospital in the afternoons and staying on duty in the operations room until late at night "in case any urgent messages arrive from Maleme".

The Athens headquarters now had little executive power. Divisional headquarters in Maleme made all decisions and, as a matter of courtesy, Athens was informed of General Student's plans, albeit usually five or six hours late. Colonel von Bulow revelled in his senior appointment and his 11 a.m. briefings to the staff were lively, informative and sometimes controversial, much to the amusement of Brigadier Schlemm who took a back seat but kept a watching brief on the proceedings and made sure that his protégé did not abuse his authority.

On May 27th a crisis arose in Athens headquarters. General Student had ordered air strikes at Galatas, Rethymno and Heraklion for that day but, due to fighter losses and pilot fatigue, von Richthofen's operational officer could only muster enough planes for one strike and Maleme was the selected target. Colonel von Bulow offered to intervene and he and Manfred hurried to Argos airfield where the *Luftwaffe* general was at breakfast with his senior officers. The reception from von Richthofen was cool but such was von Bulow's power of persuasion and flattery that the general agreed on two full air strikes, one at Soudha and one at Heraklion. Rethymno would have to wait another day.

On the return journey a jubilant von Bulow commented, "Manfred, that's the way to deal with these pompous bastards, whatever their rank. You must let them feel that any decision they make is theirs. In any case my own family in Prussia has a better pedigree than von Richthofen's and there's nothing at all he can do about that!"

On the 28th and 29th May reports arrived of a general retreat by the British from Soudha and Galatas. British and Dominion forces in Crete were commencing their withdrawal southwards from Stilos up the Apokoranas foothills to Vryses and then over the White Mountains to reach their evacuation port at Sphakia on the south coast, a distance of some forty kilometres. The retreat took two whole days with the allied forces struggling across mountainous terrain harassed by strafing attacks from Messerschmitts and Stukas.

Colonel von Bulow was extremely agitated that, as happened at Dunkirk and Greece, British forces were again possibly going to evade a trap and avoid capture by a victorious German army. He openly criticised General Student's decision to send two of General Ringl's mountain regiments towards Rethymno and only one regiment, the Hundredth, to chase the retreating allied armies across the White Mountains. The British rearguard, organised by Lieutenant Colonel Laycock, was so efficient that over a four day period, from 28th May to 1st June, some sixteen thousand troops were evacuated from Sphakia, vindicating Colonel von Bulow's exhortation to press harder on the retreating enemy.

As it was five thousand allied troops were captured on the 2nd June awaiting evacuation on the south coast of Crete. Evacuation of Allied forces from Heraklion had also commenced on the 27th May, the Royal Navy providing night convoys to ferry troops to Alexandria. Brigadier Chappell, the British commander at Heraklion, slowly pulled his forces back into the town, covered by the Yorks and Lancs and the Leicesters, whilst evacuation was proceeding from the harbour. By May 31st the Navy had evacuated nearly five thousand men but a third of these were drowned at sea with the loss to the Royal Navy of one thousand eight hundred and twenty-eight seamen, three cruisers, six destroyers and damage to seventeen other warships.

On the night of 30th May the airfield at Heraklion was taken by Major Werner's paratroops and the remnants of Captain Burkhardt's unit, pushing the Black Watch into the town itself and dislodging the Australian gun batteries from the top of the Two Charlies. It took three days for the engineers to get the airstrip serviceable. The first plane, loaded with supplies and fresh troops, landed on Heraklion airfield at midday on the 2nd June. On the 30th May the Tenth Sienna Division commanded by General Angelo Carta made an unopposed landing at Sitia and occupied eastern Crete. Ironically the same Division was involved in the battles in southern Albania with the Fifth Cretan Army. The battle for Crete ended on the 2nd June, 1941.

Headquarters staff at Hotel Bretagne celebrated the German victory on Crete with a sumptuous banquet prepared by Sergeant Fritz Schultz. By protocol, and on the orders of Brigadier Schlemm, the evening was a sombre and quiet occasion. Toasts were offered to the Führer, to the Fatherland, to General Student, to the airborne divisions and individual regiments and, most poignantly of all, to 'absent friends'. A few tears were shed as the assembled officers recalled personal comrades who had lost their lives in the battle. A special toast was offered for two brothers who had been killed in action. Lieutenant Count Wolfgang von Blucher and his brother Leberhardt both lost their lives on the airfield perimeter at Heraklion on the second day of battle. Wolfgang and his platoon were dropped in the middle of the Black Watch defending the airfield and the lieutenant was killed in a skirmish, whilst his brother Leberhardt von Blucher was shot whilst attempting to carry ammunition to the beleaguered *Fallschirmjagger*. The tragic death in battle of these two young and popular officers cast a gloom on the evening's celebrations. Towards the end of the banquet Colonel von Bulow was called away to the operations room. He returned within a few minutes and beckoned Manfred to leave the dining room with him. Outside the door he turned to face Manfred.

"We fly into Heraklion tomorrow at dawn. Major Werner's message says the airfield is now clear and safe. We will leave Eleusis at 5.30 a.m. in full mess kit, only on this occasion you should wear your helmet. We don't want a repetition of the Schiphol disaster do we?" Then with a glint in his eye he added, "Now let's rejoin Brigadier Schlemm and get to bed early. Reveille will be at 3.30 a.m."

A Dornier cargo plane droned noisily as it sped south-westwards over the gleaming blue ocean dotted with crusty brown islands of the Cyclades, some small, others large and forbidding with vast mountainous ranges splitting the land mass down its middle. Manfred clearly saw the horseshoe shaped, deep-blue lagoon of the bay of Santorini as the plane veered westwards and half an hour later banked to the right and started losing height as it neared Crete from the east. As they flew lower the pilot pointed out the island of Spinalonga, protecting Elounda, and the fishing port of Aghios Nikolaos. Lower still they flew directly over Neapolis and Malia and, on the final approach to the airfield, the island of Dia lay on the port side.

The landing was perfectly smooth and the Dornier taxied slowly up to the control terminal, coming to a halt some two hundred metres from the main building. The engines were shut off and a side hatch opened. Colonel von Bulow advanced to the open hatch and Manfred became aware of loud cheers from outside the plane. Over the colonel's shoulder he saw *Feldwebel* Schneider and three other paratroopers running towards the plane. The colonel jumped to the ground, slipped and nearly fell, but quickly recovered and started walking towards the approaching *Fallschirmjagger*. When the colonel had gone ten or twelve paces, as Manfred prepared to drop to the ground, his ears picked up a whining noise in the sky overhead.

The cheering stopped and Schneider was shouting, "Mortars, mortars, down down," as he flung himself to the ground. Colonel von Bulow hesitated for only a moment and then threw himself flat and, at the same moment as Manfred jumped earthwards, there was a vicious loud bang. Manfred's last vision was of the back of Colonel von Bulow's tunic and a group of *Fallschirmjagger* lying flat on the ground some fifty metres away. A split second later there was a loud explosion inside his head, accompanied by a vivid flash and then blackness, total blackness, as he fell sideways impelled to the left by the force of a blow from a piece of mortar shell casing which penetrated the right side of his helmet, through his skull and into his brain.

Chapter Sixteen

The Defenders of Crete,
May 20th – June 2nd, 1941
Rape at Piskopiano
Heraklion Airfield, 3rd June, 1941

When the German armada carrying its airborne divisions arrived over Heraklion at 11 a.m. on 20th May Captain David Green was in Brigadier Chappell's headquarters, now sited in a cellar in the docks. The shufti Dornier had not appeared that morning. Instead at six o'clock the sky to the north suddenly filled with aircraft. As the humming noise of their engines increased to a reverberating crescendo, like a surging wave of thunder, they came in waves, discharged their bomb loads, banked steeply and sped northwards to return to Greece. Then there was an eerie silence broken once more at 11 a.m. by the thundering noise of another air flotilla, hundreds of planes, some towing gliders, flying overhead towards the south and releasing their gliders and white parachute canopies some eight kilometres outside Heraklion. The British defenders in the town were standing fast along the shoreline awaiting an assault from the sea but, by twelve noon, it was more than evident that the main German thrust was from the air. Confused reports were also arriving of a major attack at Maleme and Khania.

David returned to brigade headquarters at six o'clock. The place was in utter confusion, officers, orderlies and wireless operators rushing around in disjointed chaos, shouting messages and giving and accepting orders. In the corner of the orderly room David saw the familiar face of Professor Pendlebury confronting a Black Watch officer, Lieutenant Gordon Hope-Morley, prodding his chest with a walking stick whilst two stern looking Cretan *kapitans* stood imperiously by his side.

"What's going to be done about it?" Pendlebury demanded in his high-pitched voice.

Hope-Morley, seeing David approach, replied, "Here's an officer who can give you the answer."

Pendlebury fixed his one-eyed gaze on David.

"Captain Green, we met in Athens. I must see the Brigadier. I have with me two of the most important *kapitans* in Crete – Manoli Bandouvas and Satanas. They have, between them, ten thousand unarmed Cretans who are ready to fight here and now. If the brigadier will give me some three thousand rifles and ammunition we'll have the Germans off the island in no time. But Brigadier Chappell won't listen. He's too busy. Busy my foot!"

David thought for a few seconds that ten thousand appeared to be a standard estimate of Cretan irregular strength. Bandouvas and his companion seemed a better class of leader than the western *kapitans*.

"Professor Pendlebury, I'll see what I can do," and turning on his heel he left the group, followed by the smirking lieutenant who had managed to get the irritating Professor and the Cretans off his back.

The two British officers entered Colonel Hunter's office together but permission to see the Brigadier was refused. David started outlining Pendlebury's request when the harassed colonel interrupted him.

"Captain Green, we've got a major battle on our hands. Tell Pendlebury and the *kapitans* to bugger off and let us get on with the fighting."

David returned to Pendlebury and apologised for the Brigadier, suggesting they should try again on the following day.

Cretan War Diary

The first day of the battle for Crete had gone well for the defenders. The German paratroopers suffered severe losses on landing at Maleme and Heraklion and, at Rethymno, they were split into two groups by the aggressive Australians. One thousand eight hundred and sixty-three German paratroopers and glider troops were killed on the first day of the assault. On the second day David took a platoon from headquarters to defend the road between the airport and the dock.

The two hillocks at the western end of the runway, known as the Two Charlies, were used by Australian artillery to pin down Colonel Bruno Braüer's paratroopers pressing from the east. The fighting during the day was intense and bitter, the Black Watch, defending the airfield, giving as good as they got, but neither side won the day. During the day the Australians on the hillock shot down nine Junker JU-52 troop carriers. Colonel Burkhardt's First Parachute Regiment was deployed to the east of Knossos and had suffered three hundred casualties and made little progress towards Heraklion by the end of the second day. On the morning of the 23rd May the future looked bleak for the German invaders. Their Schiffsstaffel was sunk without trace and their forces in Rethymno and Heraklion were contained and suffering heavy losses.

The breakthrough came at Maleme airfield. Captain Ramcke's Storm Paratroopers secured the airfield early on the second day and this allowed a constant supply of planes to use the airstrip, despite repeated attacks by New Zealand and Maori forces. During one attack along the coastal strip Lieutenant Charles Upham was subsequently awarded a VC for his valour in leading his men to within two kilometres of their objective. In Heraklion during that day Greek forces in the city capitulated, allowing the Germans to briefly enter the town from the west, but they were soon driven out by fierce counter attacks by the Leicester's and the Yorks and Lancs. The Black Watch were firmly in control of the vital airstrip. The situation at Heraklion and Rethymno remained static for 24th and 25th May but, at Maleme, the New Zealanders were forced eastwards and took up a defensive line with two Australian battalions between Galatas and the sea.

Creforce's reserve battalion, the First Welch, were pushed into the defensive line at Galatas on 25th May and after twenty-four hours of fierce fighting were surrounded and surrendered. Over four hundred of the battalion were taken prisoner including Colonel Duncan, one hundred men were killed in action and only eight officers and one hundred and sixty-one other ranks returned safely to Alexandria. On 26th and 27th May Richthofen's VIII Flotilla conducted a savage air bombardment of Heraklion, razing the town to the ground.

By the 27th May resistance to the German advance from the west was weakening despite two desperate but futile counter attacks by

Colonel Kippenberger's New Zealanders and Maoris. On the same day the order to evacuate Crete was received from London. Brigadier Hargest organised withdrawal of New Zealand and Australian forces from western Crete moving his men from Stilos across Askifou plain, and southwards over the White Mountains to the port of Sphakia on the southern coast. Evacuation from Sphakia continued until 2nd June and four thousand men were removed from the little port by Royal Navy destroyers leaving five thousand soldiers to be captured by the Germans. Brigadier Chappell organised evacuation of British and Dominion forces from Heraklion on the nights of 28th, 29th and 30th May. The Yorks and Lancs covered withdrawal of troops into the Heraklion perimeter during daytime for embarkation in the harbour under the cover of darkness.

David and his platoon came into Brigadier Chappell's headquarters near the docking area mid-afternoon on the 27th May. The dilapidated command centre was crowded with tired officers and men, some asleep, and others sitting crouched on the floor, dejected and unshaven. David entered the Brigadier's office and found Pendlebury, Satanas and Peter Ferman in earnest conversation with a tired looking Brigadier, who stopped in mid-sentence and looked towards David.

"Captain Green, Satanas has come to collect rifles and ammo' for his *andartes*. The brigade will be leaving a lot of weaponry behind over the next few days. You will help Santanas with his collection. You have my authority to confiscate any unclaimed rifles."

The brigadier wished them good luck and David and the Cretan *kapitan* spent the rest of the day scavenging amongst the retreating troops until they had collected three hundred Lee Enfields and had requisitioned three dozen crates of ammunition. Satanas and his cache of arms and ammunition, loaded on a dozen mules, left the dockside area at 4 p.m. on the 27th May.

Brigadier Chappell and his senior officers departed from Crete on HMS *Imperial* on the night of the 28th May and David and the remnants of the rear party sailed on HMS *Orion*, the last ship to leave Heraklion harbour, before dawn on 29th May. Due to its late departure the *Orion* and her sister ship HMS *Dido* were strafed at dawn off eastern Crete. The *Orion* received two direct hits and suffered many casualties amongst the seamen and troops on deck. In all, three thousand five hundred men were evacuated from Heraklion, but a fifth of this number were lost at sea. HMS *Orion* limped into Alexandria Harbour at 6 p.m. on the 30th May. The injured and dead were carried off to the military hospital in Alexandria. David and the survivors were taken to Sidi-Bishir Camp a few kilometres distance from the harbour. On the same day as David arrived in Alexandria the Italian Siena Division, commanded by General Angelo Carta, was making an unopposed landing at Sitia in the eastern sector of Crete.

Rape at Piskopiano

When David left the farm at Piskopiano on the 13th May his instructions to Corporal Anderson were clear. The corporal was to 'stay put' at the farm until David returned from his trip to Khania, probably in three or four days time. The corporal was only too pleased to remain at the farm where he helped with herding the goats and where he was near Stephia. Jim Anderson had fallen in love with the girl and, with her father's approval, she in turn welcomed the advances of the pugnacious Australian soldier. When the captain had not returned by the 19th the corporal became anxious but his comfortable situation at the farm and Stephia's blossoming love for him overrode all other considerations. As instructed Jim Anderson 'stayed put' in his Cretan love nest.

On the morning of the 20th May the noise of the bombing to the north, over Heraklion, was louder and more prolonged than usual. At midday, when the sun was at its zenith, Jim was out in the olive grove herding his goats towards the pastures and lower slopes of the Mohos hills when he became conscious of a continuous rumbling noise in the air out to sea. The noise grew in intensity and into his view in the distance over Hersonisos came a fleet of planes towing gliders and protected by a swarm of Messerschmitt fighters weaving to and fro above the air convoy.

General Löhr's Fourth Air Fleet was bringing in glider troops and paratroopers for their landings on the flat plains south and east of Heraklion. Corporal Anderson's first instinct was to make his way towards the landing site but he convinced himself of the impracticality and danger of such a move. He decided to stay at the farm. The distant sounds of battle to the north and west continued intermittently throughout the night, intensifying at daybreak on 21st May. Early that morning Jim, who had been awake most of the night, climbed the foothills and lower escarpments of the Pirgia mountains south of the farmhouse. A curtain of smoke shrouded Ames escarpment and an occasional flash of light pierced the dark, smoky sky like a searchlight beam. He stayed at his observation point on the ridge most of the day, looking northwards and wondering if any of his commando pals were involved in the battle.

He returned to the farm at teatime to be greeted by Spiros who had been into Hersonisos that morning. Spiros indicated by gestures that a large force of Germans had landed from the air, in and around Heraklion, and British and Greek soldiers were defending the town. Spiros looked at Jim and tugging at the sleeve of his battle dress, with a look of concern on his face, made gestures to indicate that he should remove his military clothing. Jim realised that, as he was the only uniformed man in Piskopiano, he would stick out like a sore thumb and might compromise the safety of Spiros and his family. Jim changed into some of Spiros' old working clothes and the addition of an old *sariki* on his head made him look Cretan but did nothing to improve his inability to converse in Greek.

The days and nights dragged slowly by. There was little abatement in the volume of noise engendered from the battle area except that on a few occasions Jim thought the fighting was coming nearer Piskopiano. On the seventh night of the battle, from his vantage point on the Pirgias, he saw a myriad of small lights out to sea off Gournes, a large convoy proceeding in an easterly direction. The lights were evident on 28th and 29th May but on 30th there were none and this coincided with complete cessation of the staccato sounds of gunfire and flashes from the direction of Heraklion. On the same day Spiros returned from Piskopiano with the news that the British had evacuated Heraklion by sea and that German airborne troops were moving through Hersonisos along the coast road to Malia and Neapolis.

Jim Anderson now knew that he had to move out of the farmhouse in order to protect Spiros and his wife and two daughters. Supplied with water, bread and cheese he established a daytime hideout some two kilometres from the farm on the southerly slopes of the Pirgia foothills, in the fork between the roads from Hersonisos to Kastelli and Gournes. At night-time he skirted back northwards around the foothills to the olive grove of the farm where he slept on open ground and spent hours in Stephia's company. The first German armoured vehicles to probe in a southerly direction came past his observation post at midday on June 1st. The German column of four armoured troop-carriers and two motorcycle machine gunners slowly ground their way past his hide and disappeared in a cloud of dust in the direction of Kastelli. There was no further activity in the afternoon and Jim made his way back to the olive grove, avoiding the roads, and arriving at 6 p.m. Near the farm he met Stephia herding goats and had a brief but passionate interlude with her under an olive tree in the hot, evening sun. Stephia left, promising to return with food and drink. Jim settled down comfortably on the ground under the shade of an olive tree and immediately fell asleep.

Jim woke with a start about an hour later. The light was fading and from the farmyard he heard men's voices singing in unison, deep guttural voices in an unfamiliar tongue. He crept nearer the edge of the yard, protected from sight by the olive trees, and saw two armed German paratroopers circling around the perimeter of the yard, where about a dozen men, stripped to the waist, were manhandling buckets of water from the well and filling up a water tank on one of four lorries parked in the yard. Jim could not understand why he had not heard the lorries arrive and wondered where Spiros and his daughters might be. Daylight was rapidly fading when a sergeant emerged from the door of the farmhouse urging the men to hurry up and fill the tanks before nightfall. Feverish activity continued in the yard amid ribald laughter and bursts of singing from the labouring soldiers.

When it was quite dark the German sergeant called a halt and the soldiers moved into the barn where they lit kerosene lamps, washed themselves and dressed before sitting in a circle on the floor to eat their rations and drink wine. The sergeant again emerged from the farmhouse carrying bottles of ouzo, cheese and black bread which he distributed amongst his men and, posting two armed guards in the corners of the yard, he returned to the house. The noise from within the barn increased in volume as the ouzo took effect. The soldiers were singing bawdy and lewd songs, cursing and swearing and emerging through the barn door on occasion to urinate against the outside wall.

After about an hour a paratrooper staggered across the yard to the farmhouse. Within a minute he reappeared with Antia, dragging her across by her wrists to the barn. A mouth organist was playing a plaintive tune and when Antia was thrust into the circle of light cast by the kerosene lamps, the whole company broke into a loud cheer. They shouted, "*Danz, Danz*", but Antia just stood in the middle cowering, trembling and begging for mercy. But there was to be no mercy from the drunken paratroopers. Jim heard Antia give one loud scream and then many stifled shouts but the noise and excitement of the soldiers left him in no doubt that she was being raped, not once, but by most of the men in the barn. One of the paratroopers on guard in the yard was relieved by a colleague and hurried into the barn to partake in raping the helpless Greek woman. Antia's ordeal went on for about an hour and was interrupted when the sergeant dragged Stephia into the barn and into the middle of the drunken, lascivious soldiers. Stephia screamed and spat but her attempts at protecting herself were futile. The men held her on the ground and the sergeant was first to take his pleasure, followed in turn by most of the other paratroopers. Jim, lying in the undergrowth some eighty metres away, listening to the screams and moans of the women and the uncouth shouts of encouragement from the soldiers, could hardly control an impulse to run into the barn and physically assault the paratroopers. But he knew that such an exhibition of valour would be of no use or help to Antia and Stephia. He kept watch on the farmhouse throughout the night.

The paratroopers were roused at daybreak, drank some coffee, returned to filling the water tank from the well, packed up their belongings and left in the four lorries at about 9 a.m. in the direction of Kastelli. Corporal Anderson waited for about fifteen minutes before cautiously approaching the barn where he found Stephia and Antia bound and gagged, lying in a mound of straw like two broken rag dolls. He released the bonds and gags and, without waiting to talk, ran into the farmhouse. In the bedroom he found Spiros bound and gagged and tied to the bedpost and, lying on the bed, was his wife, similarly tethered, with a look of terror in her dark brown Mediterranean eyes. She had been raped twice by the sergeant in full view of her husband. Jim was unable to believe that civilised soldiers could behave in such a dastardly manner. Spiros was sobbing uncontrollably at his impotence in preventing the atrocity. His wife lay on the bed staring at the ceiling, whilst his two daughters huddled in the corner of the living room clinging to each other and crying fitfully, the salty tears streaming down their faces on to the front of their torn, blood-stained blouses. Jim felt a sudden rage rise within him, a flood of anger and fury and a desire for revenge on the cowardly Germans who had brutally shattered the lives of the Constantinos family. Jim Anderson decided there and then exactly what he had to do.

Jim took his leave of the Constantinos that same day. He first went to the cache in the hideout at the upper end of the olive grove and took away one Sten gun, ammunition and a water flask. He carefully replaced the crates and resealed them with waterproof tarpaulins. Now, dressed as a Cretan farmer, he dismantled the gun and secreted the various parts and the water-bottle inside his clothing. He then took his leave of Stephia who was still in a state of shock and shattered by the traumatic events of the previous day. Hemade his way to the Hersonisos-Kastelli crossroads and, crossing over, scrambled over a low hill to reach a dried river bed which took him northwards towards the coast. After two kilometres he turned westwards passing south of the small hamlet of Koxari and, skirting around the foothills of the Apostoli hills, he made his way slowly and carefully towards Episkopi where he was some eight kilometres distant from the coast road.

Throughout the day Jim lay low and heard vehicles moving on the coast road and saw dust clouds lying over the main highway to the north. Dusk was fast approaching as he ate his evening meal of dry bread and rancid goats cheese in an orange grove on the outskirts of Episkopi. He then rested and slept for four hours under cover of a dry stone wall. At midnight he entered the darkened village and silently padded his way across the main square to take the road northwards towards Heraklion. Within four kilometres he reached the village of Aghios Ioannis, again in complete darkness, and silent as the grave. He proceeded northwards and on his left side became aware of a vertical cliff rising from the uneven hillocks. Soon after leaving the village he took a goat-herd path leading to the base of Ames escarpment and, with great care and feeling his way uphill, he ascended to the top of the ridge. The journey to this point from Espiskopi had taken two hours and in about an hour's time dawn would be breaking.

Jim selected a group of boulders on the top of Ames ridge and, inserting his body into a crevasse between the rocks, he quickly fell asleep. The chirping of grasshoppers woke him about an hour after daybreak and the sun was already fully over the horizon to the east.

He crawled out of his night bivouac and took stock of his surroundings. The top of Ames escarpment was criss-crossed and covered with irregular rock formations and large boulders. At the north end of the ridge Jim saw a Nazi flag some five hundred metres distant and, in the bright sunlight, he also made out the helmets of three German sentries standing around the flagpole. The east to west coast road, cluttered with moving vehicles, was barely discernible in the distant haze. On both sides of the escarpment the olive groves were studded with white canopies and, in some places, pock-marked by craters with trees leaning drunkenly to one side and the tails of crashed gliders standing out starkly from the green background, like white Celtic crosses. In amongst the trees he caught an occasional glimpse of German soldiers working their way through the tree-lined terrain pulling and carrying various items of equipment and bodies towards a row of lorries parked alongside the Episkopi-Heraklion road. On the left-hand side of the ridge he could dimly see the ruined buildings in Heraklion – blackened, shattered shells protruding into the smoky, hazy sky.

At frequent intervals during the morning many supply planes, Dorniers and Heinkels came in off the sea and flew in an easterly direction over Dia island and then, banking sharply, turned westwards to hit the runway at the airfield. For a few seconds the planes were visible as they swooped down near the ground and then Jim's view was obscured by the Two Charlies at the westwards end of the runway.

Corporal Jim Anderson studied the terrain in detail. He realised that a daylight attempt to cross the plains and the landing ground of the paratroopers would be suicidal and he would need to negotiate the difficult journey under cover of darkness. He had ample time to study the ground between Ames ridge and the airfield. On the western side of Ames escarpment a dried river bed ran directly northwards towards the sea and passed under the coastal road about two kilometres from the airfield and about the same distance from the small village of Amniso, which appeared to be heavily guarded by the Germans.

The hot, dry day wore slowly onwards. At midday the guards were changed at the observation point on the north end of Ames ridge and during the afternoon the volume of air traffic diminished only to return with increasing intensity in the early evening. In the evening the engineers and troops scavenging in the olive groves withdrew and returned to their loaded vehicles to be driven up the road to Heraklion. The evening was calm and peaceful except for a constant drone of aircraft landing and discharging their loads and taking off from the airfield.

By now Jim was thirsty, cramped and uncomfortable in his hideout amongst the boulders and he had drunk all his reserves of water. Dusk and night descended very suddenly as the sun sank rapidly over Heraklion. About half an hour before sunset Jim began his descent off Ames ridge using a shepherd's track leading downwards and zigzagging across the three hundred foot left hand face of the escarpment.

By the time it was completely dark he had reached the brushland on the edge of an olive grove. Striking westwards for about half a kilometre he soon found the dry river bed cutting a straight course from south to north through the olive groves and leading directly towards the coast. Within two hours he reached the coastal road near an unguarded bridge and having crossed it entered a large orange grove. The village of Amniso lay some two hundred metres to the west. Jim made his way steadily and gingerly through the orange grove, giving the village a wide berth and crawling and crouching as he advanced for the last kilometre towards the landward face of the Two Charlies. A guttural shout and a short barking laugh in the blackness above his head confirmed that these points of vantage were indeed manned and used as observation posts by the Germans.

He arrived at the chicken coops at 3.30 a.m. and was relieved to find that the two mortars and the bombs had not been discovered. Sitting in the corner of the shed waiting for daybreak he reminisced about his home and his brothers in Adelaide, about his time in the commandos, about poor old Colonel Maclean, about Sergeant Tucker and Captain Green, but most of all his thoughts were about Stephia and the horrible rape she had endured. His hate for the Germans, who had perpetrated the crime, grew within him by the minute, like a rampant cancer, and he welcomed the approach of daybreak when he might be able to avenge the atrocity.

The noise of aircraft movement on the other side of the Two Charlies began at daybreak. Six aircraft took off rapidly one after the other flying eastwards into the rising sun. At seven o'clock planes started arriving in the airport and Jim knew, from his observations on Ames ridge, that the time of maximum activity would be about an hour after sunrise. When he judged that the time was right he let the first mortar bomb drop into its canister. There was a deafening roar as the mortar shattered the wooden roof of the hut and flew into the sky to descend with a piercing whine and a thunderous bang, landing twenty seconds later on the airport runway. Jim kept running from one mortar to another:

"This one's from me, this one's from Stephia, this one's from Spiros, this one's from Colonel Mac."

He worked like a maniac and discharged seven bombs in all, changing the setting and angle of the mortars in between shots. The Germans on top of the Two Charlies soon spotted the source of the bombing. Three *Fallschirmjagger* came running down the hillside, *Schmeitzers* at the ready and, as Jim Anderson turned to load his eighth bomb, he was mown down by a fusillade of shots. He fell across one of the mortars, blood streaming from his mouth and gasping for breath.

His dying words were, "Stephia, Stephia, oh God, Stephia."

Corporal James Anderson's mortar bombardment of the airfield on the morning of 3rd June, 1941 caused the death of four German airmen, destroyed three planes on the ground and damaged many others. Twelve ground staff were slightly injured but the most severe injury was inflicted on Major Manfred Schmidt of the Eighth Parachute Regiment who was rendered unconscious by a piece of shrapnel which pierced his helmet and was embedded in his skull.

Heraklion Airport, 3rd June 1941

Feldwebel Heinz Schneider, always an early riser, woke before dawn in his tented bivouac on the perimeter of Heraklion airport on the 3rd June, 1941. He reviewed the events of the preceding week as he stretched his aching limbs and lit up the first cigarette of the day. The Eighth battalion had covered themselves with glory in the fighting along the coastal road which eventually led to the capture of their objective. The enemy, small wily Scotsmen of the Black Watch, proved tough and durable adversaries. The drop itself was a near disaster when one hundred and twenty paratroopers, including Colonel Herdich landed on the foothills of Mount Elena amongst a battalion of Cretan irregulars and were wiped out to a man.

Despite the early drawback Major Werner regrouped the battalion and, on the 27th, the 8th advanced northwards to cut the coast road between Heraklion and Malia. Advancing westwards on the 28th they were able to relieve Captain Burkhardt's beleaguered and exhausted battalion to be joined later that day by the decimated remnants of van der Hydte's paratroopers who had also been surrounded and in continuous contact with the enemy for five days.

Both these battle-weary groups were of little use during the last days of the battle and the onus for further advances westward fell squarely on the shoulders of the Eighth Regiment. Two days of bitter fighting followed as von Bulow's *Fallschirmjagger* pushed their way westwards along the coast road, fighting for every inch of territory against the obdurate and stubborn Scots. Casualties were heavy on both sides and by nightfall on the 29th May Major Werner's men were within a kilometre of the airfield. When the Eighth resumed their probing at dawn on the 30th May resistance was minimal. During the night the enemy had withdrawn to the harbour and evacuated the airfield.

Heinz Schneider led his men in the final assault on the deserted airfield which was made secure by mid-morning. He then proceeded westwards to the harbour area where there was still some desultory small arms fire but few British soldiers remained and the remnants were soon captured. The retreating British had left the airfield pock-marked with land mine craters and strewn with immobilised aircraft and lorries. *Feldwebel* Schneider was impressed at the rapidity with which the engineers cleared and repaired the runways, allowing the first aircraft to land and take off from Heraklion on 2nd June. On that day Major Werner informed Student's headquarters at Maleme and the skeleton divisional headquarters in Athens that the airfield was now open to receive planes.

Schneider took one final deep draw on his cigarette, extinguished the stub and walked across to the mess for breakfast. Within ten minutes Major Werner appeared, bleary-eyed, and announced that a message had been received at 5 a.m. that Colonel von Bulow and Major Schmidt would be leaving Eleusis at 5.45 a.m. in a Dornier with one Messerschmitt 110 as escort; estimated time of arrival at Heraklion 7.30 am. He gulped down his mug of coffee and hastily left the mess hall. Dawn was about to break as he drove his *Kübelwagen* around the airfield perimeter where his paratroops were entrenched in dugouts and gun emplacements evacuated by the British. By the time his tour was finished the sun had appeared above the horizon to the east and all his battalion, including the gunners on the *Zweikarlys*, had been informed that Colonel von Bulow would arrive in the first Dornier to land on the airfield. The men were ordered to give their colonel a rousing welcome, just as they had done at Schiphol in 1940. *Feldwebel* Schneider then took up his position next to Major Werner on the steps in front of the control tower to await the Dornier's arrival.

The first two planes to arrive that morning were not Dorniers. They were Heinkels bringing in medical supplies, food and ammunition, from Maleme. As soon as they came to a halt off the runway a hoard of engineers and paratroopers rushed forwards to unload supplies. Some ten minutes later a solitary Messerschmitt came in at pace and taxied to the fuel depot. The next plane to arrive approached from the west and flew over the airfield, before banking steeply and gliding in to land bumpily, rolling up noisily to the control tower. Colonel von Trettner, Student's operations officer, emerged from a two-seater *Storch* and walked across to join the waiting group at the control building. Whilst he was talking to Major Werner a Messerschmitt fighter flew in from the east and zoomed over the airfield and Heraklion town at a low level banking steeply and disappearing into the blue haze over the sea. And then came the unmistakable engine sound of a Dornier approaching from the east, the noise growing rapidly louder as it came into view, flying sedately on its gliding pathway to approach the runway.

Feldwebel Schneider fired a green flare which was the pre-arranged signal that the Colonel's Dornier was approaching. The paratroops of the Eighth Battalion emerged all around the airfield, holding their machine pistols above their heads, standing on parapets and sand-bagged trenches, ready to cheer their revered commanding officer. The cheering began as the Dornier's wheels touched the hard runway and continued in waves as the plane came to a halt and then taxied to within two hundred metres of the control tower.

Heinz Schneider, on impulse and unable to control his excitement, ran towards the plane as it drew to a halt and the engine spluttered and coughed as the propeller blades slowed and stopped rotating. As he ran towards the stationary, silent plane the loud cheers of the

Fallschirmjagger echoed in his ears and he was joined by two young paratroopers.

The hatch on the side of the Dornier opened and Colonel von Bulow's diminutive figure appeared in the aperture waving in the general direction of the airfield. He jumped forwards from the plane on to the ground, slipped, picked himself up and walked towards the *Feldwebel*. Major Manfred Schmidt was next to appear in the open hatch and seemed to Schneider to be getting ready to jump when he heard a different noise to the background cheers, an unmistakable whining, whistling noise, the noise of a mortar bomb overhead beginning its vertical trajectory to the ground below.

Heinz Schneider's reaction was instinctive, imbued in his brain by long months of training and combat. He flung himself flat on the ground shouting, "Mortars, mortars, down, down." As his body sped earthwards he had a brief glimpse of Colonel von Bulow stumbling to his knees and Major Schmidt airborne, half way out of the hatch and then came the horrendous bang of an exploding mortar, some forty metres to his left, which drove the breath from his lungs and seemed to turn his eardrums inside out. He got up on one knee and saw the colonel doing likewise and looked towards the plane. The inert body of Major Schmidt lay on the ground underneath the hatch.

Colonel von Bulow and the two *Fallschirmjagger* ran for shelter at the control tower. *Feldwebel* Schneider stumbled to his feet and staggered drunkenly towards the plane, his sense of balance disturbed by the mortar bomb explosion. When he was within ten feet of Manfred he realised that the major had suffered a serious wound and turning towards the command post shouted as loud as he could, "Medics, medics, stretcher, stretcher."

Feldwebel Schneider then knelt carefully by Manfred's prostrate body and took stock of his injuries. Manfred was unconscious but not dead. His face was ashen grey, with blue-tinted lips and fresh blood bubbling in a frothy mess from the side of his mouth as he gasped for air. There was a gaping hole in the right side of his steel helmet with a jagged piece of shrapnel impaled in its centre and dark, venous blood oozing gently from the edges of the cavity. Schneider's first reaction was to dislodge the shrapnel but, after touching it gingerly with his forefinger, he decided the injury required expert medical attention. Remembering his basic first aid instruction he gently turned the major's limp body on to its left side to maintain an airway and felt for a pulse in the left side of his neck. Satisfied that the pulse was strong and regular he again looked towards the central building shouting, "Medics, medics" while he fished an emergency bandage from his tunic pocket and started winding it around Manfred's helmet and the sharp, protruding edge of shrapnel. This did nothing to quell the bloody ooze which rapidly soaked the dressing and continued to seep from under Manfred's helmet down the right side of his neck and on to his tunic.

Whilst engaged in these activities Schneider was conscious that he was almost completely deaf and he did not hear the shrill, whistling noise of the second descending mortar bomb. He was half-crouched over the still figure of his company major, cradling the bandaged head in his lap, when he felt a sudden violent thrust at the back of his right shoulder which forced his torso forwards on to the major's head. He was faintly conscious of the 'crump' noise of a mortar explosion and acutely aware of an excruciating, boring pain behind his right shoulder before he passed into unconsciousness.

The second mortar bomb landed even nearer to the plane than the first. By the time the young medical officer and stretcher bearers got to the two injured men under the Dornier a third mortar bomb had been released and landed harmlessly some hundred metres away between the plane and control tower. The unqualified medical officer at first thought that he had two dead men on his hands. He was only a junior lieutenant, recently flown out to Athens from his medical school in Berlin and had arrived in Crete on the previous day. Apart from a few basic bandages, splints and instruments there was little equipment on the airfield. Manfred and *Feldwebel* Schneider were placed on stretchers and carried to the command post where further pressure dressings were applied. Colonel von Bulow, ashen-faced and trembling uncontrollably, fussed over his injured comrades, berating the medical officer and questioning his ability to deal with such severe injuries. The poor frightened sub-lieutenant, quivering in his boots, made a snap decision.

"The injured men are to be evacuated to Athens on the next plane to leave the airfield."

One of the newly arrived Junkers transport had refuelled and was about to take off. The two men on stretchers, accompanied by the over-attentive medical officer and a medical orderly, were flown back to Tatöi airfield and within four hours of their injuries *Feldwebel*

Schneider and Major Schmidt were undergoing emergency surgery in the requisitioned Red Cross hospital in Athens. As the Junkers took off from Heraklion Colonel von Bulow was heard to comment in a sad voice, "We're told that lightning never strikes in the same place twice. Well, they're wrong. In poor Manfred's case lightning has struck in the same place twice and I'm afraid the second strike may prove fatal."

Chapter Seventeen

The Desert War,
June 1940 – December 1942

Desert War Diary

Mussolini's colonial aspirations led directly to the onset of hostilities and the Desert War in North Africa in the autumn of 1940. Before World War I, Italy had acquired Libya, a part of Somaliland and Eritrea and in 1936, despite world criticism, wrested Ethiopia from Emperor Haile Selassie who was driven into exile in London. Italy entered World War II on 10th June, 1940 by invading the south of France whilst the French were in the throes of annihilation by Hitler's victorious armies. By his action Mussolini catapulted Italy into a war with Britain and France and he lost little time in his attempts to expand his Nilotic empire in East Africa. In July 1940 Sudan was invaded by the Italians, followed in August by an attack on British Somaliland. At first the Italians were successful but, as the year came to an end, British counter-attacks reversed Italy's gains and in January 1941 Emperor Haile Selassie returned to Addis Ababa to resume command of his forces and to rule Ethiopia. By the end of 1941 Italy's Nilotic empire in East Africa had been repossessed by Britain.

Italian forces in Libya, some five hundred thousand strong, posed a direct threat to Egypt and the Suez Canal. The Italian rear was protected by Vichy French occupation of Algeria, which left the field commanders complete freedom to concentrate their attention on an all-out attack on the British in Egypt. The Italian Fifth Army was deployed in western Libya whilst the Tenth Army faced the British on the Egyptian border, supported by one thousand two hundred guns, three hundred tanks and over one hundred and fifty aircraft. Facing this formidable array of military power General Sir Archibald Wavell had ninety-five thousand men at his disposal, two infantry divisions and one armoured division, severely depleted of serviceable tanks. An under-strength Anzac Fourth Division was held in reserve in Palestine were completing their desert training.

The first strike of the North African Campaign occurred on the 11th June 1940 when an armoured car of the Eleventh Hussars penetrated the Italian defences and attacked two fortresses at Capuzzo and Madalena, inflicting a few casualties on the enemy who were not prepared to counter-attack and remained entrenched in their fortress defences. Numerical odds in favour of the Italians was five to one and yet Marshal Rodolfo Grazziani procrastinated and held back his forces whilst the British were receiving reinforcements of men and tanks and establishing a defence line at Sollum.

By August Grazziani's indecision caused Mussolini to order an attack and, on the 13th September 1940, the Italians unleashed five divisions of the Italian Tenth Army against the British along a twenty mile front between Sollum and Sidi Omar. The British defenders retreated in an orderly fashion eastwards and the Italians quickly occupied Sollum and Sidi Barrani where they built a series of fortified encampments on an elevated escarpment and there the Italian thrust petered out. At this point they were still some sixty miles short of the main British defence line at Mersa Matruh.

General Ritchie O'Connor, commander of the Western Desert Force, now deployed his armour and a motorised Indian Division of thirty-six thousand men to strike into the desert some ten miles south of the Italian lines. On the 9th December 1940 O'Connor's forces advanced northwards at dead of night and, led by Matildas of the Seventh Tank Regiment, cut the coast road at the enemies rear.

Operation Compass took the Italians by complete surprise and the fortified encampments at Nibeiwa, Sidi Barrani and Bukbuk were overwhelmed over a period of five days with the capture of two hundred and thirty-seven guns, seventy tanks and thirty-eight thousand prisoners of war. Morale in the Italian army was completely shattered and the straggling demoralised troops retreated in disarray across the border into the coastal fortress of Bardia where their further escape to the west was blocked by the Seventh Armoured Division.

General Armale Berganzoli and forty-five thousand men in Bardia were ordered by Mussolini to, 'Stand and fight to the last man'. The attack on Bardia, led by the newly arrived Fourth Australian Division, began on the 4th January 1941 and, after some initial fierce fighting, the fortress was overcome and surrendered on the 5th January with the capture of forty thousand Italian prisoners.

General O'Connor's forces relentlessly continued to surge westwards, their main objective being the vital port of Tobruk, eight hundred miles from Alexandria and the same distance from Tripoli. On the 21st January Tobruk was captured by the Australians taking twenty-seven thousand prisoners and vast amounts of supplies. The road west to Benghazi was open for a further Allied advance, but events in the Balkans and the German threat to Greece impelled the chiefs of staff in London to divert a large contingent of British and Dominion forces to the Greek theatre.

Despite lack of supplies, and especially of tanks, General O'Connor continued with a two-pronged attack westwards, the Australians along the coast to take Derna on the 30th January and General Creagh's Seventh Armoured Division across two hundred and fifty miles of uncharted desert to cut the Italian escape and supply route at Msus. The Italians, in headlong retreat westwards from Benghazi and harried in the rear by the Australians, were engaged in a major tank battle at Beda Fomm on the 6th and 7th February where the Italian Armoured Brigades were annihilated.

General O'Connor wanted to press forwards to take Tripoli and expel the Italians from North Africa but General Wavell ordered a halt and from the 12th February 1941 British and Dominion Forces were on the defensive. The Allied advance into Cyreniaca was the first of the war and hailed as a momentous victory. The tactics employed by General O' Connor were innovative and completely demoralised the poorly led Italian forces. In retrospect General O'Connor should have been allowed to maintain his momentum and press forwards to Tripoli, but the exhausted British and Dominion Infantry and, in particular, the depleted armoured forces, down to thirty-five serviceable tanks, could not have been further extended.

On the day the Allies went on the defensive at El Agheila General Rommel and a light Panzer Division were disembarking in Tripoli. The Africa Corps had arrived in North Africa and Hitler had again made moves to support Mussolini and bail him out of a tricky *situation. The arrival of the Africa Corps changed the whole concept of the desert campaign in North Africa and Rommel's subsequent successes were largely modelled on the tactics employed by General Ritchie O'Connor and his three hundred and fifty mile advance into Libya between December 1940 and February 1941.*

David and his rearguard party disembarked from the shell-battered *Orion* at Alexandria on the evening of 30th May, 1941, where waiting trucks took them to Sidi Bishir Camp some ten kilometres distant from the docks. The officers were ushered into separate quarters for a bath and a change of clothing and, after a solid meal, David slept for a full eighteen hours waking at teatime on the next day. From the orderly room he sent a message to Colonel Sharples and then toured the camp area with the commandant identifying four junior officers and one hundred and three other ranks, sole survivors of the First Battalion Welch Regiment. Morale amongst the little group of survivors was particularly low. They had all lost friends and even relatives who had been killed, wounded or taken prisoner in the Cretan battle and, with Rommel's forces gathering and preparing to strike into Egypt, it looked as if these dispirited men might be asked again to face the Germans. David prayed silently they would be spared after the debacle their battalion had suffered on the killing fields at Galatas in Crete.

No. 29 Shepherds Hotel, Cairo, 2nd June, 1941

Colonel Henry Sharples, perspiring in the mid-afternoon sun, stood on an airless balcony overlooking the Nile, his battle tunic drenched in sweat. As often happened the cooling ceiling fans in rooms twenty-eight and twenty-nine Shepherds Hotel were not operating, a frequent occurrence in wartime and, for that matter, peacetime Cairo. He was rather short-tempered and longed for a cold shower and a change into a freshly laundered clean shirt. David was ushered into his presence by Sergeant Willoughby, her dyed blond hair, wet and limp and her heavily manicured face, red and sweaty. The colonel dispensed with formalities.

"We shouldn't be expected to work under these conditions, David, but there's a war on and I suppose we have to put up with it. I'm sorry that your First Battalion is in such poor shape after their mauling at Galatas. They may be expected to go up to the front line again shortly to face the Germans. So I'll come to the point. For my purposes you will remain in and around Cairo as I may need to call on your services at short notice. I've had a word with my oppo' on Wavell's headquarters staff and he's looking for an intelligence officer with a few languages up his sleeve. I've arranged for you to become a staff officer at General Sir Archibald Wavell's headquarters in Gazira. With your knowledge of Greece and Crete and your ability to speak German you'll be well placed to fill this post. Your immediate superior will be Brigadier Dorman-Smith. You will sit in on conferences at HQ and report back to me. I'm fed up with getting HQ decisions second, or third-hand and I know that Wavell is in contact with London day and night.

"Poor Wavell has had a lot on his plate since Mussolini threw Italy into the war. His command stretches over nine countries and parts of two continents and is about two thousand square miles. To defend this vast territory he has two divisions, two brigade groups, one under-strength armoured division and a camel corps of six hundred men. In June last year the main threat to us here were the half million Italians in Libya. Their battle-worthiness had not been tested and what happened is of course now history. The Italians attacked on the 30th September and advanced sixty miles into Egypt but were stopped at Sidi Barrani by General Ritchie O'Connor's division. On December 5th last year O'Connor counter-attacked with thirty-six thousand men. Our forces broke through with ease and the Seventh Armoured Division raced westwards after the retreating Italians. By the time you reached Cairo in January O'Connor had taken Bardia, captured two Italian generals and some hundred and thirty thousand prisoners. He then pressed forwards to Tobruk and Benghazi where he captured an Itie general, Elastic-Whiskers Berganzoli. There was no stopping O'Connor who wanted to drive on to Tripoli and throw the Italians out of Cyreniaca but, on Wavell's insistence, he stopped at Bedda Fomm.

"Unfortunately the Balkan problem developed and Wavell was ordered to deploy his over-stretched forces to help the Greeks. Well you know what happened there and subsequently in Crete we lost a lot of manpower and material which would have been useful in the desert against the Italians. Then on the 14th February Rommel and his Africa Corps arrived in Tripoli and changed the whole ball game.

General Neame was made temporary commander of our forces in Cyreniaca and when the German attack started in earnest in late March, the CIC sent Ritchie O'Connor back to the front to advise Neame on his defensive positions. Unfortunately, on 6th April, the generals were captured by the Germans whilst doing a recce behind enemy lines. Then things went from bad to worse and by the 28th April Rommel's forces were at the Egyptian border near Sollum. But they failed to take Tobruk, which is still invested but secure in our hands, held by the Aussies. And there they stand at the moment, the Germans some two hundred and fifty miles away from here. I gather there's a big flap on at HQ planning a counter attack, so the sooner you get over there the better. You'll get mixed up in some action I've no doubt. And remember, report back to me in person as often as you can, but at least once a week."

At 9 a.m. on the 6th June, 1941 David presented himself to Brigadier Dorman-Smith's office at the Commander-in-Chief's headquarters at Gazira. The whole place was in turmoil with senior officers rushing around from office to office, conferring in small groups and preparing themselves for the CIC's conference at 1000 hours. Brigadier Dorman-Smith, a short, thin-faced man with prominent teeth and a clipped, military moustache, could only spare David a few moments.

"You come here highly recommended by Colonel Sharples. You will work in this office and be responsible for analysing any messages received in German and Greek. I'll introduce you in a minute to Captain Denby who's our expert in Islam and covers Turkey, Iran, Egypt and East Africa. He'll fill you in and show you the ropes. For the time being stick with me. You'll get a good idea of what's happening at the CIC's conference at 1000 hours."

David sat next to his brigadier at the conference. He looked around the assembled senior officers of the Middle East Command and had a few minutes to think and meditate before the commanding general appeared. What made a military man. What attributes did an officer need to attain the highest rank. He was sure that luck and being in the right place at the right time played a large part in every officer's advancement. There were also the attributes of courage, leadership, intuition and intellect, which all high-ranking officers need to a greater or lesser degree. And then there was the physical build of the men themselves which seemed to devolve into two categories, large florid, muscular men, in boxing parlance, heavyweights, which would include "Jumbo" Wilson, Galloway, Godwin-Austen, Freyberg, Gott, Ritchie and Leese and then the lightweights, O'Connor, Harding and the man on his right, Brigadier Dorman-Smith. But lightweight in this context did not imply lack of intellect. On the contrary. The acutest brain was often encompassed in a smaller bird-shaped skull. But these senior officers had one thing in common. They all sported a toothbrush military moustache. That, David concluded, was the passport to the heights, that and, perhaps, family connections and schooling at Marlborough or Epsom.

His reverie were interrupted by a sudden hush amongst the assembly and then a scraping of chairs and boots as they all stood stiffly to attention for the entry of the commander in chief, Sir Archibald Wavell. David had briefly seen the general distantly at Hotel Bretagne in Athens and tried to recollect his physical features and there he stood, of medium height, stocky, a middleweight, but without doubt a military presence commanding attention and sporting a traditional moustache. David was not surprised to hear later that the general was an old Etonian.

"Gentlemen, please be seated. Operation Battleaxe will be launched at dawn on June 15th, in nine days' time. You've all been advised on the battle plan. The Seventh Armoured Division's thrust towards Halfaya Pass is the key to our success. We have a hundred and eighty tanks and estimated German Panzer strength is eighty or ninety. Our tanks will be supported by two hundred and fifty thousand ground troops. The enemy probably have some one hundred and eighty thousand troops, mostly Italians, facing us. There will be two hours' bombardment of the enemies' defences prior to the first assault and, during daylight hours, the RAF will conduct strafing sorties.

"Our objective is to gain a passage through Halfaya and then we shall fan out, relieve Tobruk and make an armoured dash across the desert to El Agheila to cut off the German forces around Benghazi. By this time I suspect the Italians will have thrown in the towel. Gentlemen, this is a simple plan which must succeed. I am under considerable pressure from London to win a victory in North Africa and drive the Italians and Germans out of Cyreniaca. I believe we have the troops, the will and the determination to achieve this aim and that Operation Battleaxe will be remembered forever as the turning point of our desert war in North Africa."

The general turned smartly and walked out of the room whilst his audience stood rigidly at attention, each one fired with muted enthusiasm for the forthcoming battle.

Brigadier Dorman-Smith led David back to his office where he was introduced to Captain Denby, a rotund, perspiring, pimply faced and red-haired officer of the Cheshire Regiment. In the office the Brigadier lit a pipe and spoke slowly and deliberately.

"I don't think the CIC's heart is in this particular battle. We haven't had enough time for preparation and our tank losses have not been replenished since O'Connor's brilliant thrust to Bedda Fomm. A lot of O'Connor's elite troops were dispersed and we have hundreds of green recruits in the line-up. But the CIC is being forced into action by London. As Captain Denby will know we get at least two, sometimes three, calls a week from the PM and the War Office pushing us to act. The PM in London hasn't the foggiest idea of the conditions out here. Still we have to go in as planned and hope for the best. I hope that we don't suffer too many casualties."

A week later, on the eve of the battle, the CIC headquarters emptied, leaving Brigadier Dorman-Smith, David and Captain Denby behind to 'run the show'. Between 15th and 17th June 1941 Operation Battleaxe ground on inexorably, with heavy British tank losses in frontal attacks on entrenched German positions and a loss of ninety-nine tanks in a fight to secure Halfaya Pass. The German 88mm anti-tank gun, designed for aerial defence, once again proved a decisive weapon in the battle and accounted for most of the British tank casualties.

A dejected Commander-in-Chief returned to his headquarters in Cairo on the 20th June. Brigadier Dorman-Smith commented that he had never seen his commander so downcast. General Wavell was convinced he had failed in his duty towards the War Cabinet and the British Army. Outwardly he seemed confident and capable, dealing with the daily problems on five fronts on which his troops were dispersed and deployed, but he spent more time on his own in his quarters and was not eager to meet new arrivals to the camps in Cairo and Alexandria. It came as no surprise to headquarters' staff to hear, at the end of June, that Churchill had relieved Wavell of his command, posting him to India as Chief of General Staff. His replacement was to be Sir Claude Auchinleck, with Sir Neil Ritchie to continue as Deputy Commander.

General Sir Claude Auchinleck took over command of the Desert Forces and the Eighth Army on the 5th July, 1941. He was a large, burly, red-faced man with an inevitable moustache and piercing blue eyes. Here was a titan, a heavyweight, both physically and mentally. But his second in command, General Neil Ritchie, physically a super-heavyweight, could not be classified as an intellectual genius. Auchinleck, familiarly known as the Auck, appointed General Alan Cunningham, who had conducted a dashing campaign in East Africa and liberated Addis Ababa, to command the Eighth Army. He was expected to take up his new command sometime in early September 1941. General Sir Claude Auchinleck settled down rapidly in his new appointment. He was a solid, homely and unpretentious man with an aura of self-confidence and a strong sense of 'family'. He rapidly selected his headquarters 'team' and stuck loyally by them over the succeeding months of his tenure as Commander-in-Chief for the Middle East.

His HQ team were composed of Major General Sir Neil Ritchie, General Corbet, Brigadier Dorman-Smith and Captain David Green, his special aide. Within the 'family' it soon became evident that Brigadier Dorman-Smith, or Chink as he was privately known to the general, was Auchinleck's advisor and that David was a proxy son. Avarice, intrigue and jealousy prevailed in the higher echelons of the military establishments in Cairo between 1940 and 1943 and Brigadier Dorman-Smith and General Ritchie were not everyone's cup of tea. Nevertheless, Auchinleck's stubbornness and strong sense of fair play kept the team together until near the end of his military leadership in the Middle East.

Captain Denby was inordinately jealous of David's elevation to the 'family'. Denby had worked his way through the ranks in the middle thirties and was commissioned in 1938. By sheer perseverance this undistinguished, dull and somewhat unsavoury character found himself on Brigadier Dorman-Smith's staff in Cairo. Rumour had it that Denby served with Dorman-Smith in India and Palestine as a staff sergeant and the two were involved in a scandal and, as a sop for his silence, Dorman-Smith arranged Denby's commission and his appointment to the CIC's HQ in Cairo. In any event the unimaginative plodder was now a permanent fixture on Brigadier

Dorman-Smith's staff and, all the while, Captain Denby was convinced that he was barred from promotion by his lack of public school education. He was unable to understand why a newcomer to the mess, a recent arrival in Cairo and a far more junior and inexperienced officer than himself, had been catapulted into the limelight. The uncharismatic captain could not comprehend that his qualities of plodding dependability were not exactly those that were required for an aide de camp to the CIC Cairo, the most powerful man in the Middle East.

At first David's duties were limited to organisation of transport for unit visits in the Delta and at the front. He had to ensure that contacts were established 'at the other end' to receive the general and that the officers Auchinleck wished to meet were available and present. He then accompanied General Auchinleck and, more often than not, Brigadier Dorman-Smith on field visits, conferences and sat in on discussions. The three, the general, the brigadier, and David became known as the 'Mena House Triumvirate' amongst the units stationed in the Delta. And all the while David functioned as Dorman-Smith's staff officer at headquarters in Gazira he kept in touch, from time to time, with Colonel Sharples at No. 29 Shepherds Hotel.

During the third week of July, after an 0800 hour briefing, the general requested David to stay on in his office after the others had departed. The large, muscular general filled his armchair to overflowing and gazed benignly at his junior staff officer, with a hint of a smile behind his blue-eyed gaze.

"Captain Green, one of the trials of high command is that one is bombarded with advice from all quarters, from senior colleagues at headquarters, from divisional commanders and, as you are fully aware, from London. There's been another cablegram from 'a most important person' this morning. I believe in receiving advice from all available sources and, as you are the most junior of my staff officers, I wish you to prepare a brief report setting out your own views on the battles that have been fought and the battles that may need to be fought here in North Africa. Don't consult with any of your colleagues or superior officers. I am already fully aware of Brigadier Dorman-Smith's views. I want your own thoughts and please feel free to criticise anyone, or everyone, if you think fit to do so. It's quiet at the front at present and General Cunningham is not expected until early September. Let me have your hand-written report on my desk a week from today. No copies. That's all," and David was dismissed.

David spent the next few days in a small library at headquarters where he found a 1937 treatise on *Use of Tanks in Modern Warfare* by Hobart and two German military manuals bound in brown paper, one by Captain Kurt Student on *Use of Airborne Troops in War* and the second by Major Erwin Rommel, *Use of Armour in Modern Warfare*. Hobart traced the development of the tank from its first appearance in the field at Cambrai in 1915 to present times. He advocated bigger and better tanks and upheld the thesis that wars could be won or lost by tanks slugging it out on the battlefield. Hobart's treatise was also very critical of neglect in development of armoured units after the end of the First World War.

In contrast Rommel's monograph, largely culled from Hobart's treatise, envisaged the armoured unit as a spearhead, or *schwerpunkt*, in battle, ably supported by preliminary bombing of enemy positions, "the blitzkrieg", and by mechanised infantry and field artillery. David absorbed all the facts from these articles written before the war and, from the German standpoint, confirmed by armoured strikes in Poland and France and produced his brief appraisal of the conduct of the North African campaign for the attention of General Auchinleck.

Captain David Green's Report

From: Staff Captain David Green, CIC Headquarters, Cairo, 27th July, 1941
To: Commander-in-Chief Middle East Forces, Cairo.

This report acknowledges the historical monographs of Colonel Hobart, Tank Regiment, 1937 and General Erwin Rommel, at present Commander, Africa Corps.

In general the North African landscape and terrain lend themselves to mobile armoured battles. The tank is a key weapon which will decide success, or failure, in battles in the desert. Development of armoured potential in the British army since the 1914-18 War has been tardy despite Hobart's urgings and protestations. The reasons are to be found in the 'cavalry complex', a belief in the British army that wars are lost or won on horseback and that fair play is the rule of the day. Cavalry officers look down on men who sit in perambulating steel boxes and, up until 1937, the horse was still an important factor in campaigns in the colonies. Lack of armoured strength in the British army became painfully apparent in 1938 and units such as the Yeomanry and Hussars were rapidly mechanised, but usually as light armoured regiments, thus maintaining the élan and esprit de corps *of* the cavalry. Heavy tanks were manned and commanded by personnel from engineer regiments and the ordnance corps. When war broke out and German success, using heavy tanks, in France became evident in 1940, the War Office panicked and transferred commanders from the 'light skirmishers' to the 'heavies' and this is the situation that exists today. Our tank regiments are commanded by cavalry men at heart who have not learnt the lesson that heavy tanks cannot be used for lightning thrusts and manoeuvres. The armoured divisional commanders insist on independence from infantry and artillery and tend to look down with disdain at their less mobile comrades.

The Germans, however, have taken the lessons of 1914-18 and the writings of their generals to heart. As we saw in Poland and France a Panzer group is the schwerpunkt of any attack. A Panzer formation contains motorised artillery and infantry as well as tanks and these three arms are trained together as a comprehensive unit. The basic concept of a Panzer attack is not to expose their tanks in head-on confrontation but to protect them behind a screen of anti-tank guns and infantry. These deal with the initial impact of the enemies' thrust and the tanks are released as a second phase to mop up enemy remnants, usually by a lateral hook, which brings the Panzers in on the attackers' flank, or even behind them. The vast rolling deserts of North Africa are ideal for manoeuvre of tracked vehicles. Another tenet of German training is that once the enemy is on the retreat the whole Panzer group give chase and keep up the momentum of their counter attack. In any given situation the tanks will chase faster than their support groups but as soon as they meet resistance they will halt and wait for the artillery and infantry to catch up and again re-engage the enemy. By application of these basic principles Rommel's Panzer divisions have been more successful than our own formations in the battles that have already occurred in North Africa. It is also true to say that German tanks are superior to our own in fire power and the effect of their 88mm anti-tank gun on our armour has been devastating.

In order to counteract Rommel's superiority we need to organise our divisions into brigades containing the three arms, armour, artillery and infantry. The days of the massed attack by hundreds of tanks, advocated by Hobart, are probably over. This entails restructuring our chain of command. The divisional commander should be trained in armoured warfare and each brigade should be commanded by an officer of the tank regiment. These brigades, during a battle, must remain fairly mobile, interchangeable and able to concentrate on a specific task as ordered by the divisional commander. The days of each armoured brigade acting independently is past.

In the battles fought so far in North Africa, General O'Connor got it right against the Italians but Rommel's Panzers might have proven more difficult. It is now clear that O'Connor should have been allowed to press on to Tripoli and that would have put paid to the Africa Corps' arrival.

Since then Operation Battleaxe was a shambles and an indication of how not to conduct an armoured battle. The reasons are clearly that the tank echelons were led by the 'Yoicks Tally-ho' brigade who rushed headlong at the enemy in frontal attacks and were shot to bits by German 88mm anti-tank guns.

For future battles it is suggested that three-armed brigades are formed and they should be commanded by tank regiment officers. The divisional commander must be a tank man and the general officer commanding the Corps, or Army, must also have had training in mobile armoured warfare.

At present, in North Africa, only one heavy tank brigade fits the bill. The rest are commanded by valiant, but misguided, officers who are converted cavalry men at heart.

David signed his name and placed his report in a sealed envelope.

Captain Denby was beside himself with rage at not knowing what David had been up to. He probed and questioned but David told him that it was top secret material which did not concern anyone else other than the CIC. By the time David's report was presented, General Auchinleck had been called home to London for an interview with Churchill and the Cabinet, where great pressure was brought to bear on the Auck to start an offensive in early August but he steadfastly refused. On his return the general shelved David's report, as other matters of a more pressing nature were weighing heavily on his mind, not least the impending arrival of his new eighth army commander and planning for Operation Crusader.

Twice during August the Mena House Triumvirate flew out to Mersa Matruh for conferences with General Willoughby-Norrie and General Godwin-Austen. David was not too impressed with these tank generals who showed little inclination to fit in with a divisional plan and wanted to 'do their own thing' and undertake frontal assaults on Rommel's Panzers on the principle that brute force would smash the enemy. If that was achieved they were not quite clear in their own minds what the next step might be. General Auchinleck assured the divisional commanders that General Cunningham would soon be arriving to sort things out. On the flight home the CIC confided in David that he had read his report with interest.

"But I regret that at present my divisional commanders only think in terms of fighting from a static base, with no provision for a follow up should the enemy be routed." He added, "As things stand my generals are more qualified for this type of action than for the mobile brigades you envisage in your report. I do see the advantages of a three-armed brigade but it isn't even a remote possibility at the moment."

*

General Alan Cunningham arrived in Cairo from Nairobi on 7th September to take command of the Eighth Army based at Mersa Matruh and facing Field Marshal Rommel's Panzer Army entrenched at Sollum. David met the general as he stepped off the plane at Gazala airfield and conveyed him to the CIC's headquarters. General Cunningham was pleasant and chatty. As they drove along the Sweetwater Canal towards Gazira David noticed that the man by his side was cast in the mould of a high ranking officer, a lightweight in this instance, short and dapper, with a handsome face, blue eyes and the inevitable greying military moustache. He fitted well into David's mental picture of a top brass general. He wondered how this meek and rather quiet senior officer could cope with the dashing, outspoken and often rude, Eighth Army field commanders.

General Cunningham took up command of the Eighth Army at his desert headquarters at Mersa Matruh on the 9th September, 1941 and was thrown in at the deep end. Plans for Operation Crusader were well-advanced when he arrived and it soon became evident to the senior commanders in the field that Cunningham was not up to the job, lacking experience of command at such high level. Added to this there were worries about his mental stability and suitability to hold command.

Together with Brigadier Galloway he made minor adjustments to the operational plan but, by and large, the seasoned commanders of the Desert Rats were given a free hand. The old prejudices remained. Far from, 'bringing a breath of fresh air from East Africa', Cunningham's arrival had little influence on the conduct of Crusader and the general himself was now beginning to doubt his own ability to see the battle through to the end. General Auchinleck, true to form, stuck by his field commander.

"General Cunningham is having some teething problems settling in but, mark my words, when Crusader gets underway we shall see what a dynamic leader he can be."

For a week before Crusader was launched Auchinleck's 'dynamic leader' was visibly cracking up. David accompanied Brigadier Dorman-Smith to Eighth Army battle headquarters on the 10th November and found Cunningham sitting alone in his caravan looking disconsolately at a map on the wall. He asked the question of no one in particular, "This is such a complicated jigsaw puzzle. Where are my tanks going to break out? There doesn't seem to be enough room for them to manoeuvre."

Brigadier Dorman-Smith reassured him that there were vast tracks of unexplored sand south of the battle area which might be used for manoeuvre.

"Yes," the general replied, "but Willoughby Norrie is planning a frontal attack on the German Panzers and has made no plans for his armour to outflank them."

General Cunningham rallied a little at the end of the morning and professed confidence at a successful outcome of Crusader but on the flight home Brigadier Dorman-Smith confided in David.

"That man is cracking up and is in no fit state to conduct a major battle."

David agreed and on their return to Gazala the matter was promptly reported to General Auchinleck who short-temperedly replied, "I have every confidence in General Cunningham who will command the Eighth Army in Crusader. He has impeccable credentials and I am certain he will lead his Army to a resounding victory."

Operation Crusader was launched on the morning of the 18th November, 1941. For four days, whilst the battle raged, David lived and slept in the map room at GHQ in Cairo. A confined tank battle was raging around Sidi Rezegh and contradictory reports were coming in of the number of German and British tank casualties. By the 22nd November British tank losses in the frontal attacks were astronomical, some three hundred and twenty tanks and most of the casualties were inflicted by German 88mm guns. There was no direction from the British side. General Cunningham was still confident he could drive the Germans out of Libya but had no control over his armoured divisions who, throughout the battle, acted independently. On the night of the 23rd November General Cunningham wanted to disengage his troops but was having trouble with the New Zealand commander, General Freyberg, who refused to withdraw from his forward position at Sidi Rezegh. General Auchinleck was in the map room when Cunningham's signal was received.

"Reply. No withdrawal. I'm coming up to the front to look for myself."

On 24th November the general, Brigadier Dorman-Smith and David flew to Cunningham's battle headquarters. The commanding officer of the Eighth Army was pacing up and down outside his command post asking irrelevant questions of all and sundry and making fatuous statements about the success, or lack of success, of one or other of the battles of the previous day.

David was ordered to take General Cunningham to his quarters and keep him there. General Auchinleck now took control of the battle. By the 24th Rommel was moving his forces unopposed towards Egypt, but Freyberg's New Zealanders had captured Sidi Rezegh and Rommel's Panzer headquarters was in danger of being overrun. The Germans were down to their last hundred tanks. General Auchinleck ordered his remaining armour to press on Rommel's headquarters, which led the commander, a Colonel Westphal, to recall Rommel from his strike towards Egypt. The Germans withdrew and both sides claimed victory. Operation Crusader was a draw but British armour had again suffered heavily, mainly from the guns of the German motorised artillery. Whilst the battle raged David sat in the command vehicle with a sedated Eighth Army commander who, in between fits of lucidity and remorse, slept most of the time, whilst his Army was being mauled by Rommel's forces. On the 26th November General Auchinleck relieved Cunningham of his command. His only comment was, "The man must go. I'm afraid I made a bad choice in appointing him."

General Cunningham was flown out from his headquarters to Madalena on the 27th November and, subsequently, disappeared into obscurity.

General Auchinleck was now in a dilemma. He had to appoint a field commander for the Eighth Army and it had to be a locally available senior officer. David thought the obvious choice was Brigadier Dorman-Smith, who had seen desert action and was tank-trained. General Auchinleck opted for his second-in-command General Sir Neil Ritchie, a very tall, very large, bovine type of person who was an excellent and dependable staff officer, but whose only battle experience was as a battalion commander in France in the First World War. General Auchinleck hinted that he would be around, 'to hold the general's hand whilst he is settling in'.

General Ritchie took over on 27th November and had the task of trying to retrieve a 'lost battle'. By 27th November General Freyberg and the New Zealanders had linked up with the Tobruk garrison. On the 29th November Rommel struck again at Sidi Rezegh and, after another five days of confused fighting, began a long retreat westwards to El Agheila, covered by a screen of 88mm anti-tank guns and pursued by the remnants of the British Light Armoured regiments. Rommel's long retreat with thirty serviceable tanks lasted for three weeks. On 24th December, 1941 Benghazi was liberated and Auchinleck ordered his forces to continue their pursuit of the Germans until they reached El Agheila where he called a halt.

Events in the Far East, following Britain's declaration of war on Japan after the Pearl Harbour attack on the American fleet on 7th December, made further demands on Middle East manpower to reinforce Singapore and Malaya. General Auchinleck and David returned to GHQ in Cairo on 4th December when General Ritchie was formally appointed Commander of the Eighth Army, thus confirming what was originally thought to have been a temporary appointment. For the rest of December and well into January 1942 the mood at general headquarters was ecstatic. There were parties and rounds of celebration and, at one of the binges, David managed to get Captain

Denby drunk on Pimms only to find the man was more obnoxious when drunk than when sober. GHQ staff, including drivers and stenographers, had a family Christmas lunch at the general's house in Gazira. General Auchinleck was an excellent host and made sure that all his guests, down to the sentry on guard duty, had sufficient food and drink to celebrate the occasion.

Auck's summary of the first six months of his command was delivered to a select audience at a lunch in Mena House Hotel on the 30th December 1941. Basically he described his difficulties with London and the wisdom of waiting until he had sufficient strength before attacking. He claimed that, despite heavy losses, Operation Crusader had been a resounding success and the new commander of the Desert Rats was doing an excellent job in holding Rommel at El Agheila and mopping up in Cyreniaca.

The only blot on the horizon was the intervention of the Japanese and his command was now expected to provide trained brigades for the Far East. He reported that supplies of men, material and particularly American tanks, were arriving daily and strengthening Eighth Army reserves. There were reports that during December Rommel also had tank reinforcements but, he concluded, "I have every confidence that General Sir Neil Ritchie will be more than adequate to face the challenge and deal with any further aggressive intent from the Desert Fox."

He asked everyone to rise and drink a toast to, "General Sir Neil Ritchie and his Desert Rats."

New Years Day 1942, Colonel Sharples' Briefing

David sat uncomfortably in Colonel Sharples' outer office conscious of the perspiration dripping from his armpits and soaking the outer sides of his khaki shirt. ATS Sergeant Willoughby had thoughtfully provided him with an iced lime juice when he arrived.

"I'm sorry the colonel is keeping you waiting, Captain Green, but I'm sure he'll be ready for you in a few minutes."

The minutes passed slowly as he sat in desultory silence staring at the hazy, dark mist which hung over the putrid, dirty brown Nile and not even a felucca in sight in the oppressive midday heat.

Colonel Sharples' door opened and out strode a tall good-looking full colonel in an immaculately pressed uniform, evidently a peace-time soldier who had seen little active service. As soon as David entered the office Colonel Sharples rose to greet him.

"Happy New Year to you, David. Did you recognise the colonel who just left?"

David approached his superior officer's desk, saluted, and replied, "No, Sir", and, on Colonel Sharples' instruction took a seat on the opposite side of the desk. The colonel stood up abruptly and started pacing the room, deep in thought. He was sweating profusely and, loosening his collar, pressed the bell to summon Sergeant Willoughby to bring them iced drinks. He did not speak until the sergeant had departed and they were sitting and sipping their lime cordials.

"David, I know you're cleared for security and what I'm about to tell you is highly secret. It is also probably highly irregular but if you are to work for me it's only right and proper you should know something about what's going on here and where our unit fits into the jigsaw puzzle."

He paused to take a deep breath and a sip of his lime juice and continued, "That colonel whom you saw leaving was Terence Maxwell, the new head of Special Operations Executive. He replaced George Pollock last month. The SOE is the main department responsible for information gathering and is riddled with Oxbridge dons and archaeologists. Their Cretan section is located in a small house across the road from Rustum House and is run by a very able man called Jack Smith-Hughes. Our section here has little to do with SOE though we carry out combined operations from time to time. The military section of SOE is the SIS, also at Rustum, and consists entirely of ex-army officers and NCOs trained in explosives and terrorist type activities. Now things get more complicated. The Navy has a small sabotage detachment in Alexandria, the Special Boat Section, and they run a camp for operatives at Crusaders' Castle in Athlit just outside Haifa. Narkover, the SOE training camp, is on Mount Carmel. The RAF have a wing specialising in parachute drops for operatives. Now our little group is independent of all others. Our instructions come from the War Cabinet and this means the PM himself is our boss. Unfortunately there is little communication between all these sections, especially SOE and SIS. They all plan operations and, for reasons of security, do not inform anyone else of their intentions. That's one reason why I've tried to get to grips with the problem but I couldn't budge Colonel Maxwell one inch. So I've

decided to co-operate with the naval section in Alex. As a Royal
Marine, and half a sailor, it makes sense to co-operate with the Jolly
Jacks. They plan their attacks from the sea. However I think I can
convince them that they can attack naval establishments from the land.
I might arrange for you to go for a week's course at Athlit Castle. At
least you'll be nearer the birthplace of Christ and away from this
Godforsaken country!"

The colonel stopped speaking and his pink sweaty face reddened
perceptively, realising that David was Jewish. They both burst out
laughing as David replied, "Don't forget, Colonel, we also have a
stake in Jerusalem. We were there first, at least a thousand years
before the Christians arrived!"

The colonel rang the bell for more iced drinks and when they were
alone he moved across to a wall map of Crete and, bidding David to
join him, he continued.

"Now, let's look at the wall map together and bring you up to date
with the current picture in Crete." Holding his iced drink in one
hand, the colonel, using a pointer, continued his peroration. "After
the German landings on Crete there was chaos. I needn't tell you
that. Some three thousand Cretan irregulars, not under our control,
joined the battle around Maleme and Heraklion. I'm afraid they went
berserk. After the Germans took Crete, General Student issued an
edict on the treatment of any Cretan irregulars caught in action or
carrying guns. Here I have a copy of Student's directive."

The colonel handed David a sheet of paper which he read in
silence. General Kurt Student had received reports that Cretan
irregulars were killing and garrotting wounded paratroopers, showing
no mercy and stealing equipment, guns and ammunition. He issued a
directive – 'to combat all cases of cruelty and to undertake reprisals
with punitive expeditions which must be carried out with exemplary
terror'. For proven cruelty he ordered reprisals by the units who
suffered with speed and no necessity to await a judicial enquiry, or
tribunal. The penalties ordered were: 1. shooting, 2. fines, 3.
destruction of villages by burning and 4. extermination of the male
population of the territory in question. Student's authority would be
necessary for measures three and four. David read and re-read the
directive three times, holding the manila sheet with trembling fingers.

The colonel continued, "Yes, horrific reading isn't it? Well,
Student's orders have been carried out frequently in the past seven

months. We have reports of over a thousand Cretan civilians executed and the burning of at least four villages. General Wildemar Andrae has taken over from Student, but he's as bad a butcher as his boss. As a result of reprisals the irregulars, or *andartes* as they call themselves, have taken to the mountains and seem to have sorted themselves into two groups, one lot in the White Mountains and the other group on Mount Ida."

The colonel used his pointer to indicate these mountains and continued, "Both these areas are under German control but the bit of Crete east of Heraklion is largely occupied by Italians with a considerable German presence. This area of Crete does not seem to have any *andartes* except for a Communist group in the Dikti mountains in the south around Ierapetra here," indicating again with his pointer. "The Italian commander, General Carta, and his Siena Division are based at Neapolis. I've marked the spot where you have hidden your arms on the map near Piskopiano. If the arms are still in working order you will be able to cause a lot of trouble around Heraklion and to the Ities in the eastern sector. As I told you, the Navy boys are keen to have a go at the harbour in Heraklion. I want you to go away for a couple of weeks and think about these ideas. You will need to work out how many men you need. Your equipment is already there. If it's no good I can arrange a drop, or bring the stuff in by sea. Let me have your ideas. I must repeat that the order for this mission to go ahead comes from the highest authority. All this talking is making me thirsty. Let's go down to the bar and bring in the New Year in style."

At brigade headquarters David acquired a captured large-scale German military map of Crete which was more accurate and detailed than its British counterpart. This he studied, noting the site of the cave in Piskopiano and the various routes connecting the farmhouse with Heraklion, Hersonisos, Neapolis and Ierapetra. The German map also delineated the larger goat-herd tracks over the three main mountain ranges in Crete. Looking at the map he wondered if the arms and supplies in the cave were still safe and usable and if the mortars in the orange grove behind the Two Charlies were still intact.

On a sheet of paper he made three brief headings and considered his action plan in relation to each in turn. His first decision was whether his men should wear British uniform, or whether they should be dressed as native Cretans. He decided fairly quickly that the proper dress for the clandestine operation he envisaged would have to be Cretan. The second question which occupied his mind was the relationship between his group and the SOE operatives in Crete and Cretan *andartes*. He was not overly impressed with the British agents he had met on the Greek mainland and in Crete and felt that their involvement in his operations might compromise his position, in view of their divided loyalties with the Cretan *kapitans*. As far as the latter were concerned he did not trust any of them, apart from Satanas, whom he had last seen near brigade headquarters in Heraklion on the 28th May, 1941. In any event he did not want the location of his arms cache to be revealed to any of the resistance fighters, or to the SOE, or any other irregular groups on the island. The third question to be answered was how many men and who should be members of his team. He came to the conclusion that he would need one senior NCO, probably a sergeant and five other ranks, three for general duties and two with special expertise in weaponry, mining and bombing.

In his selection David insisted that his group would not only be dressed as Cretans but should act like Cretans and have a smattering of basic Greek. The most important factor of all was compatibility, as he envisaged that his commando might be living rough, and cheek by jowl, for prolonged periods of time and any friction between his soldiers might prove disastrous to the whole enterprise. David estimated it would take at least three months to collect his group, to get them to work as a team and to teach them some basic Greek and about the lifestyle and traditions of Cretan communities. His research completed, he took his draft document to Colonel Sharples' office on 17th January, 1942.

Christmas, 1941, and the early part of the New Year, 1942, was a time for celebration and optimism in General Auchinleck's Middle Eastern headquarters in Cairo. And then the bubble burst. David was accompanying the commander in chief on a tour of inspection of a newly arrived Special Engineer Regiment at Qatira barracks, when the duty major interrupted to say that the general was urgently needed back at headquarters. Unperturbed, the general continued with his inspection and on the way back to base spoke anxiously to David.

"I expect old Rommel has attacked our positions at El Agheila. I have been expecting this to happen. General Ritchie was informed to expect an attack and I know he can deal with it. Plans have been made to counter attack at the appropriate time."

And then he fell silent and did not speak again until they were in the map room at Cairo HQ. During the journey David recalled that General Auchinleck had sent a message to Ritchie advising him to expect trouble on or about the 21st January, 1942. He had advised Ritchie that Rommel's Panzer forces were replenished and it was estimated that he now had one hundred and seventy German and seventy-nine Italian tanks at his disposal. David wondered about the source of General Auchinleck's information. Could it be a direct line from London to SOE headquarters at Rustum House or could his own commanding officer in Shepherds be the recipient of these important communications? Colonel Sharples often referred to messages received by him 'from a higher authority' and, on a few occasions, 'from a former naval person'.

The news that greeted their arrival at headquarters was much worse than expected. Rommel had smashed his way eastwards towards Msus and, on the way, surrounded the First Armoured Division south of Sidi Saleh. The fighting at this point was ferocious with heavy tank casualties on both sides.

General Auchinleck surveyed the wall map, "Gentlemen, you can see what the cunning fox is out to do. He will strike from Msus to Mechili and then to the coast to cut across the Via Balbia between Derna and Tobruk. This will isolate our forces in the area of Jebel Achdar between Benghazi and Tobruk. General Ritchie has been warned of this possibility and ordered to withdraw east if there is any danger of encirclement. The route Rommel is taking is directly in the other direction to General O'Connor's dash to Bedda Fomm last year."

The CIC's voice trailed off and he had a worried expression on his face. He turned to Dorman-Smith, recently promoted to general and said under his breath, "I hope Ritchie sees the danger. He mustn't be cut off at Jebel Achdar. He should already be falling back to Derna."

On the 26th January Ritchie ordered a general withdrawal to Derna but the withdrawal became a rout. The Fourth Indian Division, cut off at Benghazi, managed to fight its way clear. Rommel's forces entered Benghazi on 29th January and, by this time, the retreating British were holding a line at Gazala which they reached on the 4th February where the German advance was halted. The relief on General Auchinleck's face was plain for all to see. He walked around with his head held high, exuding an almost visible aura of confidence.

He was heard to murmur, "Good old Ritchie, good old dependable Ritchie. I knew he wouldn't let the side down," as if to vindicate his choice of field commander. But the Auck's confidence in Ritchie was not echoed by all and sundry. The British field commanders, with one or two exceptions, had no faith in their commanding general and General Godwin-Austen asked to be relieved of his command for this reason.

On 26th February David arranged a picnic on the banks of Lake Faioum outside Cairo for Auchinleck, General Dorman-Smith and General Godwin-Austen and there, using all his charm, the general persuaded his recalcitrant infantry divisional commander to continue fighting. He also confirmed that General Sir Neil Ritchie had his full support and would continue as commanding general of the Eighth Army. General Dorman-Smith felt uneasy and hinted to David that many field commanders were dissatisfied with Ritchie and now would be a good time to replace him. The implication of General Dorman-Smith's comment was that he, as an experienced desert field commander, should take over the Eighth Army. David sensed ambition oozing out of every pore of his superior officer. He fingered his upper lip, but his own attempts at growing a moustache were so far proving a disaster. His lack of success was more than compensated when, on March 1st, he smartly marched into the CIC's office to be told by General Auchinleck that he had, as from that day, achieved his majority and was to remain as staff major to General Dorman-Smith. His promotion was greeted with incredulity by Captain Denby.

"Fucking hell, what have I got to do to get up the ladder? I was a soldier when you was in nappies. Fuck it. I'm going to complain to General Dorman-Smith."

But he never did. David now had his own office at GHQ, staffed by an orderly room corporal and a flighty young ATS typist. His attempts at growing a moustache were greeted with derision by his colleagues. He gave it all up and decided to remain moustache-less for the rest of his military career.

Cairo was a hive of feverish activity between March and early May 1942. The Gazala line extending from the seashore to the fort at Bir Hakeim, some fifty miles inland, became a sea of mines, protected by four fortified boxes which paid eloquent testimony to General Ritchie's defensive training. Ritchie's confidence in the impregnability of his defence line grew and this was reflected at GHQ by an air of optimism and hope for a successful conclusion to the battle. The Auck was bounding around, full of energy and bristling with confidence. The only dampening effect on this air of euphoria were the perpetual, recurrent, almost daily missives from Churchill demanding action and, in many instances, indicating to Auchinleck where a counter-thrust against Rommel might be most effective.

But the Auck stuck to his guns. He was now developing the idea of amalgamating tanks, guns and infantry into mobile brigades, but this would take time and he did not wish to expose his new brigades to Rommel's Panzers and anti-tank guns until they were fully trained. Ritchie's defensive line, although debatably sound in principle, did not give the British Army a strong fulcrum for offensive action. Nevertheless Ritchie was a sound and dependable soldier and Auchinleck was certain he would use his resources to best advantage when the German attack came. As come it would.

The Commander-in-Chief constantly received accurate appraisal of German intent from his secret sources and the date of Rommel's attack was pinpointed to the latter half of May, probably around the 25th. Churchill's exhortations to attack first intensified during April and on May 10th General Auchinleck received a cryptic cable from Whitehall: 'Attack in June or resign'. These telegrams must have been worrying and goading for the Commander-in-Chief, but outwardly he remained calm and confident.

After dinner in the HQ mess during the second week in May he turned to his 'family' seated around the table and with a beaming smile said, "Gentlemen, I am constantly bombarded by 'you know who' to attack. Why should we! General Ritchie has woven a spider's web between Gazala and Bir Hakeim and we are now waiting. The Desert Fox can enter the web at any time he chooses. Once he's there he will be enmeshed and cocooned and, by a process of attrition, destroyed. The spider will then be able to gobble him up at his own convenience."

But the Fox did not play the game. Leaving the Italians to face the fixed defences in the north at Gazala, on the 27th May, Rommel struck eastwards with his Twenty-first and Fifteenth Panzer Divisions and his Ninetieth Light Armoured Division and outflanked the British defences south of Bir Hakeim. His armoured columns were now behind the Gazala defence line. He thrust to the north and was stopped at Knightsbridge by Grant tanks of the First Armoured Division, whilst further south the Seventh Armoured Division checked his advance eastward. Rommel now withdrew his armoured forces and entered the British minefield from the east.

Ritchie and his field commanders were overjoyed. Now they had the fox in the spider's web. Rommel's Panzers stayed in the cauldron in the minefield for five days. Ritchie missed his opportunity to contain him there for good and, once more, went on the defensive. By that time Rommel, replenished and rested, smashed the containing forces and then struck eastwards towards Tobruk. Rommel had again outwitted and outflanked the dour, predictable Ritchie. On the 11th June Bir Hakeim, stoutly defended by the Free French, fell and the floodgates were again open. General Auchinleck was not too perturbed by the march of events until the fall of Bir Hakeim. He realised that the Gazala defence line was lost and that the British would have to withdraw.

Churchill was urging a defence line based on Tobruk and stated categorically that Tobruk must be held at all costs. This fortress mentality on the part of the British Prime Minister did nothing to help the commanders in the field. On 12th June General Auchinleck, General Dorman-Smith and David flew to Ritchie's headquarters in the desert. They found the Commander supremely optimistic and confident of the unrealistic possibility of mounting a counter attack 'in the next few days'. Ritchie seemed completely unaware that the Gazala Line had broken and he would have to retreat, at least to Tobruk and maybe further. General Auchinleck made it clear that, "London has ordered that Tobruk must be held at all costs and, if necessary, isolated again, as it was last year". Before they left, news was received of the loss of two hundred and forty tanks in an armoured battle south-east of Ritchie's headquarters. On the flight back to Cairo General Auchinleck remained silent and pensive. His only comment to his companions was, "Ritchie is doing his best, as he sees it, but I'm afraid it's not good enough. We damned well missed the chance to kill the Fox when he was holed up in the cauldron."

In order to placate Churchill, General Auchinleck proposed a compromise defence line which included Tobruk at its base. On the following day, the 15th June, General Corbett and David flew again to Ritchie's headquarters where David witnessed a row between the two generals which culminated in Ritchie completely losing his temper, a phenomenon which no one at headquarters had ever witnessed.

Ritchie apologised to General Corbett and then, head bent low, mumbled, "We have to retire and retire fast or the Eighth Army will be cut off west of Tobruk. Tobruk must go and I want to pull back to our HQ at Madalena. Please tell the CIC that I have failed him but that I hope to bring back an intact army to Mersa Matruh."

Later that day General Ritchie gave the order to retreat – a retreat which almost became a rout, referred to by the soldiers as the Gazala Gallop. On the homeward flight General Corbett commented, "Poor old Neil. He's had enough. The task was too big for him and he couldn't adapt his thoughts to a mobile battle. You see, he learnt his fieldcraft in the trenches of the First World War."

By 18th June the bulk of the Eighth Army was inside Egypt. There still remained some thirty-three thousand troops in and around Tobruk commanded by Major General Klopper, the hero of Bir Hakeim. He and Strafer Gott were given twenty-four hours to arrange the defences of fortress Tobruk but, as was expected, though they held out for four days, General Klopper capitulated on 21st June and a South African division, an Indian division, a Guards brigade and the thirty-second tank brigade went into captivity.

News of the fall of the Tobruk reached General Auchinleck in the map room of GHQ on the 21st June, his fifty-eighth birthday. He looked around the table and spoke half in jest, "Not much of a birthday. I don't expect a birthday present from London this year."

GHQ Cairo was cast into depression and gloom and everyone spoke in whispers, as if there had been a bereavement in the family. In a way the loss of Tobruk was a 'family catastrophe'. Having liberated the port only six months previously, General Auchinleck had come to regard it as his own seaside resort. Eighth Army headquarters was now sited at Matan Baggush and General Ritchie and his staff arrived there on the 18th June and decided to make their last stand on the Matruh Line. On the 22nd June Rommel's forces reached the Egyptian border at Sollum and, on the same day, General Auchinleck paid a visit to Ritchie's headquarters. On the return flight the Auck expressed his doubts to General Dorman-Smith about Ritchie's ability to hold the Matruh Line. When they returned to Cairo headquarters David knew instinctively that the old man was depressed and desperately trying to work out a solution which would be fair and not discriminating against any member of his Mena House family. On the 23rd June he spoke to David about the inadequacies of the Matruh Line and the need for establishing a last line for defence of Egypt at El Alamein adding:

"If General Ritchie fails at Matruh we'll have to make a last stand at El Alamein. But I'm not in the business of sacrificing my boys' lives unnecessarily. We must draw up contingency plans for a withdrawal to the Delta and to Port Said and give up Egypt if necessary. The reason for us being in North Africa in the first place is to protect the Iranian oil fields and we can do this at other places apart from Egypt."

Early on the 25th June, 1942 David was summoned to the CIC's office and told that they would be flying to Matan Baggush in the late afternoon accompanied by Major General Dorman-Smith. David surmised, as he made preparation for a staff car and a plane to be available, that something momentous was afoot. On the flight operational tactics were discussed in some detail between the generals. They agreed that any army must remain mobile at all times, and, if pressed, the Eighth Army should retire to El Alamein or even further back into the Delta, maintaining their mobility. General Auchinleck stressed that under his command there would never be a 'no retreat' policy. General Dorman-Smith commented that in any future action against Axis forces the Eighth Army should concentrate on the Italians, who were always the weakest link in the enemies' defences.

A light Lysander aircraft landed at Matan Baggush at 1700 hours. General Auchinleck strode towards General Ritchie's command caravan and the two giants were closeted together for ten minutes and, when they emerged, General Ritchie had been dismissed and departed for Cairo in a staff car.

The Auck stood in the shade of a large tent flap and in a measured tone said, "I've just done the most distasteful thing of my lifetime. I hope neither of you will ever be put through the torment and torture of sacking a good friend and a brilliant officer who did his duty as he saw it but unfortunately was too defence-minded. And now we are here and here we'll stay. I shall take over command of the Eighth Army. You, Chink, will be my deputy commander and you, David, will be my staff major. I want to meet as many divisional commanders as you can muster at 0800 hours tomorrow for a briefing. I am going to do some map reading. By the way, David, there are no sleeping quarters. See if you can rig up a couple of tents to accommodate all three of us."

The commanding general's conference only lasted fifteen minutes. The theme was simply 'we must keep mobile at all times'. Tired and depressed commanders who had been moving backwards for the best part of three weeks were not too amused. Dog-tired, they wanted a few days rest and plenty of sleep. General Auchinleck was confident that they would soon have it as he had received a highly secret communication earlier that morning, the 25th June, that Rommel's attack on the Matruh Line was not expected for a minimum of three weeks and possibly four. These highly secret missives had been very accurate in the past. There was no reason to suspect this message would be incorrect.

But the Desert Fox had other ideas. Arriving in style at the Matruh line with only sixty serviceable tanks and two thousand five hundred tired, but exultant, German infantry, he knew he was facing a demoralised, but far superior, British force. Cairo and the Suez Canal were the prizes and they were within his grasp and the sweet smell of success was in his nostrils. Rommel launched his Panzer Army on the Matruh Line at dawn on the 26th June 1942. They cut through the British defences like a knife through warm butter. Two demoralised British Divisions were routed and innumerable tanks lost to a Panzer blitzkrieg. Within twenty-four hours of taking command of the Eighth Army General Auchinleck had no alternative but to order general withdrawal along the coastal route to the El Alamein defence line. The poor Desert Rats once more had to trudge eastwards through the burning sand and searing heat. The general and David, both standing in an open-roofed station wagon, moved to and fro along the road encouraging the men and trying to make light of their predicament.

The Auck, with tears in his large blue eyes, said, "David I hope we shall never again be asked to supervise the retreat of a vanquished army. At least when they get to El Alamein we have fresh divisions in the line and these poor little Rats will be able to rest and recuperate," and then, looking David straight in the eye, he continued. "Never forget a rat is at its most dangerous when it's cornered and these brave boys will all live to fight another day."

The Gazala Gallop continued until the main body of the Eighth Army were safely behind the El Alamein line.

The El Alamein defences, well-constructed and manned by fresh divisions, extended a distance of forty miles from the coast to the impenetrable Qattara depression in the south. When they reached the defences the Africa Corps were at the extreme end of a tenuous line of communication and supply, some fifteen hundred miles long, extending from Tripoli to a hundred miles inside Egypt. Rommel's advance was halted more by supply logistics than by tiredness in his soldiers or the strength of the defence line facing him. Sixty miles from Alexandria he decided to dig in and await reinforcements for the final push.

Rommel's arrival at El Alamein produced panic in Cairo amongst British civilians, non-combatants, army officers and high-ranking Egyptian dignitaries. On 29th and 30th June there was a mass exodus from Cairo to Beirut and the King David Hotel in Jerusalem. Before leaving the deserters burnt documents which caused a pall of black smoke to shroud Cairo for the best part of two days. Colonel Sharples and his staff stayed put in rooms twenty-eight and twenty-nine. The Royal Navy evacuated their base at Sidi Bashir outside Alexandria and sailed eastward. Nazi flags started appearing on balconies on some of the more prominent buildings in Cairo, ready to welcome the victorious German armies.

General Auchinleck and David were now located at El Alamein in a hastily constructed headquarters on the reverse side of Reisawat ridge. The headquarters had few amenities and at night David shared a lean-to canvas tent with General Dorman-Smith. The Auck was a tower of strength, encouraging, advising and suggesting plans of action as the necessity arose. Everyone seemed satisfied that Rommel had 'shot his bolt' and couldn't move forwards for at least two weeks. But again the British commanders underestimated the Desert Fox.

On 1st July, 1942, German Panzers pushed through the British defences, though they only had twenty-six serviceable tanks. The British held the thrust and counter-attacked the Italian Ariete Division at the south end of the line. The Italians were routed and Rommel withdrew his armour to protect the gap left by elimination of the Italian Division. Local pressure and counter attacks occurred throughout July as Rommel probed and pushed, trying to find gaps to exploit in the Alamein defences.

The defenders of El Alamein enjoyed complete air superiority and at each riposte the Eighth Army concentrated their attack on the vulnerable Italian infantry. On 8th July the Italian Sabartha Division broke ranks and bolted westwards leaving Rommel's forces spread thinly on the ground, trying to plug a gap left by the panicking Italians. A night attack by New Zealand and Indian troops cut into the Brescia and Parma Divisions and, all along the line, Italian troops were demoralised and beaten and the Africa Corps, grossly reduced in numbers, were tired and battle-weary.

Rommel, now promoted to Field Marshal, managed one more large-scale Panzer attack towards the Delta on the 13th July, 1942, but this feeble thrust was easily handled by a superior and revitalised Eighth Army. Both sides now settled down to a period of rest, resuscitation and replenishment. During these minor battles at Alamein, General Auchinleck was here, there and everywhere but the pace was beginning to tell on the Commander-in-Chief. His normally rotund face was drawn and haggard and he was uncharacteristically short-tempered and brusque. David and General Dorman-Smith, two parts of the Mena House trio, strove hard to keep potential troublemakers away from the commanding general. He had enough on his plate and yet he personally insisted on controlling every action undertaken by his Desert Rats. During a brief lull in activity he confided in David.

"I now know how General Cunningham and Neil Ritchie felt before they cracked. The only difference is that I can see the light at the end of the tunnel. It's still a bloody long tunnel."

To add to his worries Churchill's cablegrams were arriving thick and fast, urging action, which prompted Auchinleck to send the Australians into an ill-advised night attack on Miteiriya ridge. General Morshead, commanding the Eighth Australian Division, at first refused to comply with the order and it took all the persuasive powers of the Commander-in-Chief to get him to agree. London were also pushing Auchinleck to release some of his divisions to defend a potential threat of a German advance from Rostov and the Caucasus into Persia and Iraq. By the end of July General Auchinleck was at the end of his tether, both physically and mentally, and was heavily dependent on General Dorman-Smith to run the show. He still stubbornly refused to move back to his headquarters in Cairo, preferring to rough it at Reisawat with his Desert Rats.

On the 30th July the Auck convened a senior officers' conference at his Cairo headquarters at which he outlined Dorman-Smith's proposals for the future conduct of the Desert War. He announced that two new armoured divisions, armed with American Grant and Sherman tanks, had arrived together with two infantry divisions. Air supremacy would be absolute. These new divisions were to be trained in the concept of three-armed mobile units and training of these new brigades was to commence immediately but, with all the best intentions, the British attack at El Alamein could not take place until late September. The plan of attack would be a simple frontal assault with two mobile divisions hooking around the south end of the line, but north of the Qattara depression. The corps-commanders, Gott, Ramsden and Corbett felt a resurgence of hope and confidence in the commander in chief and, at his quarters afterwards having a drink with David and General Dorman-Smith, Auchinleck's engaging smile and enthusiasm resurfaced.

"I thought the conference went very well. Thank you, Chink, for letting me use your detailed appraisal. Most helpful. I truly believe the tide is turning in our favour. Rommel's forces are understrength and too extended and, with air superiority and new battle-fit divisions, we should have no trouble rolling the Africa Corps back to Tripoli and into the sea. I hope we'll all be around to enjoy the fruits of our victory."

He set down his glass and an orderly sergeant handed him a cablegram which he read twice. The colour drained from his face.

"Damn it! What does he think he can do here? I am advised," he continued, "that Winston Churchill will be paying us a visit next week. Date to be confirmed. Damn it, damn it!" he expostulated as he shredded the cablegram into tiny pieces.

The Prime Minister and his entourage arrived by air in Cairo on 3rd August. General Dorman-Smith and David were amongst the officers who met the visiting party at the airport. David was interested to see that Colonel Sharples headed the reception party and introduced the Prime Minister to other officers.

When Churchill came to face General Dorman-Smith he growled, "Where's the Commander-in-Chief?"

"He's at Eighth Army headquarters in the desert, Sir," replied Dorman-Smith and then Churchill's tired jowls broke into a half grin.

"Well, I hope I do see him. I've come a devil of a long way to pay my compliments."

Post-siesta on the following day David accompanied General Auchinleck to the embassy to meet the Prime Minister. They were together for over an hour and on the journey back to his quarters General Auchinleck was very quiet and pensive.

"He's at it already. The PM's coming out to our desert headquarters for breakfast tomorrow. I wonder what he's got in mind. Perhaps he'll lead a charge against the Panzers and rout them with his cigar! David, we'll go back up to Reisawat tonight to be ready to receive the Prime Minister at dawn tomorrow."

The Prime Minister's plane landed at Matan Baggush at 0800 hours. Considering the early hour and the PM's antipathy to early rising, Churchill was in a buoyant, jocular mood. He was given a field breakfast and then conveyed around the front line positions in a large, open, station wagon. David sat in the seat behind the conspicuous, podgy man in a white boiler suit and pith helmet and wielding a large unlit cigar. In between bouts of energetic exhortation to the men, accompanied by a wide grin and a V sign, he chatted amiably with David. The Prime Minister made oblique references to Crete and the Cretan campaign and was interested to hear of David's experiences in the conflict. David could scent Colonel Sharples' influence behind the PM's seemingly innocent questions. At the end of their trip Churchill made a point of shaking David's hand.

"Thank you very much, Major Green, for the guided tour."

The PM's farewell to the general was terse and formal. Within a few minutes the great man was whisked away to lunch in Air Commander Tedder's mess at RAF headquarters in Alexandria where a sumptuous meal had been prepared by Shepherds Hotel.

Between the 4th and 6th August David stayed closely beside his besieged, harassed and brooding commander-in-chief at Reisawat. During a stop-over on a tour of the forward defences the tired and dejected CIC confided, "I don't like it. I'm not happy with the goings-on in Cairo. All the big names are there – Smuts, Wavell, Sir John Dill and the CGIS Field Marshal Alan Brooke and I'm certain that, amongst other things, my appointment here is on the agenda. Still we can only wait and see."

Auchinleck did not have long to wait. Mid-morning on the 8th August, 1942, Colonel Jacob arrived from Cairo with a letter from Churchill. The two men were alone in the command caravan for over an hour as David hovered nervously in the background. They reappeared together and after a perfunctory handshake, Colonel Jacob turned on his heel and left. General Auchinleck returned to his caravan and sat inside, alone with his thoughts, for a long hour. He summoned David and, grim-faced, spoke haltingly.

"I knew the Prime Minister was not here on a goodwill visit. I have had a forboding this would happen. I only regret that the Prime Minister did not have the guts to tell me to my face instead of deputising one of his minions. David, I am to go and so are Ramsden, Corbett and Dorman-Smith. Our replacements are General Alexander to replace me and probably Bernard Montgomery to take over the Eighth Army. Strafer Gott had been given my job but, as you know, he was killed in a plane crash yesterday. It looks as if the whole of the command structure is to be changed. I'm not sorry for myself but I do worry about the future of my field commanders and Chink and yourself. Well now, I'm still in command of the Eighth Army and today we'll make a round of our forward positions to say our goodbyes. I will appoint General Ramsden temporary commander tomorrow and return to Cairo to tie up some loose ends. You will stay with General Ramsden until the new commander takes over. Thank you, David, for all your services for the past year. I hope your attachment to my command, and to me personally, will not have blighted your future career prospects in the Army."

They shook hands firmly and David had the feeling that the older man was on the point of giving him a fatherly hug. He watched his Commander-in-Chief fly away eastwards to Cairo with a strange sensation of loss, not just loss of a commanding general, but loss of a friend, counsellor and family member.

General Ramsden was a heavyweight, a tall Welsh Guards officer, proven in battle, reliable and a supremely efficient commander. Because of David's Welch Regiment connections the general had always teased and taunted him, referring jocularly to those "Leek eating miners from Llanelli," and "the goat-chasing Taffies".

The two got on very well together but their collaboration was only for forty-eight hours when, two days earlier than expected, General Bernard Montgomery arrived at Reisawat headquarters in a flurry of agitation and self-importance. After the briefest of conferences General Ramsden was dismissed and sent back to his division. Montgomery, lisping his 'Rs', announced, "I'm in charge here now. I'll come and visit your Corps tomorrow."

The new army commander spent a whole day with the Thirtieth Corps, where Montgomery went out of his way to ingratiate himself with the soldiers but dealt with the officers very brusquely, inferring that the Eighth Army's present predicament was solely due to their inefficiency and the more senior the officer the more culpable he was in the management of the troops under his command. General Montgomery made David feel very small and insignificant.

"So you've been on General Auchinleck's staff for over a year? A long time in anybody's book. Time for a change, don't you think?"

David's first impressions of the new commanding general were not favourable. He seemed to be an overbearing, high-handed, humourless man with an exaggerated opinion of his own abilities. The man himself was short, of slight build, with a long pointed nose and the inevitable moustache on his upper lip. In David's private estimation he was a bantam-weight, but obviously possessed terrier-like qualities and an acute brain. David concluded that he did not wish to serve with the new domineering general, a different personality to the solid, quiet, thoroughly dependable and loyal Auck. His predicament was resolved when he received a wire from Colonel Sharples ordering him to report to Unit 14, Shepherds, with immediate effect. David requested, and was granted, permission to leave Matan Baggush. As things stood he was not sorry to be going.

Colonel Sharples was pleased to see David.

"Belated congratulations on your majority, David. So you're back from playing soldiers at last, Major Green! Have you met the new army commander yet? I'm told he's already ferreting around at El Alamein and causing a lot of bother to everyone. I also expect you know who else has been in town. I saw you at the reception party at the airfield. Well, I had a long conference with a former naval person three nights ago. The Cretan enterprise is definitely on and London want to start as soon as possible. I've been working on the project all day and will be able to give you a full briefing in three or four days' time. In the meantime start gathering together your tour party and bring them up to scratch and ready to leave at a moment's notice. I've got an excellent Royal Marine sergeant for you. You'll meet him in a couple of days' time."

The colonel mopped his brow with a large polka-dot handkerchief. David stood up to leave but Colonel Sharples was not quite finished.

"David, I suppose you noticed that the foyer downstairs and the bar are fairly empty. You should have been here on 28th and 29th. There was a hell of a panic, everyone burning their secret documents and causing a thick pall of smoke to hang around Cairo for two days. We called it Ash Wednesday. Most of the admin. staff evacuated eastwards and we christened a group from Rustum House the 'Shepherds' Short Range Desert Group'. They've ended up in the King David Hotel in Jerusalem. Now some of the rats that deserted the sinking ship are coming back with their tails between their legs."

The colonel then described how he had mobilised sixteen non-combatant troops and clerks and taken them up to El Alamein where they stayed for eight days trying to help with the defences but getting in everyone's way. They were returned to base as 'superfluous to requirements'. The colonel terminated the briefing.

"Well, David, it looks like we're back in business again. Take a week off to settle in and report to this office for a full briefing at 1100 hours on August 19th. I need a few days to gather more information about the situation in Crete. Glad to have you aboard again, Major Green."

Chapter Eighteen

Commando Recruitment
Bronwen in North Africa,
August 1942

At 11 a.m. on 19th August, 1942, David reported to Brigadier Sharples' office in 28/29 Shepherds. He congratulated the brigadier on his very recent promotion and the exultant officer, already anticipating a celebration, produced three bottles of foul, lukewarm South African champagne. When two bottles had been consumed Brigadier Sharples dismissed all his staff and, sitting on his desk, looked at David with bleary eyes. David surmised that, since his promotion he had probably been on South African champagne for a day or two. 'The man must have a cast-iron stomach,' he mused.

"Well, David, we stopped old Erwin all right at El Alamein. I think that when he knew he was up against the pen-pushing brigade, he decided to dig in and call it a day. As a result of the PM's visit there have been changes here and in Crete. Colonel Maxwell has been kicked out and Lord Glenconner is our new boss. He's aristocracy and not very bright. But the worse news is that his second in command at SOE is a Brigadier Martin Kimble. He's a tubby, pop-eyed, bald little man from one of the minor regiments. He's not really seen any active service and he's a gong hunter. I don't like him at all. He's a bombastic little shit but at least I out-rank him. We won't let him bugger us about!"

The Brigadier, though obviously intoxicated, seemed to have developed a great mistrust and dislike of the second in command of SOE operations at Rustum House.

He continued, "The news from Crete is that General Andrae has been replaced by General Bruno Braüer who was a company commander with the First Parachute Battalion in the German drop on Crete. Colonel Müller has moved across to Khania and Heraklion and eastern Crete is now commanded by a Colonel Manfred Schmidt, also from the Parachute Regiment. He's an unknown quantity."

David held his breath. Could it be the Manfred he knew from Aalbrücke, his blood brother?

The Brigadier was continuing, speech slurred, "I told you about the June SAS operation in Crete. Well, some of the boys got back to Mersa by caique in late July and brought Satanas with them. The poor old fellow died of cancer at the British military hospital in Alex earlier this week. He seems to have been one of the better and more sensible *kapitans* in Crete. Well, that's life," and his voice trailed into silence.

The Brigadier rose unsteadily to his feet and, swaying slightly, spoke in a more purposeful manner.

"I have decided to put you and your commando into Crete in late November or early December. You will now need to get your team together and prepare the lads mentally and physically. You may be on Crete for a few months or maybe a year. The plan I have in mind is not a rapid raid, but will involve you and your group in a series of operations on the island. That's all for now. Shall we go down to the bar for a couple of snifters? They've got some foul locally brewed whisky which is palatable, if you push it down in one gulp."

The two officers made their way to the main bar at Shepherds, crowded with duty officers, most from non-combatant units, comparing notes on the difficult journeys they had had to endure on their evacuation to Palestine. As befitted his rank the other customers at the bar cleared a path for the newly appointed brigadier and a few were in the mood to join him in his celebrations. Brigadier Sharples' description of the whisky was accurate. It really was foul and David only toyed with his glass. The Brigadier, completely undeterred by the obnoxiousness of the amber fluid, tossed the drink back with exaggerated panache and was quickly passing the point of no return, aided and abetted by a few well-meaning, cadging fellow officers.

David meanwhile stood quietly aside, viewing the spectacle with some distaste, and wondering all the while if Colonel Schmidt was the

Manfred he knew from his days at Joachim's Grossmunde farm. His reverie was sharply interrupted by the almost incoherent brigadier.

"Oh, by the way, David, I nearly forgot. For the past week we've had a pretty dark-haired Welsh QA calling here and asking for you. She's called around two or three times. She did leave her name. It's an unusual one. She told me that if I couldn't remember it to mention 'white tit' to you. She's with 203 Field Hospital out at Qatira Camp. If you don't want to see her I'll fill in for you, though I don't think I would be of any great use to the filly tonight," and he burst out laughing, reverting his attention to another dram of fire water which had been thrust into his hand.

David's heart missed a beat. He turned to Brigadier Sharples.

"Will you excuse me, Sir?"

"Certainly, dear boy. Go and see your bit of stuff," the brigadier replied and David was out of the door of Shepherds in a flash. He commandeered an army fifteen hundredweight and a Geordie driver to take him to the transit camp at Qatira.

The British army wartime base at Qatira was a three mile square encampment surrounded by a high barbed-wire fence, enclosing sandy scrubland, on the west bank of the Nile, some four miles outside Cairo. The Victorian permanent buildings and stables at the base were relics of old colonial days when the camp housed a brigade of infantry and a cavalry troop. Subsequent demands led to its piecemeal expansion so that by 1942 it was a vast area criss-crossed by sand tracks and tented accommodation. The 203 Welsh Field Hospital, a late arrival and the second hospital on site, was allocated a position in a far corner of the military complex, abutting on the right bank of the Nile.

David's driver, a squint-eyed, sallow complexioned Geordie, was not at all pleased to be woken from his afternoon siesta under the veranda at Shepherds to take this bumptious major to a hell-hole of a base camp. An MP sergeant at the camp entrance was helpful but could only point the driver vaguely in the direction of the 203 Hospital. As he explained to David, "It's been hell here for the past month, Sir. We've got units coming and going all day and every day. There's probably ten thousand troops in camp at the moment. Still if it's a hospital it should have a Red Cross on one of the marquees or, better still, look for ambulances. Every hospital has about half a dozen of 'em. Sorry I can't be more helpful."

David thanked the sergeant and urged his Geordie driver to drive around and look for ambulances. Even so, the search took them nearly half an hour and when the hospital was finally located it had only one ambulance on site. The main bulk of its stores and equipment had not been unpacked, as the hospital was in transit, awaiting relocation, probably westwards nearer the front line at El Alamein. The 203 Hospital signpost, crooked and awry, was posted outside headquarters tent.

David ducked through the tent flaps and found a bespectacled, portly, orderly room sergeant behind a trestle table covered with sheets of paper and standing orders. The sergeant stood clumsily to attention, surreptitiously buttoning his upper fly buttons and attempting to buckle his web belt around his portly waist.

"Lieutenant Thomas," he asked in reply to David's query. "We have three of them, two QAs and a young medic. Which one do you want, Sir?"

David exasperatedly explained that the one he wanted was definitely female and a QA, a dark girl from west Wales.

"Ah, you must mean Greta Garbo. Excuse me, Sir, we all have pet names for our Qas. She's the pretty one who always wants to be alone, if you get what I mean!"

David was getting impatient with the flippant sergeant.

"Look, Sergeant, I don't care what you call her. I want to see Lieutenant Thomas and I want to see her now."

"Sorry Captain," the profusely sweating sergeant replied, "I'm not able to enter the QAs' quarters and in any case they're all on compulsory siesta at the moment."

"I don't give a damn, Sergeant, if they're on siesta or not. I want to see Lieutenant Thomas."

The sergeant scratched his forehead with a pencil and a bead of sweat ran down the pencil shaft.

"I'd better get hold of the QA orderly officer. She should be in the mess," and he waddled away leaving David standing perplexed in the semi-dark and baking hot orderly room tent.

The Geordie driver poked his head through the tent flap.

"Ready to go, Sir?"

"Push off," David replied curtly. "We'll be ready to go when I say so."

The sergeant was away for more than ten minutes. David stood in front of the overloaded trestle table watching a dozen, or more, pot-bellied flies making a meal of the remnants of one of the sergeant's bully beef sandwiches. A hand appeared in the tent flap, holding it aside for a thin-faced, middle-aged QA captain to duck into the orderly room.

"Who wants Lieutenant Thomas?"

David saluted and looked the virago straight in the eyes.

"I'm Major David Green of the First Welch Regiment. Lieutenant Bronwen Thomas is an old friend of mine. I would be grateful if you could let me see her for a few minutes."

The stern-faced captain replied, "This is highly irregular. We don't allow our QAs to meet visitors during duty hours," but then relenting. "If you are back from the front, I could let you have five minutes to speak to her in private."

David thought she was winking at him but soon realised that the QA captain had a permanent tic which involved frequent involuntary closures of her left eye.

"Thank you, Ma'am," David said with humility and followed the captain out of the orderly room to the main mess hall where he was asked to sit at one end of a long table.

The captain left and the minutes ticked by and then, like a bolt out of the blue, Bron came running into the hall, dishevelled, hair awry and clad in baggy army issue slacks and a khaki shirt at least two sizes too large for her. She looked a mess but to David it was the most beautiful mess he had ever seen. She started shouting, "David, David," almost before she entered the marquee. David stood up and Bron sprinted the last ten yards, jumping at him and throwing her arms around his neck. Her face was suffused and wet with tears and sweat as she clasped her mouth firmly on to David's lips. There were moans and sighs as they embraced. David, conscious that the bird-like matriarch might be watching, tried to fend her off, but Bron was not to be discouraged.

"Bugger old Captain Beaky. She's not going to get between me and my man."

After kissing and clutching for five minutes Bron calmed down enough to sit next to David and hold his hand.

"Well, my little general, you didn't expect to see your Welsh bint here in Cairo, did you? Bit of a surprise, I have no doubt! Still I always told you I'd get to you wherever you might be. You certainly picked a hell of a hole for this meeting. Too many randy blokes and filthy, fawning Arabs in this joint for my liking. How are things with you, David?"

David was crying silently, tears of joy.

"I've missed you, Bron, oh how I've missed you. You've been in my thoughts all the time. What happened in Swansea? The last time I saw you you were dying of TB."

Bronwen laughed.

"TB, be buggered, that bloody specialist in Swansea Gen. didn't know his arse from his elbow. The spot on my lung, which they thought was TB, turned out to be an old scar from pneumonia. They let me go back to work about a week after I saw you and I finished my course and qualified as an SRN. Then I volunteered for the QAs and, well, here I am. And I have been up to Shepherds asking after you for the last ten days. Where the hell have you been? Shacked up with some bint in Cairo somewhere I've no doubt!"

Bron started crying and David squeezed her hand firmly.

"Bron, Bron I love you. I want to marry you."

Bron looked deeply into David's eyes.

"I love you too David, but we can't talk of marriage here in this cesspit. One day, when the war's over we'll get hitched. Don't rush your fences, my little general. Let's enjoy our time together in Cairo. Now you're in charge and your wish is my command."

They kissed briefly and were conscious of a body standing behind them. Captain Morgan, whose long, hooked nose had earned her the nickname Beaky, had returned and was hovering ominously behind the engrossed couple. David stood up.

"Thank you, Captain, for your courtesy in allowing me to see Lieutenant Thomas." He could hear Bron giggling behind his back as he continued, "I wish to make a formal application to take Lieutenant Thomas out to dine at Shepherds tomorrow evening."

Bron's giggling became a torrential guffaw. The duty captain, flattered by David's formal request, agreed readily. David turned to leave.

"Good afternoon, Lieutenant Thomas. I'll arrange transport to pick you up at 1900 hours tomorrow," and, saluting Captain Beaky, he turned and left the mess tent.

The impatient Geordie driver was in bad temper, muttering and cursing under his breath, but the mood of the officer by his side was completely different. David sang, sang Welsh hymns, made pleasant and jovial conversation, but the only muttered response from the Geordie was, "Bints, bints, bloody bints."

David picked up Lieutenant Bronwen Thomas at the 203 Welsh Field Hospital at 1900 hours on the following evening and drove her to Shepherds Hotel. Bronwen was dressed in her mess kit and made a striking entrance as David ushered her into the foyer producing sidelong glances from the guests arriving for dinner. They had cocktails at the bar before entering the dining room. At the bar some of the young bucks were evidently going to press their claims for attention, but David's 'hands off' stare and seniority soon put an end to their lascivious intent.

David couldn't blame the young officers. There were only three female officers in Shepherds that night. One was a captain in the Service Corps and of barrage balloon proportions and the other a weaselly, thin, sullen officer in the NAAFI and, compared with these, Bronwen was a stunning apparition. They dined at a corner table, attentively supervised by Abdul, the head waiter, whom David had previously bribed with two hundred piastres. The food was diabolical, a cold version of curried chicken and half-cooked rice. The South African champagne was as foul as it had been the previous day, but they both drank in excess to celebrate their reunion. Inevitably David had to take Bron to see room twenty-eight where he worked and without effort they made rapid and sensually satisfactory love. Then in the aftermath of the lovemaking came the difficult questions. Why was David working from a hotel? Had he really been at Alamein when Bron called to see him? What did Brigadier Sharples have to do with David? What the hell was going on?

"I am not quite sure what to make of you, David. You tell me you've been to Alamein with General Auchinleck and yet you seem quite at home in this office where I've met Colonel Sharples two or three times."

David thought long and hard.

"Darling, it's not Colonel Sharples anymore. It's Brigadier Sharples and, yes, he is my boss. I've been up at the front with the Eighth Army headquarters but I'm also involved with Brigadier Sharples in some special duties."

Bron's eyes clouded over with concern.

"Special, special, what do you mean by special?"

David repeated, "You know I went to Oxford to read Latin and Greek. Well I can speak German and some Italian. I'm useful here in Shepherds to help them sort out the messages from foreign stations."

Bron looked concerned.

"Bloody hell, David, you're a spy."

"No, no," David reassured her. "I'm more of an interpreter of messages from foreign sources" and there the matter was laid to rest.

David did not dare tell Bron that Brigadier Sharples was planning to send him into Crete within a month or two.

One evening during the third week of August Major David Green and Lieutenant Bronwen Thomas were dining by candle-light on the balcony of the Mena House Hotel. They were well into their meal, talking, gazing into each others' eyes and holding hands when the sommelier brought along a bottle of vintage port.

"With the compliments of the two officers sitting at the corner table."

David looked over his shoulder and could hardly believe his eyes. General Auchinleck and General Dorman-Smith were dining together in a dimly lit corner and raising their glasses in a silent salute to the two lovers. David was completely taken aback but soon recovered his composure.

"Who are those officers?" asked Bron.

"A couple of friends of mine," replied David. "Come and meet them."

He took Bron by the hand to the senior officers' table, where both stood stiffly at attention in deference to a lady's presence. David felt Bron's hand perspiring in his and almost heard her knees knocking. He introduced Bron to General Auchinleck and General Dorman-Smith in turn and she was charmed by their healthy, broadly smiling faces. David thanked the generals for their kindness and hospitality. General Auchinleck took David by the hand and shook it warmly.

"Don't thank me, Major Green. Let me thank you for all your support and hard work over the past fourteen months and especially over the past four weeks."

They returned to their table. Bron was flabbergasted.

"Bloody hell, David, two generals and one of them was Auchinleck. What a nice man. I could fall for him."

'And so say all of us,' thought David as he expertly poured out two glasses of port.

*

Brigadier Henry Sharples agreed with David's basic concepts for the organisation of his small commando group. A date was fixed for the operation, code-named Codfish, to be implemented in the last week of November, or the first week of December. Codfish commando was to be taken into Crete by submarine. David's main priority now was to collect his men and give them intensive training before the start date. With the help of the brigadier he established a small headquarters in two Nissen huts at the back of Gizza barracks. One hut was converted into a dormitory and living area and the other became the operations office and, at the back, a small partitioned-off section was reserved as David's own quarters. Working in the cookhouse at brigade headquarters David had noticed two civilian refugee Cretans. One of them, Georgiou Mandakis, was pleasant, affable and spoke English reasonably well. Georgiou was only too pleased to help David in return for a cigarette issue and a bottle of Scotch. David's request startled Georgiou.

"Strip to your underclothes."

Georgiou took off his white jacket and vest and then, smiling broadly, his check trousers. He was completely naked. David felt a little abashed but Georgiou explained that Cretans seldom wore underclothes. He studied the naked man from top to toe, noting in particular the different shades of brown on the exposed parts of his body and those covered with clothing. He noted that the tan on Georgiou's face ended abruptly at his neckline and that his forearms and legs were only slightly browner than his torso. The backs of Georgiou's hands were a deep mahogany brown which ended abruptly at the wrists. The Cretan's chest and abdomen had a light yellowish-brown tinge which faded into the pristine whiteness of his buttocks. David thanked Georgiou and asked him to dress. He now knew the coloration and degree of tanning which his commando would need to simulate if they were to pass as native Cretans.

On the last day of August 1942 David paid one of his frequent visits to room 29 Shepherds. Brigadier Henry Sharples was sitting behind his desk and a pleasant open-faced Royal Marine sergeant on another chair opposite him.

"Major Green, this is Sergeant William Hubbard, just in with the last draft from the UK. I think he may be of use to you in the Codfish operation."

David looked squarely at the sergeant, now standing to attention, and liked what he saw. Sergeant Bill Hubbard was a slightly built, sinewy, dark-haired man with a perpetual smile on his face. He was a Royal Marine regular who was wounded in an abortive commando raid on the Lofotten Islands in 1940 and, after a long period of hospitalisation, had been declared fit to return to active duty. Sergeant Hubbard, a Devonian, became the first recruit for David's Codfish commando.

For the next three weeks David and the sergeant scoured the camps and barracks around Cairo and the army headquarters in Alexandria, looking for suitable recruits. They both knew the type of soldier they needed, men of dark Mediterranean mien, of equable temperament and with the ability to act independently, or as a unit, as and when the occasion demanded. Within a fortnight twelve possible candidates were selected and, with the permission of their commanding officers, transferred to Codfish depot where preliminary screening and training commenced. Without revealing their destination David explained the purpose and aims of the commando in clandestine activity behind enemy lines. Four of the men fell out within a few days and a further four were eliminated as unsuitable candidates by David after a thorough screening interview.

The four men left appeared to fit the bill. Two were recruited from the Royal Artillery Depot in Ismalia by Sergeant Hubbard and were explosive experts, one was an RASC driver from the BMH in Alexandria and the fourth a private in the Highland Light Infantry. They still needed a further general duty private, or NCO, to complete the unit.

On the suggestion of Brigadier Sharples David paid a visit to the army detention centre at Ismalia. He explained to the duty officer at the Glasshouse that he was looking for a certain type of soldier who would be reliable under stress and could stand the pressure of long periods of solitude and also mix readily with other members of the group. The military police lieutenant looked at him sardonically.

"Major Green, Sir, I don't think you'll find your ideal man in this place. Most of the inmates here are in for assaulting superiors, thieving, desertion and improper behaviour. I couldn't recommend any of them to you, Sir."

David acknowledged the difficulties but politely responded to the police officer, "Nevertheless, I would like to talk to a few likely prospects."

The military police lieutenant sent for about a dozen men and all of them were either insolent, or backward, and not at all suitable for David's needs and were returned to their cells.

"While I'm here, Lieutenant, I wouldn't mind looking around. I've never been in one of these military prisons before."

"Certainly, Major," replied the lieutenant, anxious to show off the prison and its incarcerated inmates over whom he wielded undisputed power.

As they walked around the second cell block to the accompaniment of booing and hissing which, according to the lieutenant, was standard behaviour, David heard a deep voice emanating from cell No. 23.

"Over here, Major, over here."

David looked through the bars to see the unmistakable figure of Biffo and his mind raced back to Pusey Street Primary school.

"Biffo, Biffo what the hell are you doing here?" queried David.

"I'm in 'cos I 'it an officer, Sir," Biffo replied with a wide grin on his pock-marked face, adding, "You've done all right for yourself, Sir, since we last met."

David laughed aloud much to the disgust of the MP lieutenant who asked, "Do you know this prisoner, Sir? He's a hard nut and one of the most recalcitrant men in here. We have to keep him in solitary most of the time."

"Lieutenant, Gunner Wendro and I go back a long way. I want to have a word with him in private. I will be responsible for his safety and make sure he doesn't make a run for it," and turning to the prisoner, "I want a word with you, Biffo. No nonsense and don't try to get over the wall."

David interrogated Biffo in an office in the orderly room of the detention centre whilst the MP lieutenant stood guard outside the door.

Billy Wendro had been unwillingly conscripted into the army in November 1940. He took unkindly to regimentation and had 'done a runner' on three occasions only to be brought back by the MPs. On completion of his basic training he was posted to a Royal Artillery regiment which in due course reached the Middle East in October 1941. His unit played its part in Auchinleck's offensive in November and he was then brought out of the front line to Mersa Matruh where Gunner William Wendro went on a drunken rampage in the town and was arrested for striking a military police captain. David looked at Biffo, smiling and leaning back in his chair with a cigarette dangling from the corner of his mouth.

"Do you want to get out of here?" David asked.

"What do you think, David... Sir?" replied Biffo.

David made a decision.

"I can get you out if you promise me you'll behave. I'll be responsible for you and, if you let me down, I'll have you back in here quicker than you can say shuftiwallah."

A deal was struck and Biffo was hustled back to his cell. David thanked the MP Lieutenant and with Brigadier Sharples' aid he secured Gunner Wendro's release from Ismalia Detention Centre on a temporary basis. The team for Operation Codfish was now complete.

Training of the seven-man Codfish commando started in earnest in September 1942. Sergeant Bill Hubbard was in charge of physical fitness, unarmed combat and weaponry while David took command of the general and strategic instruction for the group. He again recruited Georgiou Mandakis, this time wearing underpants to show them the areas of tanning and the paler, or whiter, skin patches which they needed to simulate a Cretan peasant. All of the party had brown knees and forearms. Selective tanning was achieved by daily exposure to the sun wearing long trousers and long-sleeved shirts. Georgiou was co-opted to supply Cretan artisan colloquialisms to supplement David's teaching of basic Greek. David insisted that Codfish commando, or Codforce, should spend day after day together eating and sleeping in a group. After a month it was evident to David and Sergeant Hubbard that the members of their force were getting on well together and melding into a happy, interdependent commando unit.

Whenever Lieutenant Bronwen Thomas was off duty a car picked her up and brought her to a place of assignation with David. Often it was Shepherds, either in Sergeant Willoughby's office, or in a room at the hotel. Sometimes it happened in another hotel in Cairo, but by mid-September David hit on a perfect place for their trysts. Dotted along the west bank of the Nile, well within city limits, were house-boats of various sizes and description. During the day some of the smaller boats were used for transportation across the Nile. At night they were moored amongst the larger pleasure boats, where Egyptian prostitutes entertained their clients. In his researches David discovered a small operator, who, for two hundred piastres a night agreed to rent out his twenty foot pleasure boat and no questions asked. The only difficulty was that his small craft, the *Isis Rose*, was not berthed permanently at any given point. Sometimes it was on its own wafting lazily on the subdued waves of the sleeping Nile and on another occasion moored precariously between two larger pleasure boats. David hired the *Isis Rose* exclusively for his own use. Bron was brought by David's driver to the boat, or she occasionally had use of a duty ambulance for her visits to their lovenest. The *Isis Rose* had a glass-sided cupola with a good wide-angle view and during the day took ten passengers precariously back and forth across the Nile. At night brown damask curtains inside the cupola excluded all light from the lovenest. Bron loved the little craft. After lovemaking she lay beside David and laughed when sometimes the next door pleasure boat rocked gently on the sleeping Nile keeping time with the sexual gyrations of a prostitute and her client.

Due to the uncertainty of Rommel's next move the 203 Western General Hospital remained in reserve at Qatira. Bron had spare time on her hands and David, though working hard during the day, had most evenings free for his tryst on the *Isis Rose*. Life was idyllic and it seemed would never end. But the lovers' days together were numbered. A week before Montgomery's attack at El Alamein, on the 17th October, the 203 Western General Hospital were moved forwards and became a second echelon field hospital for battle casualties. Despite David's enquiries he was unable to ascertain the exact location of the hospital and frequent requests to Brigadier Sharples for a few days' leave for a desert recce went unheeded.

Brigadier Sharples was now pressing David hard to get his commando group ready for their transfer to Crete. The Brigadier's intention was that Codforce would take off in early November, but 'the little bit of a fracas at El Alamein' put paid to the plan. The

Brigadier started planning for late November when it became clear that Rommel was in full retreat and that Egypt was now a safe haven for Allied forces. David's days were occupied with kitting out his men and making final arrangements for departure. Second-hand Greek clothing was provided by a quartermaster at brigade headquarters and the men's 'authentic' Greek belongings were crammed into a *sakouli*, a woollen knapsack. All the group were fitted out with a *sarikis*, black woollen head-cloths embroidered with tiny tassels. Forged papers were prepared by Professor Wassl's department. The commando were advised of the food they might expect in Crete, mainly sour milk and goat's cheese, snails in the wet season, *khorta*, a chewy mountain grass mixed with oil and acorns or chestnuts and Cretan stew which contained a variety of meats including snake, snails and, occasionally, lamb or goat. The alcoholic drink of the natives was *tsikoudia*, a very strong raki and best avoided. Cretan wine was poor in quality, vinegary, and not very palatable. The commando were told that their living quarters for most of the time would be in caves or the peculiar conical huts that were used by the farmers for milking their goats and sheep. They were made fully aware that for lengthy periods they would have to endure a troglodyte existence. Fleas and lice were endemic commensals and had to be suffered gladly.

The lovesick major was only half-heartedly interested in these preparations. His thoughts were all the time out west, where Bron and her field hospital were daily facing danger of death, injury or captivity.

On 23rd October, 1942 the Eighth Army, commanded by General Montgomery, started its assault on Rommel's Africa Corps at El Alamein. After a twenty-four hour softening-up bombardment and two days of close combat the German Panzers were neutralised, or destroyed, and the Eighth Army started their advance into Libya. By the 4th November Rommel's Panzers, now reduced to a hundred tanks, were in full retreat.

Secretly David half-wished that Montgomery's offensive would peter out in the vastness of the Sahara and the 203 Field Hospital might then be recalled to base and the Cretan expedition might be aborted. At such time he was overcome with guilt at his own selfishness. He knew that, as Montgomery's Eighth Army chased Rommel's Africa Corps out of Libya, the field hospitals moved westwards in support of the successful British attack, taking Bron further away from their safe haven in Cairo. How he longed to see her again, just once more, before he left for Crete. So much had been left unsaid and he bitterly regretted he had not formally asked Bronwen Thomas to be his wife. The only reminder he had of his paramour was a poorly developed black and white print, taken by a box Brownie, of Bron sitting smiling on a rock besides the bridge pool on the River Teifi in west Wales. And even this undistinguished photograph would have to be discarded when he left for Crete.

Brigadier Sharples' Penultimate Briefing, 30th November, 1942

"Well, David, it won't be long now," Brigadier Sharples and David were sitting in No. 29 Shepherds facing a large map of Crete. The Brigadier wielded a long pointer and embellished his statements whilst sitting in his chair.

"I'm sending you into Crete in the next week or ten days. Tim Gammon and two wireless operatives will be coming with you. You will remember Tim from Athens. One of the radio operatives is strictly mine and he's the one you'll have to use to relay and receive messages. He's going to be planted here near Tres Ekklises. You will all be going by submarine from Alexandria landing somewhere near Tsoutsouro. You'll be met by 'safe' guides, known to Tim Gammon, and taken across the narrow waist of Crete to your hideout at Piskopiano. You are the only one who knows where the goods are hidden and I want it to stay that way. You'll go dressed as Cretans and I'll explain why in due course.

"The German commander for the whole of Crete is General Brüno Braüer and his second in command is a tricky bastard Colonel General Müller. The counter-espionage officer at Heraklion, appointed in June last year, is Colonel Manfred Schmidt who has made a big name for himself, a very hard, unscrupulous Nazi. He doesn't get on well with the Italians and is apparently flirting with some Communist groups in the eastern sector, promising them arms and hoping to turn them against the Nationalist Cretan *andartes*, led by our old friend Bandouvas. A nasty bit of goods in your eastern sector is the Commie Militades Porphyroyennis whose got a strong force in the Lasithi

Mountains. Watch out for him. He's devious and ruthless and we wouldn't lose any sleep if he should disappear without trace one night.

"As you are aware, on mainland Greece there are two rival resistance factions, a loyalist or monarchist group, EAM, and an outwardly Communist group ELAS. This has not happened in Crete. Here we have independent Cretan Nationalists and the Communists who are strong ELAS supporters. There are some rumours that Bandouvas is flirting with ELAS. The two *kapitans* you have to look out for in your sector are Bandouvas and Porphyroyennis. Don't trust either of them an inch and don't give arms to either side. The SOE organisation in Crete is still chaotic. The boss would seem to be Tom Dundabin at Khania, but there are countless others wandering around. There's Xan Fielding in the western sector and in your area on the eastern side, you may come across Peter Ferman.

"As far as the Italians are concerned they are a fairly benign bunch. General Angelo Carta is in command of the Siena Division and his counter espionage officer is Lieutenant Franco Tavana. He may be a captain by now. This chap is quite humane and seems ready to do a deal at any time.

"Lastly we come to your mission. You're there to act as a thorn in the flesh of the German forces and to attempt to create a split between the Germans and the Italians. At present there are some forty thousand Germans and forty-five thousand Italian personnel on the island. Your group will carry out harassing operations around Heraklion and in the Lasithi area and perform these in the guise of Cretan irregulars and in particular Communist *andartes*. The idea is to drive a wedge between the Germans and Italians, between the Germans and the Commies and between Porphyroyennis and Bandouvas. If you get either the Germans, or Bandouvas, to eliminate Porphyroyennis this would be appreciated by my superiors in London.

"The other major task you must undertake is to reconnoitre the harbour area at Heraklion to assess the feasibility of marine sabotage conducted from the land and not from the sea. If you think something can be done along these lines you must inform me. For the past year disruption to our shipping in the Aegean by submarines and E-boats, based in Heraklion, has been considerable and a great worry to naval command in Alexandria. Well, David, that's about it. Any questions?"

David had no questions and the Brigadier continued, "I repeat again that you are my agent and directly responsible to me alone. You will have my authority to override any interference from any other agents or authorities on the island. When you get to Crete spend the first month acclimatising. After that I will look forward to receiving regular reports from you."

David rose, saluted and turned to leave. Before he reached the office door Brigadier Sharples spoke again, "I'm very sorry, David, that the Welsh beauty had to go to war and leave you in Cairo. I'll keep an eye out for her whilst you are away."

David felt himself blushing under his dark tan and for once was unable to think of a suitable riposte. He stammered, "Thank you, Sir", and walked out of room 29 past the voluptuous Sergeant Willoughby and wondered how much his commanding officer knew about his affair with Bron. He was not to know that all the officer's messes in Cairo were fully aware of his little lovenest on the *Isis Rose*. He left Shepherds Hotel that day with a heavy heart, desperately concerned that he had not married Bron in the brief three months they had together in Cairo.

*

Four days before Codforce's departure from Alexandria on 11th December, 1942, David reported to Brigadier Sharples' office at room 29 Shepherds for his final instruction.

"The intention of Operation Codfish is to place Tim Gammon and two radio operators and yourself and your six commandos on Crete, responsible only to myself and not to be integrated with other clandestine groups or *andartes* on the island. One of the wireless operators will be placed by Tim on the south of the island and he will have direct communication with this headquarters. You will have to provide a regular courier for transmission and reception of messages from this operator. You will take Codforce to a hideout near Neapolis in the north, the exact location only known to yourself. From there you will conduct clandestine operations against the Germans and, if not co-operative, the Italians in eastern Crete. You must avoid compromising the local population for fear of German reprisals.

"The disposition of Cretan resistance is known to us but, in general you must avoid direct contact with the *andartes*. Recent messages from Crete indicate that they are still not trustworthy. The area of activity assigned to Codforce is German held Heraklion and the eastern area in Crete which, as far as we know, is under the jurisdiction of General Carta and the Italian Fifth Siena Division. The local *kapitans* around Heraklion, Bandouvas and Porphyroyennis, are not to be trusted. In the south of eastern Crete near Ierapetra a Communist *Samaritis* is active. He is not to be trusted under any circumstances.

"Codforce will leave by submarine from Alexandria within the next two or three days. Tim Gammon will place our wireless operator near Tres Ekklises and your commando will be met on the beach by a Cretan guide who will take your group over the mountains to Kastelli. After that you are on your own. From there you should be able to make your way without difficulty to the arms cache. I can now only wish you luck. I'll come and see you off on Thursday morning."

David saluted, turned rapidly on his heel and left the office, sensing that the Brigadier was under great tension and that his continued presence in room 29 Shepherds would only prolong his agony.

Around lunchtime on the same day as Brigadier Sharples' final briefing David returned to Codforce base where his commando were in the mess tent. Sergeant Hubbard ordered the men to parade in their Cretan clothing, without badges of rank or other insignia. Since their appearance at brigade headquarters many complaints were received about a group of shifty-looking, wog-like characters wandering around base camp. The brigadier ordered that, on their clothing and for their own protection, Codforce commando must, at all times, wear identification badges and badges of rank. For this inspection parade all such badges were removed and the commando, including its commanding officer, were in Cretan attire including the closely woven. black bobbled *sarikis*. Each man had two daggers, one in the waistband and the second strapped to the inside of his left leg, a Sten gun slung over one shoulder with spare cartridge clips hooked on the inside of his waistband. David, similarly attired, emerged from the command post promptly at 2 p.m. Sergeant Hubbard called Codforce to attention, about turned and, walking up to David, saluted.

"All present and correct, Sir, and ready for inspection."

The sergeant then returned to the head of the line whilst David walked slowly around the front of the commando and then around the back minutely inspecting each man in detail from the top of their *sarikis* to the tips of their brown leather soled canvas shoes. He liked what he saw and, asking the men to stand at ease, he addressed them:

"Gentlemen, that's the last time I'll expect you to parade in front of me. From now on you will eat, sleep, stand, walk and talk like Greek peasants. Because that's what you're supposed to be. We're going across to Crete on Thursday. The reason we're going there is to create havoc amongst the German and Italian occupying forces. There are other people in Crete like ourselves and there are Cretan resistance fighters, but I have been ordered to act independently of everyone else. You're all well trained, fit and ready to go. I know we can do a good job. Now, Sergeant, dismiss the men and get them out of the sun. I'll give you further details of your special duties in the shade."

The men were dismissed by Sergeant Hubbard and recongregated under a canopy erected at the side of the orderly room where David again addressed Codforce, "When we are on the island we must not use our own names. I shall be called Kostas with a 'K', not Major. All of you will use the name Spiros, which will not confuse anyone except the enemy," he joked, followed by laughter from the commando.

"I've taught you some basic Greek and each one of you will have an alphabetical suffix. Now Sergeant Hubbard will be Spiros Alpha, Bombardier Ferris will be Spiros Beta, Gunner Smithson will be Spiros Delta, Private Clayton will be Spiros Omega, Gunner Wendro will be Spiros Sigma and Private Mcpherson will be Spiros Theta. The whole idea behind this nonsense is that when you are in the field and there is a chance Jerry might be listening, I want you to communicate in Cretan even if it is gibberish. We don't want the enemy to know at any stage that we are British.

"Now for your specific tasks on this operation. Sergeant Hubbard will be my second in command and will take charge if I'm away or captured. Private Clayton is our medical orderly and will act as a guard in the base camp. Bombardier Ferris and Gunner Smithson are our explosive experts and I'm sure they will have plenty to do. Gunner Wendro and Private Mcpherson will take it in turns to act as couriers and perform general duties. I want you now to practise using your new names. We leave on Thursday and I'll have a further chance to brief you on the sea crossing. By the way, are any of you claustrophobic?"

There were no answers in the affirmative and David continued, "Well, I'm glad about that because we're going across in a submarine and for the next few months you'll all be living in a cave."

Within half an hour of daybreak on the 11th December, 1942, HMS *Hyperion* edged its way slowly out of Alexandria harbour. On the conning tower stood the captain, a sub-lieutenant and Major David Green watching the two figures on the dockside getting smaller as the boat swung out through the harbour entrance into open sea. Brigadier Sharples and his buxom ATS sergeant had driven down overnight to see Operation Codfish launched.

The Brigadier's last words to David were, "Good luck, David, look after the boys."

"Thank you, Henry. I'll keep in touch," David replied.

They were two miles out at sea when the submarine commander ordered David below and remained himself in the conning tower for the first watch. David joined his Codforce commandos, the signals corporals and Tim Gammon in one of the forward messes. The navigator explained that the route to their destination was not direct, as they had to avoid German spotter planes and possibly dive bombers on the first half of the journey and surface E-boats for the last fifty miles when they would have to remain submerged for about twelve hours off Crete. The captain steered his boat on the surface in a westerly direction for about twenty miles parallel with the North African shore, veering to a northerly bearing off Tobruk and aiming towards the south-east corner of Crete.

For the land-based Codforce commando the swaying and twisting motion of the submarine on the surface was uncomfortable and this, compounded by the stifling atmosphere in the cramped mess room below decks, produced nausea and sickness in all except Biffo. The misery for the land-lubbers continued for about ten hours and only abated when the captain took his ship down to fifty feet, where the submerged boat assumed an even keel and, apart from the noise of chugging engines, an eerie silence descended on the whole company.

The crewmen spoke quietly and orders were conveyed along the craft in exaggerated whispers. Tim Gammon held a short conference with David, the signals corporal and the submarine's wireless operator to discuss coding for transfer and reception of messages. The optimum time for a submarine to get close enough inshore to safely transmit and receive signals was during the week after a full moon, when, under the cover of darkness, the boat could safely surface off Crete. For a year ahead Tim Gammon and the sub-lieutenant mariner worked out exact dates and times of transmission.

At night the submarine again surfaced and the irksome wallowing and twisting motion returned to plague the unfortunate sufferers trapped in the steel coffin. Even Tim Gammon, who had done the journey on numerous occasions, was sick. Before daybreak they were again submerged and the engines cut back to slow ahead. They were now some twenty miles from their destination and the Captain planned to have the *Hyperion* offshore at about 10 p.m. The day passed slowly, the wretched sufferers dozing amidst the foetid stench of diesel, oil and vomit. At 5.30 p.m. darkness descended rapidly over Crete and three hours later the *Hyperion* surfaced about two miles off shore. A pencil beam of flashlight from the darkness to the north indicated the site of disembarkation. Codforce commando had arrived in Cretan waters wallowing two miles off shore from their landfall on a shelving, shingly beach at Keratokombou.

Chapter Nineteen
Six Months in the Wilderness, June – December 1941 SS Rehabilitation Hospital, Havel, Berlin The Sex Hotel

Manfred Schmidt emerged from a state of semi-consciousness during the last week of July 1941. He had no recollection of events leading to his injury and his amnesia extended back as far as the long train journey which, in his befuddled mind, ended in copulation on a balcony in a Balkan railway station. He did not remember clearly if his partner was male or female and, in his vivid nightmares, sometimes it was a scowling male and sometimes a wide-mouthed, brazen harlot with a red slash for a mouth, blackened teeth and an obnoxious smell to her breath. His moments of lucidity waxed and waned but generally there was daily improvement. He was subject to fits and outbursts of violent shouting and abuse, worse at night-time. The head injury left him with intermittent headaches, a weakness in his left arm and leg and a slight slurring of his speech. By the end of July he knew his name and rank and his whereabouts and remembered the battalion's train convoy to Sofia. After this stop he had no recollection of his time in Greece and the flight to Crete or any event subsequent to his head injury, sustained on Heraklion airfield.

Major Manfred Schmidt and *Feldwebel* Schneider were evacuated from Crete in a Junker JU-88 transport plane to Tatöi airfield and then, by ambulance, to the Red Cross hospital in Athens. *Feldwebel*

Schneider's injured shoulder was dealt with speedily but the involved nature of Manfred's head injury was another matter. The German army surgeon at the Red Cross hospital cut away Manfred's steel helmet with an oxyacetylene flame guarding the underlying scalp with an aluminium sheet. Once the extent of the shrapnel wound was exposed they realised that Manfred needed expert neurosurgical attention and within twenty-four hours, still unconscious, he was transferred by plane to the Bilroth Neurosurgical Unit in Vienna, a journey of eight hundred miles which took five hours including a refuelling stop at Zagreb. The five hour operation for removal of the shrapnel and insertion of a metal plate into his temple was performed by Professor Otto Kempinski, a neurosurgeon of world repute. After a fortnight recovering, the semi-conscious patient was then airlifted to the officers' wing of a military hospital in Spandau and, after a month, transferred to the SS officers' rehabilitation centre on the banks of the Havel in Berlin.

Manfred's recuperation at this centre was rapid, aided by expert nursing care and intensive physiotherapy to his left arm and leg. Four months after the injury he was able to sit out of bed and move around the bedside with assistance. He had lost some three stones in weight. His clothes hung limply on his bony frame and his, once handsome, face was now gaunt and haggard, marred by the unsightly puckered pink scar extending forwards from his right temple on to his forehead. Added to this his head had been completely shaven for the operation and tufts of yellow, blondish hair were beginning to reappear in a haphazard fashion all over the exposed scalp. During the day his head was dressed in a white Kaplan bandage hiding the unsightly scar on the right side of his temple.

His first visitor during the last week of September was Colonel von Bulow. The 'old man' had been made camp commandant of the airborne division at Potsdam, the only purely airborne divisional barracks left after the Cretan debacle. The Count was realistic enough to recognise that he had been 'put out to grass' and this would be his last active posting in the army. He was not pleased to find Manfred in an SS hospital but conceded that the treatment available was the best in Germany. He reported that *Feldwebel* Schneider was still convalescing in Hanover but expected to rejoin the regiment at Potsdam in early October. Major Werner had been promoted to colonel and was von Bulow's second in command at Potsdam.

General Student remained general officer commanding the Parachute Regiment and his three brigadiers, Schlemm, Stürm, and Ramcke of the Storm Regiment, between them commanded a force of four thousand five hundred men, a reduction of twelve thousand since the battle of Crete. There were frequent demands for airborne battalions to fight as infantry on the Russian front. Colonel von Bulow, now in full flow, started analysing the tactics and battles of the German armies fighting in Russia but, by this time, Manfred's brain could not assimilate more facts and, indicating that he was fatigued, he thanked Colonel von Bulow for his visit and asked a male nurse to return him to his bed.

On October 10th Major General Ringl, commander of the Fifth Mountain Division, accompanied by Heinrich Himmler, came to present Manfred with a Knight's Cross decoration and later that month he received a visit from General Student, Brigadiers Ramcke and Schlemm and Field Marshal Goering, accompanied by General Freiherr Wolfram von Richthofen. The obese, medal-bedecked *Reichsmarschall* was full of bonhomie and walked around the wards with an expansive smile on his flabby face. He only spoke briefly to Manfred and the other patients but took special pains to be pleasant to the blond medical orderly who nursed Manfred. Hugo Felder was overjoyed by the attention he received from the second most powerful man in wartime Germany and for weeks after the *Reichsmarschall's* visit Hugo talked about the day when he had a '*tête à tête*' with *Reichsmarschall* Goering.

War Diary

The Eastern Front: June 1941 to April 1942

As decreed by Führer's Directive No. 21, Operation Barbarossa, the German invasion of Russia, was launched on Sunday June 22nd, 1941 along a thousand mile front extending from the Baltic in the north to the Black Sea in the south. German involvement in the Balkans and Crete delayed the original start date by five weeks. Battle tactics were based on the successful German campaigns in Poland and the Western Front – rapid penetration by armoured spearheads, bypassing and surrounding pockets of resistance, leaving the beleaguered enemy to be mopped up by advancing infantry.

For four months before the start date German forces were amassing in Poland and Rumania so that, by mid-June 1941, there were one hundred and eleven front line divisions and seventeen armoured divisions assembled for the attack. Three main assaults were planned. Army Group North, commanded by Field Marshal Ritter von Leeb and comprised of seven infantry divisions and General Hoepner's Fourth Panzer Group, were to attack Leningrad and link up with the Finnish forces advancing down the Kyrelian Isthmus.

Field Marshal Fedor von Bock commanding Army Group Centre had forty-one infantry, six motorised and nine Panzer Divisions at his disposal for an attack on Moscow. The Panzer Divisions were divided into two groups, one under the command of General Heinz Guderian and the other commanded by General Hermann Hoth. The strongest of the three army groups was in the south, commanded by Field Marshal Gerd von Runstedt. Army Group South had fifty-two German, fifteen Rumanian, two Hungarian and two Italian divisions, spearheaded by Erwald von Kleist's First Panzer Group, and air cover provided by General Löhr's Fourth Airfleet. Their objectives were Odessa and the Crimea and the eventual capture of Rostov and Stalingrad, securing the Ukraine granary and the oil fields of the Caucasus.

Opposing these German armies of one hundred and thirty-two divisions the Russians had over one hundred and sixty infantry divisions at their disposal, thirty cavalry divisions and fifty-five motorised armour brigades. The Russian commander in the north was Marshal Kliment Voroshilov whilst Marshal Semeon Timoshenko commanded the Central Armies and Marshal Semen Budenny the south. Russian reserve manpower was enormous. By the end of 1942 four hundred new divisions were mobilised and by Christmas Russia had twelve million men under arms. The poorly equipped Russian front-line troops proved no match for the Nazi juggernaut as it advanced rapidly across the open tundra capturing town after town and surrounding and annihilating hundreds of thousands of Russian infantrymen, bypassed by the crunching wheels of the Panzer spearheads.

Von Leeb's Army Group North pushed through Lithuania and Latvia with little resistance and by early October had encircled Leningrad. Von Bock's Army Group Centre had taken Brest-Litovsk and Smolensk by July 16th where the Panzer Units were halted in their *charge towards Moscow on the banks of the river Desna. By the 12th July Field Marshal von Runstedt's Army Group South was a hundred miles short of Kiev where they were ordered to pause and await further instructions from high command. Although his armies were successful in all their offensives throughout July and August, Hitler dithered and his high command issued conflicting orders to the army commanders, changing the priority of their targets on a weekly basis.*

In late July General Heinz Guderian reported to Hitler's headquarters at Wolfshanze in Prussia and made a plea to be allowed to resume the Panzer advance and take Moscow before the onset of winter. Hitler, supported by Halder and Brauchitsch, disagreed with the field commander and instead ordered Guderian's Second Panzer Division south to reinforce von Kleist's Panzer Group with the objective of capturing Kiev and opening up a gateway to the Crimea. Kiev was taken on 18th September, 1941 with capture of half a million Russian infantrymen. The Russian commander, Marshal Budenny, was relieved of his command.

Hitler and the German high command now realised that the Eastern campaign would take longer than estimated. Russian resistance, tissue-paper thin at first, was stiffening and their T-34 tanks, appearing in great numbers, were proving a match for the Tigers of the Panzers. Hitler now became obsessed with capturing Moscow before Christmas and ordered Army Group Centre to advance in force to take the Russian capital.

Von Bock's army moved across the Desna and proceeded rapidly at first but, within a week, the Russian defenders, protected by their T-34 tanks held up his advance. Added to this heavy rainfall, the Russian razputikza, *made most roads and fields a muddy morass which was an obstacle to both foot soldiers and mechanised units. The generals in the field advised the Führer that they must form a defensive line for the winter about a hundred miles short of their target but Hitler ordered them to press forward relentlessly. Operation Tufun, the delayed advance on Moscow, started in earnest on October 2nd when von Bock's Panzer potential had been greatly strengthened by the return of Guderian's Second Panzer Group from Kiev and Hoth's Third Panzer Group from the north. Guderian's Panzers pushed forward relentlessly from the south, capturing Orel on the 2nd October and encircling a whole Russian army at Bryansk a week later. Hoth's Third Panzer Group confined another Russian Army of six hundred* thousand men outside Vyasma and Marshal Zhukov, the new Russian commander on the central front, commented:

"There is no longer a continuous front in the west and large gaps in our defence line cannot be plugged because of lack of resources."

Marshal Zhukov began reorganising his defence lines when large numbers of T-34 tanks, proven in battle, came rolling off the production lines and several divisions of crack Siberian infantry became available. By mid-November the weather was worsening and movement of vehicles, including tanks, became impossible. The Wehrmacht, already exhausted by weeks of fighting, now had to cover the last forty miles to Moscow on foot. By the 14th November only fifty of Guderian's original six hundred tanks were serviceable and the central drive towards Moscow came to a standstill. Further north Hoepner's Panzers made progress through Kalinin towards the Russian capital and a detachment of the 258th Division crossed the river Narvar and entered the western suburbs of Moscow on the 2nd December, only to be driven out on the following day by a determined Russian counter attack. The formidable Russian winter set in in earnest on the 6th December and continued unabated until the middle of April 1942.

Abiding by Hitler's no retreat policy the German armies at the gates of Moscow dug defensive hedgehogs and sat out the long, hard, ice-bound Russian winter. Not so the Russian forces. Acclimatisation and familiarity with fighting in wintry conditions allowed Marshal Zhukov to mount two offensives around Moscow in the stalemate months, one to the north-west across the Moscow-Volga Canal and the second southwards towards Ryozan, separating von Kluge's Fourth Army from its armoured support. More German troops were lost from frostbite than suffered injury and death in the battles around Moscow. Zhukov's tactics at first were suicidal, frontal attacks on well-equipped and well-entrenched enemy forces. Heavy casualties forced him to concentrate his forces, mainly Siberian infantry and Cossack cavalry, into well-defined attacks on the flanks of the German Fourth Army and Panzer groups.

General Guderian was the first to withdraw and this led to an amazing upheaval in the German command in Russia, starting in mid-December with the sacking of Guderian. On December 18th the ailing Field Marshal von Bock gave up his command and von Kluge took over Army Group Centre. Field Marshal von Brauchitsch did not agree with Hitler's directives on withdrawal and resigned, whilst at the front von Runstedt, Hoepner and von Leeb were dismissed. By Christmas Eve 1941 the Fourth German Army, now commanded by General Kübler, was in a precarious position some hundred miles south-west of Moscow only protected from the Russians by some fifty surviving tanks of the Nineteenth Panzer Division. On 20th February, 1942 the Russian offensive in the central sector ground to a halt.

Zhukov now devised a plan to relieve Leningrad. On 7th and 8th January 1942 he launched an attack northwards against General Ernst Busch's Sixteenth Army, which was thrown back in disorder. The brunt of Zhukov's attack was resisted by SS General Theodore Eickes Third Totenkopf Division who held the line for seventy-three long arduous days until 22nd April when they were relieved from the west. For two months they were supplied from the air, enclosed in a pocket around Danyansk, and fought to the last man to hang on to their fragile bridgehead. Leningrad was still besieged by von Leeb's army who now advanced to hold a line a hundred miles to the east. In the south von Kleist's Panzers managed to enter Rostov on the 21st November only to be driven out five days later by superior Russian forces. A defensive winter line was then established along the River Donets.

The winter fighting took a terrible toll on German manpower and resources. Of the hundred and sixty-two combat divisions engaged in Operations Barbarossa and Tufun, by the end of March 1942, only eight were battle worthy and the sixty armoured divisions only had one hundred and sixty serviceable tanks between them, the normal complement for one division. April and May 1942 were months of replenishment for the depleted German infantry and mechanised forces. Hitler and his high command, now located in their Werewolf headquarters at Vinnitsa in the Ukraine, were making plans for the forthcoming summer offensive. Hitler's Directive No. 45 insisted that German forces attack and occupy both Stalingrad and the Caucasian oilfields at one and the same time, the former for its strategic importance and the latter for oil to keep the mechanised armies on the battlefield. General Halder and members of the senior planning staff were bewildered by this decision but Hitler, as chief of the armed forces, insisted that his directive be obeyed. The German failure to take Stalingrad in 1942 became the turning point of the war in the east *and eventually led to the downfall and destruction of Hitler's Third Reich.*

SS Rehabilitation Hospital, Havel, Berlin, July – December 1941

Ever since June 1940 and the conclusion of the battle for France, Berlin had been a city of euphoria and gaiety, fed by a continuous series of successful campaigns, engineered, and, in the people's view, commanded by their God-like leader, Adolf Hitler and exploited by the master of propaganda, Doctor Joseph Goebbels. The city soon overcame the shock of its first air raid by the RAF in August 1940 and within a week the Berliners' lifestyle returned to normal, the only tangible effect of the early raids being a compulsory blackout of the city at night. The RAF continued sporadic night bombing throughout the year but the raids were of nuisance value only. Apart from its three airfields and numerous army depots and establishments there were no industrial, or military, targets of importance for the British to attack. In any event the raids were random and the bombing indiscriminate and the British plan to terrorise the population of Berlin fell sadly short of its intended purpose. On the contrary, the Berliners came to regard the British night visits as a mere fleabite which served only to interrupt the sleep of an otherwise jubilant population.

These were heady days, the exultant Berliners revelling in the success of their armed forces – victory in Poland and Norway, conquest and division of France, victory in Yugoslavia and the Balkans and Crete and Rommel's continued advances against the British in North Africa. The whole city buzzed with excitement. The theatres were full, restaurants remained open day and night, food was plentiful and a constant flow of excited soldiers, sailors and airmen lent an air of gaiety and light-heartedness to an otherwise staid metropolis. And, to cap it all, the conjurer who had produced all this magic sat in the *Reichschancellery* and frequently appeared to address the burghers and to take a salute at gargantuan, and well-organised, military parades.

Adolf Hitler fulfilled all his promises to the German nation and then on June 22nd 1941 he ordered his hitherto invincible army to attack Soviet Russia to subjugate the *Untermenchen*. Some sceptics questioned the wisdom of his latest military exploit and, for a few days, an air of despondency descended on the city, concerned about the enormity of the task facing their menfolk on the Eastern Front. But, within a week, favourable reports of success and rapid advances on all fronts served to restore their former optimism. They were confident that the Führer would succeed again. His brilliance, both political and tactical would ensure a rapid and successful campaign which would subjugate Ivan and, as promised, allow the army commanders to celebrate Christmas in the Kremlin.

Manfred was not aware of events leading up to a German attack on the Soviet Union. Throughout June, July and most of August he was in a semi-comatose state and it was early September before his brain recommenced functioning at a level which allowed him to appreciate his surroundings and to grasp the fact that his comrades were engaged in a series of gigantic battles somewhere in the vastness of the Russian steppes. Slowly over the next month the black veil, which had shrouded his consciousness for so many weeks, began to lift and his mental awareness improved by leaps and bounds, accompanied by a dramatic improvement in his physical condition. By the end of October he had regained most of the weight he had lost and his blond hair re-grew and was combed to partially mask the unsightly reddish-pink, puckered scar on his right temple.

He was now taking an active interest in the battle in Russia and constantly reiterated his wish to get fit and well enough to join his comrades on the Eastern Front. The medical specialists at the SS Rehabilitation Centre were sceptical as to whether he would ever be well enough to rejoin his regiment, let alone take part in any active fighting. They did not bargain with Manfred's will and determination to get back to active service and continue with his career in the army.

The SS rehabilitation centre, a pre-1900 forty-bedroomed mansion on the banks of the Havel, was staffed entirely by male orderlies and nurses and commanded by SS Surgeon Colonel Blumentritt, a strict disciplinarian and an eminent neurologist. Manfred's fellow patients were all high-ranking SS officers with injuries varying from amputations to head injuries and many suffered from shell shock. Manfred was honoured to be the only *Wehrmacht* officer in the establishment. His admission to the Havel centre had been arranged by *Brigadführer* Otto Kaltenburger, the SS commander in Paris, and a personal friend of the medical director. The other patients were mainly uncommunicative and rather arrogant, seemingly resenting the presence of a *Wehrmacht* officer in their midst. He was however treated with some respect in view of the important personages who visited him at the centre in November 1941.

All the patients were segregated in separate cubicles and only met at mealtimes in the communal mess hall or in the heated bath in the physiotherapy department. Conversation, even amongst the SS officers themselves, was at a premium, the tedium relieved by a German victory in battle when the whole mess buzzed with excitement for a few minutes before a melancholic mood descended again, like a black cloud.

In early November Manfred requested a transfer, a decision reinforced by a visit from Colonel von Bulow and *Feldwebel* Schneider on 14th November. Colonel von Bulow was not surprised that Manfred wanted to 'get out of this SS cesspit'. He tried his charm, he tried bullying, but Colonel Blumentritt would not give way.

"Major Schmidt is making excellent progress and I shall have him back to your unit by Christmas."

Colonel von Bulow had to acquiesce, adding, "Surgeon Colonel Blumentritt, when our Leader is feasting in the Kremlin, Major Schmidt and I will share a meagre Christmas lunch at my mess in Potsdam. That's agreed?"

Manfred was overjoyed to see *Feldwebel* Schneider again. Schneider was recovering well from his injuries but evidently had a permanently stiff shoulder and limited use of his right arm. Colonel von Bulow commented with his blue eye twinkling, "Lucky old Schneider. He won't have to raise his arm above his shoulder again in salute! It would be an insult to our Leader if he used his left arm!"

Before he left Colonel von Bulow became more serious and referred to the Russian campaign:

"I don't think we should have attacked Russia, a bad decision by our Leader, if I may say so. Operation Tufun has now been on for two weeks. We've captured nearly two million Ivans at Bryansk and Vyasma and they're still finding more cannon fodder. The damned *razputikza* has set in and movement is difficult. Soon the snow and ice will stop our advance and then, as happened to Napoleon, we'll be sitting ducks for the Ruskies. They're used to fighting in the snow and sub-zero temperatures. We'll lose thousands of men and probably we'll have to retreat without taking Moscow. Still things look better in the south where Gerd von Runstedt is pushing on hard to the Caucasus. If we can get the oilfields and deny them to Ivan we'll win. That's my opinion, Manfred, and don't let these SS shits tell you anything different."

Manfred had to smile. For once he fully agreed with his colonel. These SS officers were first class shits, especially the higher ranks. He walked with Colonel von Bulow and *Feldwebel* Schneider to the main entrance of the hospital.

"I'll see you at Christmas in Potsdam, Herr Colonel."

Throughout November the front-line news from Russia worsened. Von Leeb's army in the north faltered outside Leningrad, von Runstedt's army group took Rostov on 21st November only to be driven back one hundred miles five days later and, in the centre, von Bock's army and Panzers had come to a muddy halt some forty miles short of the Kremlin. On 3rd December there was great jubilation in Berlin when news was received that a detachment of Hoepner's Panzers had entered the outskirts of Moscow and were within sight of the Kremlin and the Red Square. It looked as if the Führer's prediction of Christmas in the Kremlin might become a reality. But hopes of further advances rapidly diminished as reports of severe wintry weather reached Berlin and the German detachment in Moscow's suburbs was driven out by an overwhelming Russian counter attack.

Visit of Brigadführer *Otto Kaltenburger, 27th November 1941*

Visit of Reichsleiter *Martin Bormann, 30th November 1941*

Manfred lay flat on his bed, staring at the ceiling, recovering from an energetic treatment session administered by a large, beefy, tattooed physiotherapist whose thumbs were like pistons as they relentlessly stabbed and thrust into his arm and thigh muscles. He was responding to intensive physiotherapy and function in his left arm and leg improved daily. The palsy affecting the right side of his face had almost completely vanished though there was a drooping of the corner of his mouth and a weakness of his facial muscles, more marked when he smiled, which he rarely did. There was little to smile about in November 1941. His personal career in the army seemed to be over and his vision of promotion and advancement in the paratroopers lay in shreds. Survival of Hitler's Third Reich was being sorely tested on the battlefields in Russia and, after Crete, his own regiment had been disbanded and the survivors were fighting as infantry on the Eastern Front. General Student kept command of the *Fallschirmjagger*, now only one division strong and based in three centres at Hildescheim, Potsdam and Minden. Colonel Count Erich von Bulow was camp commandant at Potsdam barracks, a sinecure appointment carrying no executive power. His thoughts were suddenly interrupted by a commotion in the corridor outside the door, a clatter of stamping boots and a shower of 'Heil Hitlers'.

The door burst open and in strode the recently promoted *Brigadführer* Otto Kaltenburger, a broad smile on his ugly face and his right arm extended in salute. With a sweep of his hand the general picked up a chair and parked himself at Manfred's bedside, placing a hand firmly and familiarly on his left thigh. With a lecherous wink he gave Manfred's thigh a squeeze and, looking straight into his eyes, asked:

"How goes it, Herr Major Schmidt?"

Manfred, visibly cringing under the unwelcome pressure on his left thigh, tried to wriggle free but thought better of it and allowed the psychopath's hand to remain in place.

"I am improving slowly, much too slowly for my liking. I want to get back into action again."

"That's the spirit," the Brigadier replied. "I am up in Berlin attending an SS anniversary rally. I called in our headquarters in Prinz Albrecht Strasse and they told me you were still here in our hospital. We had a parade yesterday attended by the Führer and a wonderful party last night in the Adlon. Not as good as our sessions at Hotel Wagram in Paris. I'm sure you'll remember the Wagram parties!"

Manfred nodded briefly in reply and Brigadier Kaltenburger continued, "Well now, I thought this would be a good opportunity to present you with these," he said fishing in his tunic pocket and producing two solid silver crowns. "Officially in the SS you are still a captain but it is within my authority to promote you. I hope you'll wear your black uniform with pride from time to time, especially here in our SS hospital. I hope they're treating you well. If you have any complaints just tell me and I'll put things right for you."

Manfred had plenty of complaints but thought it wiser to stay silent, especially as the Brigadier's hand was back on his left thigh again and edging upwards towards his groin.

"Well, Manfred, I expect you're wondering what's happened in Paris since you left? Our first raid, the one on Ponthieu Street, was a great success. After interrogation the Gestapo proved that the four young men and the two women were Jewish resistance fighters and they were shot in Orly Prison in February."

Manfred's pulse missed a beat with the realisation that poor little Lise, his Parisian lover, had been executed. Kaltenburger, completely unmoved, continued in a matter of fact voice, "Since that first raid we're carrying out at least one cordon and search exercise every week. By now I've arrested some fifteen hundred Jews and I've set up an internment camp for them in north Paris. We hold the captives there for two or three weeks for interrogation and then they're deported, or otherwise disposed of, depending on their crimes. At the rate we're going, in six months' time, Paris will be a Jewish free zone."

The Brigadier paused and guffawed, "And it all began, thanks to you, with our small little raid on Christmas Eve last year."

The Brigadier removed his hand from Manfred's thigh to look at his pocket watch. "Well, time flies, I must be away. By the way Stulpnagel and Göerdler are still in charge at Place de l'Opéra. They're not tough enough with the Froggies. Thank goodness we've got the SS and the Gestapo to exercise control over the French. I don't think the two at the Place de l'Opéra have their hearts in the job."

After a final squeeze of Manfred's thigh the *Brigadführer* rose and turned to leave, but stopped at the door.

"I hear that von Bulow called to see you earlier this month. I hope he's behaving himself. Manfred, you seem to be down in the dumps. What you need is a good screw. And I'm the man who can provide it for you. I'll arrange for you to have a special week in our SS Hotel at Lindau. All expenses paid. Courtesy of the SS. I'm sure you'll be a new man when you return."

After the revolting *Brigadführer* had left Manfred agreed with him on two points. He needed to get out of the oppressive SS hospital and he desperately needed a good screw to relieve his sexual frustration. If *Brigadführer* Otto Kaltenburger could achieve these two ends for him then the visit of the obnoxious SS officer would not have been a complete waste of time.

Three days later, on the 30th November, Manfred received another unwelcome visitor. Suitably clothed he was taking a stroll along the banks of the Havel when a flustered, white-coated ward orderly came running towards him.

"Come immediately to the director's office. There's a very important visitor to see you. I think it's the Führer. At least the party arrived in a large official Mercedes with six SS outriders."

Manfred turned on his heel and walked as fast as he could towards the main hospital, favouring his left leg, and thinking, 'The Führer! Is it really the Führer? And he's come especially to see me?'

Colonel Blumentritt's office was guarded by two SS sergeants with loaded guns across their chests and, breathless, he was ushered into the office by an SS staff captain. There was one man in the office standing behind the desk, legs apart and arms on his hips. It was not the Führer. The squat, pugnacious, overweight *Reichsleiter*, Martin Bormann, stood facing Manfred. Salutes and 'Heil Hitlers' were exchanged and Bormann opened the conversation.

"Herr Major Schmidt, have you sworn an oath of allegiance to the Führer?"

Manfred was taken aback.

"Yes, Herr *Reichsleiter*, three times – once in the Hitler Youth, once with Bavarian Hussars and a third time with my Eighth *Fallschirmjagger*."

The *Reichsleiter* accepted Manfred's reply as a matter of course.

"I am here today by personal order of the Führer on a special mission. Our conversation must not be repeated outside these four walls. Is that clear, Herr Major?"

"*Ja*, Herr *Reichsleiter*," Manfred replied with trepidation.

Martin Bormann continued, "You will recall our last meeting in Paris in July 1940 after the Grand Parade? You memorised a list of names at that meeting. How many can you remember now?"

Manfred, now thoroughly alarmed and aware of the *Reichsleiter's* treacherous nature, quickly decided to play dumb.

"I can only remember two or three, Herr *Reichsleiter*. I'm afraid the shrapnel wound to my head has caused me considerable difficulties with remembering things."

"Ach so, I understand," Bormann replied and continued, "You will forget all the names on the list except one. Our Führer is convinced that a group of high-ranking *Wehrmacht* officers are plotting to overthrow him. A few on the list I showed you have been dealt with and some of the others are innocent. But there's one name that keeps cropping up and that's your ex-commanding officer, Colonel Count Erich von Bulow. I wish you to give me your views on this officer."

A stony silence fell on the office. Manfred feverishly tried to sort out his thoughts in reply to the *Reichsleiter's* question. He decided to make his answer vague.

"I don't really have any evidence that Count von Bulow has been plotting against the Führer."

"Thank you, Major Schmidt. I expected that reply but I am going to give you some information which may make you change your mind." The *Reichsleiter* paused to take a deep breath and continued, "We have interviewed the Count on four occasions and, even under pressure, he denies any knowledge of subversive elements plotting against the Führer. He does however implicate your father, Gerhardt Schmidt and, to some extent, yourself."

Manfred's head was spinning. How could Colonel von Bulow even think about branding his father a traitor. His own Papi! The ever-dependable, fanatic Nazi, more loyal to the Führer than most Germans.

Manfred replied in a strong, counter-attacking voice, "Herr *Reichsleiter*, I categorically deny that my father was at any time plotting against the Führer."

Bormann gave a fleeting smile.

"I'm sure that is true, Herr Major Schmidt, but let me give you some more facts presented to me by Count von Bulow. Your father worked closely with Hess in Munich between the years 1929 and 1935 and we all know what happened to the traitor Hess. Your father was also a close companion of Ernst Röhm and we both know what he did to himself in Lansburg Prison in 1934, but most damning of all is the Count's allegation that your father tried to enlist him to join the traitors twice during his recruiting trips to Munich in 1937 and 1938. Is there any truth in these accusations against your father?"

Manfred, in a fury, exploded, "Truth, truth, it's all lies. How can Count von Bulow speak against my dead Papi? No, no. The truth is that, on three occasions after Operation *Weseruebung*, he has tried to get me to join in his group. As you may not be aware, Herr *Reichsleiter*, I have turned him down on each occasion."

Martin Bormann's face now wore a satisfied smile.

"Thank you, Major Schmidt, you have cleared up any doubts about your father. But tell me, who are in this group of traitors you mentioned, apart from the Count himself of course?"

Manfred replied quickly, to be sure he did not change his mind, "General Stulpnagel is definitely one and I think his staff officer, Colonel Heinz Gördeler, could be another."

The *Reichsleiter*, now more than satisfied with Manfred's replies, smiled.

"Excellent, excellent, Herr Major Schmidt. I will report your co-operation personally to the Führer. I know he will be more than grateful for your help. By the way how are you getting on? I know the Führer hopes you and all our wounded heroes will be fit to re-join the battle for our Fatherland in the near future. Heil Hitler."

The *Reichsleiter's* salute dismissed Manfred who returned, head bowed, to the privacy of his own room. He sat on the edge of his bed, holding his head in his hands. What had he done? Why had he pointed his finger at Colonel von Bulow? The old man had no right to utter false accusations against his dear Papi. And then another thought flashed into his mind. What if the devious *Reichsleiter* made up the stories about the Count and his father? Oh no! He could not bear to think about it. But before he finally fell into an exhausted sleep he became more and more convinced that he had been duped into making this confession. And what would be the consequences of his revelations to the *Reichsleiter*? He feared he had signed the death warrant of the loveable, roguish, charismatic Colonel Count Erich von Bulow.

The world was stunned by reports of a Japanese attack on the American naval base at Pearl Harbour at dawn on the morning of the 7th December, 1941. Some three hundred and twenty-seven American planes were immobilised on the ground, nine battle cruisers were sunk, and a further four badly damaged and over three thousand American servicemen were casualties. Within twenty-four hours America declared war on Japan and three days later Germany and Italy declared war on the USA, honouring the Tripartite Pact of September 1940. Reaction at the SS rehabilitation centre was mixed. Most of the officers anticipated that Japan's entry into the war might take the British east to defend their colonial possessions whilst others showed concern that the might of the American arsenal and manpower

434

might tip the scales in favour of the Allies. Manfred had no specific opinions on this new development. He was now mainly concerned about returning to active duty with his parachute regiment.

The SS rehabilitation centre was virtually a prison, surrounded on all sides by a fifteen foot, barbed-wire topped, wall guarded day and night by roving SS sentries. Access to the house was through a large, embossed, wrought-iron gate and a long, straight driveway bisecting open green lawns and shrubbery. The gates were under constant guard by SS personnel and visitors needed passes to come in and out of the *Krankenhaus*.

Colonel Blumentritt had established this exclusively SS officer rehabilitation centre in early 1940 for treatment of mental and psychological disorders and amputees on the premise that the latter, by virtue of their physical disability, also had psychological problems. He believed that physiotherapy was an important factor in the treatment of mental disorder. The type of patient at the centre reflected the colonel's medical interests. All thirty inmates were either mentally disorientated, shell-shocked or amputees and most were high-ranking SS officers. The centre was virtually a well-guarded mental asylum, run and controlled by Colonel Blumentritt, who was a strict disciplinarian. Signed permits were necessary in order to walk around the garden and alongside the Havel lake and passes for a night out in Berlin, or weekends away, were few and far between. During the sunny days of August and early September Manfred was allowed outside on the lawn to bask in the sunshine, always in the company of one of the physiotherapists. As autumn approached and days became shorter he was escorted on walks on the pathways along the banks of the Havel, but never allowed near the guarded entrance gates. By mid-September he was restless and his sexual urges were returning. All through the dark weeks of semi-coma Manfred woke sweating, screaming and shouting, sometimes with an erection, and usually with his familiar nightmare about an encounter with the female Bulgarian officer.

By mid-September he was able to arouse himself sexually by remembering encounters in the past and especially by recalling his introduction into adulthood by Erika on the train journey to Winterberg. His craving for female companionship grew daily but repeated requests to Colonel Blumentritt for a pass into Berlin went unrewarded.

On the 18th September, 1941, to celebrate capture of Kiev by von Manstein's Army Group South, Colonel Blumentritt arranged a formal party in the mess dining hall, where a sumptuous buffet was displayed on a long oak table.   Colonel Blumentritt, a short, dumpy, bald-headed, bespectacled man in his late forties, welcomed the officers to the celebration.   The inmates were dispersed haphazardly around the hall, gathered in small groups according to rank and, in some instances, according to their disability.

Manfred found himself in a corner with two depressed amputees, one of whom had lost both his feet in the early battles for Smolensk. The senior ranking SS officer present was Major General Kurt Walther who was a tall, thin man and in many ways resembled the lately defected deputy leader of the Nazi Party.   His resemblance to Rudolf Hess had endeared him to his colleagues, but rumour had it that, after Hess' defection in May 1941, the general had blown his top and was removed from active service to become an inmate of the SS Havel Rehabilitation *Krankenhaus*.

The order of toasts, schnapps downed in one gulp, was preordained by tradition.   General Walther, resplendent in his all-black uniform and silver lapel badges of rank, first proposed the Führer, then Heinrich Himmler, followed by the SS *Totenkopf* Division and finally Field Marshal von Runstedt and General Heinz Guderian, the 'conquerors of Kiev'.   Three more minor toasts were offered to SS commanders in the field, all unknown to Manfred, and then the assembled company descended on the buffet table.

The male physiotherapists acted as mess waiters and brought food and drink to the amputees as well as circulating amongst the mobile guests who were now polarised into small groups.   Manfred noted two, allegedly shell-shocked, SS *Totenkopf* majors sitting together, holding hands, whilst the major general stood angrily on his own, aloof and forbidding.

Amongst the male physiotherapy waiters, Manfred settled his gaze on Hans Bendinger, a slim, effeminate blond man in his early twenties who smilingly flitted here and there carrying drinks and fussing over his charges and, occasionally, outrageously flirting with the patients. Manfred noted that in all his perambulations Hans wandered back to Colonel Blumentritt's table, where, by a gesture or a nod, he was instructed by the colonel in which direction to conduct his next sally. There seemed to Manfred to be an invisible elastic band between the surgeon colonel and the orderly, like a puppet on a string, with Colonel Blumentritt manipulating the strings.

The smoke-filled mess hall became noisy and stuffy. Manfred, unused to alcohol for a long time, felt queasy and then for no accountable reason flew into an uncontrollable tantrum shouting and blaspheming, calling the SS 'bastards and shits'. He was then violently sick over the buffet table. Colonel Blumentritt's beady eyes, shielded by his thick horn-rimmed glasses, instructed Hans to act and he gently took Manfred's elbow leading him away from the mess to his bedroom cubicle.

"There, there, Sir. No harm done. Too much rich food in the mess anyway. Come on, Sir, let me get you to bed."

Hans undressed Manfred with loving care and tucked him into bed placing a light kiss on his forehead before returning to his waiting and entertainment duties in the mess hall.

On the following day, nursing a vicious hangover, Manfred only vaguely recalled the events of the previous evening. His reception in the mess was more antagonistic than usual and he was completely ostracised by his fellow patients. The only person to speak to him was Hans Bendinger who made light of the incident and insisted on being cheerful about the whole business. Within days Manfred was strangely drawn towards the effeminate, flirtatious young adonis and began confiding in him.

"Hans, I must have a woman. My life in here is oppressive and I feel I shall go mad if I don't get out soon. I think Blumentritt has a soft spot for you," noting the proud smile on Hans' face, "and perhaps you can arrange a pass for me to go into Berlin for a night out?"

Hans smiled at Manfred. "I'll see what I can do, Herr Major Schmidt. In the meantime if I can be of any service, you only have to ask," he added with a flirtatious grin.

Nothing happened about Manfred's request and, as the weeks monotonously passed, his frustration grew apace. He thought about escaping but the institute was too well-guarded and patrolled. The only way out was by boat across the Havel, but the boathouse was empty.

It seemed to Manfred that his sole friend in the institution was Hans, the sylph-like blond transvestite, who always had a kind word to offer and seemed prepared to offer more if requested. Manfred was tempted on many occasions to invite the young man to his bed but he managed to suppress his urges until a mess party on the 18th October. This party was ordered by Major General Kurt Walther to celebrate German victories at Bryansk and Vyasma involving General Guderian's Second Panzer Group and General Hoth's Third Panzer Group. General Walther supervised the toasting ceremonies. The format was an exact replica of the party of the 18th September, except that, in the absence of Colonel Blumentritt, Manfred had the undivided attention of Hans Bendinger.

He fussed over Manfred, pouting and posturing, plying him with drinks and food and from time to time making provocative suggestions. Manfred rapidly became pleasantly inebriated. The party soon split up into diverse groups, the two besotted *Totenkopf* majors holding hands and the austere major general sitting alone and frigid looking into the distance, as if expecting an immediate catastrophe. Manfred kept drinking schnapps as quickly as Hans could produce them and it seemed only natural that he should allow Hans to guide him back to his bedroom.

Once there he passed out on his bed and the following morning had little recollection of the previous night. He had a fleeting memory of another person lying beside him in bed and of the movement of tender sensuous fingers over his naked torso. In the morning he woke with a headache and a question in his mind...

'Did I or didn't I with Hans last night?'

The question was quickly answered by the smell of cheap cologne, favoured by Hans, on the bed-sheets and a tenderness and aching in his anal orifice. He felt ashamed but could not bring himself to castigate Hans, as he was equally responsible for the previous evening's debauchery.

During the first week of November permission was finally granted by Colonel Blumentritt for Manfred, accompanied by Hans, to have a night out on the town. The wily old colonel, now wishing to regain Hans' favour, wanted Manfred to have a night's freedom in the hope that he might become embroiled with some of the ladies of the night and Hans would return to the institution chastened and repentant and ready to rush back into his welcoming arms.

As it happened the night out was somewhat of a fiasco. For the first couple of hours Manfred and Hans were together in Club Eva, a strip club, which Hans found revolting but which provided erotic pleasure for Manfred. Eventually Hans departed to another club, a well known transvestite establishment, about half a mile down the *Kufurstendam*. Left to his own devices Manfred soon found an amiable female companion to share a drink with him and later to briefly share a bed in a grotty upstairs room in a small pension near Zooplatz. His companion was an experienced prostitute and within ten minutes she had divested him of two hundred Deutschmarks and had given him very little pleasure for his money. He returned to Club Eva and tried again to pick up another female but increasing inebriation and diminishing ardour soon overcame him and he set out to walk the four miles back to the clinic where the colonel admonished him for being late.

"Where is Hans Bendinger? He did go out with you, didn't he?"

Manfred murmured an almost inaudible *"Ja"* and with a stifled *"Guten nacht, mon Colonel"*, he staggered off to bed.

After the night out on the *Kufurstendam* Hans' attentions to Manfred waned dramatically. Like a lover spurned he now transferred his affections back to the ever-loyal surgeon colonel. Within ten days Manfred had to report to the colonel that he had pain and stinging on passing water and had a purulent discharge from his penis.

The colonel examined Manfred and proclaimed, "Gonococcal urethritis or, in lay terms, a dose of clap. Sulphonamides should clear it up in about ten days, but", with a gleeful smile, "you will have to abstain from sexual intercourse with females, or males, for two months. Is that clear, Herr Major Schmidt?"

Manfred had no choice in the matter. He would have to abide by the colonel's advice. Within forty-eight hours Hans Bendinger was dismissed from the rehabilitation centre and Manfred's remaining days in the clinic were spent as a recluse, rejected and spurned by the SS officers and desperately alone and confined to his quarters for most of the time. He reflected ruefully that he could not even recall the name of the young lady from the Club Eva who had so generously bestowed her favours and a dose of the clap on him.

Manfred's last month at the SS rehabilitation centre in Berlin was a nightmare. His physical condition improved and, apart from a tendency to sudden right-sided headaches and a slight weakness of his left hand and left leg, he was nearly restored to normal. It came as a great relief when a medical board, on the 17th December, 1941, decided he was fit to return to non-combatant duties and arrangements were made for his transfer to Colonel von Bulow's Parachute divisional headquarters at Potsdam. He was pleased to be free from the shackles which held him prisoner in the SS rehabilitation centre for the past two months.

*

Manfred arrived at Potsdam divisional headquarters on the evening of December 22nd, 1941, where he received a generous welcome from the commanding officer, *Feldwebel* Schneider and Sergeant Fritz Schultz, the officers' mess chef. To ease his re-introduction into active service Colonel von Bulow made Manfred president of the officers' mess where he was responsible for catering arrangements and for smooth running of the mess. His appointment was a 'cushy number' and gave him ample time to rest and to attend daily physiotherapy sessions at Potsdam Military Hospital.

Over Christmas most of the officers, including the two colonels, went on leave for a week and, apart from three junior duty officers, Manfred had the mess to himself. The loyal mess chef stayed on duty to cater for the culinary needs of the four officers who remained in barracks. They had a quiet celebration on Christmas Eve and went to the sergeants' mess for a carol concert. By long-standing tradition, on Christmas day, the officers waited on the men in the mess hall. All in all, the Christmas celebrations were subdued, mainly influenced by unconfirmed reports of a German retreat on the Eastern Front and heavy casualties amongst the infantry from frostbite and sub-Arctic conditions on the ice-bound terrain in Russia.

Colonel von Bulow returned unexpectedly on the 29th December. On the 27th he had accompanied General Student to a conference at Hitler's headquarters at Wolfshanze in eastern Prussia. Hitler was completely irrational and domineering, raving and shouting at the general staff and issuing orders for troop movements and even counter-attacks, which the generals knew could not be fulfilled by the depleted, demoralised and frost-bitten German armies. Colonel von Bulow was amazed at the venom with which the Führer attacked his general staff, berating them for lack of willpower and initiative and castigating them for disobeying his orders. He was bitterly disappointed that Leningrad and Moscow had not been taken and that the Russian oilfields and Stalingrad were still out of reach of his hitherto victorious armies.

Colonel von Bulow confided in Manfred, "Wolfshanze is not the place to be in at the moment. Our Leader is insane and heads have already rolled and there will be many more to follow. None of the general staff are in a safe position and the high command, including Jodl and Keitel, are in a state of great anxiety waiting for the axe to fall. Kurt Student and I were glad to be out of there. The position on the Eastern Front is grave, but not yet critical. Leningrad is surrounded by our troops and there will be stalemate there for the rest of the winter. Our forces in the centre around Moscow are slowly retreating and digging in about forty miles west of the city. In the south von Runstedt's army is dug in for the winter on the banks of the Donets.

"Our Leader is now planning his next big offensive for the spring and the main thrust will be in the south to take Stalingrad and the Caucasian oilfields. We're very short of manpower but by the spring the Southern Front will be reinforced by Hungarian, Italian, and two Rumanian Armies. The quality of these satellite troops is open to question. That's why General Student was invited to Wolfshanze. Jodl demanded a division of three thousand *Fallschirmjagger* for deployment to Stalingrad in April. Brigadier Ramcke will be promoted to general and will command the division. Colonel Werner will be in command of one of the regiments. I will stay here in command at Potsdam and you will be my second in command with, of course, promotion to colonel. We shall have very few *Fallschirmjagger* left to look after, probably, with recruits, about two thousand men and most of these will eventually be used as *Wehrmacht* infantry reserves. I am very saddened, Manfred, when I see the cream of my fighting men being sent as cannon fodder to the Eastern Front. I cannot see us winning this war in Russia. If we survive this winter our forces will be so exhausted they will not be fit to move until May or June and then, if we don't get a quick victory, next winter will kill off all hopes of beating Ivan."

The old colonel was dejected and crestfallen, singularly lacking in his usual bonhomie and verve. He continued, "I'm afraid, Manfred, our Leader is mad and he will bring Germany to its knees. I truly believe, and my view is shared by many of the high command, that we should try and get rid of him and bring this war against Russia to a peaceful end."

This was the first time Manfred had heard the colonel preach mutiny, though he suspected von Bulow had been anti-Hitler in the early days. He would not condone treachery and replied, "I am certain, Herr Colonel, that the Führer knows what he's doing and that he will lead us to victory over the Soviet Union next year. After that we'll take England. After all the Führer so far has fulfilled all his promises to the German people. I believe in him!"

Now that the colonel had brought up the subject, Manfred thought it might be an opportune moment to bring up the matter of his father's loyalty to the Führer.

"Colonel von Bulow, you knew my father well. Did you think at any time he might have been disloyal to the Führer?"

The colonel replied, "What a strange question! I can't imagine you would have any doubts about your father's loyalty to the Leader. Why do you ask?"

Manfred had rehearsed his answer but now had to concoct a lie to cover the reason for his query.

"Oh, it came out in conversation at the SS hospital. General Walther tried to make allegations about my father's close connections with the traitor Hess between 1929 and 1935 in Munich."

"Balderdash," Colonel von Bulow shouted. "Your father was a staunch Nazi and, although I did not agree with his politics, I admired his complete loyalty to Adolf Hitler."

Manfred felt deflated and nauseated. Without a doubt his revelations to Martin Bormann would produce unpleasant consequences, and possibly imprisonment or death, for Colonel von Bulow. The colonel concluded the conversation.

"Talking of loyalty to our Leader I can tell you that in the past three months I have had unwelcome visits from the SS and Gestapo. I told the shits to go away and disappear up their own arseholes," he gave a short nervous grunt, not of levity, but of a man experiencing overwhelming anxiety.

New Year's Eve 1942 was celebrated with a modest party and a banquet in the officers' mess at Potsdam. General Student attended. Depressing news from the front cast a morbid gloom over the occasion. The party broke up shortly after midnight and by 1 a.m. on the 1st January, 1942 the mess was empty and silent, left to Sergeant

Shultz and his staff, who wandered around aimlessly mopping up dregs of alcohol and generally clearing the crockery and uneaten food from the dining room tables. During the hard icy winter months from early January to well into April the *Fallschirmjagger* stationed at Potsdam were in training, preparing for their move to the Eastern Front to be used as infantry. Manfred was appointed acting training major, responsible for the organisation of the *skischule* at Winterberg and for ground exercises in the Potsdam area.

Colonel von Bulow was again active in recruitment and away on frequent missions to all parts of Germany and to German units in France, Greece and the Balkans. Colonel von Bulow's heart was not in the recruitment campaign and he spoke about his misgivings to Manfred:

"I don't like what I'm doing at the present time. Recruiting men for the parachute regiment was fine, but now I'm only using the title to entice young men to enlist and to be sent to almost certain death on the Russian front. It makes me sick to think about it. In any case most of the units I visit are aware of what's happening and realise that none of the volunteers will get their wings. I am sorry to say that I am always pleased to come away from a recruitment meeting without recruiting anybody."

Manfred realised that the old man was cracking up, losing interest in the war, openly disillusioned with leadership of the Third Reich and ready to revolt against the Führer himself. Manfred felt the colonel might be in danger and confided his suspicions to Colonel Werner, who agreed that the commanding officer needed careful watching.

Twice a week Manfred attended the physiotherapy department at Potsdam Military Hospital for treatment of his weakened left arm. After a few visits he realised that he had fallen in love with his physiotherapist, a beautiful tall, slim, blonde-haired, blue-eyed, vivacious twenty-four year old woman who massaged him with the gentlest of touches. Apart from his affair with Lise Frank he had never felt like this about a female in all his years. His feelings towards Frau Giesela Steinfurt were not purely sexual. He wanted the woman to himself and forever but his ardour was not reciprocated. Though Giesela was prepared for some superficial flirtation, she had recently married a young surgeon who was second-in-command of the surgical division at Potsdam Hospital. Manfred, who had hitherto demanded sex from his female companions or forced himself upon them without invitation, now resorted to various ploys to try and bed the gorgeous Giesela. Gifts of chocolate and flowers were accepted with thanks and a beautiful smile but kissing and cuddling was '*strangsten verboten*'.

Manfred had mental reservations about his sexual prowess. He had not had a sexual relationship since leaving the Havel clinic and had lingering doubts about transferring his venereal infection, especially to such a desirable female. In the past he would not have given this consideration a second thought but with Giesela things were entirely different. He was in love and desired this gorgeous creature more than anything else in the world. His passion grew with every visit to the physiotherapy clinic, but Giesela remained unresponsive. She was happy and content with her surgeon husband and, although she found Manfred interesting and handsome, in a rugged, way, she was never tempted to break her marriage vows. She enjoyed flirting and receiving attention from the gallant major but her interests in him cut off sharply at this point. Manfred kept pressing his suit and tried all the tricks he could think of to lure the blonde Venus into bed. Never having experienced rejection, he was unable to comprehend why Giesela would not succumb to the charms and good looks of a virile *Fallschirmjagger* major and a hero of the Cretan campaign. By early March 1942 he was desperate to requite his love and proposed elopement and eventual marriage to the voluptuous physiotherapist.

Giesela realised that things were getting out of hand and arranged for a male physiotherapist to take on the patient. Her selection was deliberate. Otto Beckman was a swarthy, dark-faced, unshaven brute who believed in deep and painful massage therapy. After two visits Manfred gave up treatment and Giesela disappeared from his life. Her memory and his deep love for her, however, was to linger on for many months.

One day in early May 1942 Otto Kaltenburger, the SS *Brigadführer*, appeared at the airborne barracks at Potsdam requesting to see Manfred. He was coolly received by Colonel von Bulow who detested the SS and was of the opinion that all their officers were pimps and prostitutes. Brigadier Kaltenburger was pleased to see Manfred and, in a private interview, offered him promotion if he would transfer to the SS and return to supervise German anti-resistance campaigns in France. Manfred considered that, with his weak left arm, his future in the Airborne Division might be compromised and was sorely tempted to take up the offer. He agreed to spend a few days thinking over the *Brigadführer's* proposal. When he mentioned the offer to Colonel von Bulow the old man burst into a torrent of abuse.

"Manfred, never, never. You must not join those bastards. They'll destroy you. I forbid you to leave the regiment and that's final. You do not have my permission to transfer to the SS. They'll dangle promotion before you like a carrot. I can assure you that I'll get you promoted. You'll become one of the youngest colonels in the airborne division, if not the whole *Wehrmacht*. Stay with me, my boy."

Colonel von Bulow's pleadings saved the day and Manfred declined *Brigadführer* Kaltenburger's offer. The SS general also made another offer – ten days' leave in a rest-camp for the SS in Lindau, hoping that a break amongst SS officers might help sway Manfred's decision to join his staff in Paris. With Colonel von Bulow's permission Manfred accepted the Brigadier's offer. He was tired and needed to get away from his amorous embroilment with Giesela. Yes, he needed a break and some time to think. On May 7th, 1942 Manfred left for his ten day recuperation leave at the SS Hotel Arbeitsende in Lindau.

Hotel Arbeitsende, Lindau, 7th to 17th May, 1942

The *Schutzstaffel*, Adolf Hitler's personal army, expanded from battalion strength in 1934 by assimilation of the murdered Ernst Röhm's SA Brownshirts, to become an elite corps of thirty thousand men by the outbreak of war. As guardians of the Führer and the Nazi regime and commanded by Heinrich Himmler since 1930, the SS regarded themselves as superior to all other military and naval organisations, including the Waffen SS and the *Wehrmacht*. The SS also accumulated privileges that were the rewards of their elitist station. Before 1939 they appropriated *schlosses*, castles and large hotels at various sites throughout Germany, and these establishments were used for the sole purpose of accommodating SS officers and their families. Hitler's desire to produce a pure Germanic race prompted Himmler to designate four of these properties for the purpose of procreation between pure Aryan females and selected SS officers and, unbeknown to Manfred, Hotel Arbeitsende at Lindau was one of these. Selection of an SS officer to act as stud in a sex farm was considered an honour bestowed by the Führer and an ultimate service to the Third Reich. As a non-SS officer Manfred's selection was unthinkable but he was highly recommended by SS *Brigadführer* Kaltenburger and his blond hair and blue eyes were testimony to his pure Aryan ancestry.

The train journey from Potsdam through Brandenburg, Magdeburg and on to Zelst took four hours and a charabanc ride from Zelst to the hotel in Lindau took thirty minutes. From Magdeburg to Zelst the train carriage was full of a mixture of young and middle-aged, black-uniformed, SS officers of various rank, all fine examples of the fair-haired, blue-eyed Teutonic race. On the train Manfred was ignored, but on the charabanc a few of the younger officers engaged him in polite conversation, once it was evident that, to their complete surprise, the airborne major was to be their companion for ten days. Manfred gathered from his talkative neighbours that the purpose of the trip was a complete rest and a holiday and a chance for female companionship before many of them had to return to the fighting on the Eastern Front. The charabanc arrived at the hotel at Lindau at 4 p.m. on the 7th May, 1942.

Hotel Arbeitsende was an old converted *schloss*, enclosed within a moat, with extensive green lawns around the main building and about thirty numbered guest cottages dotted along the footpaths leading from the lodge to the hotel. New arrivals, twenty-eight in number, champagne glasses in hand, were greeted in a large reception room by SS Colonel Frankerich.

"Gentlemen, you are here for ten days as my guests. You will have plenty to eat and drink and I shall arrange female company for you. Tonight and every night we shall all dine together to get to know each other. The waitresses at the table, the cooks and the cleaning staff here are all young hand-picked German ladies. They are not to be touched or molested in any way in the *schloss*. Now drink up and go to your rooms for a rest. Put on your best uniforms and come to the dining hall by 7 p.m. for an aperitif. Dinner will be served promptly at 7.30 p.m. I will explain further procedures at the dinner table."

As ordered Manfred came downstairs from his comfortable bedroom at precisely seven o'clock. He was greeted at the door of the mess hall by Colonel Frankerich and took a glass of wine from a tray held by a smiling, tall, thin-waisted, blonde woman dressed in a white blouse and a long dark skirt. In the mess ante-room the SS officers were chatting and joking amongst themselves and, circulating amongst the guests with drinks and canapés, were about ten blonde females all dressed in white blouses and dark skirts with diamond Nazi brooches in their lapels. All the waitresses were typical Aryan females, and Manfred later learned they were all voluntarily recruited for entertainment of the SS officers. The dinner was a protracted affair of five courses served by the silent humourless waitresses. Wine was dispensed sparingly and smoking after the meal was discouraged. The serving wenches departed after coffee and the doors were locked. Colonel Frankerich offered two toasts, one to the Führer and one to Heinrich Himmler. After ten minutes' idle chatter the colonel rose to his feet:

"Gentlemen, we now come to the purpose of your holiday here. You have seen our ladies, all selected for their beauty and breeding, and all volunteers to serve the Führer by offering their bodies to you in the hope, and certainty, that they will become pregnant and produce Aryan babies to be reared by the State. We do not want emotional involvement with the ladies. You will act as studs. That does not mean you must not enjoy yourselves, so please do. In the past we tried pairing off couples for a week but this led to complaints and jealousies. So we now have a method of random selection which means that the chances of any of you sleeping with the same person twice is very remote. This method also helps the girls as they are never sure who is the father of their child. Germany needs men of pure stock to continue the fight against the Bolsheviks. So go to it tonight, and every night, for the next ten days and think male. Produce boys if you can! By the way, for those interested there will be an afternoon session each day for volunteers. I repeat – these girls are clean and wholesome and they are not to be abused or maltreated. They are volunteers and not prostitutes. So go to it."

A papier mâché replica of the lower torso of a female with its legs wide apart was produced from under the table and, as each officer's name was called he approached the table and turned a handle protruding from the effigy's navel which eject a numbered key from a vertical slot between the outstretched legs.

On the first night Manfred drew No. 21 and made his way to the small hut in the grounds which was in complete darkness. When he entered the darkened room he sensed that there was a body lying under the bed-sheets. A timid, "*Guten abend, mein* Herr", confirmed that the person in the bed was female. He undressed quickly and jumped into bed beside the naked figure. No words were spoken and the preliminary exploration of each other's bodies only took a minute. As soon as Manfred achieved an erection the girl spread her legs and allowed him to penetrate. Copulation was brief and the girl clasped in his arms was completely unresponsive. She would not allow kissing or other means of sexual stimulation. Afterwards he used his fingers to outline the nether regions of his bed-mate. She was stockily built with thick, muscle-bound thighs and firm buttocks. After intercourse for the second time he fell asleep and by the time he awoke in the morning the girl had left, having carefully folded his uniform and underclothes and shirt on the back of a chair.

At breakfast he tried to imagine which of the blonde serving ladies had been his companion on the previous night. He was told at breakfast by one of the SS officers that there were at least ten more females in Hotel Arbeitsende than males, which allowed for sickness and the vagaries of the female menstrual cycle. He was also told that once pregnancy was confirmed at three months, the girls were taken away to a maternity unit at Magdeburg to produce their Aryan prodigy. Manfred attended three of the afternoon sessions only but did not miss any of the nightly assignments.

Time passed quickly and Manfred was beginning to enjoy a sense of sexual freedom which came with uninhibited sex. He thought a lot about Giesela and sometimes imagined in the dark that he was in bed with her. With her clean Aryan looks and superb body she would have been an excellent concubine for the Nazi sex farm. He shuddered at the thought that Giesela might take part in this sexual charade and end up in bed each night with a different partner, especially some of the more repugnant SS officers. In many ways he was sorry that the ten days were coming to an end. He had certainly achieved sexual fulfilment but not sexual enjoyment. The whole business was too cold and calculating. Before he left Lindau to return to Potsdam on the tenth day, Colonel Frankerich wished him luck and thanked him for his service to the Führer and SS *Reichsführer* Heinrich Himmler.

General Ramcke's airborne division left Potsdam barracks on May 22nd 1942 bound for the Don Basin to reinforce General Paulus' Sixth

Army destined to advance on Stalingrad. Colonel Heinz Werner commanded the remnants of the combined Seventh and Eighth Parachute Regiments. This left some twelve hundred men in the Potsdam barracks under Colonel von Bulow's command and the numerical strength of the brigade was gradually whittled away almost daily by demands for reinforcements for the Russian front.

Manfred gave up any hope of seeing Giesela again. He was bored and wanted to move. The order which saved his sanity came on the 12th June, 1942 from General Student's headquarters in Berlin:

"Colonel von Bulow is to provide a major or lieutenant colonel. Duties – organisation of counter-resistance against Cretan irregulars in Heraklion and eastern Crete."

When Colonel von Bulow offered Manfred the post he accepted with alacrity, excited by the thought of promotion. Before leaving he thanked the colonel for his support over the years and made one request.

"I wonder, Sir, if you would allow me to take *Feldwebel* Schneider with me to Crete. He will never be fit for front-line duty but he could be my bodyguard."

Colonel von Bulow thought for a few seconds.

"Manfred, I think it would be a good idea for you to take Schneider with you. I will arrange his posting and rail warrants. Now that the parachute divisions are decimated I feel my days here are numbered and they will soon force me to retire. When that happens I want to be sure that my best men are in secure jobs. I also hear that there may be political pressure to get rid of me. *C'est la guerre!* I wish you and Schneider every good fortune in Crete and many congratulations on your promotion, when it comes. Now let's go down to the mess and have a damned good drink to drown my sorrows and celebrate your forthcoming promotion."

General Student's cable suggested there might be promotion for Manfred in the immediate future. Colonel von Bulow was pleased for his young protégé and reminded Manfred that he had been in Crete a year or so previously. Manfred had no recollection whatever of his flight to Crete or of the time he spent in Greece and Athens in May 1941. Successive military governors on Crete had habitually used airborne officers to command counter-resistance activities on the premise that they were the ones who had suffered most at the hands of Cretan irregulars during the airborne campaign in May 1941.

Manfred's responsibilities were to organise the defence of Heraklion, its port and airfield and to police the eastern part of Crete, which was largely occupied by the Italian Siena Division commanded by General Angelo Carta.

Manfred flew from Berlin's Templehof airfield to Rome on the 23rd June, 1942. He spent a night in Rome as a guest of the officers of the Fifth Alpine Division and on the following day completed a three-hour flight across the Adriatic to Athens. He spent two days at divisional headquarters in Hotel Bretagne in Constitution Square and was taken to visit the Acropolis and Cape Sunion. The change in temperature as he flew south was remarkable and he was issued with tropical kit consisting of a short-sleeved shirt and khaki shorts. He also took to wearing sun glasses to protect his weakly eyes from the blazing sun. The final hop from Eleusis airfield took one and a half hours and at 10 a.m. on Wednesday 27th June, 1942 he arrived in Heraklion and was driven to Colonel Müller's headquarters at Knossos, twelve kilometres south of the city.

During the flight between Athens and Crete Manfred had time to reflect on the mental and physical change he had witnessed in Colonel Count von Bulow. The grand old man was visibly wilting under pressure. He was gaunt and drawn and had lost a lot of weight. But of more importance was his loss of spirit and courage, the hallmarks Manfred had known and admired since 1938. Five weeks after arriving in Crete Manfred was not surprised to hear that, in traditional Prussian fashion, Colonel Count Erich von Bulow had committed *sippenhaft* and shot himself in his quarters at Potsdam. The official reason for his suicide was that he had developed an incurable disease. Unofficially he was under increasing pressure from the Gestapo and SS who were investigating him for treason and plotting to exterminate Adolf Hitler.

BOOK TWO

Chapter Twenty

Organisation of German Resistance, Eastern Crete 1942 – 1943

Obersturmbahnführer Manfred Schmidt arrived by a Junker JU-88 in Heraklion at 8.30 a.m. on 27th June, 1942. He knew from his war records he had made this flight a year earlier but had no recollection whatsoever of his previous visit which led to a Knight's Cross, a medal he now proudly displayed around his neck. As ordered, Manfred reported to the garrison commander at Heraklion, Colonel Heydrich Müller, at Villa Ariadne, some ten kilometres to the south and overlooking the archaeological excavations at Knossos. Manfred found the colonel in his shirt sleeves, sitting at a table on the verandah, with a panoramic view over the Minoan excavation site and the olive and orange groves extending northwards to the town of Heraklion. Salutes were exchanged and Manfred was invited to sit at a table and offered a cup of ersatz coffee.

Colonel Müller was a red-faced, balding, bull-necked man with a habit of thrusting his square, bristly chin forwards when making a point in conversation. Manfred waited. The colonel set down his coffee cup on a table and unfolded a map of Crete.

"*Obersturmbahnführer* Schmidt, you have been sent to me on the recommendation of General Braüer and your commanding officer, Colonel Count Erich von Bulow. I know you have been here before," eyeing Manfred's Knight's Cross with envy, "and I'm sure you'll do a good job for me. I had to sack your predecessor for lack of moral fibre."

Manfred knew that Major Weisman had been sent packing by Müller for his lack of aggression in dealing with Cretan insurgents.

"You have been appointed counter-espionage officer for Heraklion and east Crete. Let me show you your operational area," and both men bent forwards to study the map on the table. "Our territory is bounded by a line extending from Heraklion southwards along the road running through Knossos, Arkalohorio and Viannos to the south coast. The central and western commanders are responsible for covering the territory to the west of this line. As you will see there's only one town of note on the south coast, here at Ierapetra, and the main concentration of our forces is along the northern coastal plain.

"There are two problems facing us at present. One is the Italians and their lack of enthusiasm for counter-espionage activities and the other is the *andartes* who roam around unchallenged on the Dikti and Lasithi mountain ranges. There are two main bands of *andartes*, the nationalists under Bandouvas who hide in the Diktis and Militades Porphyroyennis, who uses the Lasithis for his hideout. These two resistance groups need to be crushed, or better still, perhaps you could set one against the other. There's no love lost between the Cretan *kapitans* and feuds between their families goes back for centuries. Much as it goes against the grain, I think we might be better off cultivating the communist with an unpronounceable name. Perhaps if we give him arms he might save us the trouble of dealing with Bandouvas' nationalists."

By now the burly, overweight, out-of-condition colonel was perspiring profusely with drips of sweat plummeting from the tip of his nose on to the spread-out map. The colonel continued, "The Italians are a miserable lot. Their general, Angelo Carta, and his whore are billeted in Neapolis. Carta is commanding officer of the Fifth Siena and Second Alpine divisions and has some thirty thousand men at his disposal. They're in control at Ierapetra in the south and Neapolis, Malia, Sitia, Aghios Nikolaos and Elounda on the north coast. Their troops are only active in the mornings and, after a long siesta, they withdraw to their garrison towns at dusk.

"Heraklion is entirely under our control and we have companies posted at five sites in eastern Crete, one at each of the ports, in Sitia, Elounda and Malia and two inland at Kastelli and Katohorio on the road between Aghios Nikolaos and Ierapetra. The companies at Sitia, Elounda and Malia are there to protect naval and telegraphy installations. The *Luftwaffe* supply us with Storch spotter planes on request and similarly the *Kriegsmarine* will co-operate with E-boat sweeps as needed.

"Major Schmidt, I have been here now for six months and have got nowhere in my ambition to crush the Cretan traitors and get the Italians to do a better job in their district. You have been highly recommended and I'm sure that you will not let me down."

Manfred smiled inwardly thinking, 'Here speaks an ambitious man who is after promotion and will use any means at his disposal to attain his goal.'

The perspiring colonel sat down and refilled his coffee cup.

"Have you any questions, *Obersturmbahnführer* Schmidt?"

Manfred remained silent for a few moments. He was also beginning to feel uncomfortable and his shirt, under the buttoned-up tunic, was saturated with sweat.

"Only two questions at the moment, Sir. Firstly, where will I be based and secondly, how many men will I have at my disposal?"

The colonel replied, "You will use this house as your headquarters but you may, in due course, decide to set up a second base somewhere in your territory. As far as men are concerned we have thirty thousand German troops on Crete at present. Twenty-five thousand are in the western sector and we have five thousand in Heraklion district. *Oberkommando der Wehrmacht* has already decided to reinforce Festung Kriti and by the end of the year we expect that there will be nearly fifty thousand men on Crete and that we shall have fifteen thousand of these based at Heraklion."

The two officers then sat down for ten minutes of inconsequential chat about mutual acquaintances and then Colonel Müller again returned to his plans for Manfred's operations.

"I suggest you settle in here for two or three days and enjoy the sun. When *Feldwebel* Schneider arrives he will be billeted near your quarters. I understand he's your bodyguard. Once you've settled in I suggest you take a platoon of motorcyclists and do an in-depth reconnaissance of your district. The Hundredth Mountain Regiment in Heraklion will provide you with a well-trained and dependable cadre. Go and visit our Italian commanders. Have a look at our outlying companies in the Italian zone. Call on the *Kriegsmarine* captain in Heraklion and the *Luftwaffe* colonel at the airfield. Under no circumstances must you go high into the Dikti or Lasithi mountains.

If you did go, probably nothing would happen, but we don't want to provoke the bandits and, if you run into trouble, try and get out without a fight. Be very careful around Ierapetra. The Italians there are frightened to go out in the daytime, let alone at night. I haven't been there myself for over two months. Report back to me in ten days." He paused and then continued, "I wonder if you could help me with a problem at this HQ. The food here is diabolical and if you could use your influence to produce a good chef from somewhere it would be much appreciated."

Manfred surmised that the corpulent colonel was fond of his food and immediately thought of Sergeant Fritz Schultz languishing in the barracks at Lübbecke.

'Why not?' he thought. 'Why not arrange for Schultz to be transferred?'

And so it happened that a message was sent requesting transfer of *Fallschirmjagger* Sergeant Fritz Schultz to headquarters' mess of General Operations East Crete, based at Villa Ariadne in Knossos.

Obersturmbahnführer Manfred Schmidt's mobile column took off from the villa in a cloud of dust early one morning in early July with the warm Adriatic sun already beginning to force its searing hot rays into the hard-baked and scorched earth. At point there were two motorcyclists with machine guns mounted in side-cars. Manfred's open *Kübelwagen* also housed a machine gun in the rear where *Feldwebel* Schneider sat precariously with his knees wrapped around the plinth of the gun. Behind them came eight other cyclists and sidecar combinations of the Hundredth Mountain Regiment, each vehicle equipped with a mounted SMG. Food and ammunition for the convoy came in a half ton truck at the rear of the column. The fire power of the small cadre was awesome as, apart from machine guns, each soldier carried a *Schmeitzer* sub-machine gun and hand grenades.

The recce party moved quickly, the main obstacle to rapid advancement being the cloud of dust which the leading vehicle produced to coat the goggles and combat tunics of the men in the vehicles behind. Manfred recced the periphery of his domain and took the group south from Knossos around the lower Dikti mountains, through the mountain village of Arkalohorio and then around the western promontory of the Diktis to reach Viannos by dusk. They made camp for the night in an olive grove some five kilometres outside the village. During the day's trek Manfred had seen a dozen or so Cretans riding mules and a few women and children in the square near the church at Arkalohorio. Standing on the open-topped *Kübelwagen* with his blond hair flowing gently in the breeze Manfred felt like Caesar leading his troops into battle.

The next day the small convoy travelled along the south coast road to Ierapetra, where Manfred met the Italian garrison colonel. Colonel Vittoro Conti was sunbathing when the dusty column arrived, unchallenged by any of the garrison soldiers who seemed totally unperturbed by the arrival of their unexpected visitors. Colonel Conti regained his composure quickly. He arranged for his German visitors to bathe and clean up and organised a sumptuous lunch in honour of a visit from such a senior German officer. Suitably wined and dined the column moved eastwards along the coast and at Anapoli turned northwards through Lathines and Marohia on the Lasithi plateau to reach Sitia in the north by dusk. Encounters with Cretans along the road were confined to farmers and, in the towns, women, children and priests. The night in Sitia was spent with the German garrison company based in the dock area. There were five thousand Italians in the garrison but little rapport between the Italians and the Germans. The *Wehrmacht* guarded the docks and approaches to the harbour.

The German captain in charge of the small garrison was disgruntled and disillusioned and held no respect for the Italians who, in his opinion, were lazy, untrustworthy and mainly interested in womanising. The Italian commander, a full colonel, refused to see Manfred which irritated him considerably, but he decided to let matters rest until he had completed his reconnaissance.

On the following day the column proceeded eastwards through Paleokastro to Vai to visit a Germany section guarding a radio installation at the easternmost point of Crete. Here the atmosphere was distinctly different. The officer in charge, Captain Bremen, gave glowing reports of the morale of his troops and how they all looked forward to a posting to Vai. One look at the place convinced Manfred that this must be one of the most desirable situations in which a fighting soldier could find himself. A small palm-fringed, sandy bay with crystal clear water made the base an idyllic location. Manfred was so obsessed by the place that his troop remained for two days, royally entertained, fed and cared for by Captain Drexler and his men. On the second day they visited the wireless station on a remote rocky point four kilometres north of Vai. The approaches to the station were well-guarded and the amenities at the listening post were excellent. When Manfred's column was about to depart Captain Drexler made a telling comment.

"Sir, morale here is good because we have no fornicating Italians to bother us."

Time came to leave Vai and the column retraced its steps along the north coastal road past Sitia towards Aghios Nikolaos and Elounda. About fifty kilometres west of Sitia they came to a junction of the main coast road and the southbound road to Ierapetra, guarded by a platoon of paratroopers based at Katohorio. The young lieutenant in charge re-enforced Manfred's suspicions that the Italians rarely moved out of their garrisons and the only predictable traffic through their junction, twice a day, were German supply convoys going to Sitia and Vai. Only rarely did a strike column of Italian infantry come through their check point and never after dark.

By nightfall Manfred's column had reached Aghios Nikolaos where he met a German liaison officer billeted with the Italian garrison. Captain Anton Beckenbauer was a disillusioned man. The Italians in the town, some two thousand strong, had no inclination to instigate belligerent action against the local communist-led *andartes*. In fact they had settled into a state of peaceful co-existence with the Bolsheviks. Captain Beckenbauer hinted that, if anything should happen, the whole Italian garrison at Aghios Nikolaos would throw down their arms and join Porphyroyennis's ELAS *andartes*.

The convoy moved northwards to Elounda, a distance of some twelve kilometres. This picturesque Cretan fishing port was guarded by a company of the SS *Totenkopf* Regiment. Four kilometres outside the port Manfred's column was halted by an efficient and surly sergeant who demanded identification and made a thorough search of the convoy. Allowed to proceed they were again stopped three times at check points on the only passable road into Elounda. Manfred was pleased by the thoroughness of their checks and when they reached the port he was even more impressed by the number of eager young soldiers in the town guarding strategic points around the harbour. The harbour at Elounda was a perfect haven for light shipping. The small harbour town was guarded at its eastern side by the elongated island of Spinalonga, which created an inland lagoon suitable for flying boat landings. On the dockside Manfred met the company commander, Captain Rudolf Schlemburg, a stand-offish, supercilious and arrogant officer who reluctantly bowed to Manfred's superior rank and paid inordinate homage to the Knight's Cross around his neck. Hospitality from the *Totenkopf* Company was austere, starchy and formal. Manfred and his troop were pleased to leave the next morning, and *Feldwebel* Schneider remarked, "If you want to stay in Crete don't pick Elounda. Select one of the Italian held towns. At least there you'll get spaghetti and a good grind."

On the following day the column moved westwards to Neapolis, to General Angelo Carta's headquarters, where they were cordially received. They arrived at midday and the general was still in his dressing gown attended by a voluptuous Italian signorina who fussed over him and pampered the balding, monocled, rotund little man. Some fine Italian wine was quickly forthcoming and the general was obviously out to please the tall, blond Teutonic major with his impressive decorations. Even more so he was anxious to avoid the possibility of contact between Manfred and his live-in prostitute Maria who flashed her eyes and wiggled her hips at the dashing paratroop major. General Carta resolved the situation in one fell swoop.

"You must speak to my expert in this field, my counter-espionage officer, Captain Franco Tavana. He knows all about local problems with the *andartes*," and with a gesture of dismissal the general yawned, made eyes at Maria and rose to return to the bed chamber.

Captain Tavana, when he appeared some ten minutes later, was a prototype Italian gigolo, suave, dark-eyed, sophisticated and persistently plausible. Manfred took to him immediately. Yes, the captain realised the Italians were not pulling their weight but he could do nothing about it. Yes, he would be pleased to galvanise the Italian garrisons into proper action. Yes, he would very much like to co-operate with Manfred to improve relationships between the German and Italian forces. Manfred left General Carta's headquarters with a distinct feeling that Captain Franco Tavana, the counter-espionage officer of the Fifth Siena Division, was his man and a valuable ally.

On the way back to Heraklion the convoy stopped for an hour at Malia. Major Enzio Berganzoli refused to be disturbed. He was in his quarters and, after all, it was three o'clock in the afternoon and siesta time. Perhaps the German officer would like to call back next day. Manfred made a note in his pocket book, 'Major Enzio Berganzoli for the chop,' and then went on to the German headquarters at Heraklion. Defence of the town against terrorist attacks had been very adequately catered for by Colonel Müller. Manfred spoke briefly to a counter-espionage captain at operational headquarters and then dismissed the mountain regiment troopers, thanking them for their protection. The men had been happy to be away from their routine, boring duties and the three hundred kilometre trip around the countryside, combined with two days sunning at Vai, was more than fair recompense for any discomfort they had suffered.

Manfred and Sergeant Schneider called at the *Kriegsmarine* headquarters on the dockside and met Captain Erwin Bucholz, a muscular, red-faced, blond, prematurely balding, man with enormous ham-fisted hands. Manfred took to him immediately and Bucholz seemed pleased to be asked to take a more active part in patrolling eastern Crete.

As he explained, "I have eight E-boats in my command but, at any given time, only three or four are at sea. I am sure the *Kriegsmarine* can do more to help the *Wehrmacht*."

Then on to the airfield where they met the commanding officer of the *Luftwaffe* ground support wing, Colonel Ludwig von Thiesendorf, who was not immediately sympathetic, but conceded that his planes might do more to combat the Cretan *andartes*. Highly satisfied, but exhausted, Manfred returned to his quarters at Knossos to prepare his report for the attention of General Andrae and Colonel Heydrich Müller.

Manfred's Counter-Resistance Report

On August 2nd 1942 Major Manfred Schmidt attended General Waldemar Andrae's weekly conference at Festung HQ in Khania. The general made a few introductory references to the problems in Crete as a whole and with the Italians in particular and then invited Manfred to present his report and proposals for dealing with the troublesome Cretan irregulars. Standing before an enlarged map of Crete and conscious of the importance of his audience, Manfred took a deep breath and launched into his pre-conceived oration.

"It is my intention that the defence of eastern Crete, as defined on the map, will have three main components and that each will be integrated and dove-tailed so that we will have a constant German presence in this part of the island for twenty-four hours a day.

"Action one: *Kriegsmarine* Captain Bucholz will arrange for four E-boats each day to patrol inshore, moving in rotation from Heraklion to Ierapetra and calling in Sitia, Khania and Vai. Vai is not a harbour but it is secluded and safe. Captain Bucholz has agreed.

"Action Two: Lieutenant Colonel Ludwig von Thiesendorf will arrange for Storch spotter planes to carry out rotational flights around and over the Dikti and Lasithi mountains three times a day and to have Stuka bombers available at Heraklion and Maleme for lightning strikes against any enemy strong points, or villages, and any targets discovered by the spotter flights. Colonel Ludwig von Thiesendorf has agreed.

"Action Three: roving patrols will be sent out daily from all major garrisons, both Italian and German, on a stop and search basis. Their itinerary will not be stereotyped and they will take different routes each day. Most resistance activity occurs at night. I propose, therefore, that we send our troops on night patrols on a regular basis and Italian troops will also be mobilised, led and directed by German officers and NCOs. That, gentlemen, is my solution to the present problem."

General Andrae was almost on his feet, bubbling with enthusiasm, but Colonel Müller remained sullen and seated.

"We've already tried all this. It hasn't worked."

General Andrae replied, "A new broom sweeps clean. Give *Obersturmbahnführer* Schmidt a chance. If everyone works together, including the Italians, we may have a lucky break. Before I leave, gentlemen, is there anything else you want to discuss?"

Manfred promptly asked, "What do we do with captured *andartes*?"

The general replied, "Shoot them."

"What do we do if we capture British officers?"

Again, the general replied, "Question them and shoot them."

Manfred then asked "What do we do if the Italians refuse to co-operate?"

General Andrae looked up in surprise, "Treat each case on its merits. If Italian officers, or men, refuse to carry out a direct order get them court-martialled in the field and, if guilty, shoot them."

The meeting was terminated and Manfred was given *carte blanche* to proceed with his proposals. Colonel Heydrich Müller was not overly pleased but, in the presence of his more senior colleague, he had to accept Manfred's plans without question.   He stood up abruptly.

"Well, I hope it works."

Manfred replied, "We'll make sure it works, Sir."

General Andrae permitted himself a slight smile.   He recognised the tension between Colonel Müller and Major Schmidt and secretly sympathised with the younger officer.   Müller, despite his obstinacy and arrogance, was an excellent officer who had served with distinction in Russia and was doing a thorough, but unimaginative, job in counter-resistance.   General Andrae appreciated that his crude, ruthless methods in dealing with *andartes* had not endeared him to the Cretans, or the Italians, who preferred a 'softly softly' approach and, whenever possible promoted peaceful co-existence.   He hoped that the methods of the new major might be productive in winning over the Italians whilst, at the same time, showing no diminution in German inflexibility towards Cretan terrorists.

Cretan Resistance Diary 1942

By mid-1942 resistance to the German occupying forces had gelled into a definite pattern with the Cretans controlling the mountains and foothills and the main part of the southern seaboard and the Germans and Italians, strongly entrenched, on the northern coastline stretching from Kastelli Kissimou in the west to Vai in the east.   In July 1942 German occupying forces in Crete were at the peak of their power. Excessive reprisals between June and December 1941 by the Germans, ordered by General Student and perpetrated by General Andrae and Colonel Müller, had been largely forgotten by the occupying forces but not by the Cretans whose instinct for vendetta still held sway.   General Student's orders, sanctioned by Field Marshal Goering, had led to the execution of two hundred males at Kastelli Kissimou, the shooting of sixty-four civilians at Kondonaki by Lieutenant Horst Trevis and burning and destruction of a host of villages, allegedly for aiding Cretan resistance fighters.

These senseless killings and reprisals between June and December 1941 resulted in all able-bodied male Cretans withdrawing into the mountain vastness of central Crete, where they formed bands of andartes *led by* kapitans, *each* kapitan *elected to leadership of his group by virtue of his position as head of a family or head of a clan.*

Unfortunately inter-clan and inter-family vendettas were still rife and even the presence of a common enemy on their soil did not erase the hatred which these vendettas generated. Consequently for the rest of 1941 and well into 1942 the Cretan mountains were occupied by bands of andartes, *varying in strength and political persuasion, but with no controlled co-ordination and no clear-cut leader to direct their efforts in resisting the occupying forces.*

This situation suited the German occupiers who were able to deal piecemeal with the bands of brigands and, with their superior fire-power, they were often able to annihilate groups in limited actions and subsequently to destroy the villages in the vicinity of the battle on the assumption that the villagers supplied and sustained andartes *with food and clothing. The Cretan fighters were severely handicapped by lack of guns and ammunition. They often resorted to using pre-1914 outdated rifles, knives and garrottes, in skirmishes with the Germans. But in one thing they were paramount and more highly skilled than their adversaries – the art of camouflage and an ability to withdraw or disappear into the ground in the hostile foothills and mountains of central Crete.*

The occupying Germans recognised that British agents were infiltrating into Crete, at first to help rescue the hundreds of British and Dominion soldiers left behind after June 1941, but subsequently in an attempt to organise the undisciplined Cretan irregulars into recognisable and efficiently led resistance units. In the latter respect they had been partially successful but the main stumbling block in all negotiations was the bartering for arms and ammunition. On some occasions the British agents in the field were convinced that the Cretans would forget their vendettas in order to obtain arms. But they were never sure that they would not use their newly acquired rifles and start their own 'private' war for mastery of a particular sector of Crete. Vendettas between the Cretan kapitans *were rife and the British were fully aware of the difficulties in dealing with individual* kapitans *but, by mid-1942, three main groups of* andartes *emerged. Western Crete and the White Mountains were under the control of the nationalist Papadakis and the communist Mandakis, Central Crete and Rethymno were administered by Petrakageorgis and eastern Crete had the nationalist Bandouvas in Heraklion and the Diktis, with the communist Porphyroyennis controlling the Lasithi ranges.*

When Manfred Schmidt arrived in Heraklion he easily identified his Cretan adversaries but had little information on British agents active in the area. He knew that Professor Pendlebury had been executed by a German patrol in June 1941 outside Khania gate in Heraklion and that a man called Peter Ferman was frequently reported by informers to be active in eastern Crete. During May, June and July 1942 British seaborne sabotage units were particularly active in Crete. Between 23rd May and 1st June sabotage teams attempted landings at Heraklion and Colonel Müller dealt efficiently with the intruders. On 9th June further British raids were conducted and six German aircraft were destroyed on the ground at a small airfield at Kastelli Pediados and a large fuel depot was successfully blown up. On the 13th June another British seaborne raid on Heraklion was more rewarding and twenty planes were destroyed on the ground. On this occasion Colonel Müller, unable to prevent the raid, blamed the *Kriegsmarine* for their lack of defence and on the 14th June vented his spleen on the Cretan population by executing fifty civilians in Heraklion. This last act of barbarism was one reason for Müller's replacement by Major Manfred Schmidt.

Manfred's arrival in Crete coincided with a wave of euphoria amongst the German occupying forces. Von Runstedt's German *Panzers* were forging deep into the Caucasus and Rommel in North Africa, some two hundred miles across the sea to the south, was knocking on the door of Alexandria and Cairo. The senior Cretan *kapitans*, Papadakis, Bandouvas and Petrakageorgis, fearful that Germany might win the war, were all anxious to be taken off Crete. On July 9th Petrakageorgis' group was successfully attacked and dispersed by German patrols at Temeneli. German counter-espionage activity on Crete was at its height and the Germans were successfully controlling the *andartes* who were beginning to panic and break up into smaller units, many disillusioned and frightened Cretans returning to their mountain villages.

In September the German high command made a change in military control. On the 7th General Bruno Braüer replaced General Andrae as commander of Festung Kriti. Colonel Müller was promoted to *Brigadführer* taking over western and central Crete and Manfred Schmidt was made responsible for eastern Crete and promoted to the rank of colonel.

The first three months of Manfred's command were idyllic. The Cretans, sensing a global German victory, began to pay court to their German overlords. Through informers there were pacifist overtures from the communist section led by Porphyroyennis and even some encouraging approaches from the nationalist Bandouvas. Manfred's command prospered. There were no aggressive actions by the *andartes* and British SOE agents were quiescent, probably influenced by the serious threat to Egypt and the Delta by Rommel's Africa Corps. The Italians emerged from their shell and General Carta started involving his troops in daylight operations against the *andartes* in the Lasithis, as well as co-operating with Manfred's infantry in night-time manoeuvres and counter-resistance strikes against the evanescent guerrillas. The fact that the *andartes* were in a state of suspension and lacked aggressive intent helped the Italians in their decision to partake in these nocturnal exercises.

Manfred's promotion to colonel on September 11th substantiated his status as head of German counter-espionage in eastern Crete. He made sure that he was regularly seen here, there and everywhere. On patrols he wore his black SS uniform embellished with his Knight's Cross and the airborne emblem on his battle-dress tunic. Thus attired he looked the epitome of a Nazi staff officer, complete with a pitted scar on the right side of his forehead and dark sunglasses. He made sure that his presence was felt at all levels and he was never happier than when standing upright in a staff *Kübelwagen*, leading a motorised column on sorties into the Diktis and Lasithis. He soon became a well-recognised and, in some ways, respected figurehead of the occupying forces. His ascendancy to power in the eastern sector coincided with General Bruno Braüer's appointment as commander of Festung Kriti. The new commander, a friend of Colonel von Bulow since the battle of May 1941, fully approved of Manfred's counter-resistance plans for eastern Crete.

Manfred maintained his headquarters at Villa Ariadne and, after Müller's departure for Khania, became the sole occupant of the house in Knossos. His weekly routine included Storch flights over the Lasithis and Diktis and flying visits to outposts at Ierapetra, Vai, Elounda, Kastelli and Katohorio. During his first two months in command he concentrated his attention on the Italian garrisons at Neapolis and Sitia. His approach to his comrades in arms was simplistic and sympathetic. The Italian commander at Neapolis was helpful but, due to pressures of command and a lustful interest in his concubine, General Carta handed most of the responsibility to Captain Tavana, his counter-espionage officer. Captain Tavana was an intelligent Roman who immediately understood Colonel Schmidt's problems. Manfred wanted Italian forces to combine in night manoeuvres against a common enemy. It was common practice for all Italian forces to withdraw into their garrison fortresses during the hours of darkness.

"Captain Tavana, the Cretan resistance fighters are mainly active at night. We need to put our men into the field after dark. It is only then we will be able to curtail movement of the *andartes*. Can you use your influence with General Carta to allow your men out of their garrisons on night exercises? If your commander is unable to co-operate, I will have to get General Braüer to force the issue. I shall arrange for your Italian sections to be led into the field by German officers and NCOs."

Captain Tavana was taken aback. His perplexed, handsome face creased with worry, "I'll see what I can do, but I don't expect a successful result in the near future."

Success of the German campaigns in Russia and North Africa helped to sway General Carta's decision. In early October he issued an order that his troops were to participate in night exercises and manoeuvres led by German NCOs and officers. This was a minor victory for Colonel Manfred Schmidt.

The Italian soldiers never really adapted readily to night sorties. Whereas their German instructors trained them in the tactic of stealth and silence, the Italians believed that a show of strength and as much noise as possible distracted would-be assailants and caused them to shy away. And so it transpired. Italian-manned sorties were not attacked by the *andartes*. The noise and cacophony of their movement regularly advertised their presence in numbers to any marauding brigands lying in wait in the dark undergrowth. It also soon became evident that these Italian night sorties were strictly confined to the main roads, despite encouragement and coercion from the German leaders. Manfred was not overly pleased with his allies but at least he had managed to get them out of their fortresses at night and into *andarte*-held hinterland.

Manfred's promotion to colonel placed him on equal terms with the pompous *Luftwaffe* commander at Heraklion. Colonel Ludwig von

Thiesendorf kept his word and Storch spotter flights over eastern Crete operated regularly, in constant radio contact with the airfields at Maleme and Heraklion and with Manfred's command post at Knossos.

Manfred was in complete accord with *Kriegsmarine* Captain Erwin Bucholz. Bucholz, a Brunswickian and ardent Nazi, had volunteered in 1936 at the age of sixteen for naval service as a 'boy'. By dint of exemplary service and utter devotion to Nazism he progressed up the ladder in the *Kriegsmarine* and now, at the age of twenty-seven, found himself commander of an E-boat flotilla in Crete. Bucholz, a beefy, florid, red-faced man with massive hands had the attributes of dependability and élan and was well suited for his command. He had had no time for the arrogant, blustering Müller who had tried to pin the June debacle on his *Kriegsmarine*. The new tall, fair-haired Nazi commander was something different. At least he had a military compatriot and comrade with whom he felt on equal terms.

Whenever possible Manfred and *Feldwebel* Schneider took the opportunity of sailing with Bucholz in his command E-boat on their routine sweeps around eastern Crete. Elounda was Manfred's favourite port of call but the presence of the *Totenkopf* battalion and Captain Rudolf Schlemburg at the base made the visits unpleasant and uncomfortable. The haven for E-boats was Vai where the small platoon of German soldiers were always welcoming and amenities for rest and enjoyment were unsurpassed.

Early on in their friendship Manfred and *Kriegsmarine* Captain Bucholz decided to make Vai their own special base. Vai is a small, sandy, palm-fringed bay at the very eastern tip of Crete. In September 1942 Manfred proposed that a small mess should be built at the end of a forty-foot jetty which provided anchorage for two E-boats at a time. This idyllic bay was approached from the west by a single-track, dusty, gravel road and the duty platoon were housed in a series of eight tents placed at intervals on each side of the road. The sea water in Vai was crystal clear and the white sandy beach contrasted starkly with the azure blue waters of the Aegean. The place was militarily indefensible but so remote and clear of the beaten track that likelihood of discovery was virtually non-existent.

The eastward E-boat patrol from Heraklion took the boat to Malia, Neapolis, Elounda and Sitia and then around the eastern tip of Crete, stopping at Vai, to the port of Ierapetra on the south coast. Manfred soon noticed that on each occasion between Sitia and Vai, when they passed two mammary-shaped rocky outcrops, Captain Bucholz disappeared below and returned to the bridge a few minutes later, flustered and suffused with an explanation that those particular rocks reminded him of the anatomy of a long-lost girlfriend from Bremerhaven. Manfred never asked, but assumed, that the *Kriegsmarine* captain's disappearance below at that particular point was connected with a craving for masturbatory relief and the E-boat crew confirmed his suspicions with lewd remarks, which they never uttered in their Captain's presence.

*

Manfred's roving patrols frequently spent a night in a German outpost in the mountain villages. Early one morning in mid-October he was sitting outside a café at Kastelli having coffee with Schneider when the wolf-whistles of his assembling patrolmen drew his attention to a dark-haired, beautiful woman walking proudly across the square and holding a toddler by the hand. She stared fixedly ahead and made her way to the grocer's, ignoring the attentions of the German soldiers. Manfred spoke to the café owner, a grey-haired, wizened old man with a drooping grey moustache.

"Who is that woman?"

The old man replied, "Her name is Stephia. Her husband was killed in the war. She lives in one of the two small cottages over there in the corner of the village square backing on to the castle wall."

Stephia and her small boy soon emerged from the grocer's and, as they started back across the square, the infant broke loose and ran across towards the café where he stopped and looked fixedly at Manfred's uniform and medals. Manfred, never at ease in the presence of children, felt embarrassed by the boy's innocent stare and then gave him a slight smile and a broad wink. Thus encouraged the toddler moved even nearer as his flustered mother arrived to take his hand and drag him away. Manfred stood up.

"What's the boy's name?"

The mother, her deep, dark eyes flashing hatred, replied, "Spiros" and yanked at the boy's arm as Manfred leant forward and gave Spiros a chunk of uneaten bread and jam and, with a flourish, his silver swastika tie pin. The youngster was overjoyed as he was led away clutching his medallion.

Manfred turned towards Schneider with a broad smile.

"*Feldwebel*, I can get plenty more Party medallions but the Party cannot provide me with a woman like that. She should be a good grind. I intend to find out."

Within three days Manfred's mobile column was back in Kastelli and he dropped a food parcel into Stephia's house. The proud Cretan woman refused to take it but within seconds Spiros, with uncanny childhood perspicacity, picked his way into the package and was eagerly tucking into a bar of chocolate, the first he had ever seen or tasted. Stephia felt quite helpless. Manfred smiled at her and with exaggerated correctness took his leave. Two visits later Manfred was invited to stay on a while and take a cup of coffee whilst he played with Spiros. And so an unlikely friendship developed.

Stephia, deprived of male company since the loss of her Australian corporal in June 1941, overcame her repugnance of the German conqueror and, though she had been raped by this man's comrades, succumbed to his Teutonic charms. Within a week they were lovers. For Manfred it was only a means of expending his virile ego, another conquest, but for Stephia it was a release of a year's pent-up frustration. She did not love the man. She hated his race and what the Germans had done to her, and her family, but at least this handsome Aryan made her feel a full woman again. She recognised that she was being used and that nothing tangible, or permanent, would come out of the relationship.

Stephia worried about his insensitivity. When Manfred came through the door of her one-roomed cottage, nearly always intoxicated, he only wanted sex and urgent sex at that, and, even in the presence of Spiros, forced himself on her to gratify his lust. Whenever possible when the colonel paid a visit Stephia sent Spiros to her cousin's house next door but, even there, the boy was able to hear the pummelling, grunting and pushing of their lovemaking. At times the one year old stood bewildered at the bedside, whimpering and tugging at his mother's arm, whilst the man in black uniform lay on top of her, panting, shouting and writhing until he subsided into a limp heap on the bed and lay there with his head next to his mother's tear-stained face. And afterwards came the good things, chocolate, preserves, tinned fruit, candy and sweetmeats. Little Spiros almost forgave, but could not fully understand, what the German in the black uniform was doing to his mother. At the end of the day, whatever was happening on the bed, or floor, of their little house, Spiros was compensated with a rare treat of chocolate or candy. For the rest of the year and until July 1943 these visits by the German in a black uniform became a regular feature of the boy's upbringing.

Captain Tavana was entertaining Manfred in the Italian headquarters at Neapolis in late November. As always Italian hospitality was lavish and both officers were slightly inebriated. They were congratulating each other on the success of their joint patrols and the consequent lack of activity by the *andartes* when Captain Tavana asked the question:

"Colonel Schmidt how would you like to meet Porphyroyennis, the Lasithi *kapitan*?"

Manfred was dumbfounded but agreed it might be an interesting experience.

Captain Tavana went on to explain, "Over the past six months I have been able to make contact with Porphyroyennis. He's not a very nice man but he's prepared to do a deal if we can supply him with arms. I'm not sure we can trust him an inch but I thought I would mention it to you as a possible line of action."

Manfred readily agreed that they should plan a meeting with the Cretan communist *kapitan* as soon as possible. Combined daylight patrols to the Lasithis were arranged by Captain Tavana with Manfred and *Feldwebel* Schneider, refusing to discard his German *Schmeitzer* pistol, both dressed as troopers in ill-fitting Italian uniforms of the Siena Regiment.

During the second week of December the third sortie was productive. A mobile column was well up in the Lasithis and resting on a rocky plateau when a single rifle shot was heard from a ridge behind the stationary convoy. The Italian troopers hit the deck like greased lightning, whilst Manfred and Schneider took cover behind one of the vehicles. No further shots were fired and, when it became evident that no one in the patrol had been hit, Captain Tavana took off his helmet and walked out into the middle of the road both arms raised and indicating that he was not carrying a firearm. Captain Tavana remained in the centre of the road perspiring profusely and ignoring exhortations from his men to take cover.

After about ten minutes two figures appeared around the corner of the road ahead, both dressed in dark Cretan garb, festooned with ammunition clips and grenades and carrying large cumbersome old-fashioned, hunting rifles. One was Porphyroyennis, the other was one of his lieutenants and both wore distinctive red feathers in their *sarikis*. Captain Tavana advanced towards them and spoke for about a minute. He then called Manfred forward to join the group.

Manfred eyed the communist *kapitan* and did not particularly like what he saw. Porphyroyennis was a short, scrawny little man with a hook nose, slight squint, black-bearded jowls and irregular blackened teeth which were only revealed when he scowled, which he did regularly. Captain Tavana acted as interpreter.

"*Kapitan* Porphyroyennis wants rifles, bullets and grenades and he wants them very soon."

Manfred replied, "I'm sure the *kapitan* wants arms but what is he prepared to give up for having them?"

The *kapitan* snarled, "No further attacks on Italian soldiers,"

Manfred replied, "And what about the Germans?"

The *kapitan*'s face was contorted in deep thought. "I cannot control all my men against the Germans but I can help them by putting Bandouvas and his Dikti battalions out of action."

Manfred thought, 'That's clever, a chance for Porphyroyennis to promote his life-long vendetta with the Bandouvas family and take pressure off the German garrison at Heraklion.'

He decided there and then that guns and grenades were to be made available to Porphyroyennis from the Italian armoury at Sitia. He also made up his mind that when all the battles were over he would take personal pleasure in eliminating this smelly, unsavoury Bolshevik from the face of the earth. The deal was settled and a pick-up point arranged on the Sitia road near Mochlos. Porphyroyennis' band were to get one hundred and twelve obsolete Italian rifles, a thousand rounds of ammunition and three crates of old fashioned, unreliable hand grenades. Captain Tavana did not report the deal to his indolent, disinterested general, but Manfred had pleasure in reporting his coup to General Bruno Braüer, who commented on the telephone:

"Well done, Manfred, I was hoping something like this might happen. If we can play Porphyroyennis against Bandouvas it will alleviate troop commitments in Heraklion. I am looking forward to seeing you at my Christmas party at Festung headquarters. Heil Hitler."

General Bruno Braüer's Christmas party at his Villa Halepa headquarters just outside Khania was a memorable affair. Manfred, together with Captain Bucholz and his *Kriegsmarine* officers, moved in a mobile column up to Khania on Christmas eve where they were entertained to carol singing at Brigadier Müller's barracks. General Braüer's Christmas celebrations began at 9.30 a.m. with an hour long church service. Then at 11 a.m. he gave his 'State of the Festung' address to the assembled commanders and officers. General Braüer reviewed the general state of the war. He considered the hold-up at Stalingrad a minor set-back to Germany's eventual success against the Bolsheviks and that Rommel's retreat to Tripoli was a tactical exercise. The old Desert Fox would forage again and retake Libya and Egypt.

He continued, "And now to Festung Kriti. Since I took command here in September I have been extremely pleased with the efforts of all my officers in the field. The last attacks by the British agents were in June and July and they were all repulsed. British secret agent activity in Crete is at a standstill. Cretan resistance forces are sitting back and re-thinking their position. They may well have made the wrong choice at the beginning and may come around to us early in 1943. I now have to commend Colonel Heydrich Müller on his suppressive activities in Khania and Rethymno. We have not had any trouble in his command since July. Heraklion itself is well under control where the Committee of Civil Advisors, headed by Colonel Beteniakis, work hand-in-glove with our military commanders and where we have at least two reliable informers sitting on the council.

"Outside Heraklion, in eastern Crete, Colonel Manfred Schmidt has worked wonders in the short time he has been with us. With the co-operation of *Kriegsmarine* Captain Bucholz and *Luftwaffe* Colonel Ludwig von Thiesendorf, policing of this area has improved immensely. Colonel Schmidt has been very successful in mobilising our Italian colleagues in Neapolis, Sitia and Ierapetra into carrying out night patrols, most of which are led by our NCOs and officers. But I think the best coup so far is that last week Colonel Schmidt, through an Italian intermediary, arranged for the communists in the Lasithis to have limited supplies of rifles, ammunition and hand grenades."

An electric, incredulous buzz spread through the audience as the General continued, "But let me remind you, gentleman, that these are obsolete First World War Italian rifles and, at worst, we have lost about one hundred and twelve useless guns but, at best, we are providing *Kapitan* Porphyroyennis with the necessary armaments to continue his vendetta against the Bandouvas group around Heraklion and in the Diktis. I need hardly remind you that with Bandouvas out of the way the whole of eastern Crete will be secure. Surveying my command I can say that, thanks to you, gentlemen, it has been a most successful few months and I have no doubts that our success to date will continue throughout 1943 until the end of the war. We shall have an opportunity to propose toasts at lunch. So I now offer you the supreme salute," and they all stood stiffly at attention, 'Heil Hitler'."

After a gargantuan Christmas lunch of wild boar, pheasant and goose the general's party continued through into the night with a profusion of toasts and each officer was required to make a speech. General Müller's speech was crude and somewhat distasteful. Manfred extolled the virtues of the Nazi party. Von Thiesendorf, in a long and dull peroration, praised *Reichsmarschall* Goering and the *Luftwaffe*. The prize speaker was *Kriegsmarine* Captain Bucholz who gave a masterly exposition of life on the ocean wave. Manfred pleased General Braüer by proposing a toast to the *Fallschirmjagger* and in particular to comrades who were buried on Crete. The general shed a tear when Maleme was mentioned, where the fate of many of his compatriots was decided in May 1941 and where many were now buried on hill 107.

The wild party finally ended around 2 a.m. when the drunken officers either fell asleep on the spot or staggered away to find a couch, or quiet corner, in the rambling villa. By order of Colonel Braüer all the officers stayed on the following day when the celebrations continued, but at a diminished tempo.

Manfred and *Feldwebel* Schneider returned to Villa Ariadne on the morning of the 27th December, 1942. On the return journey Manfred, nursing a hangover, thought over his current position in Crete. Events in Russia and North Africa were slightly alarming but he accepted General Braüer's pronouncement that 1943 would see a reversal of fortunes on the two fronts. In his own area he was king of the castle and the *Kriegsmarine*, the *Luftwaffe* and the Italian army were eating out of his hand. There were no further signs of British terrorist activity and with luck he might have solved the *andartes* problem in eastern Crete by setting the communist Porphyroyennis against the nationalists. Added to all this he had extremely comfortable quarters in Villa Ariadne at Knossos and a lovenest in Kastelli. Thoughts of the latter aroused his sexual desire and he resolved to spend the night with Stephia and not at the villa. Yes, his cup was full to overflowing. What he did not know was that on the 15th December Major David Green and his six-man Codforce commando had arrived at Piskopiano and that, within three months, they would be active in eastern Crete.

At Villa Ariadne Manfred was waylaid by Sergeant Fritz Schultz. Schultz, fawning and deferential, seemed to have something on his mind.

"Herr Colonel, I was expecting you back yesterday and prepared a full Christmas lunch for you and the staff, a sort of family Christmas amongst ourselves."

The colonel looked haughtily at his insubordinate mess sergeant.

"I thank you for your thoughtfulness, Sergeant Schultz, but I am sure you are aware that General Braüer held a high-level conference yesterday."

The sergeant accepted the rebuff, lowering his gaze to look at his boots and then quite quickly he looked up, braced his shoulders and smiled.

"But all is not lost, Sir. I managed to salvage six geese and two wild boar and we can have our Christmas party tonight."

Manfred, aware of his private arrangement to go to Kastelli, was almost on the point of calling off the dinner but on looking at Fritz's hang-dog face he relented.

"Very well, Fritzy, we'll eat early. I'm committed to be elsewhere by 9.30 p.m. so we'll dine at 7 p.m.."

"*Jawohl, mein* Colonel. 1900 hours it will be," chortled Sergeant Schultz as he turned on his heel with a broad satisfied smile and returned to his kitchens, his very own private territory, '*strangsten verboten*' to all and sundry.

Later in the day Captain Hartman produced a guest list which included *Kriegsmarine* Captain Bucholz and *Luftwaffe* Colonel von Thiesendorf. Amongst the guests there were two new arrivals to Manfred's command at Heraklion, a supply major and Surgeon Captain Frederick Steinfurt whose wife, Manfred remembered with a smile, he had ardently coveted at Potsdam Hospital. So, they had caught up with the surgeon at last and made him enlist, leaving behind the eminently desirable Giesela. He wondered who was shafting her whilst her husband was away at war.

Sergeant Fritz Schultz was ready for the colonel and his guests to be seated promptly at 7 p.m., but Manfred, carried away by the excitement of his first Christmas in command, prolonged the pre-prandial drinking session for an hour. During this time and at the table he took special pleasure in goading Surgeon Captain Steinfurt about his wife. The medic became distressed whenever her name was mentioned and Manfred took this to be due to his absence from family and home over Christmas. He discovered later in the evening that, early in October, Frau Dr Steinfurt had left the hospital and was now living with a dashing *Luftwaffe* pilot in Bückeburg. Even then Manfred was not sorry for the surgeon. He felt sorry for himself and the fact that he had not pressed his claims hard enough when he had been a patient in the hospital and had his chance to seduce Frau Dr Steinfurt.

'*C'est la guerre,*' he thought with a slight smirk.

The evening passed quickly with many toasts and it was not until the flaming Christmas pudding arrived that Manfred realised it was 10 p.m. He stood unsteadily on his feet, proposed a final toast to the Führer, downed a large brandy in one gulp and, picking up the remains of half a goose, a large Christmas cake and a full bottle of cognac rushed outside shouting for Schneider, who had been expecting the call and had arranged for two reluctant mountain regiment motorcyclists and an armed *Kübelwagen* to be ready for a night dash to Kastelli. The small convoy with headlights blazing made the journey in thirty-five minutes.

Feldwebel Schneider doubted the wisdom of this unnecessary sortie through potentially dangerous territory at night but he knew he could not influence the drunken colonel, who was hell-bent on getting to Kastelli for a night's lovemaking. In the colonel's inebriated state, and still drinking cognac from the bottle in his hand, Schneider wondered if his colonel would be up to it. The colonel was in a loquacious and kept referring to the new surgeon captain and berating his lack of sexual prowess in keeping his beautiful wife satisfied, ending up with a rhetorical question, "And where do you think she is now Schneider? I'll tell you where she is. She's being shagged by a bull of a *Luftwaffe* pilot in Bückeburg. That's where she is! What a waste of a good woman."

Manfred's head fell forwards and the brandy bottle slipped from his grasp, as he sidled into a drunken stupor. Schneider kept driving at full speed behind the two motorcycle outriders. What a dangerous waste of time! The colonel would obviously pass out as soon as he got into bed with his lover and the poor luckless woman would probably spend the night lying beside his impotent snoring body, warding off ineffectual sexual advances and trying to keep her consort as quiet as possible. What a waste! Now if Stephia would only consider him! He was fully equipped and capable of satisfying the attractive Cretan woman. But, as he drove along towards Kastelli, he knew these were dangerous thoughts. Stephia was the colonel's property.

'Hands off and concentrate on driving, Schneider.'

The illuminated convoy made good speed and arrived at Kastelli checkpoint at 10.45 p.m.

Chapter Twenty-One
The First Six Weeks at Piskopiano

HM Submarine *Hyperion* lay anchored about a mile off the south coast of Crete and, with shouts of 'Good Luck' from the Captain, David and his small Codforce, with Tim Gammon and the two wireless operators, were transferred into two large dinghies which, once loaded, moved off smartly towards the shore, an indistinct blur in the distance, a lighter silhouette in the pitch black night. They were rowed ashore expertly and silently by two naval ratings. The silence was overpowering, only the gentle swish of oars breaking through at regular intervals. After ten minutes' rowing it became evident that the guiding lights on the shore were becoming larger and penetrated further out to sea. The dinghies were about twenty yards away from a shingle beach, when they were picked up in the powerful beam of a torch and the sound of human voices on the shoreline were heard.

"There they are," in English.

And then, "The boats are coming ashore here," in Greek and with a gentle thud the keel of the boat crunched softly on to the shingle and the crewmen jocularly announced, "All ashore that's going ashore."

David was first off the prow of the dinghy landing in two feet of water at the edge of the shingly sand. He held the boat whilst the rest of his section joined him in the surf. As soon as they reached terra firma they were surrounded by some twenty excited men in dark clothing, some holding torches which they used sparingly and most shouting excitedly in Greek with a few cultured English voices amidst the general babble. David's first impression was the lack of quietness and subterfuge which pervaded the whole landing operation. He thought the German defenders must be completely deaf and blind if they were unable to see the flashing lights and hear the uncontrolled chatter of the beach reception committee. And then, in the darkness, one of the dark-garbed figures spoke in a cultured Oxford accent.

"You must be Codforce. Where's Tim Gammon and the two new wireless boys?"

David replied, "They're in the other dinghy."

The second dinghy had landed some fifty yards further down the beach.

"Good show," the black apparition replied, "let's go and pick him up."

Codforce, surrounded by some fifteen, or more, ill-defined black-faced Cretans, stumbled along the shoreline towards Gammon's reception committee which could be clearly heard congratulating the popular agent on his successful return to Crete. The beach party was now some eighty strong, mainly Cretan resistance fighters, all excitedly showing their appreciation for the return of Tim Gammon and the arrival of 'new' British agents. The two dinghies took aboard some twelve dark-clad, dark-faced anonymous persons and, with a hurried 'good luck' from the oarsmen rowed out of the limited circle of light into the vast blackness of the Libyan sea.

"It's always like this! The *andartes* are so excited to get new recruits and arms and ammunition that they turn out in force for these landings. Once they get their hands on some guns they'll disappear. I bet you that in ten minutes the only people left on this beach will be ourselves and our guides. By the way, tell your boys to hang on to their possessions and guns. The *andartes*, although friendly, are not above pinching the odd rifle or Sten gun. It's an in-built part of their tradition."

David passed on Tim's instructions to his commando and they stood firmly in a bunch with the agent doing all the bartering and talking.

One by one the *andartes* slipped away up the beach and, within ten minutes, David's commando, Tim Gammon and the two wireless operators were the only occupants of the now silent and pitch-dark landing beach at Tsoutsouro. Tim Gammon introduced the two guides to David.

"These are Niko and Spiros, both excellent guides. Niko will guide you to within ten kilometres of your base. Spiros and I will be leaving you on the way with the second wireless operator. Our first job is to get your wireless operator placed and we'll need to do this before daybreak."

The guides led the party in single file off the shelving beach into the sand-banks and then proceeded silently eastwards along a flat coastal track to reach the hamlet of Keratokombou, a distance of three kilometres.

As Tim explained, "This area on the south coast of Crete is no-man's land. The Germans cannot police it for lack of manpower and the Italians some fourteen miles to the east at Ierapetra won't come out at night and do very little reconnaissance during the daytime. If you're safe anywhere in Crete you're safe here. On the route we shall take to the north over the next two days we shall meet German and Italian troops at Anno Viannos and at Kastelli, some thirty-five miles north of Viannos, there are nearly always German roadblocks. The guides are fully aware of these potential trouble spots and will take you around them."

Before daybreak at 6 a.m. the wireless operator was planted at a farmhouse outside Keratokombou and the group advanced high into the foothills of the Dikti mountains, making camp in a cave some three miles west of Viannos. There they had a meal and were advised to rest. They were awake at midday and the guides took them northwards along the western foothills of the Diktis, taking cover when German spotter planes came snooping around. At nightfall on the second night ashore they made camp in the Dikti mountains at Geraki, which they left before dawn to proceed westwards and reached the Viannos-Kastelli road some four kilometres south of the German occupied village. There they parted company. Tim Gammon and his wireless operator continued westwards towards Mount Ida where the second wireless operator was to be placed.

Before they parted company Tim wished David luck adding, "I don't expect we shall meet again on this island. The place is crawling with our men, Cretan resistance fighters, German and Italian troops and my advice is not to trust any of them. Do your own thing. In that way you and your chaps have a chance of getting off the island alive. You can trust Niko to get you safely around Kastelli. After that you'll be on your own."

With a firm handshake and exchanges of 'good luck' the two officers parted company.

Niko now guided David and his six-man commando northwards towards Kastelli. At midday he took them off the winding road into the Dikti hills where they rested and fed themselves in an olive grove.

They were some two kilometres south of Kastelli and, as Niko tried to explain, they would have to get around Kastelli in the dark.

"Kastelli, *Germania, bom, bom.*"

At dusk, hugging the Dikti foothills, they crossed a sizeable road and, following a shepherd's footpath, reached the Kastelli-Hersonisos road just beyond Aghios Pandeleimon. After a further cautious advance of about two kilometres northwards Niko announced that this was as far as he went. He shook hands with David, gave him a hug and a kiss on the cheek, turned about and disappeared rapidly into the darkness, back towards Kastelli.

David gathered his commando around him and, crouching on their haunches, explained that they were now within eight kilometres of their base. According to the map there was a T-junction three kilometres ahead where the Gournes road joined their own and their base in Crete was five kilometres from the junction. They had plenty of time to reach their destination before daybreak but he did not wish to approach the farm at Piskopiano in the dark as this might arouse suspicion and cause the farmer to raise the alarm. They made good progress in the darkness and lay up for an hour, one hundred metres away from the farm, to await daylight. David also considered the farm might be occupied by Italian or German forces and he did not wish to lead his commando into a fatal trap within forty-eight hours of landing in Crete.

Dawn came quickly at 7.30 a.m. At one moment there was complete blackness, a minute later an inverted twilight and a minute later clear sunlight, bathing the farm in its early morning glow. Two cocks were crowing to welcome the dawn. After about ten minutes the farmhouse door opened and a bent figure appeared shuffling slowly across the farmyard to the outhouses, carrying a bucket of fodder. Spiros was out of sight for nearly a quarter of an hour, attending to his own physical needs and the hunger of his chickens. When he again reappeared in the yard with an empty bucket David got out of his hiding place. Leaving his Sten gun with Sergeant Hubbard, he walked boldly down the centre of the dirt track and up to the startled, but wary, old man who stared at him without recognition.

David had rehearsed many times how he would approach the Spiros family but when the event happened he was lost for words. He simply walked up to Spiros, took the bucket from his hand and set it aside and then, holding Spiros' hand firmly, pulled him to his body in a fierce embrace, murmuring in Greek, "Spiros, Spiros, I am pleased to meet you again."

Their eyes were only a foot apart and slowly the ageing Cretan responded with an increasing pressure of his hand grip and a violent crunching hug for the British officer.

"David, it is you, David, it is you."

They held each other for a full minute and then the old farmer led David towards the door of his house shouting, "Anna, Anna," to alert his wife.

She came to the door and gave David another embrace. He noticed that her once jet-black hair was now completely grey. The two fussed around their visitor, Anna producing some curdled goats milk. David spoke to Spiros in Greek.

"Spiros, I have returned with six comrades to fight the Germans. Do they come here often?"

"Since the debacle in May 1941 we have seen the Germans at this farm twice, the last time two months ago. They did not cause any trouble this time. They stayed in the barn and used the fields for exercises," Spiros replied.

David's heart missed a beat. "Did they find anything at the top of the olive grove?"

Spiros shook his head, "No, no, nothing. Your cave is still intact as far as I know."

"Thank God for that," said David. "Spiros, I will now fetch my men for you and Anna to meet them. Will you be able to provide fresh milk and cheese and bread for them every day? The British Army will pay you for your service."

The old man's eyes clouded over as he looked at David with contempt, "After what the Germans did to us here, raping my wife, Antia and poor Stephia, it will be an honour to provide food for you and your men. We do not have much but whatever we have we will share. I will not accept a drachma in payment from you and that's an end to the matter."

David was shocked to learn for the first time of the callous and cowardly behaviour of the German soldiers at Spiros' farm on 1st June, 1941 when Anna, Antia and Stephia were raped.

Spiros then shook hands solemnly with David and an agreement was sealed. David went back up the driveway and brought his commando to meet Spiros and Anna. They were given a platter of bread and cheese and dark, sour, curdled goats milk. Most of the commando forced the breakfast down in deference to their hosts and obviously were not impressed with the Cretan offering. Biffo ate with relish and asked for more.

Sergeant Hubbard commented afterwards, "Not like Naafi bacon and eggs we're used to lads."

To which David replied, "You'd better get used to it. That's the sort of food you're going to get for the next few months."

David then took his troop up alongside the dried river-bed, through the dense olive grove, to the apex of the triangle where the limbs of the two escarpments met and led almost vertically upwards to one of the smaller foothills in the Dikti range.

He lined his men up and then pointing dramatically at the sheer cliff face, announced, "This is going to be your home for the next few months. Thirty feet up there you can just make out a ledge with a few shrubs and small trees growing on it. Behind that ledge is a cave and, hopefully, as much ammunition and food as we are going to need. It's a big cave and has water inside. I can see you'll be asking how we get up there. Well I'll show you."

Discarding his packs and Sten gun David approached the vertical cliff and, negotiating small crevices and toe-holds, expertly climbed the rock in a matter of three minutes. He disappeared over the edge of the ledge and crossed the ten-foot, smooth, flat rock to the cave entrance concealed by shrubbery and brushwood. Sweeping the wooden curtain aside he crawled on all fours through the narrow four-foot square aperture in the rock face. Once inside and, when his pupils became accustomed to the darkness, he saw the irregular shape of the canvas crates piled high on one side of the capacious cavern. And there near the entrance, exactly where he had left it, was a coiled rope ladder. He returned outside on to the ledge and let the ladder go, fixing his end to the trunk of a short stumpy lime tree. He peered over the edge at the incredulous faces of his commando looking upwards from below.

"Gentlemen, this is your lift to Aladdin's cave. Not as good as the ones at Harrods but it's the best I can do."

One by one the commando climbed on to the ledge and then crawled into the cave. Once inside they were amazed at the depth and height of the cavern and the coolness of its interior. In fact, in

December the interior of the cave was cold, a few degrees above freezing, but distinctly warmer at the entrance.

David looked at his dumbstruck commando and smiled, "This, men, is our own private store. It may also, from time to time, be our hiding place. We'll make an inventory of the contents over the next few days. From now on there will always be one man on guard here. It's a lonely job. We have a problem with light inside the cave. In bright sunlight, only about twelve square feet near the entrance is illuminated. Whilst we are working over the next few days we will use kerosene lamps, but the supply of kerosene will only last a few days. After that I doubt if we'll get any unless we drive up to a German fuel depot and ask for some!"

At this the men laughed outright.

David continued, "Under no circumstances are you to light a fire during the day. Smoke is a big give-away and will be seen from the air and from the olive grove we came through. It's also cold in here, even in the summer, but the Aussie quartermasters have thought of everything and there are plenty of army greatcoats somewhere in these crates. As far as food is concerned we have hundreds of tins of bully beef, jam, soup and potatoes but I must warn you not to take tins out of the cave. Empty tins will be deposited at the back. Latrines cannot be provided and you must use the edges of the olive grove and the fields. Let me remind you we are now dressed like Cretans and if we are captured we'll be treated like Cretan resistance fighters and probably shot by the Germans. So let's all behave like Cretans from now on. The plan for the next couple of days is that we stay here and unpack the crates and carry out an inventory. Later this week I'll take you out in groups to give you some training in field-craft. The following week I'll take you out on recces, probably one at a time. Most of our movement will happen at night-time so I'll be instructing you on how to lay up in the open during the day. At all times remember you're supposed to be Cretans.

"We've had a long journey and I suggest we all take a rest for a couple of hours. I know you weren't impressed with the food we had this morning. It's the best the local Cretans can do. Tonight we will light a fire in here and have a brew up and some hot bully beef. The smoke won't draw attention to us at night. We'll have to open some of the crates now to get at the food and the greatcoats. By the way, there's one absolute rule. The last man up must hoist the ladder.

Biffo, go and see to it. We can't leave the ladder dangling outside the cave for any German to see! I propose we call this hideout our kibbutz."

On the fourth day after their arrival in Crete David's commandos had completed a detailed inventory of the contents of their kibbutz. Preservation of the Australian company's food, clothing and equipment had been more than satisfactory. A crate of bully beef and a carton of tea had to be discarded and a poorly packed box of service shirts had perished beyond recognition, but the weapons, mines, grenades, ammunition and rifles were perfectly preserved in their greasy envelopes protected by thick canvas bindings. In all David had at his disposal a hundred Leigh-Enfield rifles, six Bren guns, thirty-two Sten guns and about twenty landmines and twenty mortar shells. His collection of clothing included fifty khaki woollen shirts, thirty-two battle jackets and trousers, twenty-six thick khaki pullovers, thirty army blankets and thirty-two pairs of brown khaki gym shoes. As far as food was concerned the cache contained some six hundred tins of mixed comestibles, varying from bully beef and stewed steak to jam and preserved pears. Added to the list there were sundries – rope ladders, daytime and night-time binoculars, rubber tubing, bandages, plasters and pills and medicines of all description. David realised that he had enough supplies to last him and his commando for at least a year and probably longer. Much of the equipment was superfluous to his needs but he decided to keep everything. He also decided that the men would sleep in Spiros' hay barn at night apart from the kibbutz guard. But for the first week they would all sleep in the cave to get acclimatised to the conditions under which they might be expected to live and fight during their time in Crete.

The Olive Grove Exercise

Field training for David's commandos started in earnest two days before Christmas, 1942. David took his group into Spiros' fields and walked them the length of the olive grove. Eventually they squatted down in a sheltered wood beside the river bed which contained a fair amount of water.

David spoke, "Now, chaps, you've just walked through the olive grove which will be your daytime cover in the field. At the moment the ground is covered with coarse grass but between March and

November the earth will be dry and dusty and yellow in colour. You may wonder why we are dressed in these hideous coloured trousers and shirts. Well, this will be our summertime camouflage in the field. You will have noticed that the colour of our trousers conform with the bark of an olive tree. The trunks of the trees vary in thickness, shape and size but you will also have noticed that each trunk divides into two main branches some five to six feet off the ground. When you are in the open, your best camouflage will be to lay between the main branches of a selected tree and wrap your legs around the trunk. Your upper body will be in the foliage and you will be invisible from the air and, except for close inspection, from the ground. Now for the next few days we will practise hiding from each other in the olive grove. The important thing to remember is that if you're out in the open in the daytime make for an olive grove. Any questions?"

There were none.

"For the past four days you've heard and seen these small German Storch spotter planes. Never be caught in groups in the open by these planes. One man in the open on his own is permissible but more than two might be regarded as suspicious by Jerry and bring his ground troops and bombers to the spot. If you're trapped in an olive grove there will be two emergencies that may make you break cover. One is to have a piss and the answer is to do it down your trouser leg and the other is thirst. I've thought of a device that may overcome the water problem. We've got plenty of water bottles in the cave and each of you will carry a piece of coiled rubber tubing inside your shirt. You will then be able to siphon the water through the tubing without disturbing your position in the hide. Here comes a spotter plane now. Stay perfectly still and don't look up at the plane. The pilot can easily spot movement, or a white face, from the sky."

As David stopped talking the noise of the Storch's engine grew louder and the plane flew directly from north to south over the olive grove and veered off, climbing to the right, as it approached the lower reaches of the Dikti mountains.

David continued, "It seems that there are three or four of these flights each day and they may increase as the days get longer."

The commando then played hide and seek, each man taking his turn to find a tree in the olive grove and hide whilst the rest rummaged around trying to discover the concealed person. Very quickly the commando became adept at hiding and their camouflage clothing made discovery well-nigh impossible. After a week David started taking his men out singly on daylight sorties to familiarise themselves with the surrounding roads, lanes, pathways, river beds, road junctions and olive groves. The road from Hersonisos to Kastelli was particularly busy during the day and the concealed foraging party frequently observed convoys, or occasionally marching soldiers, moving along the road, the Italians noisily shouting and blabbering amongst themselves, whilst the more organised Germans moved quietly and purposefully. Later David led his men on night sorties, again to familiarise them with the lie of the land around the cave and further afield.

The best part of six weeks was taken in field craft and day and night manoeuvring and by mid-February David was confident that his small group could exist independently. The pattern of their daily routine became established with one commando on guard in the cave and a second armed commando roaming freely in the olive grove and watching over the small road approaching the farmhouse whilst the other three were engaged on patrols further afield. David himself and Sergeant Hubbard were away for days at a time doing recces and observations on the port and airfield at Heraklion. Each and every member, accompanied by David, were taken on one-day recces of the Heraklion bases moving to, and returning from, the observation point under the cover of darkness. The days were becoming longer and warmer and by mid-March David's small commando were getting ready for their first action.

Christmas Day 1942 was celebrated with a cold buffet of bully beef, goat's cheese and black bread washed down with some vinegary wine and liberal tots of *tsikoudia*. By now the farmer was providing a daily ration of black bread and cheese which was left out mid-morning by Spiros in a shiny metal churn under a sheltered ledge on the bank of the dried out river bed, about half a mile from the farmhouse. After Christmas lunch David and Sergeant Hubbard walked down to the farmhouse. David thought it ironic that he, a Jew, should be exchanging compliments of the season with Spiros and Anna, both Orthodox Greeks.

The old man was worried. He was missing his daughter Stephia and had only seen his grandson twice in the past year. He added, "I'm hearing bad news about Stephia. People tell me that she has taken a German officer into her house in Kastelli. He's the one who commands the troops in Heraklion."

David's heart missed a beat. This could be dangerous for the safety of his hideout at Piskopiano and Spiros was fully aware of this possibility. David volunteered, "I will go and speak with her myself. If what you say is true, this might be dangerous for all of us."

Spiros nodded his agreement and replied, "Marita lives in the house next to Stephia and the boy. She's the village schoolmistress. The Germans shot her husband last October in Heraklion. She hates them. I'm sure she'll be able to tell us what's going on and I know she'll keep her mouth shut. I can't understand my Stephia after what the filthy Boche did to her and Antia two summers ago."

David said, "I'll go and see Marita and tell her you sent me. In any case I want to have a look at Kastelli."

Two days later, on the 27th December, David set out alone on the ten kilometre uphill climb to Kastelli. He left Piskopiano at 3 p.m. in broad daylight, hoping to complete his return journey before curfew at 7 p.m. He was unarmed and carried only a corked bottle of goat's milk, some dried bread and a hunk of cheese in his *sakouli*. By the time he reached the German checkpoint at Kastelli he had passed three people travelling in the opposite direction, two on donkeys and one on foot. In accordance with Cretan custom these travellers passed David on the opposite side of the dirt road in complete silence and without a flicker of interest or recognition. The sergeant at the checkpoint was still in a good mood after his Christmas celebrations and David had a superficial frisking and a cursory examination of his papers and the contents of his *sakouli* and was waved through with the parting instruction in broken Cretan, "Don't forget curfew at 7 p.m."

Once inside the small fortified town he walked down the deserted street to the main square where he took a shady seat outside the café and asked for water and a glass of *tsikoudia*. The square was completely deserted. All the houses and buildings had their shutters firmly secured but David was conscious that there were many prying eyes behind the boarded windows. The quizzical inn keeper, standing in the shade of the doorway and eyeing David with a sidelong look, was evidently anxious to know what this stranger was doing in the middle of a German held fortress. At that very moment he knew that about half a dozen German soldiers were resting upstairs in his inn coming to the end of their afternoon siesta. In fact, David heard the sounds of muffled movement and talk in the upper rooms of the inn. It was time to move. He finished drinking his water stood up, slung his *sakouli* over his shoulder and walked across the square towards the castle walls.

From Spiros' description he knew Marita's house was on the road leading off the square westwards towards Aski and abutting on the castle wall. It would be the fifth in a row of small white-washed semi-detached cottages and, at the end of the row, the sixth was occupied by Stephia and her son. David walked briskly down the rutted, cratered track and strode purposefully up to the fifth door. In answer to his two brief taps the door was opened wide by a petite, dark-haired Cretan woman dressed completely in black with a handsome strong-boned face, piercing black eyes and her hair drawn into a bun at the back of her head. Marita's black eyes registered momentary fear as she took a step backwards into the one-roomed house.

In accordance with local custom David presented his greetings and those of her uncle Spiros. In true Cretan fashion Marita welcomed him into her house and immediately offered some bread, wine and cheese to the visitor. She closed the door and sat down opposite David at an ornately carved oak table, grimly arranging her skirts and patting the sides of her swept-back hair.

David spoke quickly, urgently and quietly to the staid schoolmistress sitting opposite him in the dimly lit, single-roomed cottage.

"Marita... I have permission from your uncle to speak to you about your cousin Stephia," inclining his head slightly towards the thick earth-built partition between the two houses. "Spiros is concerned that Stephia might be entertaining German officers in her home. Can you tell me about this?"

The small Cretan woman, cringing and cowering, refused to speak. She sat quietly staring at David with fear in her turbulent black eyes. David tried again but with no tangible results. Eventually Marita broke her silence.

"My cousin Stephia's private life is her own business," and then her face settled into a sullen, defiant pout.

David thought quickly, 'Why should this woman talk to a complete stranger? I could be a plant by the Germans, or from one of the *andartes* groups. Why indeed should she confide in me?'

As far as Marita was concerned the visit and interview were over and she did not want to get involved, or implicated, in whatever was going on in the house next door. The sooner this man left her house the better and yet he seemed genuine and an attractive young man and at another time and another place she might view his presence in her home from a different angle. David also sensed that the meeting was over and that he should now take his leave. Inflexibility of Cretan custom did not allow Marita to order David to leave. The visitor could stay as long as he pleased.

David sat back in his carved wooden chair and looked around the simple earthen-floored house. Next to the back door there was a half screened off area containing kitchen utensils and David guessed that the fully screened off area along the left hand side partition wall was the bedroom. The rest was the living area and apart from the carved wooden oak table and four chairs there was one beautifully carved oak trunk, of large proportions, lying against the back wall of the house under a small window overlooking the garden path and the outside wooden lavatory, erected ten feet from the sheer wall of Kastelli castle. His appreciative inspection over, David returned to face the aggressive, hawk-like, wild-eyed creature sitting opposite him.

"Marita, you have beautiful furniture in your house," fingering the top of the oak table.

Marita's piercing eyes became perceptibly softer as she replied, "Yes, it was made for me by my man, Hermanos," and suddenly she seemed to get smaller and withdrawn as, head bent forwards, she started to cry and her shoulders quivered as she wept.

David made an immediate decision. He took Marita's hand and held it gently.

"Look Marita, Spiros has told me all about Hermanos and the Germans killing him at Heraklion. I think the man that ordered those killings is the one that comes to visit Stephia. Can you help me in this? I will tell you that I have been sent to Crete to get rid of this German and as many of his kind as possible. Marita, I need help to do this. Will you please help me?"

The shuddering of the shoulders stopped, the tear-stained face looked up and, with fiercely flashing eyes, she spat out.

"The bastards killed my Hermanos. I do miss him so. He was so gentle and kind. Yes, Mr Englishman, I will help you with your plans though how I can be of any use I cannot see."

490

David thought her alertness in picking up his faint Oxford accent was commendable and then he remembered that she was the one, and only, school teacher in Kastelli.

Stephia's Story As Told By Marita

"Stephia came to the house next door in August last year. She was nearly four months pregnant. Spiros told us about the rape by German soldiers at Piskopiano and Stephia's previous involvement with an Australian corporal. We did not know and still don't know who the father was. We were able to let Stephia have the house, as it belonged to Hermanos' father. Hermanos and I were married in July 1939. He was a master craftsman, a carpenter and a little older than myself," looking coyly downwards.

David guessed that she was in her late thirties.

"Stephia is a strikingly beautiful girl and, in her pregnancy, she blossomed into a magnificent woman. The German soldiers made passes but even they, pigs as they are, did not try any nonsense with Stephia. All the while I had Hermanos here with me and they left me alone. Little Spiros was born in December last year and he's just over a year old now and a lovely little boy. Everything was fine until May this year when Hermanos had to leave Kastelli in a hurry. Rumours of a round-up were getting stronger and, as he was one of the last few younger men left in town, we were certain he would be taken away. My Hermanos went north to Heraklion and joined Bandouvas' group. He was captured in a raid near Gournes and shot the next day on the 15th June. The two German officers involved were a Captain Hartman and a Colonel Müller. I believe this Schmidt has replaced Müller in Heraklion."

Here she paused and sighed, reliving her last moments with her beloved Hermanos and then proceeded slowly.

"Without male protection the German rats started sniffing around these two houses. The Italians are worse. They always come around with a smile and are extremely polite but once they're near they pounce like tigers. Stephia has a good method of protecting herself. She simply shouts 'rape, rape', at the top of her voice and this gets rid of unwelcome visitors. Myself, I keep a loaded shotgun in that trunk and would not hesitate to use it if needs be."

David interjected, "If the Germans search the house and find the shotgun you'll be executed."

Marita looked him straight in the eye.

"Mr Englishman, I'm prepared for that. I would then be able to join Hermanos but I would make sure that I took at least one of the pigs with me." Marita refilled her cup of water. "Stephia and I were very good friends and of course we had little Spiros to care for. We made private jokes about the ways we used each day to thwart the advances of the soldiers. We did of course have to cross the square for groceries and water and I had to go to the school. So we became experts at keeping the vandals at bay until late September when something snapped in Stephia. It all happened when that handsome brute Colonel Schmidt appeared on the scene. I don't know what went wrong. She might have been wanting a man," blushing, "and there were no eligible Cretans in Kastelli. He is a handsome blond monster with blue eyes. He is very polite but only seems to want one thing," again blushing, "and that happens next door where I can hear everything going on. If you listen carefully you'll hear Stephia move around and the little boy talking."

There were a few moments of complete silence in the gathering gloom and David heard the sounds of movement next door and some incomprehensible chatter from an infant. Marita got up to peep through the shutters and returned.

"It's getting darker outside. You will miss the curfew." David thought for a moment.

"I'll be all right. I'll get through the cordon somehow."

Marita returned to her seat, "I won't light the lamp. I'll show you a way of escape through the back garden before it gets too dark."

She took David down the outside pathway bounded on each side by five foot dry stone walls and at the back of the lavatory there was a narrow overgrown path running along the base of the circular castle wall. She pointed in one direction.

"About twenty yards down there's a breach in the castle wall, through which you can get into the castle grounds. At the base of one of the turrets on the right hand side of the castle there's another gap in the outside wall which leads you down to the valley below. The descent is very steep but when we were youngsters we used to go down to the river bed below to collect snails and *khorta*."

The two hand-in-hand then returned to the small house and sat at the table. Marita, now relaxed, continued, "Well, what can I tell you about this German swine? He's very generous. He gives Stephia plenty of food and wine and Spiros always gets chocolate and sweets. He visits Stephia at least twice a week and his visits are for one hour, or two, most times. He never stays overnight. But when he's making love I can hear everything through the wall and that upsets me. I sit here and cry for Stephia, little Spiros and uncle Spiros. At first I would take the little one in here during the colonel's visits but things changed last month. Stephia told me that she was in love with the German brute, a friend of the man who ordered Hermanos' execution. I could not believe my ears. I have not spoken to Stephia since. She tries to make contact but I ignore her. I turn my back on her. It's very difficult living next door, cousins and ignoring each other. The little boy keeps coming around asking for his Auntie Marita." She started sobbing again.

By now it was completely dark inside the house and outside in the lane. Some of the cottages had faint lights in the windows but there were no civilians walking the streets. There was an occasional noise from next door and around 6.30 p.m. the pleasant soothing voice of a mother cajoling her infant to sleep and then complete silence, except for soft shuffling and clinking of pots and pans as Marita prepared a nondescript stew for supper. David stationed himself by the window looking through a narrow gap in the slats of the shutter on to the outside street. There was a glow in the sky over the village square and occasionally a voice raised in conversation or laughter, German voices and German laughter of the off-duty garrison. Supper was ready at around 8 p.m. David and Marita ate in silence. There was complete silence from next door and Marita confided that Stephia and her infant went to bed early when her German visitor was not expected.

After the meal David announced that he would depart through the back of the house and through the castle grounds. Marita did not think this was wise.

"The ground is unfamiliar and the descent at night dangerous. No, you must stay here tonight and leave before daybreak."

David saw the logic of her reasoning and agreed.

Propped by pillows he stretched out between two chairs near the shuttered front window, whilst Marita retired behind the screen some ten yards away. David heard her snuggling and stretching under the bedclothes. He subdued an urge to go and join the waif-like little figure, so alone and so brave, lying quietly, almost within touching distance.

He dozed, only to be woken suddenly by a banging sound from the road outside, and raucous German laughter. Her peered furtively through the window slats and saw three uniformed figures standing in a group outside Stephia's front door. One German soldier was holding a flint lighter, whilst another held two plucked chickens aloft and the third was banging continually on Stephia's door. The soldier holding the light shouted, "Let us in, you Cretan beauty. You can have these two chickens if you let us in for half an hour. We know you're officer's meat but the three of us can give you a time to remember."

David tensed and felt Marita standing behind him, shivering, shaking and sobbing. He heard little Spiros bawling his head off in fright. He held Marita close to him. Even though he was not a tall man her head only just reached under his chin. He pressed her closely to him and realised that the frightened little woman in his arms was completely naked.

The drunken soldiers now turned their attention to Marita's door banging loudly and shouting, "Let us in, little school teacher. I bet you've got a tight little pussy. The three of us could teach you a thing or two but if you want these chickens you will have to give us something for them."

Marita trembled in his arms and within a minute the inebriated soldiers backed off and moved further down the street to regale other housewives with their lascivious requests. As their shouts died in the distance Marita remained securely clutched in David's embrace. Between sobs she explained that for the past week, and over the Christmas period, the German soldiers at the Kastelli were becoming more daring and she feared that one night they might force an entry into her house.

"I will shoot myself first before letting them have their way. Come over here," and she moved across the packed-earth floor to the small partitioned-off kitchen, where David saw a shotgun propped against the wall. "It is loaded and ready for use. I get it ready every night, tonight especially. I could not be sure about your intentions!"

David was unable to speak. He simply leant forwards in the darkness with his hands holding Marita's naked hips and kissed her gently on the forehead.

The sequence of events over the next two minutes were so rapid and inexplicable that David was unable recall them clearly the next day. Suddenly Marita's arms were around his neck and pulling his head downwards on to her upturned open mouth. Her kisses were so passionate and urgent that David lost control over himself. Marita tore at his belt whilst he clasped her firmly and tried to find her nipples with his lips. The small, sex-starved, woman was strong and physically insistent. She quickly pushed David backwards on to the bed and leapt across his thighs guiding his pulsating erection inside her and then she pumped and bored with such ferocity that David reached his climax within half a minute.

They then lay side by side, neither speaking, Marita occasionally whimpering and sobbing, consoled by the perplexed David who could not fathom the reason for this woman's unexpected, but pleasurable, sexual outburst. Could it be the pent-up frustration of eighteen months without a husband or could it have been fear generated by the bawdy German soldiers? Whatever the reason he had enjoyed the experience and started thinking about Bron. And then after a few minutes' rest Marita's small childlike fingers were exploring his nether regions producing a second erection. This time David dictated the tempo of their lovemaking. He controlled his thrusting and, lying on top of Marita, made sure that she had her own orgasmic release before he committed himself to full ejaculation. They once again lay side by side and fell into a deep sleep in each other's arms.

The couple had been asleep for nearly two hours when all hell broke loose. They were awakened by the noise of motorcycle engines revving in the road outside and, even through the shutters, bright vehicle lights were visible in the street. They both leapt out of bed and rushed to the shuttered window. Marita reached it first.

"Quick, quick Englishman, out the back. The German colonel has just arrived next door."

Then, even as she spoke, they heard a deep cultured German voice shouting outside Stephia's door.

"Open up, Stephia, it's me, Manfred."

Clinging together they heard the door open as little Spiros started to scream, woken from a deep sleep. Marita spun around towards

David and whispered urgently, "Quick, quick, out of the back into the castle."

David struggled with his trousers while Marita unbolted the back door and held it open for him. He grabbed his *sariki* and *sakouli* and made an urgent exit. As he sped down the garden path he clearly heard the loud voice of the German colonel in Stephia's house.

"I've brought you a goose and chocolate for Spiros and you can have the rest of this brandy. Can't you shut up that bawling kid? Get ready Stephia, but first I must have a piss."

David was half-way down the garden path when these last words were uttered. He remembered he had not made arrangements to visit Marita again and started back towards the half-open back door. Then the door on the other side of the dry stone wall was flung open and the bulky figure of a tall blond man was silhouetted in the light shining from the room behind him. He was so tall that he had to stoop and bend his head to get through the doorway. By the time he lifted his head again David was within two feet of Marita's open door. The half-naked German looked over the wall and straight into the steely grey eyes of the British officer. He shook his head and by that time David had reached the sanctuary of Marita's cottage and the door was pulled tight, but not firmly closed.

David again had Marita in his arms and he held her closely, neither daring to breath or speak. They heard the German officer urinating against the wall, humming to himself and grunting as he expelled the last drops of urine. Stephia's back door was still open when David heard his loud voice.

"Stephia, does the woman in the next house have a man?"

Stephia's replied, half-choking with laughter, "A man, Herr Colonel? She lost her man last year and she is now frigid."

"Ah so," replied the German officer, "but I thought I saw a face with peculiar grey eyes in the back garden."

Stephia's voice in the background replied, "It must be the brandy, Herr Colonel. Come to bed, Manfred, and forget about it," and then the door slammed shut.

Marita softly closed and bolted her back door, wrapped a blanket around her thin muscular body and then sat with David in a chair near the partition wall. For the next two hours they were entertained by noisy grunts and groans of attempted lovemaking two feet on the other side of the earthen wall. The colonel, it seemed, had drunk too much to be effective. Stephia, sometimes cajoling, sometimes chastising and sometimes giggling did her best to arouse her stuporous, impatient partner, who was alternatively laughing at his own sexual incompetence, then swearing for the same reason and eventually snoring loudly as he fell into a drunken sleep. The charade did not end with the loud snoring. After half an hour of relative silence another attempt was made to arouse the colonel's sexual ardour. This was a brief interlude which was again repeated an hour later and then, apart from loud snores and two bouts of crying from little Spiros, tranquillity was restored to Stephia's cottage.

It was now 1.30 a.m. on the 28th December. David was stiff and uncomfortable but Marita had revived some of her vitality and insisted on another session on the bed which had to be conducted in complete silence. David hesitantly obliged and afterwards spoke to Marita in a whisper:

"What I want you to do, my little schoolmistress, is to make it up with Stephia. I don't want to upset old Spiros unduly. I shall tell him tomorrow that Stephia has been seeing a German officer but that it's now finished. If you become friendly with Stephia again you might be able to find out the colonel's plans and movements. I now know who he is. I knew him as a boy in Germany in 1930. His name is Manfred Schmidt. He's a bully and a braggart and I will do everything in my power to get rid of him. If I can find out his future movements this will help me a lot. I rely on you, Marita, to do this. I will call and see you as often as possible and will use the castle route. After tonight, even if you have no news for me, I will call and see you again."

His voice trailed off, leaving Marita with a promise that his calls would not only be to collect information. Marita sealed their agreement with a long passionate kiss. Two hours before daybreak David left the cottage in Kastelli by the castle route. The descent from the castle was not as hazardous as Marita predicted and an hour after daybreak he was six kilometres along the valley floor between Kastelli and Piskopiano. After daybreak the winding road some three to four hundred feet above his head became busy with early morning traffic. He was well protected from sight amongst the boulders and trees and as he trudged steadily northwards he had time to think. So his blood brother was now in charge of counter-resistance in Heraklion and eastern Crete. He had to thank the Nazis for his family's ejection from Germany in 1931. He had to thank the Germans for the loss of his best friend in Oxford. He had to thank the *Luftwaffe* for killing his father and mother and he had to thank German paratroopers for killing Dickie Campbell. This indeed was a formidable thank you list which he was eager to repay. All his hatred and pent-up feelings became focused on one man, Colonel Manfred Schmidt. This man was now within his grasp in Crete. As the day got warmer and he struggled along the rock-strewn valley and the Dikti foothills he resolved that, all else apart, his main mission on Crete would be the elimination of Colonel Manfred Schmidt, his erstwhile blood brother and now his hated and loathed enemy.

*

"*Feldwebel* Schneider, I had a funny experience last night! I saw a man with a distinctive pair of steel-grey eyes over the back garden wall in Kastelli. I only saw him for a second but I'm convinced that I have seen those eyes before."

The colonel was addressing his trusty *Feldwebel* as their *Kübelwagen* lurched and dived over the pitted road from Kastelli to Hersonisos.

The tactful *Feldwebel* replied, "Well, Herr Colonel, you were a bit worse for wear last night but if you want me to check on it I will do so."

"No, no," replied Colonel Schmidt. "I'll deal with the problem myself. The woman in the next cottage is a frigid shrimp. You're probably right. It must have been the brandy playing tricks with my eyesight."

The rough journey continued in silence, the colonel brooding and nursing a splitting headache, but still convinced that in his alcoholic haze of the previous night he had seen a pair of grey eyes over the stone wall of Stephia's cottage. The eyes were unmistakable. Where had he seen them before? He pondered and worried and then in a flash, at a check point outside Gournes, the answer came – David Grünberg his blood brother. But this was inconceivable. The Grünberg family were probably incarcerated in Dachau or Belsen and David, a boy of his own age, would almost certainly have been eliminated by the Gestapo. Manfred considered that the final solution for the Jews was one of the better things Hitler had introduced into

Nazi Germany. So forget it. But still the lingering, nagging, doubts remained. The small convoy was now approaching the guardpost outside Villa Ariadne and he would have other things to worry about, not least the arrangements for a New Year's Eve party in two days' time.

Chapter Twenty-Two

Eastern Crete,
January – February 1943
Meeting with Corporal Dai,
1st May 1943

The *Luftwaffe* pilot was getting fed up with the irritating colonel sitting behind him in the two-seater Storch spotter plane. This was the third time he had been instructed to fly southwards along the western foothills of the Diktis at a dangerously low level of two hundred feet. Looking in his rear-view mirror he saw the blond, tanned colonel, hair streaming in the wind, wearing dark sunglasses and sporting a white silk cravat trailing behind his neck. The colonel always wore a white cravat on these sorties, his concept of the daring and risk of spotter flights which the pilot had come to accept with equanimity. This was to be the last sortie of the day. A wintery sun was setting in the west sending its slanting rays into the slate-grey sides of the Dikti foothills. Colonel Schmidt had indicated that he had seen 'something' in an olive grove as they flew directly southwards from Piskopiano. He himself had not seen a thing and concluded that the man sitting behind him was only being pernickety asserting his authority on a junior flyer.

A sharp jab in the back of his left shoulder and a finger pointing earthwards drew the pilot's attention to a glistening metallic object, reflected in the sun's rays and lying at the edge of a large triangular olive grove and near the left bank of a dried out watercourse. The pilot thought, 'that could be anything' but instinctively made a 'fix' on his spotter map held on a clipper board and securely fixed to the fuselage of his cockpit. He acknowledged that he had seen the object and, in order to show his interest, banked to the right and for the fourth time flew over Piskopiano on a fixing sortie. Satisfied with his mathematics he gave the colonel a thumbs up sign, banked northwards, and flew into the setting sun towards Heraklion.

When the Storch plane returned for a third run over the olive grove David became concerned that the German pilot might have seen something. He and five of the commando were well inside the cave and out of sight. Only Biffo was absent down at the farmhouse and David trusted him to conceal himself. The flights had, weather permitting, been going on once or twice a day since their arrival. When the plane's engine was heard approaching for its fourth run David became convinced that they had 'spotted' something unusual around the farmhouse.

"They're on to something lads. They may pay us a visit tonight or at the crack of dawn tomorrow. So we'll have guards out all night on a four-hourly rota, one at the head of the farmyard track where it joins the road to Piskopiano, one in the farmyard and one on the high ground half way up the olive grove and of course one here at the cave. One of us will have to do an all-night guard duty and Sergeant Hubbard and I will take the road and farmyard guard points from 4 a.m. onwards. I am going down to the farmhouse now to see if Biffo's found any reason why the Jerry plane was showing an interest in us."

"Send for Captain Hartman," Manfred commanded as he sat in the map room of Heraklion airfield with Colonel von Thiesendorf and the Storch pilot in attendance. The pilot was excited and now convinced that he and the blond-haired colonel had discovered a vital military secret in an olive grove south of Piskopiano. Captain Hartman arrived in a flurry and Manfred took him to a large wall map.

"Hartman, you will take a small section to Malia and lead an Italian recce platoon to this point here south of Piskopiano. I've seen a suspicious object in an olive grove," indicating with his finger, "and I want you and the Italian soldiers to be at the farmhouse before dawn and into the olive grove at first light. You are to lead the recce and report back to me at Villa Ariadne tomorrow morning. Good luck."

Captain Hartman in a *Kübelwagen* with two German NCOs, arrived at the Italian garrison headquarters in Malia at 2000 hours.

"Impossible, Captain Hartman. Not enough notice. Besides we're not fully trained for night patrols."

Major Berganzoli, the Italian commander, was pacing around his small control room in a bath of perspiration. Captain Hartman swallowed his frustration.

"Major Berganzoli, this order comes from Colonel Schmidt and he has the authority of General Braüer to proceed with the attack. I am to lead your storm platoon on the recce."

Major Berganzoli stopped pacing and turned to face Hartman, his dark eyes flashing malice.

"You are to lead my men into the field? Let me remind you, Captain, that I am commander of the Italian forces at Malia and if we are to go into battle I shall be the one to lead them. I cannot disobey this ridiculous order from your headquarters, but I shall take my boys on this patrol and be in charge of the operation. Is that understood?"

Captain Hartman nodded and Major Berganzoli concluded, "You may come along as observers if you so wish. You'll see how efficient the Siena Division are in action."

Captain Hartman cringed inwardly and, as it transpired, he had every reason to have misgivings about the Italian major's ability to conduct the recce. Unfortunately Major Berganzoli outranked him and there was nothing he could do about it. Major Berganzoli now became a veritable cyclone of activity. He shouted orders and counter-orders, woke up the whole garrison, pored over detailed maps of the area and, by and large, made mountains from molehills. Twice he wanted to call the operation off and was continually asking to change the time of departure. Italian officers and men ran here, there and everywhere, each with his own mission, but none of them clearly briefed as to how the issued orders would fit into the reconnaissance plan. Major Berganzoli had now escalated the sortie into a major attack on a heavily defended position.

The disorganised rabble eventually took to the road at 0600 hours, led by Major Berganzoli who insisted on travelling in a light tank whose rate of progress slowed down the whole convoy. Captain Hartman and his German NCOs, as instructed, brought up the rear. By daybreak they were approaching the outskirts of Hersonisos and, an hour later, after a very cautious approach, Major Berganzoli's tank led the recce convoy into the centre of Spiros' farmyard and trained its gun on the farmhouse, with the echelons of motorised troops in their vehicles behind it. Through a loud hailer the major commanded the occupants of the house and the outhouses to come out with their hands raised.

David, who had been on point duty at daybreak, heard and witnessed the noisy approach of the Italian vehicles from Piskopiano. He withdrew to the steep scrub-sided escarpment on the edge of the roadside where he had a good view of the farm and heard the orders issued by the Italians and Germans in their vehicles. He looked with wonderment at the two Italian troop carriers cowering behind Major Berganzoli's little tank, all the soldiers sheltering in their vehicles, pointing their loaded guns at the buildings. The scene at the farmhouse was chaotic and reminded David of a market day in Llanybydder.

A German officer, standing on the roof of his *Kübelwagen*, shouted at the tank from which Major Berganzoli refused to emerge until the house had been 'cleared'. The German captain was clearly urging the Italians to get into the olive grove and start the search. But Berganzoli was adamant that he had to clear the farmhouse to protect his rear and, in the meantime, he was staying safely inside his tank. Captain Hartman and his two NCOs now sprinted across the yard and began banging on the farmhouse's wooden door with their rifle butts shouting "*Raus, raus, hande hoch, hande hoch*" and within seconds Spiros and Anna appeared in the doorway with their hands held high. Major Berganzoli's upper body now appeared in the turret of the tank. He was brandishing a sword and shouting, "Fix bayonets and charge."

The Italian soldiers in the troop carriers began emerging in ones and twos with bayonets fixed and ran towards Captain Hartman's group holding Spiros and Anna hostage at the farmhouse doorway. The Costantinos were hustled inside and the soldiers entered the small house, rummaging indiscriminately. Berganzoli then turned his eager soldiers loose on the outhouses which were searched noisily and meticulously with no results. Only then, after thirty minutes in the yard, did the major declare, "Our rear is safeguarded. Now let's go for the olive field."

Turning about, brandishing his sword aloft, he led a charge into the olive grove with the disbelieving Captain Hartman bringing up the rear. The incongruity of the situation almost made David laugh as he observed the antics of the Italian infantry darting in and out amongst the olive trees, brandishing their bayoneted rifles, led by a diminutive officer shouting contradictory orders at each turning. And then a shout went up just underneath David's hideout on the bank of the dried out stream.

"Eureka, eureka."

A group of soldiers had found the shining object and were inspecting it with exaggerated respect. It was Spiros' milk churn. Major Berganzoli and Captain Hartman arrived simultaneously. The major was standing over the churn and pointing to it with his sword.

"There you are, Herr Captain, only a milk churn after all. Go and tell your colonel about our prize."

Captain Hartman was furious.

"Continue the search, Major Berganzoli, this may be food left for the *andartes*."

Major Berganzoli sneered, "I can see you're not a country lad. The farmer here has a large goat herd and he milks his goats at various places around the farm. This is one of them. Tip up the churn,"

The sergeant did as ordered spilling a trickle of stale curdled goat's milk on to the ground.

"Satisfied now, Captain Hartman?" asked Berganzoli.

But the German officer and his aides were already striding away back to the farm. Shortly afterwards the chatting and laughing Italians strode back to their vehicles and left the farmyard in a cloud of mid-morning dust.

Captain Hartman's report to Colonel Schmidt did not please the eastern Crete commander. He berated the captain for not having insisted on taking control of the exercise. The outcome was, as the colonel might have expected from the Italians, a mixture of chaotic organisation and élan. Italians made good bullfighters and lovers but poor soldiers. Whatever had happened to the fighting qualities of the Roman centurions in Caesar's army?

"Captain Hartman I am going to recommend your transfer back to Germany, or Poland, where I hope your talents will be more appreciated than they are here."

The captain was dismissed and the following day Manfred paid a call on General Carta in Neapolis.

"General Carta, your commander in Malia, Major Enzio Berganzoli, must go. Yesterday he messed up a patrol to Piskopiano. I sent Captain Hartman to lead the reconnaissance but Major Berganzoli over-ruled him. I am sure you are aware, General, that night reconnaissance by your troops are to be led by German officers and NCOs. This was agreed last month."

General Carta, sweating profusely, took off his glasses and looked at Manfred.

"Colonel Schmidt, may I draw your attention to two facts? The first is that this was a daylight exercise and the second is that Major Berganzoli outranked your captain and had every right to lead his troops on the reconnaissance. I also need not have to remind you that the outcome was a fiasco, the finding of a shiny milk churn in an olive grove, hardly a military success!"

Manfred felt his whole body bursting with rage and towering over the diminutive general, glowered at him menacingly. General Carta continued, "I intend looking on this fruitless reconnaissance as a preliminary exercise of co-operation between German and Italian forces in eastern Crete. I sincerely hope you will do the same. Major Berganzoli remains in his post at Malia."

Manfred knew he was beaten and backed off. Even General Brauer, when approached, felt he could not support Manfred.

"A storm in a teacup," as he put it, adding, "It's not worth crying over spilt milk, or even a spilt milk churn!"

During January 1943 General Müller strengthened his stranglehold on resistance forces in Crete. All local commanders were ordered to undertake snap searches and to use cordon and search tactics. If any suspicious agents were captured at these searches they were to be summarily executed and in most instances the nearest village, or villages, to the point of capture were to be razed to the ground. With the influx of fresh troops General Bruno Brauer was also actively engaged in strengthening his northern coastal defences and he planted a large garrison on Askifou plain. In response to General Müller's prompting Manfred arranged his first cordon and search exercise in late January. The target was to be Gournes, twelve kilometres east of Heraklion. With a flash of arrogance Manfred invited General Carta to:

"Come to see how it's done."

General Carta politely declined, having a prior engagement, and sent Major Berganzoli and Captain Tavana along as observers. Manfred was suitably rebuffed but had no objections to the company of Captain Tavana with whom he could, at least, have an intelligent conversation.

Colonel Manfred Schmidt's cordon and search attack on Gournes on the 24th January, 1943 was a textbook example of Teutonic thoroughness. An hour before dawn motorised infantry drove through the sleepy streets to occupy the docks area, closely followed by foot soldiers who were strategically placed on the coast roads to the east and west of the town and astride the small road junction to Anapoli. Further units surrounded the small fishing port in a cordon of steel. At dawn, one of Captain Bucholz's E-boats appeared at the harbour entrance. For twenty-four hours on January 24th no one was allowed to enter or leave Gournes and the Germans undertook a house to house search. Anyone found harbouring a resistance suspect or having a firearm in the house was to be arrested. The build-up to the exercise went like clockwork and the efficiency of the searchers was a feature loudly acclaimed by Captain Tavana and the subdued, and largely ignored, Major Berganzoli.

At the end of twenty-four hours only three men were arrested, all elderly Cretans, two for harbouring pre-1940 rifles with no ammunition and the third, the captain of a small fishing smack which was allowed out at dawn by the E-boat but was promptly arrested, and the catch confiscated when the boat returned to harbour in the evening. These three old veterans were taken to Heraklion for further questioning. On the 27th January Colonel Manfred Schmidt ordered them to be shot for subversive activities. The sentences were carried out on the 28th January. After this incident General Müller became known amongst Cretan resistance as the Butcher of Crete and Manfred received the nickname the "White Angel of Gournes", referring to his sun-bleached hair. General Müller's attack on Azigonia on the same day proved 'more successful'. Seventy-eight Cretan suspects were executed and three villages razed to the ground.

*

By February Major David Green's commando had settled in at Piskopiano. There were regular daily recces into surrounding areas and David, sometimes alone and sometimes with one armed commando as a bodyguard, was frequently away from the kibbutz for three or four nights and at these times Sergeant Hubbard acted as base commander.

Accompanied by Biffo, David set out westwards in early February to contact Bandouvas, the nationalist leader around Heraklion, who reputedly was flirting with ELAS and the Germans, at one and the same time. All Bandouvas' efforts were centred around accumulation of arms, but what he and his followers would do with the weapons was not clear. To reach Arhanes, one of Bandouvas' hideouts, took two days and nights and the crossing of six partially dry river beds. Biffo was an excellent guard on these sorties, alert, quick-thinking and thoroughly dependable. The two reached Arhanes on the second night and slept in the village inn.

David let it be known that he wanted to meet Bandouvas. No one spoke directly to the two but towards evening a swarthy, dark-faced man with long drooping moustaches approached them and asked in Greek, "What is your business?"

To which David replied, "My business is personal. I met Colonel Bandouvas in Heraklion in May 1941. I have information for him."

The dark Cretan sidled up to the pair, "Tell me. I will convey your message to Colonel Bandouvas."

David replied, "I will only speak to Colonel Bandouvas."

The smelly Cretan departed but reappeared an hour later.

"The colonel will see you."

He insisted on blindfolding David and Biffo and they were led behind his donkey for two or three miles. At one stage the swarthy guide asked, "What if you're informers?"

David replied, "If we are then you can do away with us."

He felt Biffo squirming at his side.

After a long journey over very rough ground the blindfolds were removed, their arms were taken away, and they were ushered into a dimly lit cave. In the middle of the cavern a blazing fire was being used for cooking and heating and about a dozen assortedly dressed men were sitting around warming themselves. One stood up and approached David. He was short, stockily built with a drooping grey moustache and he spoke in Greek.

"Ah, so you want to see me? Well, here I am."

And looking closer at David he asked, "Have we met before?" David reminded him of their brief encounter in Chappell's dockside headquarters at Heraklion. The old man's face brightened up a little.

"And who sent you, my little man, to see the great Bandouvas?"

David replied without hesitation, "I am sent by Winston Churchill. He wants to help Cretan fighters."

"Well," said Bandouvas, "give me some guns and bullets and we'll get rid of the Germans. The Italians will turn and run once we've beaten Butcher Müller and his gang."

And then David asked about the communists. Bandouvas' face became a mask of ferocity.

"The ones on Crete are scum and deserve to be eliminated. Give me enough guns and I'll get rid of Porphyroyennis, Samaritis and Bodias. But to do this I need guns. My EAM compatriots on the mainland are quite sympathetic. They might give me guns to get rid of the Bolshevik vermin in Crete."

David realised that the vendetta principle was represented strongly in Bandouvas' thinking. He felt he had to placate the *kapitan*.

"I'll be in touch with Mr Churchill in London. If anyone can help you he can."

The nationalist leader of eastern Crete then invited David and Biffo to share a meal with them, a foul smelling goat stew laced with *tsikoudia* to make it palatable and washed down with liberal portions of nondescript wine. David struggled with his food but Biffo devoured everything placed before him. They were led back over the mountain pass by the same guide and had their blindfolds removed in Arhanes an hour before daybreak. Their guns were not returned to them.

The first courier run to the south was planned for the 13th February. Biffo accompanied David on the first trip. He thought hard about the best method of getting his messages south to Keratokombou. Parts of the journey involved travel along established tracks and roads and could be accomplished by riding a mule or donkey, but the mountain passes and the shepherd's trails were best negotiated on foot. Messages were received and transmitted at Keratokombou by direct open transfer from a submarine with no codes involved. David's messages for transmission were memorised by the courier. Written messages were tied to the inside of a donkey's tail, near its anal orifice, using the animal's hair as a string.

The route David chose avoided Kastelli and the four-road junction six kilometres east of Arkalohorio where German checkpoints might be expected and also the road junction five kilometres west of Viannos. From Piskopiano the two couriers took a donkey eastwards along the Gournes road and moved southwards at Stenatilo into the Dikti foothills. The road then became a mountain path winding southwards through Aski, Kastamonitsa, Geraki and into Nipiditos. From this point, having abandoned their donkey, they moved south-west along a dried river bed to Kassanos and then southwards through Martha to Kertokombou. The distance involved was about forty-five kilometres, but it took a day and a half to complete the journey. The first message from Cairo was brief and hardly worth the danger and distance travelled for its collection.

"Hope you're settled in. Work on the spaghetti boys. More soon." David was able to report his meeting with Bandouvas and confirmed they were in a position to 'go to work'. In a matter of an hour the messages were received and transmitted and the courier party retraced their steps to Piskopiano. David made Biffo his chief courier and Gunner Paul Smithson acted as deputy. Between them they did the Keratokombou run every month or six weeks.

To David the message from Cairo was clear – concentrate on the Italians. From time to time his recce party came across an Italian patrol, always identified by their noisy perambulation and their extreme reluctance to leave the beaten track even for a call of nature. If he was to contact the Italians it would be in broad daylight and on one of the open roads. They never strayed into the hinterland and they were hardly ever abroad at night. He intensified his recces on the larger roads east of Piskopiano and found that the inland road between Gournes, Tzermiado and Neapolis were frequently used by Italian convoys and the pattern of Italian patrols were always constant. The lead vehicles were two motorcycles followed by an NCO in an armoured car. Behind came two or three troop carriers, each holding twenty men, followed by the commanding officer's armoured car, protected at its rear by another armoured jeep and two motorcyclists. The officers in charge certainly took no chances of being involved in any frontal action which the convoy might encounter.

Within a matter of days David had seen four of these lightly armoured convoys moving along the Gournes-Tzermiado road. He picked his spot carefully along a straight stretch of road with no overhanging cliffs and no excessive shrubbery on either side. It was a sunny, hot afternoon when David heard and eventually saw the Italian convoy approaching. With arms outstretched he stepped into the middle of the road and brought the convoy to a halt. The motorcyclists unclipped their rifles and a sergeant from the lead armoured vehicle came towards him with his automatic carbine poised for action.

"Could I speak to your commanding officer, please?" asked David in impeccable Italian.

The sergeant stopped in his tracks. "What do you want with him?"

David replied, "I have information which will be very useful to your captain."

The sergeant, still keeping David covered with his carbine, ordered one of the motorcyclists to the rear, "Get Captain Tavana up here quickly," and turning to David he added, "If you're playing any tricks, watch out, I'll blow your head off."

Captain Tavana appeared and was agreeably surprised to hear David speak in a cultured Italian accent. He looked around and into the distance and then returned his gaze to the short Cretan with steely-grey eyes, still holding his arms aloft in the warm midday sun. He turned to the sergeant.

"All right, Sergeant Bracchi, you can put your gun down. This man is unarmed," and then turning to David said, "And what can I do for you, or, more precisely, what can you do for me?"

David lowered his arms, "Captain Tavana, I am here with one of the *andartes* groups and they wish to make peace with the Italians, but not with the Germans. If there's a way you can suggest that this could happen please inform me. I am sure that my group would be anxious to co-operate with you against the common enemy."

The Italian smiled and laughed, "And which group do you represent?"

David replied, "It's a large group that once supported the King of Greece. Not so any more. We have lost many of our *andartes* through defection."

Captain Tavana was almost laughing aloud when he asked in perfect English, "And is this group British-led?"

David replied in English, "Of course, my dear Captain, who else?"

Captain Tavana then became serious.

"I am not empowered to make any deals as you will appreciate. But I will pass on your message to my commander-in-chief. In the meantime I can take it that your so-called group will not attack Italian soldiers."

David replied, "On that, as a British officer and a gentleman, you have my word."

They were about to part when Captain Tavana asked, "How can I contact you?"

David replied, "Some two kilometres south of the junction between Gournes and the Kastelli-Hersonisos road there is an icon. Twenty paces behind the icon you will find a bald rock-face. If you scratch a 'T' on the rock and add a number then I will meet you at the junction at twelve noon on the day specified by you, provided of course the Germans have not placed search parties in the area."

"Agreed," said Captain Tavana who seemed to be on the point of moving forwards to kiss David on both cheeks.

They parted company. The convoy proceeded eastwards and David returned to the hideout at Piskopiano, having picked up Sergeant Hubbard who had, all the while, been lying fully armed and concealed in a trench some fifteen yards off the edge of the road. David was pleased with his afternoon's work. All he now had to do was to get the Italians to supply guns to Bandouvas and for both to unite and drive the Germans out of eastern Crete. But he did not wish this to happen until he had settled his score with Colonel Manfred Schmidt.

On the 1st March, 1943 David was making his way west from Piskopiano to spend a night of observation on Ames ridge overlooking Heraklion airfield and harbour. He was conscious that it was St David's Day and remembered the celebrations with the First/Fifth in Northern Ireland and the vile leek-eating ceremony, when newly arrived junior officers ate a raw leek and downed a quart of ale. Whenever his thoughts turned to his regiment he inevitably ended up thinking about and pining for Bron. He was four kilometres west of Piskopiano and approaching the third dry river bed on his journey when he heard the unmistakable sound of a Welsh song being alternately hummed and sung:

"*Myfi syn fachgen ieunanc ffôl, Yn byw yn ôl fy ffansi, Myfyn bugeilior gwennith gwyn, Ac arall yn ei fedi.*"

The voice came from a typical Cretan farm-hand who was languidly hoeing the earth around the base of an olive tree. David approached the Cretan from behind and coughed politely. Two deep brown, startled eyes looked across at David and the singing and hoeing stopped abruptly. David walked to within ten yards of the crouching Cretan now holding the hoe menacingly in both hands, stopped, and simply said, "*Shwt mae heddiw?*"

The Cretan's face registered perplexity, amazement and fear. He stood his ground, mute and ready to spring. David smiled.

"I heard your song. It's a Welsh one and a favourite of mine. What the hell are you doing out here? Let me tell you I'm a serving officer with the First Welch. I'm afraid we lost most of our boys at Khania here on Crete."

The last statement broke the ice. The pseudo-Cretan visibly relented. His grasp on the hoe relaxed and his face cracked into a lop-sided smile.

David continued, "My name is David Green, Major Green. What are your last three?" he asked referring to the last three digits of enlistment in the British Army.

Like a robot and holding the hoe as if it were a rifle, the crouching figure stood to attention and announced, "Corporal David Griffiths 2175394 RASC. Sir."

"Well, Corporal Griffiths what are you doing here?"

The corporal dropped his hoe and leant against the trunk of the olive tree.

"I was left behind, Sir, but I'm happy here working on this farm. I've heard there have been some officers wandering around Crete trying to get blokes like me back to Cairo to fight again. Well they won't get me to go. I've had a belly-full of fighting. You're not one of them are you, Sir?"

David laughed. "Of course not, Corporal. But I am here on some special business. Now tell me how you came to be here?"

Corporal Dai Griffiths, now completely at ease, sat with David in the shade of an olive tree and related his story.

"I was in North Africa in a cushy number driving top brass around Cairo and Alex when I was sent with the First Welch to the garrison depot at Khania. There I drove the commanding officer, Colonel Daddy Duncan, for a while but I got moved on to general duties and," with a wry smile he added, "I lost my cushy number because I got drunk one night and crashed the colonel's Humber. He wasn't very pleased."

"I don't suppose he was," David interjected, "so what happened afterwards?"

Dai continued, "Jerry came in May and I was sent up in a convoy with a New Zealand lot to a place called Prison Valley. Mad buggers, the New Zealanders. The commanding officer was a Colonel Kipperberger, or something like that. One morning he came around and made everyone at HQ grab a rifle and go up to a ridge. The German paratroopers were all around us. I hadn't shot any bullets in anger up till then, but we learnt quickly and then this New Zealander, Sergeant Upham, led a charge to the top of the hill. He was cool as a cucumber. He sat on a wall shooting at the Germans until they pulled back."

David interrupted, "Sergeant Upham got a VC for that action."

Corporal Griffiths continued, "VC be buggered, he deserved more than that. Anyway we pulled back and someone shouted for a driver to take some wounded to hospital in Soudha. Three of us Royal Army Service Corps blokes took a three-tonner each and off we went. I followed the lorry in front. The sergeant in charge in the first lorry had lots of arguments with sentries at road blocks and threatened to shoot quite a few people on the way. Anyway he got us clear of Soudha and then it was dark and we apparently drove around Rethymno through a German checkpoint. Some fifty miles further on I ran out of petrol. I had six wounded men in the back of the truck and by the time we ran out of juice two of them were dead and another two almost gone. An RASC sergeant took the two living ones on to his lorry and drove off. I waited around for a while until the two other poor buggers died and then I started walking eastwards towards the rising sun. I laid up in the daytime and moved at night. There was fighting all around me and, though I can't understand German, I was certain they were Jerries in the fields around Heraklion. I kept going and after about a week landed up here sometime in early June, probably the 2nd or 3rd. Old Spiros at the farm took pity on me and took me in and he has an elderly daughter who looks after me. I dig his fields and look after his goats. By the way, Sir, how's the war going? Is it true that we are winning in Egypt?"

David confirmed that Rommel was on the run in North Africa and that the Germans were deadlocked at Stalingrad.

"Bloody good," said Dai, "I'm glad I missed those battles, especially the one in Stalingrad. I expect it's bloody cold out there."

David rose to his feet and was about to leave when he asked the RASC corporal, "What did you do in civilian life Corporal Griffiths?"

"Me?" Dai replied, "I was a mechanical genius. I could fix anything from a motor car to a washing machine or a fountain pen."

'Good,' thought David, 'his mechanical abilities might be of use to me,' and turning to the corporal he added aloud, "I'll be coming around this way quite often. We'll have another chat when we meet again. By the way, you've got a nice singing voice. Let me wish you a happy St David's Day."

The corporal's face broke into a wide grin.

"St David's day be buggered. *Dydd Gwyl Dewi*. Well, would you believe it! I'll have an extra drop of *tsikoudia* to celebrate tonight. Well, well, well."

As David walked briskly away across the olive grove Corporal David Griffiths thought, 'I wonder if that bloke's genuine? He could be a Jerry plant looking for British deserters on Crete. I'll lay low for a few days and try and avoid him next time.'

David also reflected on his contact with the singing mechanical genius from Llanelli, or Sospan as Dai would have it, and wondered, with a smile, if all Cretan farmers were called Spiros.

Communication with Bandouvas and Captain Tavana was fairly easily accomplished. David now faced the problem of finding Militades Porphyroyennis, the communist leader in the Lasithis and eastern Crete. During the last week of March he took Sergeant Hubbard into uncharted territory in the Lasithi mountains. They went fully armed carrying two Sten guns each and their *sakoulis* bulging with hand grenades, food, spare water and sufficient supplies to last six days. They journeyed mainly some three hundred metres inland, parallel with the coastal road, making wide detours around towns and larger villages. They reached Kalahorio fifty kilometres from base after two days and then trudged upwards into the Lasithis to reach Meseleri on the evening of the third day. This, David decided, was a likely contact point with the Lasithi *andartes*.

Meseleri was a typical Cretan mountain village, a clutch of small, single-roomed houses arranged around a large square with a church prominent at one end and a two-storey village inn at the opposite end. There were three entry roads leading into the square at three of the corners, the church occupying the fourth corner. David and Sergeant Hubbard approached the main square by the larger road from Kalahorio. On this road, about two kilometres outside the village, they constructed a small hide about ten metres off the roadside where they left two of the Sten guns and all their grenades and *sakoulis*. David made sure they each took a red-marked cartridge holder along with their Sten guns.

In Meseleri they walked boldly across the deserted village square, sat on some hard wooden chairs under the shade of an eucalyptus tree and placed their guns prominently on the wooden tables before them. Bread and cheese, some wine and *tsikoudia* were ordered and eaten and all the while the newcomers were deliberately ignored by the local Cretans and even the innkeeper, sullen, and monosyllabic, would not be drawn into conversation. David and Sergeant Hubbard spoke to each other quietly for over an hour. Occasionally one of them raised his voice and uttered the name Porphyroyennis. At such times, through the corner of his eye, David saw the inn keeper visibly stiffen when the name of the *andartes' kapitan* was mentioned. A modest tariff for the food and wine was paid and the two commandos left just before sunset to spend an uncomfortable night at their hide.

Mid-morning on the following day David and the sergeant returned to Meseleri and took their seats outside the inn, parking their Sten guns on the wooden table. The place was ominously quiet and they both had an uncanny feeling of being observed by unseen eyes. They chatted quietly together and took some wine keeping a weary eye on the square.

At around midday, Sergeant Hubbard, without raising his voice or his head, whispered, "I think we've got visitors. I've just seen someone move behind that low wall near the church."

Within seconds they both became aware of dark figures appearing fleetingly in doorways, heads appearing over a whitewashed wall and then a few armed figures materialised at the three exit roads carrying shotguns. David was about to speak when he felt the jab of a hard object in the small of his back. Turning around he looked into the vicious eyes of the ugliest face he had ever seen on a human being. Four bandits had emerged stealthily from the inn door behind them. Sergeant Hubbard also had a large, evil-looking, downright ugly man prodding him in the stomach with his rifle barrel.

Two of the bandits were ordered by Mr Large to search the commandos. This they did with some pleasure and banter but found nothing. The Sten guns were picked up and handed to the large ugly man and the smaller, uglier bandit. The larger of the two was spokesman.

"What do you do here?"

David replied, "I wish to speak to Militades Porphyroyennis."

The smaller man spat on the ground.

"What do you want with him?" asked the larger spokesman.

"I will only speak to Porphyroyennis," said David.

At a nod from the smaller, ugly-faced bandit David and Sergeant Hubbard were prodded forwards into the square, which had quietly filled with thirty or more people, all in some sort of mixed uniform and all carrying weapons, but very few firearms. The men in the square formed a human corridor from the inn to a small corner exit road which led by devious mountain tracks over the Lasithis to Ierapetra. It was obvious to David that he and Sergeant Hubbard were going to be encouraged to run the gauntlet and take this exit route.

David turned sideways towards the sergeant and, speaking quietly and rapidly, said, "Sergeant, on my command, make a dash for the left corner road, the one we came up this morning."

Behind their backs the larger lieutenant and the small ugly commander were standing on a step receiving cheers and stiff armed salutes from their soldiers.

The very ugly man spoke, "I am Samaritis. I am the commander of all forces in Lasithi. These men," spitting towards David and Sergeant Hubbard, "are traitors. Let them go and tell Porphyroyennis, Bodias, Bandouvas, Papadakis, the Butcher Müller and Churchill that I am master of Lasithi. To save their lives they must run the cordon now," and, with that, David and Sergeant Hubbard were prodded forward and started running between the rows of *andartes*.

When they had gone some forty yards David heard Samaritis cursing as he tried to release the Sten's safety catch. The men in the cordon were aiming blows at their heads but the two commandos sprinted forwards and then, after covering another twenty yards, David shouted "NOW" and they both veered off sharply to the left and raced towards the exit road.

As they rounded the street corner David heard the unmistakable 'plop' of a Sten bullet hitting a wall above his head. Samaritis had obviously negotiated the problem with the safety catch, but handling a Sten was a new experience for him and his aim was out, too high, a common fault with inexperienced Sten gunners. The fleeing couple were still in full view of the square and the Sten was firing, but no bullets arrived.

"Blanks," shouted David and they kept running.

The big, ugly bandit also having trouble with his Sten safety catch, crouched down to hold the gun between his legs and fumbled for the catch, inadvertently touching the gun's hair trigger. A dum-dum bullet tore through his face and forehead splattering bone and brain over the white-washed walls of the inn. Samaritis in a rage kicked the dying body of his lieutenant as he withered and squirmed on the ground and holding his Sten aloft ran across the square shouting, "After them," and "Follow me." The two fit commandos had a good head start and the bandits, mostly elderly men, were no match for the fleeing Britons.

David and Sergeant Hubbard did not stop sprinting until they reached the hide and recovered their hidden *sakoulis* and Stens. There they paused for breath.

"That was a close call, Sergeant Hubbard. What did you make of that lot and of Samaritis?"

"Not a lot," the sergeant replied and continued, "Why did you shout blanks, Sir, as we were running?"

David gave the sergeant a brief smile.

"Before we came I filled the two red marked Sten cartridge clips with one live round at the lead and then all blanks. So Samaritis now has two Stens and two cartridge clips containing blanks. They won't be much use to him. Tell me Sergeant, how many men and guns did you count on that square?"

"I thought there were some twenty-seven men there, Sir, and a dozen, or so, old rifles and shotguns," the sergeant replied.

"Just as I thought," replied David. "You know what that cordon was all about? They were trying to force us to leave by the right-hand corner road where I expect the rest of Samaritis' group were lying in wait. There would then have been a turkey shoot and we would have been the turkeys. I don't expect we would have made it. Well, we're all right now. Off we go" and the two started jogging downhill into the valley below Meseleri towards Kalahorio.

After they had gone about two hundred yards David stopped and started chuckling.

"What's the matter Sir?" asked the sweaty-faced sergeant.

"I was only thinking what old Churchill would think if he knew the ugly bastard Samaritis had included his name on a list with the Cretan bandits and Butcher Müller."

Sergeant Hubbard laughed and they both chortled as they moved briskly westwards across the Lasithi plains, with its myriads of windmills, towards Piskopiano.

They rested that night on the eastern Dikti foothills some two kilometres outside the village of Tapes. Both were exhausted by the day's exertion but just before they fell asleep David, in a nostalgic mood generated by the days activity, told Sergeant Hubbard about his relationship with Colonel Manfred Schmidt, the White Angel of Gournes. He explained about their blood brother relationship and concluded, "So you see I have a special interest in the White Angel. I hold him and other Nazi thugs responsible for evicting my family from Germany, for the death of my parents in London, for the death of my best friend at Oxford and of Dickie Campbell here in Crete. I know it's absurd to focus all one's hatred on one man but that's how it is. Whatever else I do in Crete, I'm out to get Manfred Schmidt. In the land of vendettas this will be my personal vendetta."

For a while David was lost in thought and spoke again, "By the way, Sergeant Hubbard, and not that it matters, you do realise I'm Jewish?"

The sergeant turned over sideways, nestling into the hard ground for comfort, "I had guessed, Sir. Why else would you call our hide at Piskopiano a kibbutz?"

The pre-arranged date for David's next meeting with Captain Tavana was at twelve noon on the 29th March near the icon on the Hersonisos-Kastelli road. The Italian captain, immaculately dressed as always, turned up unarmed. His first comment to David was, "Tommy, I think it's silly we should meet without weapons. If we are attacked by anyone we would be sitting ducks."

David agreed and the suave Italian, lighting a cigarette in a holder continued, "Well, Tommy, the ball is on your side, or is it the ball is in your court? How can I help you?"

David replied, "I have three questions to ask you. The first is: do you have contact with Porphyroyennis and if so can you arrange for me to meet him?"

The Italian's face screwed up quizzically.

"The first answer is yes and my second answer is no. I do not think it wise for you to get involved with Porphyroyennis."

David accepted the Italian's rebuttal without question.

"Secondly, Captain Tavana, have you met Samaritis?"

The Italian's face creased in a wide smile.

"No, but I would like to. He sounds like a ferocious character, an Al Capone of Crete."

"Well," said David, "I would advise you to steer clear of Mr Capone. He's not at all a nice fellow. I met him. Like the rest of them he wants arms and from what I've seen of his *andartes* they are old, poorly trained and only have outdated shotguns for firearms. There's about ninety of them at present on the western Lasithis around the village of Meseleri."

"Thank you, Tommy, for this information." Captain Tavana replied, "I'll pass it on to my superiors. Perhaps a punitive expedition to this area might prove fruitful. Is that all, Tommy?"

"No," David replied, "What can you tell me about Colonel Manfred Schmidt? About his background?"

Captain Tavana was smiling again.

"Colonel Schmidt is my colleague in arms. I have always found him fair to deal with but completely ruthless in his actions against transgressors. He is from Munich. His father held a high position in the secretariat of the Bavarian Nazi Party in the thirties. I believe he died of cancer in 1939. Colonel Schmidt, illogically, blames the war, and especially Britain, for his father's death but I cannot see how he can blame the British for a malignant tumour. He has an inborn hatred for the British. So look out, Tommy, your head will be on the floor – or is it block? – if you're caught. Incidentally he has a Knight's Cross, the highest German decoration and was wounded in the battle for Crete in May 1941. His injuries have left him with a weak left arm. Will that do for you, Tommy? Why did you want to know about the colonel?"

"Just curiosity, just curiosity," David replied.

As they parted, Captain Tavana shouted over his shoulder, "We'll keep in touch, Tommy, and don't forget to come armed next time."

Chapter Twenty-Three

The Ambush, 27th April, 1943

Colonel Heydrich Müller arrived unexpectedly at Villa Ariadne on the morning of the 10th April in a foul mood. He closeted himself with Manfred in the operations room and harangued and badgered him on the lack of anti-terrorist initiative in his territory. The colonel pointed out that ever since Gournes, Manfred's command had not achieved anything spectacular.

He continued, banging the desk, "Look at my command in western Crete! We executed thirty-two terrorists last month and have destroyed five villages for harbouring *andartes*," and he began to enumerate his successes by counting them individually on the fingers of his left hand, "Platanias," the thumb, "Stilos," the forefinger, "Fournes," the middle finger, "Galatas," the ring finger and, "Asigonia," the little finger. "And what have you been doing here in Heraklion? Bugger all."

Manfred was quick to recognise that at least three of the villages mentioned by Müller had been dealt with during the summer and autumn of 1942 but, in the current electrifying atmosphere, he was not going to question the veracity of the general's statement.

"What's wrong here, Colonel Schmidt? Is Captain Hartman not pulling his weight? If he's the problem I can get General Bräuer to remove him immediately."

Manfred wanted a scapegoat and Captain Hartman, who seemed to be losing enthusiasm for killing Cretans and burning their villages, seemed the obvious choice. Manfred looked at the fat, posturing, perspiring bully of a colonel sitting behind his desk and spoke quietly and deliberately.

"Herr Colonel, we have had no trouble with terrorists in my territory since my cordon and search exercise in February. Not one, I repeat, not one of my soldiers has been killed by terrorists. We have lost two of our men in a road accident but neither of them were killed by the enemy. And may I remind you, Herr Colonel, that I have a large area to cover with the troops available to me. The Italians are taking greater responsibility for daytime searches and are showing greater enthusiasm for action. But I do have to agree that Captain Hartman has been in his post too long and a replacement with new ideas would be welcome."

A week later General Braüer visited Heraklion and had a private interview with Manfred. Colonel Müller's policies were discussed in some detail and it was agreed that Captain Hartman should be replaced at the earliest convenient moment. Over mid-morning coffee and cognac Manfred approached the general and presented his private views on future developments in eastern Crete. The general listened intently.

"Herr General, there are particular problems in my command here in the east, which Colonel Müller does not have to contend with in western Crete. The first is the Italians. They are responsible for holding Malia, Neapolis, Aghios Nikolaos, Sitia and Ierapetra. Their aggression is improving and they are now starting to get out on night patrols. The funny thing is that the bandits seem reluctant to attack the Italians and my own men are always happy to lead them day or night, knowing that they'll be immune from danger. As far as the *andartes* are concerned, the chief figure is Militades Porphyroyennis and, as you know, he's on our side after we arranged transfer of some old Italian rifles to his group. There are a couple of minor bandits about the place. Yanni Bodias and Bandouvas are active around Heraklion, but we have the Council of Advisors in Heraklion eating out of our hands and Colonel Beteniakis handles Bodias without difficulty. And then in the Lasithis a new man has appeared, a fellow called Samaritis. He's a communist, but Porphyroyennis will have nothing to do with him. I intend making Samaritis the next target for a combined attack between us and the Italians. On Colonel Müller's advice I have put in for Captain Hartman's transfer back to Germany. Looking to the future, should it happen that we have to evacuate Crete I assume there are contingency plans?"

General Braüer nodded his agreement and Manfred continued, "Well, Sir, I wish to make a plea that Aghios Nikolaos and Elounda should become two of our main evacuation ports, especially, Elounda, where there is a natural bay suitable for fairly large troop ships,

E-boats, U-boats and a safe landing area for flying boats. I wish to develop this corner of Crete into a German base guarded by a ring of steel. My present difficulty is that the base is occupied by a company of *Totenkopf* Stormtroopers and they are a law unto themselves."

Manfred paused and sipped his brandy.

"I suppose there would be no chance of replacing these Hitler hotheads with a company of good old-fashioned *Fallschirmjagger*?"

General Braüer's face broke into a wide smile.

"I sympathise with you Manfred but even I cannot work miracles."

"Well, General Braüer, there's one other point. *Kriegsmarine* Captain Bucholz and I have developed the harbour at Vai into an area for rest and recreation for our troops. It's completely sheltered and safe. I intend building a small officers' mess at Vai. Captain Bucholz will bring in the materials by boat and as soon as the mess is ready I am going to transfer Sergeant Schultz there for the summer. I will invite you to the opening ceremony."

General Braüer sat back in his chair and thanked Manfred for his report.

"I agree that Captain Hartman will have to be replaced as soon as convenient. I agree to your proposal for a combined attack on Samaritis and his group and suggest you make it early next month. I don't know if I can help you with the *Totenkopf* Company at Elounda. As you know they do as they please and they receive their orders directly from Berlin. Go ahead with Vai. It sounds a great idea and, if I can, I assure you, I will be at your opening ceremony. I'll be sorry to see Schultz leaving this villa. He's such a marvellous cook. Which reminds me," he said, rising and patting his stomach, "isn't it time for lunch?"

*

Apart from Bombardier James Ferris who was out on guard duty at the farm, the whole commando were sitting around a small fire eating their supper out of mess tins, a congealed mass of corned beef and mashed potato lightly fried in olive oil, prepared by Biffo. This dish had become standard fare for the cave-bound commandos. After their meal they took it in turns to wash the mess tins in the dark, tepid, clearwater pool at the back of the cave. By April the height of the water in this pool had shrunk considerably, since cessation of the rainy season in early February, and David advised they should use water sparingly throughout the summer. Biffo, appointed spokesman by his compatriots, approached David.

"Sir, the boys are getting restless. We want some action. Is there any chance of something happening this month?"

David looked around his group and at their eager faces.

"Sergeant Hubbard and I have been discussing a convoy ambush. We think we've found the right spot. All we have to do now is to check on a few details and the operation may be on. I'll let you have more details in about three days' time."

That night and for the whole of the next day David was away reconnoitring the proposed ambush site. On his return he had ten minutes' private conference with Sergeant Hubbard and then called the commando together under a large olive tree at the head of the grove. The makeshift conference was interrupted once by the appearance of a Storch spotter plane and, after the all clear, David spoke to his group tracing a crude map in the earth at the base of the tree.

"The German forces in our area are based at Heraklion, Aghios Nikolaos and Elounda with a few at Sitia and Vai. Their supply and reinforcement convoys have to travel along the coast road from Heraklion. Sergeant Hubbard has established that their supply convoys leave Heraklion twice a week, on Monday and Thursday afternoon and return on Tuesday and Saturday morning. I propose to hit one of these convoys at a point on the coast near Stalida, which is about a mile this side of Malia. The attack must look as if it is being carried out by the local bandits, who, in the Stalida area, are controlled by Yanni Bodias. So we'll wear a little red feather, or piece of cloth, in our *sarikis* for this operation. The direct distance from here to Stalida is about ten kilometres but, by the time we've got around the base of the Mohos mountains it'll be around twelve kilometres, an easy distance to get there and back in one night. Three preliminary trips will be necessary to get our equipment out to the target area. We'll attack on the evening of the 27th April."

The site for the attack selected by David and Sergeant Hubbard, seemed ideal for an ambush. Between Hersonisos and Malia the coastal road hugged the shoreline except at one point about two kilometres west of Stalida, where the road made a long, curved, two kilometre inland detour around the base of a three hundred foot high hill with a sheer drop on the landward side of the road and an almost vertical rise to the cliff face on the seaward side. David's reconnaissance was directed towards the sea-facing edge of the mountain shelf. The only access to this area was by an irregular shepherd's path clinging to the cliff edge and in some places overhanging the vertical two hundred foot drop into the blue Aegean sea below. David's recces had not been in vain. About forty feet down from the edge of the shepherd's path he saw a narrow ledge and, abseiling down the steep cliff face, found a small shallow cave with a narrow entrance, only fifteen foot in depth and quite invisible from the landward side. On his next visit David brought two Lee Enfield rifles and a supply of ammunition and left them in the shallow cave. In turn he took each of his squad out to their operational site and showed them where they should lay their landmines, where their targets might be on the road and the escape route after the attack.

The principle of the ambush was simple. David and Sergeant Hubbard at each end of the escarpment would set up their Bren guns to cover the road two hundred feet below. Sergeant Hubbard would be in pole position at the Hersonisos end of the escarpment and signal the approach of a convoy. Biffo and Gunner Smithson would place three mines in potholes at the Stalida end of the curved arc and then move swiftly along the road towards Stalida and plant another two mines in the road a kilometre further on, their actions covered by David's Bren gun on top of the escarpment. Once their mines were laid Biffo and Gunner Smithson were to retire into the olive groves and make their way into the Mohos foothills and back to base. As soon as the last vehicles in the convoy had disappeared around the bend of the arc Bombardier James Ferris and Private Clayton were to lay three mines in the road at the base of the arc covered by Sergeant Hubbard's Bren gun. They were then to retreat south into the Mohos foothills. Under no circumstances were the mine laying commandos to hang around and watch the action.

The purpose of the attack was to isolate the convoy in the curved road between the two machine guns on the escarpment. The Germans would find great difficulty in ascending to the top of the escarpment to get at the Bren gunners, and, due to the steep drop, their vehicles would be unable to get off the landward side of the road. If the Germans radioed for help David surmised it might come from Malia, but more likely, due to German mistrust of the Italians, from Heraklion. Hopefully the relief column might get entangled in the secondary mines and lead to more confusion and destruction. At the end of the briefing David asked for any questions. Biffo immediately sprang to his feet.

"'Ow will you and Sergeant Hubby get off that fucking 'ill?"

"A good question, Biffo. Sergeant Hubbard and I will hole out in a small cave until dark and then make it for home. If that doesn't work we'll have to swim for it," and turning towards his sergeant he said, "You can swim I hope, Sergeant Hubbard?"

"It's an insult to ask a sergeant in His Majesty's Royal Marines if he can swim, Sir!" the sergeant replied good humouredly, adding, "I won't mind the swim but we'll need a parachute for the jump into the sea and I don't fancy that."

*

Colonel Manfred Schmidt personally supervised arrangements for the supply convoy before their journey to Elounda, Sitia and Vai on the afternoon of Monday 27th April. He would not normally be involved, but on this day he was sending Sergeant Chef Fritz Schultz in a transport lorry full of kitchen equipment and stores to set up an officers' mess at Vai. *Feldwebel* Schneider would accompany the convoy to look after the sergeant and his culinary paraphernalia. The convoy was constructed as usual of two motorcycles and sidecars with mounted machine guns in the lead, followed by two light tracked armoured vehicles and the commander in a *Kübelwagen*, followed by four lorries with infantry replacements and stores and another light armoured vehicle bringing up the rear.

The pace of the convoy was determined by that of the slowest vehicle, in this instance the light tracked armoured vehicles, whose maximum speed was twenty kilometres per hour. The journey to Vai, including stops at Elounda and Sitia was expected to take around five and a half hours. The convoy moved out of Heraklion barracks at precisely 1500 hours with a grim-faced Sergeant Schultz, not entirely happy with his new appointment, sitting at the front of his supply lorry, glum, and resigned to a long, hot and sweaty journey. *Feldwebel* Schneider sat at his side, happy and smiling and looking forward to a few days in the sun at Vai.

The young under-officer in charge of the convoy had only arrived in Crete a week previously and this was his first military assignment.

He was nervous and anxious that he should not make any mistakes and kept moving his *Kübelwagen* up and down the line of the slowly progressing convoy. They stopped at Ilithia for a water break and outside Gournes for a light meal and coffee. Sergeant Fritz Schultz, sweating and uncomfortable in the afternoon heat, kept grumbling but the more philosophical Schneider took it all in his stride. By the time they cleared Hersonisos the convoy was already half an hour late and the harassed under-officer ordered maximum speed. This meant that the leading light-tracked vehicles had to press on as hard as possible whilst the faster lorries bunched up behind the leaders and the convoy became more compact. Approaching Stalida the leading motorcycles, weaving in and out to avoid the potholes, were some forty yards ahead of the convoy when, on a long arced bend in the road, there was a loud 'crump' and the leading tracked vehicle lurched to a stop and skewed across the road with one of its tracks blown apart by the explosion. The rest of the convoy came to a juddering halt.

Feldwebel Schneider was the first to react. Shouting, *"Minen, minen,"* he leapt out of the cabin of his lorry, pulling the blabbering Sergeant Schultz behind him and crawled under the supply truck, his *Schmeitzer* sub-machine gun at the ready. The startled young under-officer was in a complete panic. He ordered his *Kübelwagen* driver to try and get past the stricken vehicle and in their efforts set off the second mine which blew the fragile *Kübelwagen* and its occupants to smithereens.

Feldwebel Schneider now took charge. Ordering the troops to disembark from their lorries, he led a party of four, crawling on their hands and knees, searching for further mines. A third mine was discovered quite quickly, defused and discarded over the steep edge of the road. *Feldwebel* Schneider now ordered all the soldiers, most of them green and battle-shy, to take cover under their lorries and wait further instructions. The two motorcyclists came back to join the column and positioned their machine guns on either side of the stricken armoured vehicle.

Under the supply lorry Sergeant Schultz was shaking like a jelly, cowering and blabbering on the ground, holding his head in his hands.

"Sergeant Schultz, stay where you are. Don't move," and as he stood up Schneider thought, 'The colonel will never forgive me if I lose old Sergeant Schultz.'

He then raced back to the tail end of the convoy. The light-tracked vehicle at the rear was attempting to turn round in the narrow road. *Feldwebel* Schneider ordered it to stop manoeuvring. He took hold of its radio and got through to Heraklion headquarters. The duty major was incredulous.

"Mines, mines. I can't believe it. Probably a blown track"

Schneider pressed a button on the hand-set hard.

"Listen you pompous idiot, we're under attack out here. The under-officer and his driver have both been killed. We cannot proceed because the damaged vehicle is in the way and we cannot retreat because the second armoured vehicle is unable to turn in the road. Get Colonel Schmidt for me."

The major, now alert, replied, "There's no need for that, I can deal with the situation."

Schneider stiffened with rage, "No, you bloody well can't. Get Colonel Schmidt now."

It took about a minute to get Manfred on the radio at Villa Ariadne.

"Schneider, what's going on?"

Schneider replied, "We've been stopped on the road some three kilometres outside Stalida by mines. The under-officer and his driver are dead. I can't retreat or advance. It's very quiet out here at the moment. I'm expecting an attack any minute."

Manfred, studying his map replied, "Stalida, Stalida, you haven't got very far have you? That's near Malia. I'll see if I can get the Italians to move across to you from Malia. Bugger it, that Italian Berganzoli would probably take a whole day to get up off his arse. I'll get a flying relief column from here. It should be with you in an hour."

Schneider sighed with relief. He knew he could trust his boss to help him.

"Thank you, Sir."

Colonel Schmidt came over the air again. "Hell, Schneider, I've just realised Schultz is on that convoy. Is he all right?"

Schneider half-smiled "Yes, he's fine, Sir. He's lying under the stores lorry at the moment and – Jesus Christ," he screamed, as he heard the first crump of an exploding hand grenade. "It's starting, Sir. I thought we would be attacked. I have to go and organise our defence. *Rot Scheint Die Sonne*, Sir," and, with that, he slammed down the hand-set and, as he raced towards Schultz's vehicle, he heard the bullets from a Bren gun directing an enfilade on the stranded convoy from above.

The ambush was achieved with perfect precision. A sign from Sergeant Hubbard in his Bren gun pit some two hundred yards to his right indicated the approach of the convoy which came into view ten minutes later. The convoy, moving at a fair speed in close order and in a cloud of dust entered the trap and the lead vehicle blew up and blocked its progress immediately below David's observation post. Two hundred feet above the convoy David witnessed the *Kübelwagen* blowing up and the subsequent actions of the soldiers down below in trying to dislodge the stricken vehicle and to reverse or turn about the armoured vehicles at the rear. All the while he knew that his men were laying mines on the road a mile behind the convoy and getting away into the valley below and up into the Mohos hills. An hour before the convoy arrived Biffo and Bombardier Ferris had placed three mines on the road below him and then, with a thumbs up sign from Biffo, they moved down the dusty, red road towards Stalida carrying three further mines. By the time the lead motorcycles of the convoy arrived Biffo and Ferris were well out of sight. And then the long awaited sign from Sergeant Hubbard came, a long wave of both his outstretched hands, indicating that the mine layers on the Hersonisos side of the trap were now well clear and under cover. By this time the German convoy had been stationary for about fifteen minutes.

David guessed they would be lying under and behind their vehicles wondering what would happen next. Well, now that he had received the sign from Hubbard, he would not keep them waiting any longer. On a ledge to the right of his Bren gun position he had laid out a dozen hand grenades. Methodically he took one at a time, removed the pins and lobbed them over the edge of the precipice. After ten seconds in the air the grenades exploded, some harmlessly on the rock face above the convoy and some in the steep valley below the road, but three reached their target. He heard screams from the trapped soldiers as hot shrapnel from the exploding grenades tore through their limbs and bodies. And then he directed an enfilade at the convoy with his Bren gun. Hitting the lorries and troop carriers was not difficult but he found that achieving a hit on a human target was not easy. Someone down there was organising the Germans into a sound defensive group. Every twentieth bullet in his Bren magazine was an incendiary. One of his bullets hit a fuel tank which burst into flames and for the next twenty minutes black smoke billowed over the battlefield, obscuring the targets.

Some indiscriminate rifle and automatic fire was returned from below but the main danger came from machine guns mounted on the sidecars. On four occasions the Germans attempted to use these guns, but each time David was able to pick off the operator and he was sure that at least four brave German soldiers lay dead, or wounded, around their mounted guns. By now Sergeant Hubbard had moved nearer David's position and was engaging the tail end of the convoy, keeping the Germans pinned down.

The action now subsided into a relatively quiet affair, with sporadic bouts of Bren fire as targets presented themselves. The two British commandos were awaiting the arrival of the relief columns before they disengaged. Schneider and his men had been trapped on the road for nearly two hours. One officer and five soldiers were dead and at least twelve men were wounded. Sergeant Schultz was still alive and well under his truck, bemoaning his fate and praying to his God to get him out of the pickle.

David was surprised to see that the first signs of relief came from the east. The Italians at Malia, led by Major Enzio Berganzoli in his light tank, took to the road and advanced cautiously westwards. They saw the black cloud of smoke some two kilometres away and Major Berganzoli became even more cautious. He ordered three luckless soldiers to walk in front of his tank to look for mines. About a kilometre away from the black smoke one of them found a landmine and panic set in. Major Berganzoli ordered an immediate turnabout and, in the manoeuvre, his tank ran over one of Biffo's carefully secreted landmines and blew the undercarriage of the flimsy tank to bits. Major Berganzoli's driver and navigator were killed and the major suffered painful shrapnel wounds to his buttocks. The Italian armoured column limped back to Malia, bloodied, and never to reappear.

Meanwhile Manfred's relief column were through Hersonisos and fast approaching Stalida. They too saw the black pall of smoke on the coastal road and made every effort to get there quickly. Manfred's *Kübelwagen* miraculously threaded its way through the hidden minefield without contact but the first armoured troop carrier blew up with a loud bang, disgorging its occupants onto the sides of the road. Most of the soldiers were stunned and deafened, some slightly wounded, and three killed outright by the blast.

Sergeant Hubbard opened up with his Bren gun and sprayed the newly arrived column with bullets. He suddenly realised that his Bren magazine was nearly empty. He retreated backwards from the crest of the escarpment and made a sign to David that he was out of ammunition and withdrawing. David was also low in ammunition and after a final burst into the massed lorries below, he withdrew and, retreated with the sergeant over the crest of the hill towards the cliff edge. They picked their way across the rocky surface of the escarpment, reached the perilous shepherd's path along the cliff edge, threw their Bren guns into the sea and using a rope previously concealed by David, descended on to the ledge in the cliff face and crawled into the small cave. There, sweating, panting and exhilarated they shook hands formally and lay flat on the ground immersed in their private thoughts. Eventually Sergeant Hubbard spoke.

"I don't think I could jump from here if we had to."

"No," replied David. "It's a bit high but we'll get away over land as soon as it gets dark."

They had nearly two hours to wait for darkness.

*

When Colonel Manfred Schmidt realised that the relief convoy he was leading was under attack he radioed Captain Bucholz in Heraklion.

"How quickly can you get an E-boat to the escarpment about three kilometres west of Stalida?"

Bucholz thought quickly at the other end of the connection.

"Let's see, E 472 is on its way from Sitia and should, at the moment, be off Malia. I'll ask it to speed up and get there as quickly as possible. What's the problem, Manfred, old chap?"

"We're in the shit here, Klaus. There are a few terrorists on the escarpment above us. I need your help to flush them out."

By the time he finished speaking *Feldwebel* Schneider and Sergeant Fritz Schultz, shaking from head to toe, appeared from behind a stranded lorry. Manfred looked at the sergeant cook.

"Schultzie, are you all right?"

Sergeant Schultz tried to pull himself together.

"Can't complain, Colonel Schmidt, but I'm afraid the kitchen equipment is *kaput.*"

Manfred grunted.

"Ach so, Schneider. Get thirty men and follow me. We're going up to that ridge to flush out those bandits before dark."

"*Jawohl,* Herr Colonel," Schneider replied, ready and anxious to have a go at the adversaries who had pinned them down with deadly accuracy. Schneider quickly gathered a fully armed section of mountain infantry and at a run they began to follow the striding, white-haired, hatless colonel who was, by this time, nearly half way up the side of the escarpment. At the top Manfred made them spread out in a line and they walked forwards, guns at the ready, the whole length of the rock-strewn ridge, like beaters in a pheasant shoot. But no *andartes* were discovered. Manfred then ordered his men to concentrate on the cliff edges. A sudden shout from one of the soldiers, pointing out to sea, drew attention to E 472 nosing swiftly around the point some three hundred yards off shore. Manfred stood on the cliff top waving to the E-boat and the lieutenant in charge of the boat acknowledge by flashing his searchlight.

Darkness was approaching when a flash of light out at sea drew David's attention to the presence of an E boat, very close to shore.

"Damn it," David muttered through clenched teeth. "We're in trouble, Sergeant Hubbard. There's an E-boat out there signalling to the cliffs close above our heads. I expect our friends are up there..."

At that moment the silence was broken by a loud hailer, a German voice from the E-boat.

"I've got a good view of the cliff under you, Sir. There's a sort of ledge some thirty metres to your left. That's the only possible hiding place on this stretch of cliff." The hailer's voice stopped with a crackle.

Manfred paced thirty metres to his left and Schneider, bending down, spotted the tied end of the rope in the coarse grass. The soldiers collected in a bunch around the end of the rope. Manfred, peering over the cliff edge, saw the ledge on the sheer cliff face some forty feet below. He looked around.

"I want a volunteer to go down this rope on to that ledge."

A fresh-faced, blond youth stepped forward. Manfred looked into his eyes.

"There's an Iron Cross in this, whatever happens."

Without hesitation the young soldier took off his pack, picked up the rope and started abseiling down the rock face. David and Sergeant Hubbard became aware that there was someone descending from above, as the end of the rope started moving and small pieces of rock and stone came hurtling down past the open end of the shallow cave. Sergeant Hubbard thrust David aside and took out his commando knife. A pair of black leather boots appeared, dangling in front of the cave entrance, and then, with the next abseil, the boots planted themselves firmly on the ledge and a man's hip and belt appeared. Sergeant Hubbard, with an expertise born of his commando training, aimed the sticker in an upward direction at the man's abdomen. There was a loud scream from the soldier on the ledge and then a shout, "*Wir sint hier*", as the stricken man, bent double and letting go of the rope, plunged with flailing limbs into the dark sea below. The loud hailer was in action again.

"Your bandits are on that ledge. Do you want me to blast them out with my Bofors? Move away from the cliff edge."

But Manfred did not move away immediately. He was so close to his quarry that he wanted to finish the job himself. Schneider suggested lowering a stick bomb on the end of the rope. Manfred was prepared to try anything. The rope was retrieved and a stick grenade tied to its end. The grenade was then hurled out to space and on its return Schneider expected it to hit the ledge and explode. In the event nothing of the sort happened and the grenade clanged harmlessly against the rock face without detonating. The light was fading rapidly and time was being wasted. Manfred admitted defeat and ordered his men back a safe distance, waving a white handkerchief, indicating to the E-boat captain he should commence firing.

After the stabbing, Sergeant Hubbard withdrew into the cave and began assembling and loading the 303 rifles. David was pleased to see that it was semi-dark and then, suddenly, he heard a command from out at sea, "*Feuer.*"

All hell was let loose. Bofors shells started ripping into the rock face above the cave entrance showering the ledge with white chalk and causing deafening reverberations inside the cave. The two commandos were quickly covered with white dust, and were practically stone deaf. David realised the boat's gunners were aiming high as they were too near the target for accuracy. The gentle sway of the boat at anchor made their aim erratic. But it would only be a matter of time before a lucky single shell entered the cave entrance and blew both of them to kingdom come. And then suddenly a searchlight partially illuminated the inside of the small cave and the Bofors shells were hitting the rock face nearer the cavern's entrance. David picked up his rifle and squirmed on to the ledge, followed by Sergeant Hubbard, and there they lay, side by side, covered in white dust, each squinting into the strong glare as they pumped bullet after bullet at the blazing searchlight three hundred yards away. One of the bullets was successful and shattered the glass lens and the shooting stopped abruptly.

Without hesitation David took hold of Sergeant Hubbard's hand and they both rose to their feet on the ledge. Without prompting or urging they simultaneously took off into the dark night plummeting rapidly downwards for one hundred and fifty feet into the cold deep sea. They surfaced within ten yards of each other and began swimming westwards alongside the base of the vertical cliff. They had progressed about thirty yards when the light beam again appeared over their heads and the thump, thump, thump of the Bofors recommenced, faintly audible to their deafened ears. They swam for about a mile and landed on a flat shingle beach about ten kilometres east of Hersonisos. From their landing point they were within eight kilometres of the kibbutz. Gunner Smithson and Biffo were already safely home and Private Clayton and Bombardier Ferris returned early the following morning, having spent the night on the Mohos hills.

*

"What went wrong this time, Colonel Schmidt?" asked the sneering *Brigadführer* Müller, who had flown in for a post-mortem on the debacle at Stalida. He had been promoted to Brigadier a week previously.

He continued, "General Braüer is extremely displeased and wants reprisals. Only last week you were telling me how safe you had made Crete for the German forces and here we are now with one officer dead, nine soldiers killed, one unnecessarily on your orders, and fifteen men with severe injures. Added to this you managed to get two Italian privates killed and that shit Berganzoli shot up his backside. The question is, who did it and did we kill any of them and, more to the point, what are we going to do about it?"

Manfred disliked the Brigadier intensely but on this occasion he did have a point. He had botched up the whole business. He stood up and looked squarely at the general whose heavy jowls were quivering with rage.

"I accept full responsibility for what happened yesterday. I believe the *andartes* carried out the attack. I am making full enquiries, but Colonel Beteniakis assures me that Yanni Bodias was not involved and I do not think Porphyroyennis would attack so far to the west. This leaves just one man, the new, self-appointed Bolshevik commander in the Lasithis, Samaritis, though where he got his hands on British grenades, Bren guns and mines I have no idea. The Tommies must have supplied them to him. You ask – did we get those men on the ledge? I am certain we did. The naval Bofors' bombardment was frightening and Lieutenant Neuberg, commander of E 472, is of the same opinion. I sincerely hope that Samaritis was one of the bandits on the ledge. I have sent some men up there today to have a look at the cave and to collect the bodies. As for what has to be done in reprisal, I will ask for your expert advice."

The Brigadier, slightly mollified by the request for his advice, banged the desk in front of him.

"As you have no hostages, you have to get some. The nearest village is Stalida. You and the Italians must cordon and search the place, get a few men in the net, execute them publicly and burn the place down. Don't leave it for longer than a week. These Cretans have a short memory and will forget the reason why they are being punished. By the way, I see that Hauptmann Hartman is still here. When will you kick him out? Soon I hope. I have to return to Khania urgently. Heil Hitler," and he stood up, saluted, and stalked out of Manfred's headquarters.

Colonel Schmidt fixed the 2nd May as the day for a cordon and search exercise in Stalida. The Italians, on General Carta's authority, refused to co-operate and even Major Berganzoli, who had suffered more than most, refused to consider reprisals. So the Germans did it alone. Five men were arrested in the small village, four in their seventies and the fifth, a young, good-looking, thirty year old mental defective with an estimated mental age of nine. They were carted off to Heraklion and shot on Colonel Schmidt's orders on the 4th of May.

Stalida was razed to the ground, first by a sea bombardment from E-boats and then by fire. The surviving Cretan inhabitants fled and never returned to their seaside village. David's post mortem on the action at Stalida concluded that it had been a complete success as his commando had not suffered casualties. He regretted the loss of two Italian soldiers and that made it imperative that the perpetrators of the attack were seen to be Samaritis' group. The German reaction to the ambush was unforgivable and the shooting of four elderly men and a thirty year old mental defective as reprisal was indefensible. These atrocities, together with the burning of Stalida, ordered by Colonel Manfred Schmidt, strengthened David's resolve to get rid of the White Angel of Gournes at the first possible opportunity.

Chapter Twenty-Four
Eastern Crete, May – June 1943
Attack on Vai

Throughout May and most of June 1943 David's Piskopiano commandos were content to limit their activities to local recces and guard duties at the kibbutz. David in the meantime continued his long distance observation at Heraklion and kept up his visits to Marita's house in Kastelli. By now she and Stephia were again firm friends. Marita turned a blind eye to the visits of her German colonel and aided and abetted Stephia's indiscretions by looking after little Spiros when she wanted to be alone with her German lover. During the early part of 1943 information about Colonel Schmidt's movements was sparse, but in late May David learnt from Marita that Stephia had been ordered by her German colonel to the seaside at Vai for the months of July and August. Little Spiros was not invited. Marita readily agreed to look after the boy as her school at Kastelli would be shut for two months and Marita could devote all her time and attention to her young nephew.

David assimilated this information with interest. If Stephia was at Vai for any length of time it followed that Colonel Manfred Schmidt would be a frequent visitor to the seaside camp. The more he thought about it the more it made sense. Perhaps he should take part of his commando to Vai for a week or two in July? Why not? And if he had the chance he might settle his score with the blond Nazi colonel.

Communications from Egypt were singularly unhelpful, encouraging David "To keep in touch with the Wops," and, "Try to get at the Commies."

With the former request he had no difficulty as Captain Tavana was only too pleased to talk and practise his English and, when he learnt that David had studied languages at Oxford, he was over the moon. Captain Tavana had a pleasant, likeable disposition and this, combined with his outgoing personality, made him an interesting companion and yet, in the middle of an inconsequential conversation, he often threw in gems of valuable information. He had accepted that Samaritis carried out the Stalida ambush and, as two Italians had been killed, he thanked David for warning him against the vicious *kapitan*.

"He's turned out to be a bad chicken, or is it egg? My general would never have any dealings with such a man, not unless he changes completely. The Germans wish us to join them in a big campaign to surround Samaritis and capture him. I'm not too keen on working with the Germans on this plan. With them everything is so serious and if they can't have their own way they just shoot people. The Nazi general in western Crete, Müller, has a bad name and I fear that our Colonel Schmidt is destined to follow in his foot-treads, or is it footsteps? A pity, I like Colonel Schmidt but I cannot condone what he did to the poor people at Gournes and now at Stalida. He's going to be leading our combined attack in the Lasithis in the first week of June."

This was indeed important information. It meant that during June the coast roads in eastern Crete and the Lasithis would be crawling with Germans and Italians. As a result of Captain Tavana's information David planned his movement to Vai for the 28th June. He would take Sergeant Hubbard and three commandos with him and would introduce Corporal Dai Griffiths to the commando. Sergeant Hubbard had met Dai on a few occasions and the two got on very well together. When Sergeant Hubbard saw him during the last week in May they chatted amicably for a while and then the sergeant posed the question, "Dai, we're planning a trip to the seaside for two or three weeks. Would you like to come along?"

Dai rested his spade against a tree.

"I dunno, Sergeant Hubby. I'll think about it."

Sergeant Hubbard got up to leave.

"I'm sorry, Dai, I want the answer today. Think about the paddling and the girls."

Dai perked up, "Girls, girls, what girls?"

"There's always girls at the seaside," the sergeant replied.

Dai mellowed, "All right then, I'll come along. Do you want me to drive?"

"Drive, be buggered," replied Sergeant Hubbard. "It'll be shanks's pony all the way. We'll be travelling light so just bring a *sakouli* and some food and water. I'll pick you up when we're ready to go."

Dai responded, "I'll be ready. I only hope the trip is worthwhile."

*

On the 9th June 1943 Manfred took a combined Italian and German force on a seven day punitive exercise into the Lasithi mountains. He knew from the beginning that it might be a complete disaster. The Italians insisted on bringing all their home comforts with them and what should have been a mobile column became a disorganised, desperately slow-moving, almost immobile convoy. The noise and clatter of the movement of the Italian strike force gave fair warning to friend and foe alike that they were approaching. Consequently the bandits and local inhabitants disappeared and melted into the vastness of the majestic Lasithi mountain ranges. But one bonus emerged from the whole enterprise.

Captain Schubert, who had replaced the long-suffering Captain Hartman on the 3rd June, introduced a technique of lightning strikes on the smaller far-flung villages. While the Italians were still getting organised at Tzouerloti Captain Schubert and his heavily armoured, but highly mobile, motorcycle platoon went rampaging over the Lasithis causing havoc and panic amongst the local inhabitants. And his method of dealing with suspects was malicious and uncompromisingly ruthless. This mild-mannered, bespectacled, balding thirty year old Schwabian charmed and placated his captives, but, once a decision was made, the same gentle, school-masterly man personally conducted the execution without trial and without any sign of remorse. His usual comment at the end of a long day in the field was, "It's all in a day's work." Next to Müller and Manfred Schmidt he rapidly became the most hated German in Crete.

Manfred's mammoth exercise in the Lasithis involving some three thousand German and Italian soldiers produced a paltry total of thirteen suspects, twelve of whom were detained by Captain Schubert's mobile column and all of whom were summarily executed by the same person. Of Samaritis and his band of *andartes* there was no sign. The wily *kapitan*, with his depleted force of some sixty-four men, withdrew to the highest peaks in eastern Crete and went to ground near the mountain village of Sitanos.

Colonel Manfred Schmidt was luxuriating in a foam bath at Villa Ariadne having arrived home late the previous evening, covered in the dust and grime of seven days in the field and having had twelve hours' uninterrupted sleep. He was reflecting on the operation and quietly pleased with his achievement when, without ceremony and unannounced, the bathroom door opened and the pugnacious figure of *Brigadführer* Müller thrust itself into the room. One look at his loathing face convinced Manfred that he was in for a roasting from his malicious superior. He managed to stifle a groan as he made a pretence of trying to get out of the sunken bath. The brigadier wasted no time.

"Colonel Schmidt, I bring you congratulations from General Braüer on your 'successful' operation. Successful, my arse. With three thousand men at your disposal you should have had a better haul than thirteen bandits. And I hear that support from Colonel Plevres did not materialise."

Manfred felt his face getting redder at the mention of Plevres, the nationalist *andartes* leader in the Lasithis. Before the exercise he and Captain Tavana had made contact with Plevres, who promised support in hunting down Samaritis in return for rifles and ammunition for his men. About eight hundred nationalists turned up at the Italian base camp and some five hundred rifles and ten rounds of ammunition per person were issued to Plevres' men. Within three days, as the army got higher and higher into the mountains, Plevres, his men and their rifles disappeared into thin air. Manfred had been secretly praying that Brigadier Müller did not know all the details of his deal with Plevres.

The general apparently did and continued, "The only man to come out of this mess with any distinction is Captain Schubert. His mobile company captured twelve men and dealt with them in the prescribed fashion. And what of the Italians? They're still no fucking good. Can't you get the lazy bastards to move off their backsides and do some fighting, instead of just jabbering? I gather they caught one bandit, who had been hiding for two days in their cookhouse and thought he was in the safest place. He was wrong. The safest place for the terrorist was in the field. Three thousand men could only capture thirteen in one week! I can't believe it! Now my orders are these. You must let Captain Schubert have a free hand. Get him and his men out to the Lasithis again as quickly as possible. Capturing this damned Samaritis has become top priority. General Braüer wants him alive or dead. Now get out of that bath and get to work. There's plenty for you to do."

The general turned on his heels and strode away. At the door he stopped, his hand on the ornamental door knob.

"I've got one bit of news for you. The *Totenkopf* in Elounda are moving out at the end of this month. General Braüer has arranged for a parachute battalion, the Fifth, to replace them. The Fifth had a bad mauling near Kursk and are down to two hundred and fifty men. I expect you'll be pleased to see some paratroopers in Elounda. Heil Hitler."

Müller turned and was gone as Manfred executed a parody of a Nazi salute in his bath.

"Pleased!" he muttered to himself, "I'm over the moon! Schneider, Schneider, come here quickly. I've got some great news. Good old General Braüer has worked a miracle, despite that bastard Müller."

The euphoria over the posting of paratroopers to Elounda soon overshadowed his depression at Müller's drubbing.

"Schneider, open a bottle of our best champagne," and, though it was only eleven o'clock in the morning, *Feldwebel* Schneider and his bath-robed colonel drank to the Fifth *Fallschirmjager* Regiment.

Colonel Schmidt's punitive expedition was generally regarded as a success despite the contempt and ridicule expressed by *Brigadführer* Müller, as he had demonstrated that, in eastern Crete, the Germans and Italians were prepared to take on their adversaries on their home ground. Manfred very quickly adopted Brigadier Müller's suggestion that Captain Schubert should have a free-roving mobile hit squad and within days, Commando Schubert was formed and dispatched back into the Lasithis to hunt for Samaritis.

For the rest of June Manfred busied himself with arrangements for establishing a small officers' mess at Vai. On the 15th June Sergeant Schultz and his kitchen equipment were transferred by E-boat and Stephia and two ladies from a brothel in Heraklion arrived a week later. The grand opening night was to be Saturday 27th June. *Kriegsmarine* Captain Bucholz was invited and General Bruno Braüer, who declined, and his place was taken by Lieutenant Lautermann, newly arrived commander of E-boat 459. Sergeant Schultz was instructed to prepare a grand banquet to celebrate the opening of the new mess. By the time the three German officers arrived in Vai for the official opening, David, Sergeant Hubbard, Corporal Dai, and three commandos were safely ensconced in a cave at the base of a cliff some two kilometres east of the newly erected officers' mess.

*

Gunner Peter Smithson arrived back in the kibbutz slightly out of breath. It was a scorching hot day and he had been on local patrol. Disarming his Sten gun he turned to David, "There's a fresh message on the Icon stones, Sir. It reads TIX."

David became fully alert. By arrangement with Captain Tavana a suffix 'X' meant urgent, the same day if possible. The chosen time was an hour before dusk, as the Italian wanted to be back in the safety of his garrison before nightfall. When David arrived Captain Tavana was sitting on a large boulder, smoking a cigarette held in a long holder.

"Tommy, you're a bit late," he opened with a quiet chuckle.

"I'm sorry, Captain Tavana, I was held up."

The Italian looked alarmed.

"Who held you up? Do you mean it was a stick up?"

David laughed, and the Italian joined him, ending his laughter with a loud burp. Captain Tavana had been drinking and was in an expansive mood.

"Well, Tommy, old fellow, I have to tell you that I've been out in the field for a week with Colonel Manfred Schmidt and my German colleagues. We went east to the Lasithis chasing after your friend Samaritis. There were over three thousand of us crawling all over the place but we didn't get Samaritis. We, or rather the Germans, executed twelve bandits. We caught one gangster hiding in our cookhouse. He thought he would be safe there, but the Germans took him away and shot him. The poor chap was more than seventy years of age and crippled with arthritis." Captain Tavana stopped to light another cigarette. "What I wanted to tell you is that Colonel Schmidt and I made a deal with Colonel Plevres. He would get rifles if he assisted us in catching Samaritis. We gave them five hundred rifles and some ammo' and they started off with us into the hills. Within three days they had all disappeared. Poor old Colonel Schmidt, was, how you put it? Up the Greek without a piddle."

David laughed and corrected the captain. "No, no, you mean up the creek without a paddle."

Captain Tavana settled down and continued his monologue.

"I suspect Plevres might join Samaritis, in which case Colonel Schmidt is in the shit."

He giggled again and then pulled himself together.

"But there's bad news. Colonel Schmidt now has a new man, a very dangerous and nasty man in the field. His name is Captain Schubert. I met him briefly. He looks a quiet pleasant sort, but he's poison. He's the one who personally executed the twelve Cretan bandits and the one we caught in our cookhouse, I wanted to warn you, Tommy, about the little weasel. Tell your British friends in Crete to look out for him." Captain Tavana stood up and flicking the ash from the end of his cigarette. "I must go, Tommy, it'll be dark soon and we've had a party going in the mess in the Neapolis since we returned from Lasithi, celebrating another famous victory!"

And with another burp and stifled chuckle Captain Tavana walked down the road into the rapidly gathering dark moonless night.

The Attack on Vai, 27th June 1943

David's patrol reached Vai on the afternoon of the 23rd June. Keeping mainly to the roads, but diverting into the fields and olive groves at the slightest sound or indication of trouble, they circumnavigated the small camp at Vai and instinctively made for the high ground and cliffs on the shoreline to the east. There David found a broken cliff-face pathway which zigzagged down to sea level on to a narrow, shingle beach and an entrance to a shallow cave. The cave entrance was invisible from the sea, protected by another rocky outcrop and a small island thirty metres offshore. The water between the beach and the island was some fifteen metres deep. The commando party deposited their heavy *sakoulis* at the back of the cave and rested for a while. Lightly armed with a Sten gun and two spare clips and two grenades each David and Sergeant Hubbard carried out a recce of the camp.

The German encampment at Vai was constructed on each side of a narrow, palm-fringed dirt road running alongside a white sandy beach with a wooden, recently built, mess hut and a jetty at the eastern end of the bay and a row of ten tents erected at regular intervals along the edges of the sandy beach track. David concentrated his attention on the mess hut and jetty, which they had approached from the east through a sloping, wooded hill. The rickety jetty was some forty metres in length, supported by thick poles and rubber tyres. At that moment there were two small rowing boats tied to the pier and they clearly saw an armed sentry standing at the landward end of the jetty. The windowless officers' mess was a wooden construction, thirty foot square with a front door leading on to the beach path and, at the rear, another door leading to a corrugated lean-to, which served as a kitchen. Clustered around the lean-to were four small sheds, one a toilet, one a supply hut and, by the evidence of cycle tracks in the sand, the other two contained motorcycles.

In the early evening sun the camp was relatively quiet. German voices were audible on the beach and in the water and David thought that he heard a female voice at one stage. An occasional German soldier, in shorts and shirtless, walked in and out of the tents and two soldiers in uniform guarded the west end of the beach track, where the road entered the small encampment. David reckoned that there were about twenty-four men in the camp and there were three guards to contend with and probably a fourth at night-time. The camp at Vai provided men to man an observation and wireless post on a promontory four kilometres to the north, at the tip of Alero peninsula.

David and Sergeant Hubbard were crouched in a screen of trees some thirty yards behind the little wooden mess, when a short, roly-poly man emerged, sloppily dressed in a white apron and carrying a bottle of schnapps in one hand and a packet of cigarettes in the other. He was obviously the camp cook coming out of his kitchen for a breath of air, a smoke and a drink. David observed Sergeant Fritz Schultz through his binoculars. Rivulets of sweat were pouring down the fat German's shoulders and collecting in a puddle at the upper end of his corpulent belly. The man's red heavy jowls sagged visibly and he was constantly chattering and moaning to himself, a cigarette clenched between his lips, and swigging at intervals from a schnapps bottle.

David thought, 'This is the picture of an unhappy man who would prefer to be in a *weinstube* in Munich rather than sitting in this hot, sizzling hole in the middle of nowhere.'

On the way back to their hideaway David spoke to Sergeant Hubbard.

"Sergeant, I'm a bit worried about Biffo and Dai. They seem to be bickering a lot. Did you notice that, before we left, I asked them to prepare supper? Dai volunteered and Biffo went into one of his Cockney sulks. I hope they don't rock the boat."

Sergeant Hubbard reflected for a few moments.

"As I see it, Sir, these two chaps are wise in different ways. Biffo is streetwise and cunning, a crafty little bastard if ever there was one, and Corporal Griffiths is wise in the ways of nature and things mechanical. They'll make it up, especially if we see some action."

"I hope you're right," David replied. "I didn't know you were a philosopher, Sergeant!"

Sergeant Hubbard's prophecy proved to be correct. When they returned to the cave Biffo and Dai Griffiths were sitting together chatting amicably. Dai was twisting and turning some wire into a sort of basket.

"What are you up to Corporal?" asked David.

"I'm making a lobster pot, Sir. I reckon there's some lobster out there. There's plenty of fish. We caught these mullet in ten minutes."

The innovative Welshman had fashioned a hook from a sharp safety pin and with some binding cord and using mussel as bait had caught four large mullet. Biffo was fascinated in helping Dai with construction of his wire lobster cage.

Dai continued, "I saw the markings of rabbits or hares on the cliff-top. I made a few snares and I'll set them tonight."

Biffo exploded, "You'll never catch a rabbit with that bit of wire!"

Dai replied, "Wait and see, boyo, wait and see."

They barbecued the fish for supper and Dai had his lobster pots down next day. The following evening there were two large lobsters in the pot and the remains of a dead rabbit.

David gathered his team together on the second day after their arrival at Vai.

"The reason we are here is to kill some Germans and one German in particular, a large blond colonel. My information suggests he will be visiting here any time now and may stay overnight in the camp on the beach. I don't know the exact day, but I hope to find out tonight. While we're here one of us will be on guard at the top of the cliff day and night. If a stranger approaches, bolt down to the cave. Sergeant Hubbard and I will keep the camp under observation. There are about twenty-four armed Germans in the camp. When our target arrives we'll attack at night with Sten guns and grenades. There are four guards on duty, two at the head of the beach road, one at the jetty and one roaming around. Sergeant Hubbard and Biffo will take out the two at the camp gate, Corporal Griffiths will deal with the one on the jetty and I will get into the wooden mess from the back. There are ten bivouacs on each side of the sand track perfectly placed for grenading. We may have a bonus. There may be an E-boat tied up at the jetty. I leave it to you, Corporal Dai, to think out a way of putting the boat out of action. When we've completed our mission we'll gather outside the wooden building and make our way back here. I'll run through the plan with you again before we attack. By the way, Biffo, I'll take one of the lobsters and by tonight I want you to get hold of a long stick and tie the lobster to its end."

For the rest of the day David kept the camp under observation. Mid-morning two motorcycle and sidecar combinations arrived from the west, and the driver and co-pilot were replaced by two soldiers and the vehicle disappeared westwards again in a cloud of dust and sand. The fat sergeant in the cookhouse came out repeatedly to the store huts, to use the lavatory and to have a surreptitious drag on a cigarette. From midday until teatime the whole place was silent, the only visibly activity being at the beach road guard-post and on the jetty. In the early evening the men started moving around – some went to bathe in the sea and some came to Sergeant Schultz's cookhouse. And then just before dusk David saw Stephia's tall, erect figure emerging from one of the smaller tents near the officers' mess. The upper half of her body was wrapped in a red towel as she strolled proudly along the dust road to a shower house near the beach. Cat-calls and whistles from the soldiers in their bivouacs did not deter her. She walked at a leisurely pace, head held high, responding to the soldiers taunts by sticking out her tongue and tantalisingly lifting one edge of the red towel to reveal a bare midriff. David was mesmerised. She reminded him so much of Bronwen, tall, straight-backed, dark-haired, flashing dark eyes and walking tall and proud.

David returned to the back of the cookhouse as the light was fading. As he surmised, the fat sergeant cook came outside his kitchen to sit on a wooden chair, illuminated by a kerosene lamp from within the cookhouse. He lost little time in lighting a cigarette and uncorking his schnapps bottle. David gave him ten minutes to relax and then, as the sergeant's head was nodding, he edged forward and held out the long bamboo rod, dangling a lobster some three feet away from the sergeant's face. The befuddled cook gave one snorting snore and his head jerked upwards to look straight at the extended claws of the dead crustacean.

"*Mein Gott, langoustine,*" and then he saw David standing in the shadow at the edge of the dimly illuminated background.

"*Wer ist da?*" the sergeant croaked.

David kept dangling the lobster and advanced into the arc of light. Sergeant Schultz was completely bemused. David smiled and blabbered in Greek and the sergeant kept repeating, "*Nicht verstehen, nicht verstehen.*"

Then his slow-thinking brain clicked into gear. This local fisherman wanted to barter his lobster for something, probably schnapps or cigarettes. Both were offered to David. He refused the drink but took the cigarettes. David then pointed to the large cookhouse water-container. Schultz understood. He filled a flask with fresh water and a deal was made. David had his fresh water and Schultz had his lobster.

On the following day Sergeant Hubbard kept the German camp under observation whilst David rested. He reported that an E-boat, E 479, came into the jetty around teatime. A naval officer got off for about twenty minutes and the E-boat sped away again westwards towards Sitia. At dusk David again took a lobster to Sergeant Schultz, who was half-expecting him, and smiled as he carried the large crustacean into his kitchen, returning with fresh water, chocolate and cigarettes. The sergeant had a curious habit of muttering under his breath and David was unable to make head or tail of the fat man's blabbering. On the third day another E-boat, E-434, called at Vai and sped off westwards but that evening the sergeant outside his cookhouse was in a state of agitation. He clutched a lobster in one hand and held five podgy fingers in the air, expostulating, "*Ins morgen, ins morgen.*"

David nodded his head and held up his own hand to indicate the number of lobster needed by the sergeant on the morrow. David surmised that a big party would be held in the mess on the following night, Saturday 27th June.   He returned to the cave and faced his team.

"The show's on tomorrow night, probably around 2200 hours. It'll be dark by then and all soldiers, apart from the guards, will be in their tents. Let's run over the plan of action again."

*

Colonel Manfred Schmidt was enjoying the sea voyage, clad in a white sweater and wearing his peaked cap back to front, much to the amusement of Captain Bucholz and Lieutenant Lautermann, commander of E-432. Saturday 27th June was a beautiful day and the powerful boat skimmed over the smooth surface of the azure blue Aegean like a greyhound in full flight. On its way from Heraklion to its mooring at Vai Manfred chatted amiably with his colleagues.

"Wait till you see the girls I've got lined up for you. Remember, the one called Stephia is mine. And I wonder what culinary delight old Fritz will cook for us. It's a pity General Braüer couldn't make it, but you're not unhappy about that are you, Lautermann?"

Lieutenant Lautermann feigned surprise.

"I thought you told me General Braüer was the second choice. Now I feel offended!" and the three burst out laughing in the cockpit of the speeding E-boat.

On Saturday 27th June David had a busy day. He was up early and down at the back of the cookhouse at breakfast time. Sergeant Schultz saw him lingering and dismissed a trooper who had been helping him clear up after the meal. That morning Corporal Griffith's trap had only caught three small lobster and David now presented these to the sergeant, whose face dropped when he saw the size of the catch, muttering to himself in German, "This is not enough *langoustine* for everyone. The girls will have to go without."

Sergeant Schultz was also dismayed that he would have to forego his ration, as he had become extremely partial to lobster meat in the past three days. David was paid off as usual with water, coffee and cigarettes and quickly disappeared back into the trees on the side of the hill to his vantage point overlooking the bay.

The hours passed slowly but, as evening approached, he saw E-boat 432 gently edging its way towards the wooden jetty. A blond man in a white pullover disembarked and then a larger, burly man, also dressed casually. They walked quickly up the jetty and were soon out of sight and into the officers' mess. The crew of E 432, ten in number, worked rapidly to secure the mooring ropes and within ten minutes a fresh-faced young lieutenant was piped ashore and disappeared into the mess. The *Kriegsmarine* crew then left their secured ship, guarded by one of their number. David surmised that the E-boat was tied up for the night and, as it began to grow dark, returned to the hide to make final preparations for the forthcoming attack.

David and his small commando were in position on the wooded hillside behind the officers' mess at 2100 hours. From this vantage point they dimly saw the back of Sergeant Schultz's kitchen and the outside sheds and, over the top of the mess, the guarded barricade on the beach road was faintly visible. The jetty and E-boat were out of sight behind a rocky bluff. David indicated the route that Sergeant Hubbard and Biffo must take to reach the road checkpoint and he whispered to Corporal Griffiths, that, to get to the jetty, he and Private Clayton would have to pass the back of the kitchens and then take a narrow path down towards the beach and the water's edge. They were all armed with Sten guns and grenades and had blackened their faces and hands. But things were not going according to plan. The *Wehrmacht* soldiers were celebrating with their *Kriegsmarine* colleagues and were gathered in one of the larger tents used for messing in the daytime. Not to be outdone, the officers' mess was ablaze with light and pulsating with *Tanzmusik*, played on an old wind-up gramophone. 2200 hours came and went, as did 2300 hours. Half an hour later, the cacophony from the men's mess tent came to an abrupt end as did the dance music and revelry from the officers' mess.

David whispered to his colleagues, "We'll take off in fifteen minutes. Sergeant Hubbard and Biffo first, and then you, Corporal Griffiths, two minutes later. Try and get the guards silently and look out for the roamer. I'll attack the officers' mess ten minutes after you have all left. The signal for a general engagement will be my Sten and grenades in the mess. When you hear me firing give them all you've got and double off back here. We'll then take off together."

Between 2130 hours and 2300 hours Sergeant Schultz had visited the back of the mess for three cigarettes and innumerable gulps of schnapps from a bottle secreted behind one of the sheds. He was getting steadily drunker. He was acting as a mess waiter and very unhappy at the lowly and menial tasks he was expected to fulfil. His 'tut tutting' and muttering indicated his obvious displeasure at what was happening in the mess.

By 2315 hours David could wait no longer. Sergeant Hubbard and Biffo were despatched on their circuitous route to the roadblock followed by Corporal Dai and Clayton who disappeared down the narrow sand track towards the beach. David now had to wait ten minutes and hope none of the others ran into trouble with the guards and set off the attack prematurely. He tensed himself ready to rush the back door of the kitchen when Sergeant Schultz appeared for the umpteenth time, on this occasion to urinate, quickly followed by a fresh-faced, dishevelled, boyish naval lieutenant who urinated where he stood outside the kitchen door. David gave him two minutes to settle back into the party and then made up his mind – NOW.

He rushed down the hill and through the back door of the mess into Schultz's kitchen which was a disorganised mess of pots, pans and crockery. On a wooden stool in the middle of the kitchen Sergeant Schultz was slumped forwards. He lifted his head slowly, his eyes flickering recognition, as David came forward and smashed the butt of his Sten gun into the cook's forehead. Sergeant Schultz fell backwards in a crumpled heap. The way through from the kitchen to the mess was draped with a grotesquely coloured, beaded curtain and chinks of light came through between the beads from the room beyond. Thrusting his Sten gun forward David rushed through the flimsy curtain and immediately began firing at point blank range at the figures seated around the table. In that instant he thought he saw Stephia's face and he certainly saw the back of a burly man immediately in front of him slumping forwards on to the table as the bullets raked his back. The women were screaming and the men shouting. Someone to his left lifted the end of the table and turned it on its side, scattering lighted candles on to the floor and throwing the mess into darkness. David gave two quick bursts, one to his left and one to the right. The screams of the women and the grunts of the men indicated that his bullets were finding targets. He had only been in the mess room for fifteen seconds when he became aware of the 'crump, crump' noise of exploding grenades from outside the building. He sprinted towards the closed front entrance but, before opening it, drew the pins out of two grenades and tossed them indiscriminately into the darkened room where the women were still screaming and a man was sobbing and moaning.

David threw open the front door to be confronted by a soldier with his rifle at the ready. The German soldier, unsure as to whether David was friend or foe, hesitated for a split second. In that brief time his fate was sealed. David's Sten gun bullets thumped into his body almost cutting the man in half as he fell to the ground at David's feet with his *Schmeitzer* still cradled in his arms. David stepped over the body and saw two dark figures coming towards him in the glow of the burning tents alongside of the beach pathway. Sergeant Hubbard and Biffo had completed their run of terror down the corridor between the tents, throwing grenades into each open-mouthed canvas bivouac. The three turned in unison and ran around the outside of the officers' mess. At the back they found Sergeant Schultz attempting to kick-start a motorcycle combination. He was swaying and unable to keep his corpulent body in the saddle with blood streaming down the side of his face on to his grubby white vest. With an apology, "Sorry about this, old fellow," David struck him again on his forehead and the blubbery mass of flesh fell in an inert heap at the very spot where his officers had been urinating earlier in the evening.

Corporal Dai and Private Clayton came running along the path at the back of the mess.

"Quick, Sir, come with me," and accompanied by David, they returned to the end of the jetty.

The dead body of the *Kriegsmarine* guard was lying at the water's edge. Dai took David on to the jetty and then lifted up two strands of binding cord.

"Give one of these a good yank, Sir, and I'll pull the other."

David did as instructed and then Dai shouted, "Run like hell, Sir."

They were only halfway back to the mess when the E-boat exploded and an orange flame shot into the sky. Pieces of hot metal showered down on to the roof of the mess which caught fire. By now Biffo had the engine of the motorcycle combination revving. David jumped on the pillion. Corporal Dai filled the combination seat and James Clayton and Sergeant Hubbard, Sten guns blazing, sat astride the combination.

"Full speed ahead!" David shouted and as Biffo opened the throttle they trundled past the lifeless figure of Sergeant Schultz and moved sedately up the pathway between the blazing tents. A few desultory shots were fired from the darkness behind the camp, but the aim was poor and the motorcycle, yawing like a beleaguered circus act, strained and skidded its way out of the camp and along the coast road towards the west. David ordered full headlights and the old bike struggled and puffed until it finally ran out of steam three kilometres north of Paleokastro. The bike was discarded at the side of the road and Corporal Dai could not resist the temptation to place a booby trap under the useless vehicle. David, collecting his breath, turned to the corporal.

"How did you manage to blow up the E-boat, Dai?"

"Simple," replied Dai. "Did you know that half those Aussie grenades you gave me are incendiaries? Well, I jammed two over the petrol tank and we both pulled pins out on the jetty."

"But how did you know where the E-boat tanks were located?" asked David.

Dai tapped his nose in the darkness.

"I told you, Sir, I'm a mechanical genius."

The five commandos moved off the road, took stock of their ammunition and food supplies and proceeded swiftly westwards away from the road and away from danger, or so they thought. As they started their slow climb up the Lasithi foothills David exhorted his men.

"Come on lads, we've done a good job at Vai. Now let's put as much distance as we can between ourselves and that place," and then he thought about Stephia.

'Poor Stephia and poor little Spiros. Had he shot her in the darkened room?'

He couldn't tell. He was certain that his bullets had found two of the males sitting around the dining table. He hoped and prayed that one of them might have been the White Angel of Gournes. If he had been successful then, as far as he was concerned, his job on this godforsaken island was complete. He felt genuine remorse at having had to clout the mess sergeant twice on his head. The poor chap was obviously in Hitler's Army under protest.

The first man to recover at the camp in Vai was Sergeant Fritz Schultz. He was lying face down in a small pool of his own blood and in a patch of sodden earth impregnated with human urine. He sat up and looked at the wooden mess roof ablaze. Fritz staggered through his kitchen and parted the beaded curtain. He was immediately conscious of the smell of burning flesh. Two women were sobbing in the darkness and a man, undoubtedly Colonel Manfred Schmidt, shouting, "Get me out of here. What the hell's going on?"

Fritz returned to the kitchen and with shaking fingers lit a kerosene lamp. He then returned to the smoke-filled mess hall.

"Sergeant Schultz, here, Sir. Where are you?"

The colonel was lying on the floor pinned down by the capsized mess table and by the inert body of Stephia, lying across his face, her left breast squashed firmly on to the right side of his forehead. She was dead and had taken the full blast of one of David's grenades. Slumped in one corner was Captain Bucholz, also dead and shot through the chest and head. Crouched forwards in a kneeling position against the overturned table was Lieutenant Lautermann with one of the Heraklion females across his knees moaning and mumbling feebly, bleeding profusely from a large gaping hole in the region of her left hip. The third Heraklion woman was cowering in the far corner of the mess, her face in her hands, quietly praying.

There was blood everywhere and by now gaps were appearing in the roof of the mess as burning strips of wood fell onto the floor and on to the carnage below. One strip of burning wood had ignited Lieutenant Lautermann's left trouser leg and the flesh was beginning to scorch. Sergeant Schultz stood still for ten seconds, taking stock of the human mess he saw before him. He was sorry for Stephia and the poor woman from Heraklion whose life was ebbing away in a series of groans and sighs. He had grown fond of these three ladies and enjoyed looking after them and caring for their every need. And then the voice again intruded into his thoughts.

"Fritz, what the hell are you doing? For Christ's sake, get me out of here."

Always slow-thinking and slow-acting, Fritz now acted with assurance and uncharacteristic agility. He set the kerosene lamp on a chair, pulled the sobbing Cretan woman from the corner by her hair and pushed her out into the night. He prised Lieutenant Lautermann's body away from the table and laid the second Cretan woman, also dead, by his side. The large dead naval captain was still obstructing the table and Fritz had to use all his strength to drag his body away into the kitchen. He was then able to move the heavy mess table off the colonel's chest and to lift Stephia's body off his face.

"I've been hit in the shoulder, Fritz, get a doctor," and then, realising his stupidity, the colonel added, "Get me to a doctor quickly."

Fritz was not a medical expert but he realised that Colonel Schmidt was able to move his shoulder and recalled that he did have trouble from a weakened left arm as a result of a previous injury.

"What about the others here, Sir?" asked Sergeant Schultz.

"Get me to a doctor quickly," shouted the enraged colonel. "I'm the important one here."

Fritz himself, covered in blood from his forehead gashes, replied, "*Jawohl*, Herr Colonel."

He propped Manfred up against a table leg and took a strip of table cloth, binding the colonel's shoulder as best he could. He then took another strip of cloth and bandaged his own forehead.

Outside the kitchen he realised that one of the motorcycles had disappeared but the reserve cycle was still locked in a small shed near the outside lavatory. Once the bike was started he returned to the smoke-filled mess and assisted his colonel outside the back door. Manfred sniffed the air.

"Have you pissed yourself, Sergeant Schultz?"

"No," replied Fritz, but he had to agree with the colonel that there was a pungent uriniferous smell in the air.

Manfred was bundled into the side-car and Fritz, having armed himself with a *Schmeitzer*, took the driver's seat. They had only gone some twenty yards along the sandy beach road when a *Wehrmacht* corporal stepped in front of the motorcycle waving them to stop.

"We have a dozen badly wounded men here, Sir. What shall we do with them?" Colonel Schmidt looked at the man without pity.

"Can't you see I'm badly wounded myself? Drive on Sergeant Schultz."

Schultz did as he was ordered and, though a timid driver at normal times, he covered the thirty kilometre drive from Vai to Sitia in record time.

The motorcycle combination reached the harbour at Sitia at 0120 hours and an Italian medical officer was summoned. The colonel, by now regaining some of his composure and feeling guilty about deserting his detachment at Vai, ordered the doctor to treat his wounds first and then take a convoy of armed men and an ambulance to Vai.

The Italian doctor pronounced that Manfred's injuries were quite superficial.

Manfred, enraged, replied, "They may be superficial to you, you Italian quack, but I'm the one who's suffering."

As the medical officer was about to leave Fritz Schultz fell flat on the floor in a dead faint. A combination of stress, excitement, blood loss and the sweet smell of ether all contributed to Fritz's collapse.

The Italian doctor proclaimed, "Quite the worse head injuries I've seen for a long time. It's amazing how this brave man was able to drive all that distance in his state. Get an ambulance and take him to hospital," and turning to Manfred, "and you, Sir, can spend the rest of the night here. Tomorrow you may rejoin your command at Heraklion."

Manfred stalked out in a fit of rage. What did the Italian quack know about injuries? He would report to Heraklion tomorrow and get Surgeon Captain Steinfurt to check him over. He was certain that his injuries deserved a bar to his Knight's Cross. But his hopes of glory were soon dashed. On the following day Captain Steinfurt pronounced his injuries trivial, just a graze on the shoulder, and said that after a few days' rest he would be able to resume active duties.

*

David was driving his little group hard. By the second night they were on the southern escarpment of the Lasithis, traversing a pathway from east to west about a kilometre north of Stavrohori. The men were tired and wanted to rest but David encouraged and cajoled them to keep going. During the day they saw evidence of frantic German and Italian activity on the road between Sitia and Ierapetra and David knew that many of these convoys were searching for the perpetrators of the Vai massacre. The elation he had felt at the successful conclusion of the Vai attack was beginning to wear thin. He was glad to have his commando back in the mountains once more and knew that he would have to call a halt soon for a night's rest.

It was already dark and his men, now pausing every hundred yards to regain their breath, were reaching the end of their tether. During one of the pauses David heard an unmistakable sound, a German voice somewhere in the darkened skyline above his head. He led his group off the irregular track into a thicket and they lay on the ground, hearts beating faster, the weariness of a few moments ago now replaced by an acute alertness, as the adrenaline took hold and they were aware of the noisy approach of the enemy. The German party descending from a higher plateau made no effort at concealment or stealth. The leader was carrying a flashlight which he used from time to time. As they drew nearer David began to pick up the gist of their loud conversation. The torch bearer had a deep guttural voice.

"Why the fuck does that little Himmler give me all the dirty jobs? Why didn't he pick on Sergeant Kuntz and his section for this trip?"

The man behind the torch bearer replied, "You know Sergeant Kuntz is Captain Schubert's pet. In any case it's also common knowledge that you're the best sergeant in the company!"

There were a few stifled giggles from the soldiers at the back of the fifteen man section. The torch-bearing sergeant spoke indistinctly.

"I suppose you're right, Engelbert, but why does the captain want the firing pins tonight? Why can't he wait till the morning?"

Engelbert's reply was lost in the vast still darkness.

David gathered his group around him and whispered, "That was a German patrol. They're going downhill to get supplies. We can't take them on, but we could perhaps clobber the supply depot. We'll follow them down the mountain."

The small commando kept their distance behind the German party stealthily descending the worn shepherd's path and then, quite suddenly, the Germans came upon the small mountain hamlet of Orino. David pulled up his own group on the path some hundred metres short of, and above, the village square. The loquacious German voices intensified and the commando's view of the dark square was helped by frequent use of flashlights. They saw that there were about fifteen motorcycle combinations neatly parked under a camouflage net in one corner of the square and the largest building in Orino, the church, was a German storage depot for arms and ammunition. Corporal Dai rubbed his hands at the sight of the motorcycles.

"I'd like to have a go at them, Sir. I've got some fuse flex in my *sakouli* and if they're full of petrol I reckon I can blow up a few."

After fifteen minutes the laden German supply troop reassembled and returned uphill and, as they passed the commandos' hiding place, the leading torch-bearing sergeant was still vociferously complaining.

"I told you, Engelbert, this would not be a midnight jaunt. Look at us now, laden with grenades, firing pins, ammunition and odds and sods. We're like fucking pack mules. It'll take us at least two hours to get to base. I'm going to complain to his Royal Highness Schubert when we get back."

"You do that. You do that," replied the panting Engelbert, half stifling a laugh, which was taken up by most of the trudging group behind him.

The sergeant's loud, guttural voice castigated the whole squad. "It's not a fucking laughing matter," as the Germans continued to struggle uphill with their wearisome loads.

David waited for twenty minutes. He estimated, by observation, that there were three or four guards in the small hamlet. He suspected that one soldier guarded the cycles and the second the entrance to the church whilst two or three rested inside. The voices of the guards and soldiers inside the church were heard wishing each other, "*Guten nacht*", and, "*Schlaffen sie gut*", and then, eventually, there was complete silence.

A soldier on guard duty revealed his position by striking a match to light a cigarette under an orange tree at the bottom of the church steps, which made Sergeant Hubbard's task easy. In a minute or so he had silently disposed of the guard by garrotting. Dai and Biffo then went silently to work removing the petrol caps of the motorcycles and inserting a fuse flex into each tank. There were fourteen motorcycle combinations under camouflage netting and within two minutes twelve of these were 'fixed' and wired up to one main flex. Sergeant Hubbard and David stood at the open church door ready to rush in and overpower the sleeping guards when, well above their heads, they heard the unmistakable staccato fire of small arms being used in close combat. The noise of the skirmish brought a sergeant and two sleepy-eyed soldiers on to the church steps. One of them had picked up a rifle but they all fell within seconds to rapid fire from Biffo and David's Sten guns.

David shouted to Sergeant Hubbard, "Go up the track and have a shufti. Dai, can you blow up this supply depot?"

Dai again rubbed his hands.

"I won't have time to fix explosive charges. I reckon it'll have to be incendiary grenades. We could use the Germans' own stick bombs. When I light the flex leading to the motorcycles we'll have twenty seconds to get clear of the square."

As David was about to reply Sergeant Hubbard came running across the square up to the church steps, breathless and panting.

"The whole bloody place up there is crawling with bandits."

David acted speedily.

"We're getting out of here and down that road to the left. Dai, light the fuse and Hubby and I will lob grenades into the church. We'll have about twelve seconds to clear the square. Go NOW."

The fuse was lit, the grenades were thrown and the five commandos raced across the square and down the exit road. The first grenade went off in exactly ten seconds and then another a second later followed by an enormous bang and sheets of flame as the ammunition in the church exploded en masse. There was the rustle and crash of falling debris as the commandos ran down the sloping road and then, at around twenty seconds, a sudden whoosh as sheets of flame shot twenty metres in the air and the first motorcycle blew up. As they ran Dai was counting, "Three... four... I'm disappointed Sir, five... I thought I'd fused twelve of those bikes, six..." and they continued running.

They were nearly clear of the square when David became aware of a ricochet of bullets whizzing above their heads and with a sudden lurch Private James Clayton fell forwards flat on his face in the dusty road. Sergeant Hubbard stopped and knelt down by the inert body of the commando. In a matter of seconds the sergeant realised that James Clayton had been shot by a stray bullet that had gone straight through his skull and that the commando was dead. He leapt to his feet and continued running down the exit road to catch up with his fleeing compatriots. Weariness was again setting in and, when they had put three kilometres between themselves and Orino, David took the commandos into an orange grove and they fell to the ground into a deep, all-embracing sleep of physical exhaustion.

Samaritis' *andartes*, flushed after their annihilation of the German supply column on the mountain, rushed down the path towards the village. About fifty metres short they were greeted by the first grenade blast in the church and then the enormous bang as the whole church exploded. As they cautiously approached the square the motorcycles started exploding one by one. They reached the square just in time to see the last of the fleeing commandos scurrying towards the exit road. The *andartes* let fly with their carbines, more in anger and frustration than in any hope of hitting a target in the poor light, but a lucky bullet hit one of the fugitives in the head. They were infuriated at not having acquired any arms from the night's action and took their revenge on the dead British commando. His body was dismembered and thrown piecemeal into the village well in the centre of the square at Orino.

On the following day Captain Schubert came down from the mountain to Orino. A house to house search by the Germans produced five hostages, two middle-aged women, two elderly infirm men and a boy of twelve years. They were all executed on the spot by Captain Schubert and their bodies dumped into the well to join the mutilated body of Private James Clayton. The village was then burnt to the ground and Orino was erased from the map of Crete.

Chapter Twenty-Five

Eastern Crete, July – August 1943
Call to Festung HQ
Trouble at the Kibbutz

For two days following the Vai debacle Colonel Manfred Schmidt's headquarters at Heraklion was unusually quiet. Manfred at least expected a visit from *Brigadführer* Heydrich Müller and then on the 2nd July the peace was shattered when two coded messages were received from Festung HQ. The first message was brief and cryptic and read:

"Information. General Bruno Braüer relieved of command as from 0800 hours on 1st July 1943. *Brigadführer* Heydrich Müller promoted to full general and will assume command of Festung Kriti as from this date."

The second message chilled Manfred to the marrow.

"From General Heydrich Müller, general officer commanding Festung Kriti: Colonel Manfred Schmidt is ordered to report to General Müller's headquarters, Khania at 1100 hours on 3rd July, 1943."

Manfred held his head in his hands. So this was it. General Müller was going to have the pleasure of sacking him now that he did not have General Bruno Braüer's protection. He was dreading the thought of tomorrow and of meeting the newly appointed general face to face. His head started aching and his left shoulder became painful and affected movement of his left hand. He cancelled all his duties that day and retired to bed.

Promptly at 1100 hours Manfred, left arm in a sling, marched into the general's office, saluted and remained at attention until curtly ordered to sit. General Müller was seated in General Braüer's chair, crouched over some papers, enjoying the discomfiture of the commander from eastern Crete.

"Well, Colonel Schmidt, I expect you're wondering what this urgent meeting is about. As the new commander of Festung Kriti I should be considering getting rid of you but I'm not going to. Your track record during the past weeks has not been encouraging. That debacle at Vai cost us an E-boat and the lives of two naval officers and six *Kriegsmarine*, as well as eight *Wehrmacht* soldiers, not to mention two of the three Cretan whores you had brought to the mess to entertain your friends. And yesterday I received reports that your Captain Schubert has lost nineteen men and ten motorcycles in the Lasithis."

Manfred thought to himself, 'Captain Schubert is now MY captain.'

The general seemed to have forgotten that the idea of giving Schubert free rein had been his and now Manfred was being blamed for Schubert's mistakes. At that particular moment Manfred wished General Müller would send him home to Germany.

Standing in front of Manfred, legs apart, hands on hips and jaw thrust forwards the general continued, "No, Colonel Schmidt, I will not make things easy for you by sending you home. As things stand you have a good relationship with the Italians. I can't stand the bastards myself. They're lazy, inefficient and only interested in fornicating. OKW have informed me that Mussolini's troops in Italy, on their own soil damn it, are low in morale and are showing signs of wanting to capitulate. This would leave our troops in Italy in a serious position. If it happens here on Kriti you have my permission to shoot any of them that refuse to continue working with us. Start putting pressure now on that useless man Carta and make sure the Italians stay in the battle on our side, whatever happens in Italy. The second reason I want you to remain is that your paratroopers are now occupying Elounda and Aghios Nikolaos. As a senior officer in the *Fallschirmjagger* you will have their respect. Elounda is an ideal base for supplying eastern Crete and for sea plane flights and E-boat sorties. You will fortify that area and make it a safe haven for our troops. I believe the *andartes* in the area are relatively friendly. Work on Porphyroyennis and get him to lie low. As well as all this I expect you to continue punitive expeditions into the Diktis and Lasithis and you will give Schubert another chance. He doesn't deserve it but I'm feeling in a benevolent mood today."

Manfred thanked the general and asked his permission to withdraw. The general, inflated with his own importance, strutted across the room and theatrically produced a bottle of French cognac.

"You know, Colonel Schmidt, that I do not drink before sundown. Today, I will make an exception," and, filling two large glasses, he proposed a toast. "To Festung Kriti and to the future Festung Elounda."

Manfred reluctantly downed his drink wishing to be away from the hateful and bombastic commander. On the return journey to Heraklion he had time to think.

'Yes, we will work hard and create an impregnable eastern German base at Elounda.'

Manfred was now determined that Festung Elounda would become a reality.

Trouble at the Kibbutz

David's commando group, reduced from six to five after the tragic and unlucky shooting of Private James Clayton, took eight long weary days to get back to their base at Piskopiano. German and Italian activity along the main roads was intense and they were forced to lie low in the daytime and travel cautiously at night. After their escape south from Orino they travelled westwards along the southern coastal foothills of the Lasithis and then across the wide valley of Katohorio, skirting south to reach Viannos where they turned north along the courier route to reach the cave at Piskopiano. The exhausted party, after nearly a month in the field, were pleased to rest their weary limbs in their haven. But they returned to a crisis.

Private Iain Mcpherson had suffered a nervous breakdown. Mcpherson, an introverted quiet Glaswegian, had taken to his bed about a week after their departure. He refused to do guard duty, drank and ate very little and spent his day either sleeping or lying flat on his back and staring at the darkened ceiling of the cave. Bombardier Ferris tried coaxing and bullying him, but to no avail. David approached him quietly and took hold of his hand.

"What's the matter, Jock?"

Mcpherson lay staring straight through David who repeated the question, "What's bothering you Iain?"

The Scot replied, "Nothing," and turned on his side with his back towards David.

David gently shook his shoulder, "Tell me what's wrong."

"Nothing, Sir," was the stifled reply.

David persisted, "There's something bothering you, Private Mcpherson. Are you feeling ill or in pain?"

"No Sir," came the whispered reply and shake of his head. David was too tired to continue.

"We'll have a good chat in the morning," but the chat had to be postponed until the evening of the following day.

The four tired commandos slept soundly until teatime. By the time they were up and about Private Mcpherson was sitting in the back of the cave staring abjectly at the entrance. David ordered all the others to leave and took the commando out into the bright sunlight to sit on the ledge outside the cave entrance. The disorientated soldier blinked and covered his eyes and started sobbing uncontrollably. Eventually David was able to prise information out of the mentally sick Scot. He was apparently frightened of going away from the cave; he was frightened of staying in the dark inside the cave; he mistrusted and disliked his colleagues; he was fed up of being on guard duty day in and day out; he disliked Crete; he 'wanted to be away from here'; he wanted to get home to Glasgow and, if David did nothing about it, he would probably shoot himself. David waited until the torrent of self-pity and self-recrimination ceased and then spoke softly to the suicidal soldier.

"Private Mcpherson, I think I know how you feel. All of us would like to get out of here and go home. But we can't at the moment. What I suggest is this. I'll take you down to the farm tomorrow and you can stay in the farmhouse all the time with Spiros and Anna. The only thing you have to do is to stand guard at the farm during the night. There will always be another sentry at the top of the farmhouse lane. If you do this for me I promise I'll get you back on the first possible boat to Alexandria where you can have treatment. Is that a fair deal?"

Private Mcpherson nodded his agreement and David concluded the interview by adding, "There's a good chap. I knew you wouldn't let me down."

But his concern about the sick commando continued for the next few days. In effect his six-man commando was reduced to four, but he had recruited Corporal Griffiths who, on their arrival back at Piskopiano, had insisted on returning to his own farm with a parting shot:

"If you're going to the seaside again, let me know. I'll bring my bucket and spade with me next time."

On the same evening as David's interview with Private Mcpherson, Bombardier Ferris returned breathless from a local patrol and reported, "There's something big going on with the Ities. There are four 'X's on the rock behind the icon."

Captain Tavana evidently had some important information for David. When they met at the icon, an hour before dusk on the following day, Captain Franco Tavana was not in his usual jocular mood and his normally pleasant smiling face was creased with anxiety.

"Where the hell have you been, Tommy? I've been up here at least ten times in the past month and you haven't shown up. I thought perhaps the Germans, or the *andartes*, had caught you. But then I would have heard about it if they had. The bloody place has been in turmoil for the past two weeks. Our blond colonel friend was nearly killed in an *andartes'* attack at Vai, but he survived."

David glanced towards the ground to mask his feelings. The Italian captain failed to notice David's disappointed look and continued, "And then two days later Commando Schubert were attacked by Samaritis' bandits and they lost all their motorcycles and supplies. As a result of these two raids, two *Kriegsmarine* officers were killed at Vai and five sailors and eight *Wehrmacht* soldiers. Two Cretan women were also killed. One of them was Colonel Schmidt's – how you say? – 'bit of stuff' from Kastelli. Samaritis killed eighteen of Captain Schubert's soldiers in the Diktis. The butcher General Müller has replaced Braüer as military commander of Crete and has ordered full reprisals for the killing of the German soldiers and *Kriegsmariners*. For the past ten days we have been motoring around the Lasithis and Diktis picking up hostages for the Germans and helping to burn down their poor villages. Whenever I can we let the hostages escape and try not to burn their homes too efficiently. I think this vendetta by General Müller will go on again for at least a week."

The captain paused for breath and his face clouded even further in despair, "But, Tommy my friend, the worse thing of all is that a military junta is trying to get rid of Mussolini. You may not think much of him, but Il Duce is a great man. He rebuilt Italy after the Great War and united the many different sections and provinces. He captured Abyssinia in 1935, Albania in 1939 and Greece last year. But for some reason the military commanders want to be rid of him and this makes me sad. You will have heard that your forces and the Americans invaded Sicily three days ago?"

David had not heard but the news helped to revive his spirits. Captain Tavana now paused to light a cigarette and continued, "I expect the next step will be the invasion of Italy and when this happens I think Italy will surrender and the Germans will pull out. But what will happen to us here in Crete? I think we will be forced to support the Germans. If we don't, the Butcher will get us shot. David, I want you to tell your superiors how helpful I have been to you. I want you to ask them if I can become a prisoner of war in Egypt. I don't want to serve under Müller. Can you fix it for me?"

The Italian captain was near to tears and David felt sorry for him. On impulse he took the Italian's hand and held it briefly.

"Franco, I will see what I can do for you."

Captain Tavana's fears for the future of Italy were not ill-founded. Mussolini was deposed by a military junta at the end of July and, on the 8th September, 1943, the Italians concluded an armistice with Allied forces, who had already landed and were fighting the Germans on Italian soil.

*

Throughout August David's commando remained entrenched and safe in their cave hideout. Private Mcpherson rarely visited the kibbutz. As a form of therapy Spiros used him in the olive groves as a farm-hand and he slept at night in the farmhouse. Members of the commando saw him daily in the olive grove. Sometimes he seemed alert and chatty, but most of the time he was morose and turned his back on his comrades, or walked away. David counselled the rest of his commando to treat Mcpherson gently and not to pressurise him into conversation if, by his actions, the man indicated he wanted to be left alone. By the end of August it was evident to David that the Scot was not recovering from his depression and that he would have to evacuate Mcpherson soon before he either took his own life, or compromised the safety of the rest of his colleagues.

In August David visited Marita at Kastelli. He spent the night in her small house with little Spiros, now nearly two years old, sleeping peacefully in his cot at the other end of the room. David's sense of propriety would not allow him to make love in the same room as the child and for this purpose he took Marita outside into the back garden, where their urgent copulating did not disturb the boy. The house next door, Stephia's house, was empty. Spiros often asked for his mother and Marita consoled the little boy and reassured him that his mother would soon be coming home. Spiros, with the innocence of youth, accepted her explanation. After their first passionate embrace Marita's deep, dark-brown eyes looked up at David and her troubled voice quivered as she spoke.

"Englishman, do you know what happened to Stephia?"

David was prepared for this question and had decided to lie.

"I went to Vai after the German colonel, but Samaritis' men got there first. I heard afterwards that two German officers were killed and many men wounded. There is also talk of the death of two Cretan women. Stephia could have been one of them."

The small fragile figure in his arms started convulsing and sobbing.

"Poor Stephia, poor Stephia, we've heard here that she was shot by the *andartes*. But the colonel, the White Angel of Gournes, got away. He's been up here once to Stephia's house and rummaged around for a few minutes. I don't know what he was looking for. Thank goodness he didn't come in here. Little Spiros is now alone in the world, but I will look after him and when he's older I'll take him down to his grandfather's farm at Piskopiano. The little boy is no trouble at all," and she began sobbing again with tears flowing. "Poor Stephia. She did not deserve this. To be shot in cold blood by her own people when she should not have been there in the first place. Poor Stephia," and the sobbing continued intermittently for another ten minutes.

David's guilt about the part he had played in Stephia's death was overwhelming but he knew that his first priority was preserving the integrity of his commando. The blame for the massacre at Vai must be laid fairly and squarely on the shoulder of Samaritis and his *andartes*. David continued seeing Marita, mainly for his own sexual gratification, but he found the visits increasingly stressful, especially when little Spiros kept crying for his mother. He remained steadfast in his resolve not to disclose the truth to Marita. He did not wish her to know that he had been the assassin who had killed Spiros' mother.

In the early hours of the morning of September 1st, 1943, Bombardier Ferris woke up with a belly ache. He went outside the cave and vomited over the ledge. When he returned Biffo volunteered.

"Pregnant again, Ferry?"

At which they all laughed. Bombardier Ferris offered his opinion.

"I think it's something I ate. Could have been that cheese we had for supper."

Biffo replied, "Nothing wrong with the cheese. I had two platefuls and I'm okay. More likely it was too much *tsikoudia*. You'd better lay off the hooch. It'll rot your liver."

Bombardier Ferris was known to have a liking for strong, unadulterated spirit and the stronger the better. On the following morning the bombardier announced that he felt much better and went out on a local patrol with Sergeant Hubbard. He vomited again during the day and, when he returned in the late evening, he was pale, feverish and anorexic.

He complained to David, "I've got a gut ache which started around my belly button and has now moved to my right side. I've also got the runs."

David had a cursory look at the bombardier's abdomen and when he pressed in the right side the stoic little Glaswegian flinched and groaned.

"It might be your appendix, Bombardier Ferris."

"Can't be that, Sir," the bombardier replied "I've had it out at the Glasgow Royal."

David looked again and noticed a long irregular scar in the right side of the corporal's abdomen.

"I expect it'll settle down, Bombardier. You can rest all day tomorrow and we'll see how things are in the evening."

When David returned from his patrol on the following evening Bombardier Ferris was very sick. His eyes were sunken and his cold perspiring face was ashen-white under his tan. His abdomen felt board-like to David's palpating fingers. The bombardier was uncannily cheerful.

"Pain's gone, Sir, and I feel like something to eat."

But when he took a mouthful of water he was immediately sick, bringing up dark, bile-stained vomit. He continued vomiting on and off during the night and by early morning, on the 4th September, his general condition was deteriorating, though the dour little Scot kept cheerful and insisted that, "a wee dram of Glenfiddich will put me right".

David ordered Sergeant Hubbard to make a stretcher from a sheet of canvas and two poles and they lowered Bombardier Ferris to the ground on ropes and brought him down by stretcher to the farm. By the time they arrived old man Spiros had harnessed a donkey to a ramshackle cart and the sick commando was strapped securely to the back of the cart, his legs dangling over the end of the short dray. Spiros led the donkey out of the farm and David walked alongside the sick corporal, who was alternately swearing and cursing in an incomprehensible Glaswegian dialect and passing out into a deathly coma from time to time. They took Bombardier Ferris to a Cretan doctor in Hersonisos. On the way they had to pass through two German checkpoints, one south of Piskopiano and the other on the outskirts of the town. On both occasions the cortège was waved through when the *Wehrmacht* sergeant saw the serious condition of the man on the back of the donkey cart.

The Cretan *iatros* made a diagnosis of peritonitis and advised that the patient needed urgent surgery which could only be undertaken in Heraklion. He offered to accompany Spiros to the hospital and, after injecting the bombardier with a large dose of opiate, the donkey cart and its two attendants left for Heraklion, a distance of thirty-six kilometres, a journey which took them six hours to complete and, for most of the time, the prostrate figure on the back of the dray was silent and lifeless. David hid in a barn in Hersonisos for the rest of the day and made good his return to the cave at Piskopiano after nightfall.

He took Sergeant Hubbard aside and whispered, "Sergeant, I don't think Bombardier Ferris is going to make it. When he left with Spiros and the doctor he looked dead to me. The Cretan doctor thinks he's got peritonitis. The poor chap is delirious and may let slip the position of our kibbutz. We will all muster before dawn tomorrow and, apart from the sentry on duty tonight, we'll position ourselves around the farmhouse and the approach road. We may have unwelcome visitors at any time. Our commando is getting a bit thin on the ground with the bombardier out of action and poor old Private Mcpherson a useless misfit at the farmhouse."

The commando remained at their sentry positions all day. Spiros returned in the late evening and reported that the sick patient had been admitted to the civilian wing of the military hospital at Heraklion. Both he and the Cretan doctor were questioned about the home address of their patient. Spiros admitted that the best they could do was to say that he came from a farm some two kilometres west of Pirgia.

Spiros added, "When we left the poor boy, he was deathly pale with shallow breathing, which occasionally stopped for many seconds. When I saw them cart him away into the hospital I thought he was dead. There were many German soldiers in the hospital grounds. I wanted to stay to see what happened to your comrade but the *iatros* became very agitated and insisted on getting away. I had to go with him. I'm sorry to have abandoned the bombardier but there did not seem to be anything else we could do."

David clasped the old farmer's shoulder.

"Spiros, you have done everything I could have asked of you. I thank you and I hope that what we have done will not bring the Germans to Piskopiano."

As David left the farmhouse he caught a glimpse of Private Mcpherson sitting idly near a barn door. He did not seem concerned or interested in the fate of his fellow Scot and colleague.

The Hospital at Heraklion

When Student's paratroopers overran Heraklion on May 30th, 1941 they found part of the main hospital had been used by the British garrison to treat their casualties and many of the more seriously wounded soldiers were still occupying hospital beds. The hospital was requisitioned for use by German military and naval personnel and all civilian patients were ejected. Over the following twelve months, and after negotiation with the Committee of Civil Advisors, a forty-bedded civilian wing was allocated to the Cretans, manned and administered by local doctors. On the 5th September, 1943 a moribund patient was admitted to this civilian wing and was at first seen by a Cretan doctor.

At that time the overall commanding officer of Heraklion hospital was the recently promoted Major Steinfurt and, since his arrival in Crete in December 1942, he had insisted on examining all surgical patients, military and civilian, admitted to the hospital. Consequently he was quickly summoned from the officers' mess to see Bombardier Ferris. Peritonitis was diagnosed and, though mystified by the presence of a scar in the right side of the patient's body, he advised an emergency operation which he personally performed. At operation he confirmed virulent generalised peritonitis due to a perforated appendix. He removed the appendix and placed drains in the abdominal cavity.

While the patient lay naked on the operating table the colonel was surprised to find a tattoo on his left upper arm, a small green flower and written underneath the words, 'All my love Annie'. The 'Cretan' patient lingered on for two days, mainly in a semi-comatose condition, but during lucid periods he shouted and sang English ditties and sea shanties. The German surgeon major was soon convinced that his 'Cretan' patient might be a British agent. He thought he should report his suspicions to Colonel Schmidt but he disliked Manfred so intensely that he decided to wait and observe the outcome of his surgery. The outcome was inevitable. Bombardier Ferris died at 6.30 a.m. on the 8th September.

On the evening prior to his death Surgeon Major Steinfurt had asked the dying patient in English, "Where is your home in Britain my son?"

The bombardier replied, "Glasgow, Sir," and began to sing in a quiet, croaky, dry-mouthed voice, "I belong to Glasgee, dear old Glasgee town."

"And where are you based in Crete, my boy?"

"In Pissypano," the delirious Scot replied and then the interval of lucidity ended and the patient fell into a coma, with shallow sighing respirations, from which he did not emerge. By morning he was dead, lying in a pool of his own blood-stained vomit and foul-smelling excreta.

Later that day Surgeon Major Steinfurt called on Manfred Villa Ariadne. Manfred, with a mocking smile on his face, sat at his desk.

"And what can I do for you, Herr Surgeon Major?"

Major Steinfurt felt the hostility and sarcasm in the seated officer's voice. He was sorely tempted to turn on his heels and walk away from the odious man. And then he reasoned, 'It's my duty to report these matters,' and, clearing his throat, he proceeded.

"Two days ago a very sick man was admitted to the Cretan wing of my hospital. He had peritonitis and I operated on him. He died this morning."

"Well," said Manfred, "You can't expect to save everyone and what's the worry about losing one more Cretan bastard?"

The medical major flushed.

"It's not that, Colonel Schmidt, but it's that fact that he had an English tattoo on his arm and spoke to me last night in English."

"What did he say?" asked Manfred, now fully alert and interested.

"He said he was from Glasgow and that his base in Crete was at Piskopiano. I checked with the Cretan doctor who first examined him and was told that the man was a farmer from Pirgia. I think he might have been a British agent."

Manfred jumped to his feet and exploded.

"Why didn't you tell me this before he died?"

The surgeon major replied, "He was in no fit state for questioning at any time and I was only able to speak to him on one occasion and that was last night."

Manfred glowered at the red-faced surgeon.

"The trouble with you damn medics is that you don't think about these things. We could have been on to a good thing if my men could have questioned him," and then, turning to the wall map, he exclaimed, "Piskopiano and Pirgia. Here they are. Very close to each other, some three kilometres apart. You may go, Major, and sharpen your wits. Make sure you report any of these events to me in future without delay."

The flustered major left the commander's office, seething with rage. As he passed through the door he heard Manfred bellowing for his orderly sergeant.

"Get Captain Schubert here immediately," and the German plans for a cordon and search of Piskopiano and Pirgia were formulated. At Captain Schubert's insistence both villages were to be razed to the ground after the hostages had been despatched. A date was fixed by Colonel Schmidt and Captain Schubert for a dawn attack on the 11th September, 1943, but the attack did not materialise on that day. On the 8th September Italy signed an armistice with the Allies and all hell was let loose in Festung Kriti.

The Italian Armistice, 9th September, 1943

Manfred and Captain Schubert were busy with preparations for their planned attack on Piskopiano and Pirgia when General Müller burst into headquarters' office at Villa Ariadne in a raging temper.

"Well, the bastards have done it this time. The bloody Italians signed an armistice with the Allies yesterday and that leaves us here in Crete in one hell of a mess. The worst area is yours here in east Crete, Colonel Schmidt. You'll have to take over the Italian defensive positions at Neapolis, Sitia and Ierapetra. To do this you need more men. I've ordered a division to move today from Khania. This will give you some three thousand extra German troops to take over the Italian defensive positions. You may have to abandon Ierapetra if there are insufficient troops to go around. Now let me tell you how we'll deal with our gallant Italian Allies," and with a flourish the general planted a typed sheet of paper on Manfred's desk. He continued.

"My instructions are on this paper. That bastard General Carta has three options. The first is to keep his arms and serve under our control. The second is for us to disarm them and use them for non-combatant duties and a third is, if they refuse either of these measures they will be interned as deserters. Any Italians fraternising with, or selling arms to, the enemy will be shot. Colonel Schmidt, I order you to take an armoured column to General Carta's headquarters at Neapolis today and give the bastard this ultimatum. I don't care how you do it, but make it clear to the *schweinehund* that Italian troops will be shot if they desert their posts or make a run for it. Report to me at Khania later today."

The general and his aide turned on their heels and stormed out of the villa to the waiting car and armoured escorts.

Manfred wasted little time in getting across to Neapolis. He took Captain Schubert and his mobile commando with him for protection and, as always, Sergeant Schneider sat at his side in the staff *Kübelwagen*. On announcement of the Italian armistice General Angelo Carta had withdrawn all his troops into their garrisons to await further orders. When Manfred's convoy reached Neapolis the outskirts of the town were deserted and all road blocks and military outposts were unmanned. Manfred ordered his heavily armoured column to drive straight to the Italian barracks. After some delay at the main gate, and threats from Manfred, they were allowed in and drove across the barracks square to General Carta's quarters. The general, flanked by four senior staff officers and Captain Tavana, was standing behind a long desk with a picture of Mussolini prominent on the wall behind them. After an exchange of salutes Manfred was the first to speak.

"I have been delegated by General Müller to bring you these orders," placing the ultimatum on the desk before the Italian general.

General Carta picked up the document, read it through slowly, and, looking across at Manfred, spoke in halting German.

"I would have thought that, in view of the seriousness of the occasion, General Müller himself might have made this visit. I have already discussed the actions we will take with my staff and we are all agreed that Italian forces in Crete will remain under arms and will submit themselves to control by German officers. Tell General Müller that none of my troops will be deserting or joining the irregulars and, if that happens, we will deal with it ourselves. I can give you my word that any one of my men breaking the rules will be shot."

Manfred was taken aback at the ease with which the frightened Italian general had accepted General Müller's ultimatum and was pleased to get away quickly and report the results by telephone to Festung headquarters in Khania. General Müller was still seething at the Italian treachery, bellowing over the telephone, "I hope the fornicating Wop keeps his word. Keep a careful watch on the Italians, Colonel and, at any sign of trouble, call me. I know how to deal with deserters. You will also need to keep an eye on the *andartes*. They'll be hanging around like vultures hoping to feed off Italian meat and to get hold of their rifles. All the reserves should have reached you by now so instruct them to shoot on sight and to be utterly ruthless in snuffing out any resistance. Is that clearly understood, Colonel Schmidt?"

Manfred replied with authority, "*Jawohl*, Herr General. Your orders will be carried out to the letter."

Later that day Manfred inspected the German reserves now assembled in the *Wehrmacht* barracks at Heraklion. They were a mixture of young boys, some of them barely seventeen years of age and tired old soldiers, many recruited from reserved occupations and from the supply cadres of the *Wehrmacht*. He ordered a grand parade for the morning of September 12th and addressed them en masse.

"General Müller's orders are clear. You are to shoot on sight any suspicious person, Italian or Cretan, and villages near the site of the incident are to be burned to the ground. Don't wait for orders from me. Just do it. Some of you will be posted to Italian garrisons in the main towns. Don't take any orders from Italian officers whatever their rank. Our own *Wehrmacht* officers are in charge. Most of you will be organised into storm companies and you will be in the field most of the time, asserting our control over Cretan resistance forces. Captain Schubert will instruct you in the techniques of cordon and search and of elimination of Cretan fighters and burning their villages. We have very little time to prepare and we must start our operations within forty-eight hours. Let me remind you that the fate of Crete is in your hands. It is our duty to ensure that Festung Kriti is not captured by the enemy and that we keep it in our hands for the Fatherland and for our Führer. Heil Hitler."

In the event, instructing the new recruits proved to be more complicated than expected. They were not ready to take to the field until the 17th September and, even then, Captain Schubert was not entirely happy with the quality and ability of his new stormtroopers.

Cretan Resistance Diary May 1941 – October 1943

When General Student's air armada and paratroopers attacked Crete in May 1941 reaction from the Cretan population was unexpectedly violent. Though poorly equipped the Cretans, traditionally proud and aggressive, ruthlessly attacked Student's Fallschirmjagger *and there were many reports of wanton killing of wounded, and sometimes defenceless, German soldiers. No prisoners were taken. The attacks of the Cretan irregulars were in the nature of a popular uprising against the invaders and were not controlled or co-ordinated by British and Dominion commanders. Once the British had been driven out of Crete, German reprisals, ordered by* Reichsmarschall *Goering were both swift and horrendous in their scale, involving mass killing of captured Cretan males and bombing and burning of Cretan villages.*

At the onset of winter in 1941 nearly all able-bodied Cretan males had taken to the mountains where they wandered aimlessly forming themselves into small armed bands, acting independently and frequently mistrustful of each other. Each leader of a group of andartes *strove to assert his authority over other groups and some of the* andartes *themselves moved from one group to another in the hope they would eventually end up with a winning* kapitan. *Desertion was rife and many of the* andartes *became informers against the* kapitans *and sadly, sometimes, informed on their colleagues to the Germans. These disparate groups roving the mountainous highlands of central Crete confined their attacks to ambushes and sniping on German columns.*

When this happened the German reaction was always violent. Arrest and execution of all males in the villages nearest to the incident and often burning of Cretan dwellings was the norm. This situation continued throughout 1942 but, by the autumn of that year, definitive leaders were emerging often under surveillance by British SOE agents. The established kapitans *at the end of the twelve month struggle were also developing political ambitions and, whilst the majority of* andartes *were Cretan and nationalist, some communists became affiliated to ELAS on the mainland. By the end of 1942 Crete was parcelled into various overlapping sections, each territory controlled by one nationalist and one communist* kapitan.

In western Crete the emerging nationalist kapitan *was Colonel Papadakis, whilst Mandakis became the spokesman for the communists. Around Rethymno the nationalist Colonel Petrakageorgis held the reins whilst in eastern Crete Bandouvas controlled the nationalists around Heraklion and Yanni Bodias ruled the weaker communists. British SOE agents had two informers on Colonel Beteniakis' Committee of Civil Advisors in Heraklion – Georgio Dendovakis and Miki Akoumianakis provided valuable information on German military intent to the British agents. Heraklion was heavily garrisoned by the Germans and Cretan resistance fighters never felt strong enough for direct confrontation with the occupying forces in the town.*

Further east the nationalist Colonel Plevres held command in the Sitia district and there were two militant communist leaders operating in the Lasithi and Dikti ranges – Militades Porphyroyennis based mainly around Aghios Nikolaos and Samaritis who roamed the Lasithis and held the Italian garrison at Ierapetra under siege. A further group of communists with ELAS affiliations were located in the Diktis and led by a benign, almost fatherly kapitan, *Mitsos O Papas. Each of these groups, despite having a common ideology, were aggressively militant towards each other and all attempts at unification met with failure, largely due to the differing personalities of the* kapitans. *The armed brigands stayed in their mountain retreats, jealously guarding their territories, wary and suspicious of each other and of any strangers and only descending occasionally into the foothills to snap at the heels of the German occupation forces. The Italian forces were rarely attacked by the brigands, with the exception of Samaritis, who relentlessly harried the Italian garrison at Ierapetra.*

Samaritis became the most hated kapitan *in eastern Crete, hated not only by the German and Italian forces, but also by his own communist comrades Porphyroyennis and O Papas. Born in the gorge of Samaria in south-west Crete he developed into an ugly, bitter and sneering man who in late 1941 formed his group of some fifty militant* andartes. *He soon quarrelled with Mandakis, the emerging communist* kapitan *in western Crete, who was instrumental in driving Samaritis eastwards, where he set up his cell in the Lasithis and became a thorn in the side of the occupying forces.*

*The sudden collapse of Italy on the 8th September, 1943 provided a golden opportunity for Cretan resistance fighters to take over eastern Crete but, as a result of their general unpreparedness, lack of communication and inter-*kapitan *vendettas, the opportunity was lost. Between the 9th and 16th September 1943 eastern Crete was ripe for plucking from the German and the Italian occupation forces, but the chance was missed and the resistance fighters had to wait another fourteen months before they were able to descend from their mountain retreats and re-occupy the northern coastal towns of Crete.*

For the first week after the armistice declaration all Italian forces remained alert and fully armed and closeted in their garrison towns at Malia, Neapolis, Sitia, Aghios Nikolaos and Ierapetra. General Carta's instructions were definite and unequivocal.

"All Italian forces will remain alert and in battle readiness within their garrison barracks. They are not to provoke incidents with the local population and they are to co-operate with German reinforcements when they arrive and to subordinate themselves to the

command of the Wehrmacht. *Anyone caught deserting, or selling arms to the enemy, will be shot without trial."*

General Angelo Carta had grave misgivings about the future of the troops under his command. He was not sure all of them would obey his orders and many would desert rather than serve under the Germans. He also recognised that many of his men were corrupt and, if given the opportunity, would readily lay down their arms and sell them to Cretan irregulars. He knew that he would not be strong enough to impose the death penalty on his fellow countrymen and this factor, together with his hatred of the German military commanders and General Müller in particular, prompted him to start secret negotiations with British agents to get off the island. Whilst he spoke with conviction to his troops about the ultimate penalty for desertion, General Carta was planning his own escape from Crete.

As soon as the Italians withdrew into their garrison towns the andartes, *emboldened by the lack of military activity on the roads, came out of the mountains and occupied the foothills, gradually encroaching on the garrisons. Bandouvas moved south from the Dikti mountains towards Viannos. Yanni Bodias, the communist, moved his men to the outskirts of Heraklion. Samaritis invested Ierapetra. Porphyroyennis moved from the Lasithis into Aghios Nikolaos, whilst Colonel Plevres the nationalist leader occupied the main part of Sitia. The* andartes *were not well co-ordinated and their plans for the future varied from one group to the next. Samaritis and Porphyroyennis were after guns, mainly aimed at strengthening their own forces for a fight against the nationalists. They envisaged that the defeated Italians would readily lay down their arms and hand them over without dissent. Due to the lack of communication and co-operation between the disparate groups a glorious opportunity was lost for the Cretans to disarm the Italians, eject the Germans and take over the whole of eastern Crete, excluding Heraklion and Elounda. The* andartes *descended on the Italian garrisons like vultures collecting around a kill and, like the birds of prey, spent most of the vital days after the armistice bickering and quarrelling amongst themselves, only pecking irregularly at the Italian carcass.*

Within a week the German military machine had swung into action; Italian garrisons were taken over by German officers, whilst the roads and strong points were re-manned and defended by Schubert's mobile stormtroops. Bandouvas attacked Viannos on the 14th September and the German outpost was overrun. Bandouvas' troops then swept southwards towards Ierapetra but within five days a German force of eighteen hundred men, led by Jagdcommando *Schubert, decimated the* andartes *and drove them westwards to Sphakia where Bandouvas was evacuated by British agents in early October 1943.*

During the crucial week following the Italian armistice David kept his commando strictly confined to the cave and farmhouse area at Piskopiano with two sentries on duty day and night. The road to Kastelli became extremely busy. Groups of shabbily dressed Cretan irregulars, some armed with out-of-date Italian rifles and some carrying old fashioned pre-war shotguns, moved northwards towards the coast. The origin of this nondescript rabble was unclear. A few were undoubtedly Bandouvas' men and on the 9th September a large party of his troops passed through Piskopiano moving southwards towards Kastelli and Viannos. During the week Spiros' farm had four groups of unwelcome *andarte* visitors. In true Cretan fashion Spiros fed and watered them and eventually they departed. Amongst these bands David was able to identify supporters of Yanni Bodias and Samaritis. But none stayed more than a few hours before moving eager-eyed and expectant northwards towards the towns of Malia and Neapolis. And then on the 15th September the tide turned and the road southwards towards Kastelli became blocked by fleeing *andartes*, all trying their hardest to get back into the vastness and safety of the Dikti mountains.

Once the German military juggernaut woke up to the perils of leaving large areas of eastern Crete undefended, the roads, both major and minor, were intensively patrolled, the cross-roads manned and the outer perimeters of the larger towns defended in depth. On the 17th September a mechanised column of eighteen hundred Germans passed through Piskopiano heading south to Viannos, where Bandouvas and his two hundred and fifty *andartes* were entrenched. This heavily armoured convoy easily ousted Bandouvas and forced him and the remnants of his *andartes* to flee westwards.

During this chaotic period David became extremely concerned about the safety of his hideout. He had a mentally sick commando on his hands and Private Mcpherson was virtually under house arrest in the cave and had to have one of the other commandos constantly acting as a guard to prevent his escape. The intense German activity continued for three weeks.

During the first week the commando had a scare when a column of twenty motorcycles arrived at the farmhouse. David feared the worst, but the Germans were only in the farm for half an hour before they departed in a cloud of dust and continued their journey southward towards Kastelli. Spiros later confirmed they had run out of drinking water. Most nights David and Sergeant Hubbard patrolled the local areas. They soon established that there were German troops in road blocks at Piskopiano and at Pirgia. David's commando could do little else but sit tight and wait.

Persistent pressure affected everyone's morale and they all became short-tempered and morose. Biffo started quarrelling with Gunner Smithson and it took all of David's ingenuity to stop the two coming to blows. Two months had elapsed since a message had been received from Cairo and David considered the courier journey to Keratokombou too dangerous to undertake. The pressure on his little troop was increasing daily and, by early October, it became evident that something would have to be done to alleviate tension in the stifling hot hideout. During the first week of October the number of convoys on the Kastelli road lessened and the manned outposts at Piskopiano and Pirgia were withdrawn. Platoons of Italians led by German officers took over the duties of patrolling the roads during the day and defending the garrison towns by night.

On 15th October, 1943 David and Sergeant Hubbard, on a routine patrol, found a large new 'X' on the rock behind the icon on the Kastelli to Hersonisos road. In response to Captain Tavana's signal David cautiously approached their rendezvous at dusk on the evening of October 17th. He found the captain sitting hunched on a rock, puffing dejectedly on his cigarette and his *Kübelwagen* and driver parked some fifty metres down the road. When David appeared from the bushes behind him the captain's face lit up in a brief smile of recognition but almost immediately his features settled into a worried look of utter despair.

"Tommy, am I glad to see you. We're all in a bloody mess. The Germans have taken command of all our forces and are giving us hell. It's been particularly bad since General Carta, Brigadier Gandolfo and two senior colonels deserted our headquarters at Neapolis. I believe that one of your British agents called Ferman got the general away. Do you know him, Tommy?"

David shook his head and Captain Tavana continued, "I'm frightened for my life, Tommy. Colonel Schmidt is already reducing Italian officers to the ranks. I will not let that happen to me, Tommy," and his eyes flashed in a brief glimmer of defiance. "What I want is to surrender to the British and to be taken to North Africa. Can you arrange this for me? If your agents can get General Carta away under the nose of the Germans, why can't they do it for me?"

David felt sorry for the bemused and confused Italian officer and wanted to help him. The next lift from the island would be on the nights of the 19th, 20th and 21st of October. He had a sick man in his commando who had to be evacuated and he also urgently needed to contact the wireless operator at Keratokombou. He resolved to make a courier run to the south and to take Captain Tavana with him.

"Captain Tavana, I'll try and get you out of here next week. Turn up an hour before nightfall next Friday. We only travel at night and we'll travel light, only a small *sakouli*. I shall be armed and I'll leave it to you if you decide you want to carry a firearm. With all these Germans about the place we may run into trouble on our journey south," and, clasping the Italian's hand, David concluded, "See you on Friday and don't forget, only a light pack."

David turned about and disappeared into the bushes to retrace his steps across the fields and olive groves to the hideout. As he wearily plodded towards Spiros' farm he thought to himself, 'Have I done the right thing? If Tavana turns up I'll take him with me. If he doesn't I'll go south anyway and put Private Mcpherson on the boat.'

The Italian captain appeared at the appointed hour on the 17th October. Much to David's dismay he was flamboyantly dressed in his best mess kit, complete with ceremonial sword and a red-banded, peaked *kepi*. His large heavy *sakouli* was bulging with wine bottles, bread and cheese and to complicate matters he insisted that his batman-driver should accompany him. The driver carried an even larger haversack which contained many of the captain's personal belongings and more bottles of wine which, as Captain Tavana explained, were for, "Emergency use only in case we get thirsty on the journey."

There was no time to argue. David accepted Captain Tavana's driver as a passenger but insisted his *sakouli* had to be divested of most of its clinking wine bottles. The captain himself covered his light blue uniform with a dark grey cloak and inserted his bright red cap into his *sakouli*.

"Tommy, I want to look good when I surrender to the British."

The incongruous party of four set out in single file in the gathering gloom, four paces apart, on their journey south to Keratokombou. David led the group with Mcpherson behind him, the Italian driver, Giuseppe, next and Captain Tavana bringing up the rear. David insisted on strict silence when they were marching in the dark. For safety reasons David had to take the party up into the mountains to avoid Kastelli. Progress was correspondingly slow and laboured and by dawn on the following morning they rested in a cave near Nipiditos where they ate some bread and cheese and drank sparingly from Captain Tavana's wine supply.

During that day it became evident that a bond was developing between Mcpherson and Giuseppe. The Italian driver had a broad open face, always smiling to reveal two rows of flashing white teeth, beneath a drooping jet black moustache. He had taken a liking to Private Mcpherson and mothered him all day. Despite language difficulties the two became inseparable and this suited David as it removed the worry of shepherding his sick commando over the mountain trails.

Late morning a small German motorcycle convoy rode into Nipiditos. David's 'hide' in the hills was about a kilometre north of the village and for two hours they heard the soldiers shouting to each other as they searched the houses. Apparently satisfied that there were no males to take hostage in the village, the small convoy left in a flurry of dust early in the afternoon. The party moved out of their hide two hours before dusk and, following a dried river bed, they safely crossed the Kastelli-Ierapetra road and proceeded southwards from Kasanos through Martha and, bypassing Viannos, reached the sea at Kertokombou just as dawn was breaking on the 19th October.

David found them a safe hide just north of the small seaside fishing village and set out to make contact with his wireless operator at the farm at Tres Ekklises about two kilometres to the east. The red-haired wireless operator had disappeared. The Cretan farmer explained that there had been intensive enemy activity in Keratokombou about a fortnight previously and the British agent had dumped his wireless into the farm well and taken to the hills.

The farmer added, "I am not surprised the man took off. He was becoming very nervous and, at the slightest hint of German or Italian movement, he sped into the hills. When he dumped the wireless I knew he would not be coming back."

David thanked the farmer and returned to Keratokombou.

The format for meeting the British boat was well established. One of three beaches to the west of Keratokombou, each about a kilometre apart, was used and the contact points and landing areas varied each month. The shore party kept an eye on all three potential landing sites on the appointed dates. David spent the nights of the 21st and 22nd on a cliff overlooking the beaches. That a landing was imminent was clearly evident from the sudden appearance of shadowy dark figures wandering along the cliff edges and taking great care to avoid contact with each other. And then the expected signal, a subdued flash repeated three times, came from the wide open dark sea on the night of the 21st October. David returned to collect his charges and by the time they had descended the cliff the confined beach was alive with dark shadowy figures moving silently around from place to place either singly or in small bands.

David kept his small party in a tight group just under the shelter of the cliff face. His attempts at identifying some of the ghost-like figures in the dark proved futile and there were no clues from the speech of the beach party. Everyone seemed to converse in Greek whispers. Two dinghies were guided into the small cove by intermittent torch flashes from one of the Cretans, standing up to his waist in the surf. As soon as the dinghies hit the shale they were half-dragged out of the water and the number of figures collecting around the boats increased when the occupants jumped ashore. The excited babbling of the whole group rose to a crescendo as both sides slapped each other's backs and pumped each other's hands in greeting and then David heard an English voice rising from the centre of the human mass.

"I say, hold on chaps. Take it easy. Are Codforce here by any chance?"

David sprang forwards, shouting, "Here, Sir."

A tall willowy figure in naval uniform pushed his way forwards and, taking David's elbow, walked him up the beach towards his three companions. He introduced himself.

"I'm Captain William Greyshaw, I've been told that your wireless operator needs to be pulled out. Is he one of these?"

David replied, "No, Sir, I've been to his station and he's gone. But I do have a request. Can you please take Private Mcpherson with you? The poor chap's flipped his lid."

The captain agreed and David continued, "I also have an Italian captain who wants to surrender to a superior British officer. I will explain to him that your rank is superior to his. As you will see, in a minute, he's fully dressed for the occasion! His name is Captain Franco Tavana. He won't go across to Alex without his batman, so if you agree to take the captain you'll have to agree to take Giuseppe as well."

The captain replied without hesitation, "That's all right. We'll be a bit cramped on the old tub but we'll manage. Let's get this bit out of the way."

David turned about and introduced Captain Tavana to Captain William Greyshaw. The Italian, standing stiffly at attention, withdrew his ceremonial sword from its scabbard and presented its hilt to the tall shadowy figure before him declaring:

"I, Captain Franco Tavana of the Fifth Alpine Regiment of the Italian armed forces, formally surrender to you Captain Grey... sha and offer you my sword as a sign of my sincerity. I also offer the surrender of Private Giuseppe Venaldi who wishes to give himself up to British forces."

Captain Greyshaw half-stifled a giggle at the formality of the Italian captain's request.

"On behalf of the British naval forces in the eastern Mediterranean I accept your surrender and that of Private Venaldi. You can keep your bloody sword. Now let's get off this beach."

As they moved quietly down the beach the naval captain again held David's elbow and drew him aside.

"I've a message for you from Cairo. You will know the source. Your boss is going to send out a small naval unit to attack Heraklion harbour from the landward side. They should be with you on the drop next month, or in January. Cairo are particularly interested in submarine activity in Heraklion. The German subs have been playing havoc with us in the Med recently. Cairo want you to have a look around Heraklion and see which way is best to attack. They also need specific information as to the frequency of visits and numbers of subs in the harbour at any time. If you send a courier down here for the November drop there should be further information for you."

David thanked the naval captain who re-embarked on the over-laden dinghy. David barely had time to shout good-bye and good luck as the boats were manoeuvred out to sea and, in the beam of a torch, he had a last glimpse of Captain Tavana standing unsteadily and proudly in the dinghy, his right arm held in rigid salute.

"Goodbye Tommy, thank you for your help. Captain Tavana will always remember the brave British officer who got him off this dreadful island."

The boat quickly melted into the pitch-black night and, after a shout of good luck from Captain Greyshaw, the dinghy was gone. David felt alone and within ten minutes of the dinghy's departure he was alone. The shrouded dark figures scuttling around the beach disappeared into thin air. As he trudged back up the beach David reflected that, nearly a year earlier, he had landed on a similar beach with six commandos. Now there were only three left with him at Piskopiano. He had acquired a good man in Corporal Dai Griffiths but they were getting a bit thin on the ground. He consoled himself by thinking about the naval commando reinforcements expected to arrive in December. He thought about his own self-appointed mission. Would he ever be rid of Colonel Schmidt and in the bargain Captain Schubert and the filthy scoundrel Samaritis?

*

Manfred Schmidt was extremely pleased with the way his troops recovered control of eastern Crete after the Italian armistice. On the evening of October 20th he sat with Captain Schubert and *Feldwebel* Schneider on the balcony at Villa Ariadne sipping a cognac and admiring the incandescent sunset. He was relaxed and at peace with the world.

"Gentlemen, today I received a message of congratulation from General Müller on the way we succeeded in our counter-resistance campaign after the Italian armistice. As you will recall, the general was not pleased with a week's delay before we went into action, but, as you rightly pointed out Captain Schubert, the reinforcements he sent us were raw recruits and needed some training before they were unleashed into the field. When you got going, Captain Schubert, you soon had Bandouvas and his bandits out of Viannos and by now probably out of Crete. Luckily the Italians caused us no trouble and have stayed locked in their barracks. With judicious selection some of their troops will be joining our own men in patrols and searches. As you will recall, General Müller was most displeased when the Italian fart Carta and three of his senior officers escaped from Neapolis. But that's over now. He mentioned Samaritis in his message, stressing that this Cretan swine is now our No. 1 target, especially after what he did to me and poor old *Kriegsmarine* Captain Bucholz at Vai. So, Captain Schubert, Samaritis becomes top priority. The trouble is that he's so elusive, sometimes operating in the Diktis but more often than not in the Lasithis. We must, between us, devise a plan to eliminate Samaritis and his vermin. Have you any suggestions, Captain Schubert?"

The weasel-faced, bespectacled captain replied promptly, "The trouble with Samaritis and his group is that they will not come out into the open and fight. They only attack small numbers of our troops, just as they did to my *Jagdcommando* in Sitanos. I think the only way to bring him to battle is to use decoys, two or three of our men in a small village in the mountains with the rest of us lying concealed in a circle and allowing free access for Cretans. Word will soon get to the bandits that there are two or three isolated Germans in a village. This should bring the *andartes* down from the mountains and we'll let them through and then – 'snap' – the circle will close. I would use Italians as decoys, but, as you know, Sir, before you could say 'Heil Hitler' they would be gone. So we'll use volunteers from our own ranks. I'm sure there'll be plenty of takers."

Manfred looked at the blank-faced, staring-eyed captain.

"That's a good plan Captain Schubert. Work on it. We'll get together tomorrow over a map and select suitable villages for Operation Decoy. In the meantime *Feldwebel* Schneider and I will be spending more time at Elounda. I intend strengthening the defences there and making the area a second Festung in Crete."

Manfred leaned back in his chair and smiled.

"A toast to the elimination of Samaritis and to our new Festung Elounda," and turning his back on Captain Schubert he raised his glass in a silent toast to the setting sun.

Chapter Twenty-Six
Eastern Crete, November 1943
Loss of Courier
Obliteration of Pirgia and Piskopiano

"Biffo, we must all pull together. You must try and get on with Smithson. We're too small a group to have fights amongst ourselves."

David and Biffo were on guard at the farmhouse and Biffo was cleaning his Sten gun.

"I know, Sir," Biffo replied. "But I can't stand the little shit from Coventry. I will try my best, Sir," but David knew that the proud, fierce, little Cockney would never make it up with the equally stubborn Midlander.

And so the bickering continued and all David could do was to ensure that they were never on duty together or alone together in the hideout. As there were now only four left in his group it meant that he and Sergeant Hubbard could not be away from the cave on patrol at the same time.

The possibility of an attack on Heraklion harbour entailed frequent three-day trips to the observation point on Ames escarpment, where, with binoculars, David had a good view of the airfield and a partial view of the harbour. He could clearly see the entrance and its port and starboard lighthouses, which had been converted by the Germans into searchlight and light artillery emplacements. His vigilance and observation was rewarded early one morning in November when he saw two U-boats entering and one U-boat leaving the harbour.

The entrance to the harbour was guarded by a heavy wire mesh which was winched into position from a tanker, permanently anchored on the starboard side and fixed to the wall on the port side of the harbour entrance. The anti-submarine net was lowered to the sea bed to allow ingress and egress for submarines and surface vessels. Once the U-boats were inside the harbour they disappeared from view behind a large shed on the dockside, which David took to be submarine pens. Heraklion harbour was always congested with tankers and cargo ships, E-boats and sometimes Italian destroyers and frigates. After a few weeks David became convinced that if a landward assault on the harbour was feasible there would be rich pickings for the attackers. His next task was to discover an approach to the harbour and for this purpose he would need Sergeant Hubbard's assistance.

On his third solo patrol to Heraklion David found Corporal Dai Griffiths in an olive grove one kilometre west of Episkopi. As always he was humming a Welsh hymn, oblivious to his surroundings, and perfectly content to be sitting under an olive tree in the weak afternoon sun, tending to the goats. David approached him quietly.

"*Shwt mae Dai?*"

The corporal jump to his feet but on recognising David his face broke into a broad grin.

"Hello, Sir. Excuse me for not saluting. My 'ands are all tied up with these ropes"

David also smiled.

"We haven't seen anything of you since our trip to the seaside."

"No, Sir," the corporal replied, "I've been busy here and for the past six weeks Jerry's been sniffing around. I took to the hills. What the hell stirred up Jerry? It must 'ave been something big."

"Yes," David replied. "The Italians pulled out of the war in September and the Germans had to take over defence of the whole of Crete. They're settling down now."

"Bloody hell," exclaimed Dai, "Who would have thought they'd give in? I bet old Musso isn't very pleased."

"I don't expect he is," replied David, "he's been kicked out of Italy. Now, Corporal Griffiths, I want you to help me again. I've had to send Private Mcpherson back to Alex. I'm having trouble with Biffo and Smithson. They're quarrelling all the time and I need someone at our base to keep the peace. Will you move in with us for a few weeks? There's another attack brewing and I have to make preparations. I need Sergeant Hubbard with me on patrol."

The corporal spent a few moments in pensive thought.

"Good old Hubby. How is he? I'll join your group in a couple of days' time after I've had a good chance to say goodbye to old Spiros and his family."

"Excellent," said David. "I'll be coming back this way in two days' time. I'll pick you up. I know that Sergeant Hubbard will be pleased to see you."

Corporal Dai Griffiths' reintroduction into the Piskopiano kibbutz paid immediate dividends. He was well liked by both Biffo and Gunner Smithson and the hideout settled into an uneasy truce. David and Sergeant Hubbard were consequently released to conduct reconnaissance of the Heraklion area in the certain knowledge that their hideout was safe in the care of the Royal Army Service Corps corporal.

David had spent a long arduous day at his observation post on Ames ridge, sipping sparingly from his water supply, dozing quietly in the warm midday sun and scanning the coastal road, the airfield and the harbour through his binoculars, taking care not to expose the lenses to the sun's rays. By now he was immune to the discomfort of his hide and to the proximity of the German observation post above his head. From time to time he picked up snippets of German conversation, sometimes laughter, coughs and occasionally swear words. Sergeant Hubbard had left him an hour before dawn to scan the other side of the fortified German observation point on Ames ridge.

The warm sun dipped quickly behind the mountains over his left shoulder and darkness descended rapidly, like a black curtain, obliterating his view of Heraklion and its environs. He lay completely still in his observation hide awaiting the sergeant's return and a little concerned that, an hour after sunset, he had not arrived and then he heard the unmistakable scratching sound of someone moving on the ground some twenty yards behind his back. Within thirty seconds Sergeant Hubbard flopped by his side, breathless and palpably excited.

"I've found a way down to the sea, about a mile east of the airfield. You can't see it from here, Sir, but on the other side of this hump there's quite a deep watercourse which leads northwards towards the coastal road, passes under a bridge and then, within three hundred yards, runs into the sea on a shingle beach. There's some barbed wire on the beach but the local fishermen have made gaps in the wire. There are also four fishing boats pulled up on to the beach. There were no oars in any of the boats, but I found them hidden under a small hut at the top of the beach. I spent the day sunbathing, and I'm sorry I was a bit late getting home."

David digested Sergeant Hubbard's information.

"Good work, Sergeant. For what distance would we be exposed to the Krauts above us?"

The sergeant replied, "I reckon that from the other side of this rock we would only be visible to Jerry for some four hundred to five hundred yards, half a mile at the most. After that I was well into the olive groves. The only other tricky spot is at the coast road where the dry river course dips under a bridge. On the other side of the road, within forty yards, I was into a bank of sandy scrubland."

David thought for a few seconds.

"This is useful information, Sergeant. It might be an answer to get us to the harbour."

Sergeant Hubbard nodded his agreement and added, "I must point out, Sir, that on the beach we're still nearly two miles away from the harbour gates and there's the airfield in between."

"Thank you, Sergeant Hubbard. Now this is what we'll do. We'll hang about here tonight and you can take me along the route tomorrow. So let's get some sleep and we'll move out an hour before dawn."

Major David Green and Sergeant Jim Hubbard were a day late getting back to the kibbutz where Corporal Griffiths was uncharacteristically agitated and bothered.

"I'm glad to see you, Sir, and Sergeant Hubby. Biffo and Gunner Smithson have been at loggerheads since you went on recce. I have had to work hard to keep them apart. The main bone of contention at the moment is who is going to do this month's courier run. Biffo reckons he should go because he's more experienced. Gunner Smithson doesn't agree. You'll have to sort this one out pronto, Sir."

David ordered the two dissidents to meet him.

"Now, look, you two, this nonsense has to stop. We're only a small unit and I can't have this quarrelling going on. The next courier run will be done by Gunner Smithson. I need you here, Biffo, in the kibbutz. That's my final decision and I don't want to hear any more about it."

Biffo appeared to be mortally wounded and retired to the back of the cave to sulk whilst Gunner Smithson brightened visibly, cheered by his mini-victory. The gunner left for the beach rendezvous on the 20th November, 1943, a mission from which he did not return.

The Ambush at Geraki

Gunner Smithson and two *andartes* were on their return journey from the beach at Keratokombou and were approaching the hamlet of Geraki. The gunner walked along behind a donkey, with a jaunty step, pleased with his management of the drop on the beach. As instructed by Major Green he made contact only with a senior naval officer. A verbal message from the naval captain confirmed that a sabotage party would land in December to augment David's commando. There was also a coded message packed in a small waterproof canvas capsule to be delivered to Major Green.

In the confusion on the beach Gunner Smithson became involved with a party of four newcomers, British agents led by a Captain Ransom. The newly arrived captain took charge of the beach party and made contact with two Cretan guides. Their packages and *sakoulis* were packed on Gunner Smithson's donkey and the small party left the beach in single file moving northwards from Kertokombou. Captain Ransom and his wireless operative left the party at Nipiditis and the remaining three trudged along behind the donkey towards Geraki. On the journey up from the beach the gunner took an opportunity, during a rest period, of tying the encapsulated message on the inside of the donkey's tail using one of the animal's tail hairs as a tie.

As the party approached Geraki they saw the small, sleepy village, some half a mile ahead, shimmering in the mid-afternoon, watery sunlight. One of the Cretan guides led the donkey into a deserted and ominously quiet village square followed by Smithson and the second guide. The donkey trotted towards the village well and water and the thirsty perspiring travellers gathered around the parapet of the well. Suddenly, out of thin air, about a dozen fully armed German soldiers appeared wielding their *Schmeitzers* and advanced rapidly to surround the startled group clustered around the well. One of the Cretan guides now moved away from the group and, unmolested, ran across the square to one of the houses.

"*Hande hoch.*" The Germans prodded Smithson towards the village church where Captain Schubert strutted around arrogantly bellowing and shouting at four semi-naked, prostrate Cretan males lying face down on the floor. The captain now turned his attention to the newcomer. He ordered his soldiers to strip the gunner completely and search his clothing which they did without finding any incriminating evidence. His wrists were then bound tightly behind his back and he was made to lie down with the other unfortunate Cretan captives. At that moment a large sergeant came in carrying a dismantled Sten gun and three hand grenades.

"Captain Schubert, this was found on the donkey."

The captain's face screwed into a sardonic smile, "Well, well now, what have we here? Are you Captain Ransom? Speak!" and he started kicking the defenceless gunner, continuing for a full minute. A this juncture the gunner realised that he had been betrayed by one of his Cretan guides.

When the irate captain became tired with toe-capping his prisoner he shouted at a fat sergeant.

"Sergeant Friedlander, load these men on to a truck. We'll take them up to Heraklion for questioning."

The semi-naked men were frog-marched across the square and loaded on to a waiting truck. Gunner Smithson found himself sitting at the end of the line of captives near the tailboard of the lorry, with an armed German guard sitting on the opposite side. The fat sergeant, perspiring profusely and mopping his brow, propped his *Schmeitzer* against the tailboard just underneath the gunner. He was chuckling loudly and searched in his pocket for cigarettes and matches. Smithson strained at his wrist bonds and, finding a sharp-edged screw, cut through the rope strands on its serrated edge. His bonds sprang loose. He looked across at the German soldier facing him, his gun on his lap and his helmeted head downcast, as he struggled to keep awake.

Gunner Smithson glanced downwards at the sweaty bald head of the fat sergeant who was now contentedly puffing on a cigarette and, on impulse, sprang across the lorry, snatched the dozing soldier's rifle, smashed its butt into his face and leapt over the tailboard, landing on his feet next to the corpulent sergeant. Sergeant Friedlander had no chance. The agile fit commando used his rifle butt to smash upwards into the sergeant's face, crushing the cigarette into the left side of his jaw to fuse with the spatulate remains of his flattened nose. Smithson grabbed the sergeant's *Schmeitzer* and dived under the lorry where he lay flat on the ground. Two armed guards from inside the lorry landed almost simultaneously at the tailboard. The commando fired and at a range of ten feet heard the thud of bullets as they tore into the legs and nether regions of the two German soldiers and their sergeant. When he emerged from under the lorry there were three writhing, screaming bodies lying on the ground behind the vehicle.

The shooting alerted the Germans in the village who came running down the road, guns at the ready. Gunner Smithson had a forty yard start, but his attempt at escape was futile. On his left side the cliff face rose vertically and on his right side the edges of the road dropped precipitously, almost vertically, some two hundred feet to the valley below. As he pushed his body to the extreme, he heard the bullets zipping above his head and thudding into the rocks on the side of the road. He quickly looked ahead. The first corner in the road was still some eighty yards away and he knew he could not make it. The gunner made up his mind in an instant and, veering to the right side, jumped off the edge of the road.

Still clutching the stolen *Schmeitzer* he fell rapidly and hit the top of a large tree, which partially broke his fall. His body teetered amongst the branches and then he was falling again until a terrific jar of pain shot up his spine and his limp body lay stretched across a large branch. The pain in his back was unbearable. Through narrow slit-like eyes he looked upwards and saw three, or four, vague figures standing on the edge of the road, their guns at the ready. With one supreme effort, Gunner Smithson raised the end of his *Schmeitzer* and pulled the trigger, spraying bullets roughly in the direction of the indistinct figures standing above him. One of the grey figures came slithering down from the road to land in a heap at the base of the tree.

His last thought was, 'Why didn't I let Biffo come on this trip?'

A stream of bullets from above came tearing into his unprotected body blowing him away into dark oblivion. Within two minutes Captain Schubert arrived on the scene and went completely berserk. Looking down at the two dead bodies below, and conscious of the fact that this one bandit had killed one of his soldiers and seriously injured Sergeant Friedlander and two other troopers, he took his sidearm out of its holster and, screaming invectives, pumped six more bullets into the dead body straddling the tree below. Turning on his heel he strode back towards the village screaming orders. The six remaining captives in the lorry were unloaded, marched back to the square, lined up against the church wall and executed. Captain Schubert himself took great pleasure in executing two of the captured Cretans.

A few days later Biffo took David aside.

"I'm sorry about Smithson, Sir. I should have gone on that trip."

From the original seven in their commando they were now down to three, augmented to four by the recruitment of Corporal Dai Griffiths. David consoled himself that his difficulties would resolve when the naval contingent arrived, but when were they going to appear? Could it be the December drop or would it be in January? He resolved he would be present for both of the next two beach reception parties.

On the 17th December 1943 David took Biffo and Sergeant Hubbard with him to Tsoutsouro, twelve kilometres west of Keratokombou. As usual the beach was crowded with chattering, wraith-like, figures wandering aimlessly to and fro. David kept his group in a tight bunch and when the dinghies appeared and started unloading he immediately picked out the naval party by their efficiency and discipline. The leader was a short, thin, blond-haired man issuing abrupt commands to four burly, blue-coated matelots who were unloading heavy canvas packages and parcels and lying them gently on the beach.

As David approached the newcomers he thought, 'So these are the new recruits. They look an efficient bunch.'

David introduced himself to the blond-haired officer who turned to face him and saluted, then quickly dropped his saluting arm when he saw that the senior officer and his attendants were dressed in Cretan clothes.

He stammered, "I'm Lieutenant Napier, Royal Navy."

"I'm pleased you've arrived, Lieutenant Napier. Your men will be a welcome addition to my commando. Apart from Sergeant Hubbard here and Gunner Wendro, I have one other man back at base."

The young naval officer looked perplexed.

"Didn't you get the November signal from Cairo? This is going to be a solo effort. These men with me are from the ship's company," and, turning around, he dismissed the sailors who returned to their dinghies and rowed quickly away into the dark night.

David's heart sank.

'Only one man for an attack on the harbour!'

Lieutenant Napier turned to the canvas parcels on the beach.

"These are limpet mines. I have the detonators about my person. The mines are mounted on slings. I'll take two. The other five will have to be distributed amongst your men. Now let's get off this beach."

David had misgivings about the attitude of the young naval lieutenant who seemed to be over-anxious to take control of his commando. He shrugged his shoulders, picked up two twenty-five pound mines and walked off the beach behind the young Leviathan.

The party trudged eastwards in silence, their speed considerably hampered by the heavy weight of the mines slung around their necks. Lieutenant Napier was armed only with a pistol and was clothed in naval-blue, serge uniform with badges of rank and he wore a peaked cap. In daylight he would stick out like a sore thumb. An hour before dawn David pulled the party off the road into a small cave about three kilometres south-east of Thrapsano. After a light meal and an hour's rest Lieutenant Napier proposed they should move forwards. David thought this would be an opportune moment to have a friendly chat with the lieutenant. He invited the young officer to accompany him outside and, squatting in some bushes, spoke calmly and with authority.

"Lieutenant Napier, I shall have to put you in the picture. One thing. We don't move around in daylight unless we have to. The Germans have about thirty thousand men on the island and, as you will see later, they're all over the place. We also have to look out for spotter planes. Now if you keep wearing your uniform you'll be spotted easily. I advise you to change into Cretan clothes. My little commando live in a small cave, not much bigger than this one. We live on top of each other and it's important that we get on together. My men use Christian names amongst themselves. They call me Sir and they'll call you Sir, but there's no reason why we can't use our own Christian names. Mine's David."

The young naval man blushed and looked away from David.

"I respect your authority Sir, but, on active duty, I cannot agree to wear any clothes other than my service uniform. And another thing,

Sir, my mission is a solo effort. Your brief, with due respect, is to get me overland to the target. Once there I'll be on my own. And I'm sorry I can't agree to call a senior officer by his Christian name."

David was taken aback by this speech from the junior officer. He put it all down to inexperience and youthful exuberance and he was sure that Lieutenant Napier's attitude would change in due course. It took most of David's ingenuity to keep the new arrival under cover in the cave and its environs. The party had only traversed about twenty-five kilometres on the track from the beach-head and there was a similar distance and more to be covered on the following night. During the day enemy activity was evident on the Thrapsano to Kastelli road and low flying Storch spotter planes passed overhead on three occasions.

David led the party northwards at dusk, skirting Kastelli on the westward side and ascending the western foothills of the Diktis and finally descending towards Kalahorio. The descent was difficult and the heavy limpet mines slung around their necks made their movements slow and laborious. David, head lowered by the pressure of the straps on the back of his neck, suddenly heard a slithering noise behind him in the darkness and then a loud 'snap'.

"Damn and blast it!" Lieutenant Napier's voice carried far in the still night. "Damn it, damn it, I think it's broken."

David dumped the mines and crawled back to the writhing figure lying across the footpath with his right leg outstretched and immobile. The young officer was in great pain and through clenched teeth said, "I think it's broken, Sir."

David bent over him.

"Let's have a look," he said as he gently untied the boot-lace, but the slightest movement of the right boot caused the lieutenant to yelp in pain. Crouched over the protesting young man David spoke gently in his ear, "Samuel, you may have broken your ankle. We're right out in the open here and we've got about three kilometres to go to our hideout. Do you think you can stand with help?"

Lieutenant Napier replied, "I'll try, Sir."

"Well let's get going," David urged, as he pulled the lieutenant to his feet and placed an arm around his shoulder.

The lieutenant's two mines were transferred to Sergeant Hubbard and Biffo. The rest of the journey took nearly two hours and, by the time they got to Piskopiano, the olive grove was bathed in early-morning, wintry sunshine. Lieutenant Napier was hauled into the cave using two ropes and placed on a palliasse at the cave entrance and the limpet mines were stowed on ledges at the back of the hideout. Despite Lieutenant Napier's protests David cut the right boot off to reveal a large, swollen and extremely painful ankle.

"I'm afraid, Samuel, that this is going to lay you up for a few weeks. We'll have to delay the attack until next month, probably the first moonless night at the end of January."

Lieutenant Napier protested, "No, Sir, I'll be all right in about a week. So the plans must go ahead this month."

But on the following day it was evident to everyone that the lieutenant's swollen, bruised and painful ankle would not be able to bear his weight for many weeks. And during the prolonged period of enforced inactivity the naval officer became demanding and insufferable.

*

On the 14th December, 1943 General Heydrich Müller convened a conference at his Khania headquarters. Manfred and Captain Schubert were in attendance. The general had aged considerably and, in the process, had lost much of his arrogance and self-confidence. The general's troops were having a hard time from resistance fighters in western Crete and, by comparison, his worries about eastern Crete, even after the Italian armistice, were negligible.

"Well, gentlemen, I thought we should have a meeting to discuss plans for the conduct of further operations in eastern Crete. The Italian armistice has apparently had little effect on our defences and I'm pleased that the Italian troops are fully co-operative, though they are a bit slow in coming out of their hiding holes to take an active part in our patrols. The defection of General Carta and his senior officers has been no loss at all to us. By the way, that fellow Captain Tavana, who took him out of Crete?"

Manfred did not have the answer. He suspected British agents but, in order to avoid a long harangue from the general, he replied, "We're pretty certain it was Samaritis."

The general bristled and his face became suffused.

"That bastard again. When in God's name are we going to get rid of Samaritis?"

Manfred had anticipated this question and turned to Captain Schubert.

"With your permission, General, I will ask Captain Schubert to outline our plans for dealing with Samaritis."

Captain Schubert nervously cleared his throat and in a trembling, high-pitched voice addressed the assembled officers.

"I have studied the habits and movements of this bandit in great detail. He operates on the western side of the Lasithis and on the eastern side of the Diktis, but I am now convinced that his main centre and source of recruitment is on the Lasithou Plateau, here in the Dikti mountains," rising and pointing to the area on a wall map and continuing, "centred around the villages of Pskiro, Aghios Georgios and the town of Tzermiado. We will take two divisions, one Italian and one German, on a punitive patrol to this area," and, turning towards Manfred, he added, "Colonel Schmidt has worked out the detailed plans of this exercise."

Manfred now took his cue from the counter-espionage captain.

"My plan, Sir, is to use Italian troops at Neapolis for the eastern approach to the plateau and our own troops moving from the western side. The Italians will not be allowed to operate alone and will be led by a brigade of my best stormtroops. The combined forces of divisional strength will move westwards into the Diktis from Neapolis and divide into two prongs, one to move southwards to Tzermiado and the second to Aghios Georgios. This attack should flush Samaritis and his bandits out of these towns and make them move westwards across the Lasithou plain where they will be met by my own division of mountain troops. The attack will be co-ordinated so that the *Wehrmacht* will be in position two days before the arrival of the column from Neapolis. My division will move southwards from Hersonisos through Gournes to form a ring of steel to the west and south of the Lasithou plateau. All roads and mountain tracks leading from the plateau will be blockaded so that all enemy forces will be encircled. An order will be given that any Cretans moving in or out of the plateau are to be shot on sight."

The commander of Festung Kriti nodded his approval.

"Excellent, excellent, Colonel Schmidt, and when do you propose mounting this attack?"

Manfred was again prepared for this question. He was aware that his wily superior would be sending messages to Berlin claiming full credit for the plan of attack but there was little he could do about that.

"Well, Sir," he continued, "I don't see that we can be ready for a month or six weeks."

General Müller snorted. "Why the delay, Colonel Schmidt?"

"It will take us a month to get everything ready. I suggest the second week of January."

The general reluctantly agreed.

"Very well. Press on with the arrangements. Have you any other actions up your sleeve?"

Manfred replied, "As a matter of fact we have, Sir. I received information in September that there may be British agents operating in the Piskopiano area. The Italian debacle put a stop to our plan. I still think that it would be worth a cordon and search exercise and have instructed Captain Schubert to wipe out the villages of Piskopiano and Pirgia. I thought I would wait a week or two. Perhaps we could give the bandits a Christmas present."

The general beamed and gave one of his rare smiles.

"Excellent, excellent. I fully approve," and, turning towards Captain Schubert, "Make sure, Schubert, that you give them a good lesson. If you capture any British agents I want them here for questioning by the Gestapo,"

He then turned towards Manfred, "And how is Festung Elounda coming along?"

Manfred was taken by surprise.

"Everything is fine, Sir. My *Fallschirmjäger* are all well dug in and I have further plans to strengthen the Festung. I would appreciate a visit from you, Sir, to advise on the defences."

Manfred's flattery produced dividends.

General Müller was lost in thought for a few seconds.

"Yes, yes of course, I'll be delighted to come and visit you, if I can fit it in my schedule."

The general stood up, a gesture of dismissal. He eyed Manfred and Captain Schubert.

"Last Christmas General Bruno Bräuer had a grand party here in Villa Halepa. This year we have little to celebrate. We've been pushed out of North Africa, our troops in Russia are stuck around Stalingrad and there's heavy fighting in Casino in Italy. Hardly the background for celebration. I will be ordering a quiet Christmas for all units on Kriti. Each commander will make his own arrangements. That's all."

In acknowledgement of the general's salute, Manfred and Schubert responded with traditional 'Heil Hitlers', turned on their heels and marched out of the general's office.

*

David was not looking forward to Christmas day. He had agreed that his men could decorate the cave with eucalyptus twigs and mistletoe and Biffo was allowed to open six tins of bully beef to prepare a hash. Two of Spiros' chickens were killed and cooked in the farmhouse and two bottles of *tsikoudia* and four bottles of wine were provided by the generous Cretan. The group were given a liberal ration of *tsikoudia* on Christmas Eve and Corporal Griffiths led them in communal humming. On Christmas Day David carved the chickens with ceremony, wearing Lieutenant Napier's cap as headgear. But the jollity and comradeship was contrived and artificial. All the while the naval officer was a damp squib, casting a shroud of gloom over the festive celebrations. He objected to decorating the cave with paper and streamers; he objected to their attempts at jollity and singing and, most of all, he objected to David wearing his naval cap on Christmas day, as he put it, "desecrating the King's uniform."

To avoid contact with the supercilious young naval officer, Sergeant Hubbard, Biffo and Corporal Dai found every excuse to absent themselves from the cave. David couldn't blame them. He found it difficult to keep his temper with Lieutenant Napier and no matter how hard he tried he was unable to discover anything likeable about the young man.

The only son of a retired vice-admiral, Lieutenant Samuel Horatio Napier had been groomed for service in the Royal Navy. Schooled at Eton he had enlisted at the age of seventeen as an officer cadet at the Royal Naval College, Dartmouth. Shortly after his commission in October 1941 he came under the influence of Brigadier Sharples who, with his father's connivance, arranged the young lieutenant's transfer to Alexandria early in 1942. After two months on seagoing missions on the destroyer *Juno* he was seconded by Brigadier Sharples to Athlit

Castle Special Boat Section Training Centre near Beirut, where he instructed agents in the art of marine sabotage. His arrival in Crete was the result of his own proposal to Brigadier Sharples that he should 'have a go' at the submarine pens in Heraklion Harbour.

After a few days' lying flat on his back with his injured ankle suspended in a canvas sling the pain began to ease and Lieutenant Napier began asking questions about the proposed raid. David kept fobbing him off for about ten days and then matters came to a head when they were alone in the cave.

"Major Green, I need to know about the raid. A few preparations need to be made. I repeat, your job is to get me to the harbour. I should also tell you that the boss has ordered that you and your commando are to return with me to Alex after the show."

David smiled at the younger man's use of SOE and RAF jargon. David crouched on the cave floor next to the injured lieutenant.

"Right, Samuel, I'll run through the plan with you. We've recced the harbour from all aspects and a direct approach from the south is impossible. The German defences are too strong. The only way to get to the harbour is from the sea. Sergeant Hubbard and I have found a dry river course which runs into a small shingle beach about a mile east of the airfield. This beach is used by a local fisherman and we'll take one of their boats to row round to the harbour entrance. We'll have to attack under cover of darkness. There's an anti-submarine net at the harbour entrance which is winched up and down from an anchored ship. To get into the harbour we'll need to scale the westward side harbour wall and lower you and the mines into the water. There will be a swim of about four hundred yards to the target. When you've finished we'll get out the same way, depending on what happens in the meantime. Both the lighthouses at the harbour entrances have searchlights and machine gun emplacements. If they come into action my men on the harbour wall will deal with them. The first moonless night is at the end of the second week in January and the next opportunity after that will be during the last few days of the month. When we go will depend on you and how soon your ankle mends."

Lieutenant Napier unsmiling and serious replied, "I'll be all right by January. I must say it sounds like a lousy plan to me."

But, for want of a better arrangement, the plan was adopted.

*

Colonel Manfred Schmidt spent his Christmas Day with the Fifth parachute battalion at Elounda. Accompanied by *Feldwebel* Schneider he returned to Villa Ariadne on the evening of the 26th for Sergeant Schultz's special Christmas dinner to which all the garrison officers at Heraklion were invited. As always Schultz, by now fully recovered from his head wounds, excelled himself and managed to include lobster and wild boar on the menu. The drinks and toasts came think and fast. At around 9 p.m. Colonel Schmidt took Schubert aside and guided him out on to the balcony.

"My old commanding officer of the Eighth Paras, Count Erich von Bulow, once told me about Christmas holidays on his father's Prussian estate. On the day after Christmas they went on a wild boar shoot. I have an idea. Why don't we go shooting tomorrow morning? Samaritis is the target. Are your *Jagdcommando* ready?"

"*Jawohl, mein* Colonel," the thin-faced captain replied, his eyes glistening with anticipation.

"Good, good," said Manfred. "Go across to Neapolis tonight and get those Italians out of their bunks and whorehouses. They'll need to move out by four o'clock. I'll bring our division out from Hersonisos. If we leave now we should be in position just after dawn. Once we've encircled the Lasithou plateau we'll press towards the centre and squeeze old Samaritis out of his hideout, like a pip from an orange. Remember, Captain Schubert, speed is essential. We'll meet on the plateau tomorrow evening."

The ill-judged attack on Lasithou Plateau was a complete failure. A German column from Hersonisos, led by Colonel Manfred Schmidt, reached its objective on time and took up defensive positions on the roads and villages lying on the western and northern sides of the plateau. They also reached Tzermiado and held the road junction to Neapolis. Captain Schubert and the Italians from Neapolis did not reach their positions until early evening and even then the German brigade was first to appear. Captain Schubert was fuming. The Italian commanders and most of their troops were getting over their Christmas festivities and, despite Schubert's urging, would not muster until daybreak, by which time the German support column had moved out. The late appearance of Captain Schubert's column left a large gap in the Lasithou cordon for two kilometres on each side of Aghios

Georgios. Through this gap Samaritis and about three hundred armed *andartes* made good their escape south-eastwards, up and into the uninhabited highest ranges of the Lasithis.

Three old men were taken prisoner at Tzermiado and one middle-aged man at Aghios Georgios. All were executed on the spot and the village of Aghios Georgios was burned to the ground. Manfred sat in his command *Kübelwagen* fuming and staring straight ahead with the burning, smoking village behind his back. Captain Schubert appeared from the gathering gloom and saluted.

"You wanted to speak to me, Herr Colonel?"

"Yes, Captain Schubert, I most certainly do!"

He stared at Schubert, his steely blue eyes flashing contempt. He needed a scapegoat.

"You've done it this time! I hold you fully responsible for this fiasco here today. When I get back to the villa I shall recommend your dismissal to General Müller. Now get out of my sight and take those bloody Italians back to Neapolis with you. Drive on, Schneider," and the dust flurries from the *Kübelwagen's* spinning wheels covered the cringing counter-resistance officer with a fine veneer of chalk and grit.

Colonel Schmidt now ordered his troops to return to Hersonisos and Heraklion. The convoy travelled with exposed headlights and Manfred kept two crack motorised companies in the rear and under his personal command. He sat in the command *Kübelwagen*, silent and brooding for most of the journey. Schubert had let him down. Schubert must go. He would recommend to General Müller his immediate transfer as soon as he got back to the villa. And then he remembered the unfinished business at Piskopiano and Pirgia. Schubert had already made plans to cordon and search these two villages. The little shit of a captain must not be allowed credit for these two raids. He would be near Piskopiano on their return route to Hersonisos. Why not use his two companies for the search? Why not indeed?

"*Feldwebel* Schneider, move along the convoy and get the commanders of the two storm companies to meet me. I have decided that we'll take out Piskopiano and Pirgia on the way home."

In the cave at Piskopiano on Boxing Day festivities petered out into silence at around 7 p.m. Corporal Griffiths was on sentry duty and the rest, huddled in their greatcoats, lay on the floor trying to keep warm in the cold interior of the cave, Biffo scratched from time to time attempting to alleviate the annoying itch of his lice-infested body. At about midnight David woke, disturbed by an unusual noise – the constant hum of moving vehicles in the distance. He left the cave and stood on the ledge outside. The humming noise came from the east, from the Hersonisos to Kastelli road, and he saw a dim light on the horizon shining over the top of a low hill on the left hand side of the olive grove. He was conscious of movement on the ground below the ledge and, after exchanging passwords, Corporal Griffiths appeared at the bottom of the rope-ladder, whispering, "What's Jerry up to, Sir? There's something big going on."

David replied, "I think it's a convoy. Stay where you are. I'll wake Sergeant Hubbard and we'll go and have a look."

The sleepy-eyed sergeant was also mystified by the noise and faint glow in the sky behind their backs.

"I'll take Biffo to the hill above Pirgia to have a shufti. You stay here, Sergeant. Corporal Griffiths will return to his post. If either of you meet with any trouble, get back to the cave. Biffo and I will be back before dawn."

The journey in the darkness from the hideout to the mountain top above Pirgia was uphill and took over an hour. From his vantage point on the hill David was able to look over Pirgia, dark and silent, and the road junction on the Hersonisos to Kastelli road. German troop carriers, nose to tail, were travelling southwards towards Gournes. All the vehicles had shaded headlights and David realised that, counting the number he could see and estimating the number that had passed through, there must have been a thousand or twelve hundred Germans on the move. He watched the road until the tail of the last lorry passed to the east and out of sight and noted the Germans had left two lorries and a platoon of men guarding the 'T' junction. He concluded there must me something big going on in Gournes and made his way back to the cave.

"Sergeant Hubbard, about twelve hundred German troops have passed through in the direction of Gournes. They've left a platoon guarding the road junction and this probably means they're coming back fairly soon. I need a twenty-four hour watch on the road junction. You take night watch and I'll relieve you at dawn."

"What do you think Jerry's up to?" asked Sergeant Hubbard.

"I don't know," David replied, "but I agree with Corporal Dai; it's something big."

Cordon and Search at Pirgia

David relieved Sergeant Hubbard at the Pirgia observation post just after daybreak. Sergeant Hubbard had counted twenty vehicles in a German convoy streaming back through the 'T' junction during the night and now only the barricade platoon was left in position. David glanced down at Pirgia village on the other side of the hill where there was some activity. Two Cretan women were wending their way to the well and a few playful children ran hither and thither on the small village square. On the other side of the high vantage point, through his binoculars, David observed the road junction on the Hersonisos to Kastelli road. Two trucks were parked off the road and a machine gun was mounted behind a large rock overlooking the junction itself. The outpost was commanded by a young lieutenant and manned by twenty-four troopers who spent the morning sitting in the shade, smoking and chattering amongst themselves.

At midday, the reason for the retention of a German section at the 'T' junction became abundantly clear. David heard a fast moving convoy approaching from the north along the road from Piskopiano. The vehicles became intermittently visible on the winding road. The convoy consisted of two motorcycles at the point, two troop carriers and a *Kübelwagen* and two motorcycles at the rear. There was only one road in and one out of the small hamlet which consisted of twelve houses clustered around a small square nestling on the very edge of an almost vertical cliff face. The convoy sped into the middle of the square and, as the trucks crunched to a halt, armed soldiers leapt out of the back and raced towards the houses crashing their way through the doorways and shouting, *"Raus, raus"*.

Within seconds the occupants were ushered out of their houses at gunpoint and made to stand in a line in the middle of the square. The clattering and shouting continued for ten minutes. The soldiers reappeared and formed a cordon around the hapless Cretans. The *Kübelwagen* doors opened and a tall officer dressed in a black SS uniform and wearing sunglasses appeared, closely attended by a *Feldwebel* with his *Schmeitzer* at the ready.

Through binoculars David had a good view of the officer's face, and clearly saw the Knight's Cross hanging around his neck. The troops let him through to inspect the Cretan captives. There were fifteen persons in the line-up – seven women of varying ages dressed in black, three children of around five or six clinging to their mother's skirts, one toddler in his mothers arms and two middle-aged and two very elderly men. David kept his glasses on the officer's scowling face and, as if by request, the SS officer removed his black peaked cap to reveal a mop of blond hair, bleached almost white by the Cretan sun and mopped his brow with a white handkerchief. The irregular scar on his right temple was visible. David felt a chill pass down his spine. He was looking close up at his adversary and enemy. Yes, this man was definitely Manfred Schmidt, his blood brother from their early days in Germany. He was mesmerised by the face which filled the lenses of his binoculars. His target was so close he felt he could reach out and touch him.

David's preoccupation with Manfred nearly caused him to miss the next sequence of events. One of the Cretan elders was on his knees pleading with the German officer, whilst the women and children were clustered together in a wailing group. David saw the blond colonel's lips move and heard the words, "*Nein, nein*", and then a few seconds later, "*Scheisen, scheisen*". The German colonel placed his cap firmly on his head, turned on his heel and walked back towards the *Kübelwagen*. A few of the German troopers made threatening gestures with their rifles but not a shot was fired. Colonel Schmidt paused at the door of the *Kübelwagen* and again turned to his troopers, "*Scheisen, scheisen*, I order you to shoot," he shouted.

No one moved a muscle. The enraged colonel snatched Schneider's *Schmeitzer* and ran back to the front of his troops. Legs apart and firing from the hip he discharged a full clip of bullets into the writhing mass of screaming villagers standing before him. The little toddler fell from his mother's arms and attempted to get to his feet. The enraged SS colonel showed no mercy. The wide-eyed Cretan boy was shot at point blank range and died instantly. One or two limbs in the slaughtered mass on the ground were still twitching. The colonel shouted his orders in a loud barking voice.

"Finish them off and throw the bodies into the well. Erase all traces of the shooting and then burn down the village."

David watched with horror as the bodies were dispatched into the well, the ground around the massacre area washed and the houses burned one by one. And all the while the German colonel sat impassively in his *Kübelwagen* with his ever-faithful *Feldwebel* sitting at his side. Throughout the slaughter David felt impotent and helpless. He could do nothing to help the poor inhabitants of the village of Pirgia but the incident he had witnessed strengthened his resolve to get rid of the White Angel of Gournes, the perpetrator of the atrocity.

The rape of Pirgia had only taken about one hour. The German convoy left northwards and when he checked on the road junction David found that the barricades and soldiers had also departed. He left the observation post with a heavy heart, almost in tears. He had covered half a mile when he heard bursts of firing from the north followed within twenty minutes by a dark pall of smoke rising into the air. Piskopiano was receiving the same treatment as Pirgia had suffered. David shuddered and with caution made his way back to the cave in Spiros' olive grove.

Chapter Twenty-Seven

Eastern Crete, January 1944
Attack on the Submarine Pens

New Year 1944 was a depressing time at the cave in Piskopiano. A mood of despondency descended on the commando quartet, not helped by the constant nagging and unreasonable demands of Lieutenant Samuel Napier. By now he was hobbling around the cave but had to avoid putting all his weight on the damaged ankle. Every day he insisted on running through the plan of attack on Heraklion harbour, picking holes in the operation and occasionally coming up with useful advice, some of which David adopted. It was Lieutenant Napier's suggestion that the limpet mines might be floated to the target on cork trays. He also asked for a snorkel to approach the submarine pens. David fashioned a few snorkels from short pieces of rubber tubing and hollowed out bamboo canes. By mid-January Lieutenant Napier was able to stand on his right foot, though certain movements were painful. He insisted the raid should go through as scheduled towards the end of January. During the third week of January David took his commando away from the cave and outlined the plan for the raid and the task each one would be expected to fulfil.

He concluded the briefing, "Our task is to get Lieutenant Napier to the target and get him out after he has placed the limpet mines. This will be our last raid in Crete. Afterwards we move south for evacuation off the island. I rely on you chaps to make sure this raid is a complete success."

New Year's Eve 1944 was not a happy time for Colonel Manfred Schmidt. He was beginning to regret his impetuosity at Pirgia. General Müller, for some reason, had not taken kindly to the suggestion that Captain Schubert should be repatriated to Germany.

606

Müller blamed the Lasithou debacle on Manfred, considering that the timing of the attack was ill-conceived and that he, Manfred himself, should have taken control of the Italian column. So the weasel Schubert was to remain. Manfred made certain that, in future, Schubert got all the dirty and dangerous tasks. In fact he gave Schubert an ultimatum, "Get Samaritis by March or I'll personally demote you to the ranks."

27th – 28th January, 1944
The Raid on the Heraklion Submarine Pens

The raiding party left the kibbutz at 3.30 p.m. on the 27th January 1944. Heavy rain had fallen over the previous three days which made the ground wet, the river swollen and the rocks slippery and treacherous. Lieutenant Napier had prepared himself for the thirty kilometre trek by taking brief walks in the olive grove. He declared himself fit and, despite heavy bandaging, the ankle still gave him pain on movement. He had also insisted on wearing his naval uniform and reasoned, "If I am captured, I'll not be shot as a spy. This uniform will protect me."

The men between them carried five limpet mines with cork backing slung around their necks, Sten guns and hand grenades, two rifles, a large tin of black pitch, wire cutters, grappling irons and ropes. In deference to his damaged ankle, the naval lieutenant only carried his Sten gun, two snorkels and three grenades packed in a *sakouli*. The limpet mine detonators were shared between David and Lieutenant Napier.

They left on a dull, dank afternoon with low clouds and drizzle reducing visibility to thirty or forty yards. David took a well-tried route westwards towards Episkopi. Progress was slow, due to the heavy load each man was carrying and to difficulty in crossing the narrow rivers which were now in spate. David warmed to the grim-faced naval lieutenant. Despite the pain each step brought him he kept pace with the group, never complaining and stoically stifling his desire to cry out. Weather conditions aided and abetted their venture. There were no spotter planes aloft and they did not encounter any foot patrols.

Darkness came rapidly around 5 p.m. and by this time they were well clear of Episkopi and, moving further westwards, they picked up the river which skirted the westward side of Ames ridge and began to follow its right bank northwards towards the sea. David ordered maximum caution around the base of Ames rock where he knew the German look-out posts overhead had a view over the river bed, but in the pitch-black darkness and inclement weather the Germans' field of vision was obscured. Once they were under the cover of trees in an olive grove David called a halt. They had been struggling along for three hours and, soaked to the skin, tired and exhausted were all ready for a rest.

David explained, "We're now about two hours away from the beach. When Sergeant Hubbard and I recced this route we used the dried river bed for cover, but, as you see," pointing to the torrent of rushing water on his left hand side, "this will not be possible. We'll rest here for thirty minutes. We're making good time. The next obstacle will be crossing the coast road about eight miles ahead of us. On a night like this I don't expect the German patrols will be too active. After crossing the road we're only about a quarter of a mile from the beach."

The whole party were given a liberal tot of *tsikoudia*, and, as they moved out, Dai Griffiths commented in a voice loud enough to be heard by the rest, "Biffo, I told you I wanted to go the seaside again, but I didn't think I'd be carrying a tin of black paint and a brush. I was hoping to bring my bucket and spade with me."

Biffo snorted, "Hard luck, Dai! Don't worry. We can go paddling when we get there."

They negotiated the coast road without difficulty and arrived on the beach at 9.30 p.m. Lieutenant Napier now proposed he should take control of the operation. He was sitting on the shingles, his back propped up against an overturned boat and his right leg stretched out before him. The swelling around his right ankle was reappearing and, though the gritty young man would not admit it, he was in great pain. David crouched down beside him.

"Samuel, I will have to pull rank on you. You're not fit enough to take over. I'll get you to the target. After that you're on your own. Rest that foot of yours. We'll be off the beach at midnight."

David now made preparations for the raid. The beach was only forty yards long and twenty yards deep, heavily fortified with barbed wire, through which the Cretan fisherman had cut a path to allow access for their boats to the estuary and the sea. David allowed his men to rest while he took one of the limpet mines into the sea. The mine, buoyed up by the cork base sank under the surface of the water for about two inches. In its submerged position the mine became a heavier weight and David concluded it would take the full strength of a man to pull two of these mines behind him and swim at the same time. At that moment he made up his mind that he would have to go along with the naval officer into the harbour. He returned to his commando group.

"Right, Sergeant Hubbard, have a look under that shed for oars and break into the shed and see what you can find. We definitely need rowlocks and some cloth to baffle the oars. Corporal Griffiths and Biffo, get painting."

The craft they had selected for the raid was a broad-beamed, white rowing boat, now lying keel upwards on the beach. Corporal Griffiths and Biffo took it in turn to paint the hull of the boat and the oar blades with black pitch. The boat was man-handled into the water and all equipment stowed away. David went through the inventory carefully – grappling irons, ropes, wire cutters, five limpet mines slung on their cork bases, two rifles and two snorkels. Each man was armed with a Sten gun and three grenades and Lieutenant Napier and David carried three detonators each. At ten minutes to midnight David gathered his group together for their final briefing under the lea of the fisherman's shed. Lieutenant Napier was now on his feet, in great pain, grimacing at each step but he managed a wan smile. Corporal Griffiths inquired politely whether he would be able to swim with his badly injured ankle.

"Don't worry, chaps. We lads of His Majesty's Royal Navy are at home in the water!"

David admired the tenacity and courage of this young naval officer who was about to put his life on the line.

Heraklion's commercial deep harbour had been completed in 1937. Mainly used for cargo ships it also became a base for trans-Aegean ferries and luxury liners. Some of the local fisherman moored their boats in the 'new' harbour but the majority continued to use the old town harbour. The new harbour was constructed by creating a five hundred yard dog-leg breakwater on the western side and a shorter one hundred yard breakwater on the eastern side. The harbour entrance was fifty yards wide and each breakwater was guarded by a forty foot lighthouse showing a red port light and a green starboard light. The Germans had captured and occupied the harbour on June 2nd, 1941 and fortified the defences with roving patrols on the breakwaters and machine gun and searchlight emplacements in the lighthouses. The whole harbour area was a mass of warehouses and storage tanks. Two submarine pens were constructed in 1942 at the dockside end of the eastern breakwater which was heavily defended and patrolled by the *Kriegsmarine*. Their three-storey quarters and supply depots were located fifty yards across the road from the harbour wall. Apart from E-boats, no other vessels were allowed to anchor near the pens.

On the night of the 27th January, 1944 there were two U-boats in the pens, lying snugly against the harbour wall and draped in wire camouflage netting. One E-boat, E-579 was berthed some thirty yards to the seaward side of the pens, under the eastern breakwater, which was heavily patrolled by sailors moving about disconsolately in the dark, heads down in the persistent drizzle. Their *Wehrmacht* comrades patrolling the longer western breakwater were equally miserable in the wet, cold and dark night.

David looked at the faces of his men in turn and took a deep breath.

"Well, chaps, this is it. Biffo and Corporal Dai will row us across the harbour entrance to reach the western breakwater. I need not repeat that complete silence will be essential. When we get there we'll cross over the breakwater and into the harbour itself. Dai will stay in the boat, Sergeant Hubbard and Biffo will get on to the breakwater with rifles and deal with any guards and shoot out the searchlights if they are turned on. Lieutenant Napier and I will go into the harbour with our mines. We'll be away for about forty minutes and Sergeant Hubbard and Biffo will keep our escape route clear. Any questions?"

Lieutenant Napier spoke up immediately.

"It's been agreed that I go in alone, Sir. I insist we keep to the arrangement."

David turned towards the young lieutenant.

"Samuel, you know you can't swim four hundred yards and trail four of the limpets behind you. It's physically impossible. I tried the weight of one limpet in the sea and I can assure you that two will be the maximum that anyone can tow, especially if we have to use our snorkels."

Lieutenant Napier replied, "Then I'll only take two, Sir."

David interjected quickly. "If you do, it will diminish your chance of success. You told me yourself you need two limpets for each submarine. There could be two U-boats in there and you may need help to get into the pens. No, Samuel, I'm coming with you and that's an order."

The naval lieutenant looked down and added rather petulantly, "Once we're on the water I'll be in charge of the operation."

"Agreed," David replied and smiled inwardly.

He would have to give Samuel his head. The naval officer had come a long way with one purpose in mind. Now that they were within striking distance of their objective he would give Lieutenant Samuel Horatio Napier his moment of glory.

The raiding party left the beach, to the accompaniment of Biffo's question, "Any more for the *Skylark*?", before midnight. Lieutenant Napier ordered Dai and Biffo to row directly northwards out to sea for about a mile towards the invisible island of Dia. The night was pitch black, the sea choppy and the little rowing boat sank to its gunnels with the weight of the raiding party. Within ten minutes they were bailing out furiously. After fifteen minutes' rowing Lieutenant Napier dramatically whispered, "Hard aport," and steered the boat westwards. They knew they were abreast the harbour entrance when they saw a faint glow of green and red navigation lights towards the shore. Lieutenant Napier guided the raiding boat towards the lights and steered it expertly past the red glow, aiming the boat at the western breakwater at the bend of the dog-leg in the harbour wall. The seaward side of the breakwater was bolstered by very large boulders and covered with barbed wire.

Sergeant Hubbard was first ashore with wire cutters and cleared a path through the wire up to the thirty foot vertical harbour wall. He then used the grappling irons and rope to scale the wall and disappeared over the top. Biffo, carrying the Sten guns and a rope ladder and two rifles was next up to join Sergeant Hubbard. They lay still and quiet together for a full minute. There were no patrols or sentries about. Sergeant Hubbard crawled across the breakwater and tied the rope ladder to a bollard, letting the end of the ladder drop into the water in the harbour. David and Corporal Griffiths then formed a human chain to hand the mines and wire cutters up to Biffo on the parapet. Finally Lieutenant Napier was helped to the end of the grappling iron rope and, by pushing from below and hauling from above, he reached the parapet. David was the last up the rope. Corporal Dai Griffiths returned to the rowing boat to bail out, sit, and wait.

At the top of the harbour wall David pointed out the green and red lights a hundred yards to the left and the direction of the submarine pens to Lieutenant Napier. The lieutenant was first into the water, his primitive snorkel in position, wire cutters tied to his waist, and detonators safely tucked inside his naval tunic. The four limpet mines were gently lowered to him and then David followed with spare wire cutters and two spare detonators inside his shirt. Sergeant Hubbard pulled up the rope ladder and stowed it behind the bollard. He leant over the edge of the harbour wall, whispered, "Good luck, Sir," and then took up his position near a bollard, whilst Biffo concealed himself along the edge of the harbour parapet. They now had to sit and wait, prepared to deal with any sentries that came along, rifles loaded, and ready to fire at the harbour searchlights if they should be turned on.

The three hundred yard swim to the pens, towing a pair of semi-submerged twenty-five pound limpets, was slow and laborious and took the two raiders nearly twenty minutes. They were both exhausted when they reached their target. David was first to arrive behind the moored U-boats whose sterns were sticking some twenty feet into the harbour, hemmed in by a curtain of tough, weighted camouflage wire-netting. They were both panting heavily and gasping for breath. David held his wire cutters in one hand and pointed with his other to the netting. Lieutenant Napier gave two brief nods of his head and they both submerged to cut a hole in the netting below the waterline. Lieutenant Napier unhitched his limpet mines and handed the straps to David. He then dived and went through into the pens surfacing between the sterns of the two moored U-boats. David pushed two of the mines through the gap in the wire, and the lieutenant took them to the starboard side of one of the submarines, took a mine off its cork base, inserted the detonator and with a loud 'clunk' fixed the activated mine near the U-boat's engine room. He then swam around and repeated the procedure on the starboard side of the second U-boat and then returned to the hole in the net to collect the two remaining mines from David.

Clinging to the wire netting, their faces about a foot apart, gasping for breath, the young officer whispered, "David, I only need one. I think there was someone in the engine room of the second sub and they may soon raise the alarm. Take the last limpet and see if there's any metal you can clamp it on to. I'm going to place this one near the magazine of the first sub. Good luck, David."

He took a deep breath and dived under the water between the adjacent hulls of the two U-boats.

David murmured, "Good luck, Samuel", under his breath and swam strongly to the left of the pens, guiding himself by instinct towards the pier.

As he swam his head bumped into a thick anchor chain and within five strokes he reached the stern of an E-boat. His mind flashed back to his basic weaponry training. He recalled the instructions for priming a magnetic mine. Selecting a spot midship he attached the limpet to the underside of the boat by plunging a detonator half-way into the socket and turning it anti-clockwise until he felt a clunk. Further downward pressure on the detonator and a final clockwise turn activated the explosive charge. At that very moment he heard German voices and shouting on the quayside. Flashlights were being used in the submarine pens.

A guttural German voice shouted, "There's someone in the water. Raise the alarm. *Achtung, achtung.*"

David did not wait a moment longer. The fuse time for the detonators was twenty minutes and eight minutes had already elapsed since Samuel had primed his first limpet. The clatter of voices from the shore was increasing in intensity. It was time to go. He thanked God for the swimming training he had undertaken at Oxford and incongruously started thinking, about Percy and Wooley and dear old Daima at Rotherhithe Grammar School.

David had swum a hundred yards before the eastern end of the harbour burst into light. Probing fingers of a searchlight on one of the lighthouses made an arc around the submarine pens and then flashed up and down the breakwaters. Instinctively David clasped the tubing of his home-made snorkel between his teeth and continued swimming two feet under water. The searchlight failed to pick up the tip of his snorkel, and, as suddenly as the light came on it disappeared and the harbour was again dark and almost peaceful. Fifty yards further on a flare lit up the harbour for forty seconds. David had anticipated this and he was underwater and snorkelling within a trice of the bright light appearing. When the third flare went up he was within twenty yards of the breakwater and the rope ladder. He was also conscious of a lot of shouting and firing on the breakwater above his head. He climbed up the ladder and dropped to the ground next to Sergeant Hubbard.

"How many of them up there?" indicating the port lighthouse.

"Three or four I reckon, Sir," replied the sergeant. "I'm pretty certain I got a couple. Head down," shouted the sergeant as another flare lit the sky.

"Is Lieutenant Napier safely across and in the boat?"

"No, Sir," replied Sergeant Hubbard. "He's not made it back so far."

"Well," David said, "if he's not here by now he's not going to make it. We'll give him another minute and then we'll have to leave."

As he finished speaking another flare lit the sky and Biffo started firing from the other side of the breakwater.

"They're coming along the wall behind you, Hubby. There's about twenty of them about two hundred yards away. I think I bagged one of them. And can you tell Dai to shut up? He's shouting from the boat all the time, 'What the hell's going on up there?' If he wants to know, why the hell doesn't he come up and find out?"

The flare-light faded abruptly. David shouted, "Now," and dashed across to join Biffo on the other side of the harbour wall.

"Give me your rifle and Sten, Biffo, and get down into the boat." And then, looking across his shoulder, he shouted, "Sergeant Hubbard, it's time to go. I'll cover you. Get across here now."

He started spraying the lighthouse with indiscriminate Sten fire. Sergeant Hubbard joined him in seconds and abseiled down the rope into the boat. David lay flat on the breakwater parapet for fifteen seconds while another flare fizzled out into the harbour water and then, disengaging the grappling iron and rope and throwing them into the sea he clawed his way down the breakwater face to reach the rocks below and jumped into the boat.

"Row like hell, boys. Not the way we came. Go down past the old harbour and keep close inshore. I expect the balloon to go up in about five to eight minutes' time."

And then he fell silent, a prisoner of his own thoughts, David reasoned that Samuel had enough time to get clear and should have made it back to the pier before him. What could have happened to him? He was a strong swimmer and not in trouble when he left David to place the third limpet. Had the Germans on the pen quayside got hold of him? He uttered a silent prayer for the lieutenant's survival. The rowers were working hard at the oars. Biffo spoke to Dai through the corner of his mouth.

"Just like the fucking Oxford and Cambridge boat race, Dai."

David overheard the remark and barked at the oarsmen, "Make sure the dark blues win," a comment which was completely lost on both Biffo and Corporal Dai.

They had safely passed the entrance to the old harbour when the bang came, a loud reverberating crack, accompanied by a sheet of flame and followed later by a second equally loud crescendo and again, after half a minute, a third explosion. David thought about the third bang. It could either be his E-boat limpet, or might be Samuel's third plant. In either case, by the sound of it, a lot of damage had been inflicted on Hitler's *Kriegsmarine*. But at a price. David was now certain that Lieutenant Samuel Horatio Napier was lost, probably killed in action. They rowed westwards close inshore for a further mile and, before landing, all non-essential and incriminating equipment was dumped overboard. The commando landed on a beach at Ammondara at 3 a.m. on the 28th January, 1944. They buried the boat in a sand dune and immediately proceeded inland. Two nights later they were back in their cave at Piskopiano having spent one night, and part of a day, in an orange grove on a fertile slope two kilometres north to Kato Arhanes. During the day German patrol activity along the Arhanes to Heraklion road intensified, frantic searchers for the perpetrators of the attack on Heraklion harbour.

*

Manfred Schmidt retired to bed early on the 27th January, 1944. He had dined in Heraklion with Major Oberhaus, the garrison commander and drunk the best part of two bottles of wine and innumerable glasses of cognac. *Feldwebel* Schneider drove him home to the villa and put him to bed, where he fell into a drunken sleep, only to be rudely awakened at 2.30 a.m. by a duty orderly sergeant.

"Heraklion on the telephone, Sir. Sounds urgent."

Manfred, bleary-eyed and with throbbing temples, picked up the bedside phone.

"What's the matter, Major Oberhaus?"

The man on the other end of the phone was clearly agitated.

"We think there's been an attempted raid on the submarine pens in the new harbour."

Manfred exploded. "You think, you think, you damned fool. Has there, or has there not, been an attack on the harbour? If you've woken me up to tell me you only think there's been an attempt I can assure you you'll be severely dealt with."

The major in Heraklion was palpably trembling.

"Well, yes, Sir, there's been an attack on the harbour. Two of our searchlights have been put out of action and the *Kriegsmarine* around the pen have seen something in the water. They're investigating now and I've ordered a search of the harbour. I thought I should inform you, Sir."

Manfred was now calmer.

"Yes, yes, of course, Oberhaus, thank you. I'll be down right away."

Calling for his servant he dressed quickly and Schneider, also alerted, brought a *Kübelwagen* to the villa steps.

As they drove at speed through Khania gate a mighty explosion rent the air followed by another two in quick succession.

"Jesus Christ," Manfred exploded. "What the hell was that? It sounds as if the whole harbour has blown up. Drive to garrison headquarters."

The whole place was in chaos with officers and orderlies running around indiscriminately shouting orders and counter orders. Manfred found Major Oberhaus in his office with a *Kriegsmarine* lieutenant. The major turned to face Manfred.

"Thank God you've arrived, Sir. Lieutenant Thonn has brought news that two U-boats and an E-boat have been damaged and the *Kriegsmarine* have suffered many casualties. Lieutenant Thonn thinks it's been an attack by a one, or two-manned, submarine. How it got through the anti-submarine net is a mystery."

Manfred looked haughtily at the garrison commander, "Oberhaus, do you think the attackers could have shot the searchlights from under the water? No, this is a land attack. Put out a general alarm and seal off all exits to the harbour. No one goes in or out of the town without my permission."

At dawn on the 29th January the rope ladder was found.

"Oberhaus, that confirms this attack was from inland."

Later that morning the mangled body of a fair-haired British Royal Naval officer in uniform was recovered from the harbour enmeshed in a tattered and torn camouflage net. Manfred now changed his tune.

"Oberhaus, I told you all along that this must have been a seaborne assault. That's the *Kriegsmarine*'s responsibility. General Müller is on his way here. I suggest, if you want to keep your job, you play down the rope ladder and you concentrate on the British naval officer's body. General Müller will not be pleased if the *Wehrmacht* is blamed for not repulsing this attack."

Manfred's prediction was correct. General Müller arrived mid-morning and gave a severe dressing down to Manfred and Major Oberhaus, but kept the majority of his venomous invective for the unfortunate Lieutenant Thonn, the sole representative of the *Kriegsmarine*. Much to Manfred's relief, at the end of the day, blame for the lack of defence of the submarine pens at Heraklion was placed fairly and squarely on the shoulders of Admiral Doenitz's *Kriegsmarine*. Manfred had no doubt in his own mind, however, that the raiders had got into the harbour over the western breakwater, which was patrolled by his *Wehrmacht*.

Naval War Records, 1944

In July 1944 Lieutenant Samuel Horatio Napier RN was awarded a posthumous Distinguished Service Cross, the highest decoration the Navy can bestow, apart from a Victoria Cross. The citation, prepared by Brigadier Sharples, read:

'That the said Lieutenant Samuel Horatio Napier RN did, on the 28th January, 1944, conduct a single-handed assault on submarine pens in Heraklion harbour, Crete, and destroyed two U-boats and an E-boat and, as a result, lost his life in the service of his country.'

There were no citations for the deeds of Major David Green, Sergeant Jim Hubbard, Gunner Wendro and Corporal Dai Griffiths RASC.

Chapter Twenty-Eight
Eastern Crete, February – April 1944
Death of Captain Schubert
and Samaritis
Abduction of General Kreipe

For the whole month of February 1944 the four-man commando in the kibbutz lay low. After an initial surge of frenetic activity German patrols gave up their search for the perpetrators of the attack on Heraklion harbour, but they took their revenge on the inhabitants of Amniso and Remna, small hamlets on the outskirts of the town. Twenty elderly Cretan males and four females were publicly shot and Colonel Schmidt, Major Oberhaus and Lieutenant Thonn were made responsible for carrying out the executions.

Morale in the kibbutz was at a low ebb and the loss of Lieutenant Napier during the action in the harbour had affected the whole commando. David had a guilt complex, blaming himself for not returning to the pens to look for the lieutenant before he swam away. And yet, in his own mind, he knew he had done everything humanly possible in the harbour on the night of the raid.

As the short sunless days and the long cold wintry nights went by the loneliness and isolation in the cave became oppressive, the lice more irritating, and for days on end communication between the commando was reduced to bare essentials. Even the normally cheerful Biffo was silent and moody and Corporal Griffiths had withdrawn into his shell. David realised that something would need to be done if he was to keep his unit intact. Matters came to a head on a dismal grey morning in late February. David and Sergeant Hubbard were sitting at the cave entrance delousing, each attending to his own colony and lost in private thought. Biffo was on sentry duty at the farmhouse road and Corporal Griffiths was out scouring the foothills for food. Sergeant Hubbard looked up, a juicy louse impaled between his thumb-nail and forefinger and spoke.

"Sir, I wish to request evacuation to Alex."

David, half-startled by the suddenness of the request lay aside his 'crap-catcher' trousers and looked into his sergeant's eyes. Hubbard continued, "I feel, Sir, we have done enough here. Our last raid was a huge success but I wish to be back in the swim again doing normal military duty. I'm missing out on promotion by being stuck on this lousy island."

David replied promptly, "I'm glad you brought this up, Sergeant Hubbard. For the past three weeks, ever since our raid on the harbour, I have felt a tension in the kibbutz. You know the other two better than I do. How do you feel about them?"

The sergeant thought for a few moments.

"Corporal Griffiths won't wish to go. He wants to get back to the farm. I'm not sure about Biffo. You'd better ask him yourself, Sir."

When David and Biffo were alone later that day David asked the question.

Biffo replied, "I've been thinking about this for a couple of weeks, Sir. If I go back to Cairo I'll probably end up in the glass-house pronto. So I'll stay on here, Sir. As you know I like the food and the company." and then, for the first time in weeks, the little Cockney's face broke into a broad grin.

David now considered his own position. His mission in Crete had been accomplished. There was every reason for his return to Cairo and Brigadier Sharples' last message confirmed that his commando must evacuate to Alexandria after the Heraklion harbour raid. And yet, he had unfinished business. The White Angel of Gournes was still alive and well, Samaritis was still rampaging in the Lasithis and the butcher General Müller was still commander of Festung Kriti. Mentally he relived the day when he had seen the butchery at Pirgia and his blond-haired blood brother executing the villagers. Since that day his resolve had never wavered. He would kill Colonel Manfred Schmidt before he left Crete.

After their meagre supper that evening he addressed his small group.

"We've been under a lot of stress during the past three weeks and I believe the time has come for us to get out of Crete. We can't get away in one group so Sergeant Hubbard and Corporal Griffiths will go on the March pick up. Biffo and I will stay on till April or May. I still have one or two matters to deal with before I leave. We've had a good run together and I'm sorry that we have to break up. I will go down to Keratokombou next week to see if there are any final messages and make arrangements for you, Sergeant, and Corporal Dai to get away."

Corporal Griffiths responded immediately.

"If it's all right with you, Sir, I don't want to get out. They'll pick me up as a deserter in Alex. I'll stay with Spiros and see the war out."

David agreed. "If that's your decision, Corporal Griffiths, it'll be all right with me."

David left a day early to meet the February drop. He planned to call in Kastelli on the way to Keratokombou. By the end of February 1944 Kastelli was only lightly defended by the Germans. David had not seen Marita for four months, not since the Italian armistice. In darkness at about 7 p.m. he approached her back door through the castle grounds and up the garden path, tapping lightly on her window. He heard little Spiros chattering excitedly inside the house. There was a delay. Slowly the door partially opened and the barrel of a shotgun appeared pointing directly at his face. He pushed the barrel gently aside and whispered, "Marita, Marita", through the half-open doorway. The gun barrel was withdrawn, the door flung open and Marita was in his arms sobbing and clinging to him and pulling him gently into the one-roomed house. Spiros, wide-eyed and inquisitive, was lying on the bed in the dimly lit room. David and Marita disengaged from their embrace. She looked up at him, tears streaming down her face.

"Mr Englishman, I thought you were dead."

David took her hand gently and they both sat on the edge of the bed next to the young boy, who now had his arms around Marita's neck and was looking with awe at the stranger who had interrupted their ritual cuddle. Marita took David's hand and guided it to her abdomen. He felt a hard tumescence in the lower part of her belly and pulling his hand away, clutched Marita and Spiros in his arms, hugging them both fiercely and pulling her to him in a long embrace.

"Marita, Marita, how long have you been pregnant?"

She was now smiling. "The baby is now four months old, Englishman. Here give me your hand and you'll feel him kick."

And once again David's hand was placed on Marita's pregnancy. He was filled with joy and disbelief. He was going to father a child and, far from being resentful and recriminating, Marita was proud and pleased to carry his child. They sat together on the edge of the bed for a long time holding hands and kissing. Little Spiros fell asleep on the bed. They did not make love. In the embrace of this tiny Cretan school teacher David felt at peace. They discussed the future and it was agreed that after the baby was born Marita would move down to Spiros' farm at Piskopiano to be near David. David left Marita and the sleeping boy two hours before dawn. He wanted to be well clear of Kastelli by daybreak.

At the beach at Keratokombou the naval dinghies came ashore at 0300 hours, disgorging a few black-clothed figures on to the beach followed, after an interval, by a naval lieutenant protected by three armed matelots. After the usual spate of back-slapping and hand-shaking David managed to pull the lieutenant aside.

"I'm expecting a message from Shepherds."

The young naval lieutenant looked at David in surprise.

"Are you Green? There are no messages for you except that someone on the beach will contact you."

"Thank you," said David and handed over a coded message with details of the Heraklion harbour raid. The naval officer now moved away to another group of men crouched around a large crate which had been discharged from the second dinghy. David turned to walk up the beach and in the semi-dark came face to face with a greyish silhouette of a large man dressed as a Cretan. The silhouette spoke perfect English.

"I'm Paul Ransom, I saw you speaking to the lieutenant. You must be Green. Cairo has been trying to get in touch with you for six weeks. I've got a receiver in the Lasithis. The message is that your group is to get out as soon as possible but there's one more job to do. There's going to be a big show near Knossos sometime in April. Cairo wishes you to recce the area and look around the German HQ at Arhanes and Villa Ariadne, the general's residence at in Knossos. If you've any information for Cairo I can transmit it for you. You'll find me in the Lasithis near the village of Tapes. Just get to the village and hang around. Someone will let me know you're there and I'll get in touch with you. Good luck, Green," and, with a light tap on David's shoulder he turned on his heels and disappeared into the darkness towards a steep cliff at the upper end of the beach.

February 1944 was one of the coldest and wettest months within living memory. Despite General Müller's prompting Manfred had to cut back his field operations to a minimum. General Müller's demands on his eastern command were increasing, but at the same time many of his units were being withdrawn and sent back to Germany for redeployment on the Italian or Russian fronts. The general also ordered reassignation of Italian troops in eastern Crete. The garrisons at Ierapetra, Malia, Neapolis and Sitia were to be gradually withdrawn and relocated in Khania where Müller was creating a seventy kilometre Festung. By March 1944 Ierapetra and Sitia had been completely evacuated by the Italians. The southern town was occupied by Porphyroyennis' communists and Sitia was taken over by Colonel Plevres' nationalists. Elounda was still strongly held by German forces who only partially controlled Aghios Nikolaos where Porphyroyennis and Samaritis were vying for control of the small sea port. Samaritis also had his eye on Heraklion, where Yanni Bodias held sway for the communists, and Bandouvas, now returned from North Africa, commanded a large force of some two thousand men in the lowland foothills around Heraklion.

A year previously Manfred had had thirteen thousand Germans and thirty-five thousand Italians at his disposal to defend eastern Crete. By March there were only some five thousand Italians and barely six thousand German troops left in the province, insufficient to defend all the main centres under his command. Manfred ensured that fifteen hundred of his best troops, including his beloved *Fallschirmjagger*, were stationed in Festung Elounda. Major Oberhaus had a similar number of men available for the defence of Heraklion. Punitive expeditions were curtailed and the troops under his command were ordered to concentrate on defence rather than attack.

After a partial German evacuation of Ierapetra and removal of the Italian garrison, Samaritis' and Porphyroyennis' *andartes* encroached on the town. Manfred trusted neither of these unsavoury characters, but, of the two, he favoured Porphyroyennis. Samaritis remained a thorn in his flesh. Informers at Heraklion headquarters reported that

Samaritis' group of four hundred men were active in the eastern Diktis near the village of Males.

"Fetch Captain Schubert."

Manfred and Major Oberhaus were scanning a wall map of Crete at their Heraklion headquarters.

"Major Oberhaus, as I see it, Ierapetra is being invested by the Cretans from two sides, Porphyroyennis, from the east and Samaritis from the west. I wish Porphyroyennis to take the town as I have a sort of working arrangement with him. The bastard Samaritis is based in the mountains near Males. I want his group destroyed once and for all. I will send *Jagdcommando* Schubert in after them. As you know I don't like Captain Schubert but I have to admit he's the best man I've got for this kind of job. If Schubert fails me this time he'll be kicked out or, better still, I'll demote him to the ranks."

Major Oberhaus nodded his head in agreement with his colonel.

Since January 1944, Captain Schubert had been in the doldrums but now a glorious opportunity arose for him to redeem his previous misdemeanours and to reinstate himself in favour with his commanding officer. Like a mistreated wolfhound, beaten and battered by its master, he came cringing back to lick his master's boots and invite more punishment. This was his chance for glory. He preened his straggly moustache and made a mental reservation that, on this occasion, he would succeed and destroy Samaritis and his Bolsheviks. He had one nagging concern about the operation. Due to demands for manpower from Müller's headquarters his *Jagdcommando* had been pruned to sixty-eight men. He was confident, however, that Samaritis' poorly equipped and badly organised *andartes*, though around four hundred strong, would prove no match for his heavily armed, battle-trained *Jagdcommando*.

Jagdcommando Schubert's armoured mechanised column left Heraklion on the 28th February 1944. By now Viannos was a no-go area for the Germans and Schubert took his convoy along the north coastal road, through Neapolis and Aghios Nikolaos to swing south at Kalahorio through the village of Kalamafka to reach Anatoli, where they sat astride the road from Males to Ierapetra. Captain Schubert ordered his troops to advance northwards along the Males road, where they made first contact with Samaritis' *andartes*. True to form Samaritis, after firing a few desultory shots, immediately evacuated the hamlet and took his men into the higher ranges of the Diktis. Mechanised movement beyond Males was not possible.

Captain Schubert, cognisant with Samaritis' tactics, ordered Sergeant Weiskopf to take half the *Jagdcommando* and pursue the *andartes* on foot. Sergeant Weiskopf's platoon advanced higher an higher into the Dikti mountain range. They dug in on a flat plateau. The *andartes* were in position about a mile westwards at the top end of the plateau. Samaritis then made a costly miscalculation. He underestimated the strength of the German patrol and ordered a direct frontal attack on Sergeant Weiskopf's position. A bitter hand-to-hand battle ensued and more than fifty of the *andartes* were killed or wounded and only four of the *Jagdcommando* were casualties. Samaritis, his nose bloodied, withdrew and Sergeant Weiskopf sent a message back to Males requesting further instructions.

Captain Schubert then made the first of his two fateful decisions. He ordered Sergeant Weiskopf to press on with his attack. He anticipated that Samaritis would either ascend higher into the Diktis or would come south along an earth road to meet the south coastal road at Mourines. His second unsound decision was to divide his own force into two groups, leaving a sergeant and fifteen men to guard the motorcycles at Males and taking the remaining seventeen soldiers to the coast road to establish a welcoming committee for Samaritis at Mourines. His plan was tactically sound but it misfired with serious consequences for the *Jagdcommando*. Within two days Sergeant Weiskopf's platoon were surrounded and isolated on a mountain top above Males. One by one they were picked off by accurate sniper fire and when they were reduced to ten men Sergeant Weiskopf surrendered. No mercy was shown. The unfortunate soldiers were disarmed, stripped of their clothing and summarily executed. Only two of Sergeant Weiskopf's platoon successfully made the journey back to Males. Samaritis, flushed with success, now ordered his *andartes* to retake Males and, after a short, feverish battle, the small village was overrun. The rearguard of Schubert's *Jagdcommando* were overpowered and those German soldiers not killed in action were shot in the village square. Samaritis himself, full of pomp and arrogance, supervised execution of the German defenders.

Prompted by the prospect of acquiring more rifles and ammunition, it was now Samaritis' turn of to make a fateful decision. Instead of pressing on eastwards to Ierapetra he ordered his followers south-westwards along the coastal road to Mourines, where Captain Schubert and seventeen of his *Jagdcommando* were expecting Sergeant Weiskopf's victorious troops to arrive from the north. Instead Samaritis' *andartes* came streaming down from the east to engage the lightly defended German outpost. The battle for Mourines lasted two days. One by one Captain Schubert's beleaguered section were picked off by snipers. The casualty list mounted. By the 11th March Captain Schubert and his small encircled force were reduced to eleven exhausted men. Ammunition was running low and the wounded could not be looked after.

On the night of March 12th, Captain Schubert and his remaining eleven commandos made a dash westwards on their motorcycles along the south coast road towards Viannos, hotly pursued by Samaritis. At this point Samaritis should have called a halt. Instead he ordered his men to continue harassing Schubert's depleted group. At first the Germans had an advantage as they travelled on their motorcycles, but this soon disappeared when they ran out of petrol at Loutraki some four kilometres east of Anno Viannos. From now on Captain Schubert and his eleven men would have to walk back to Heraklion. For the next few days, whilst the *Jagdcommando* trudged northwards, the Bolshevik *andartes* harried and sniped at their heels and three of the eleven men fell to snipers.

Captain Schubert hoped to find a friendly face at Kastelli but the garrison had been withdrawn two days previously. With his eight remaining commandos he pressed on resolutely northwards and at around 4 p.m. on March 16th he led his bedraggled party into Spiros' farm at Piskopiano, where the exhausted commandos gratefully fell to the ground in the outhouse. Captain Schubert posted a sentry, ordered his men to fill their water bottles from the well and joined his commando on the grimy floor of the barn. The small remnant of his sixty-four man commando had been hustled and harried by Samaritis for five sleepless days and nights and they were all soon in a deep sleep, completely oblivious to their surroundings. Even the concealed sentry posted at the top of the farmhouse lane was soon fast asleep, slumped over his rifle.

Biffo was on sentry duty when the bedraggled remnants of Schubert's *Jagdcommando* came shuffling down the road from Kastelli. The group stopped to rest at the farmhouse junction and Biffo, concealed some forty yards away in a thicket, heard the

German captain giving orders. How he wished he could understand the barbaric language. If only Major Green were with him he would be able to understand every word. After all they used to call him the Kraut in Pusey Street school! The German captain got to his feet and led seven of the Germans down the lane towards the farmhouse, leaving one soldier on guard at the T-junction, concealed behind a rock thirty yards in front and below Biffo's vantage point. Biffo waited patiently. There were no signs of activity at the farmhouse and within thirty minutes Biffo was certain that the German sentry, slumped forwards over his rifle, was sound asleep.

This was too good an opportunity to miss. Crawling forwards silently he approached the unconscious sentry, now snoring sibilantly and, slipping a wire noose around his neck, garrotted the German with expertise and expedition learnt during his commando training in Cairo. The dead German, divested of his rifle and ammunition, was pulled out of sight into a copse. Biffo then began moving backwards along the edge of the steep escarpment towards the cave.

He had scrambled some fifty yards when an unexpected movement on the Kastelli road, some hundred and fifty yards away, caught his eye. Biffo crouched low and watched the road and soon realised that the movement he saw were two men approaching cautiously one on each side of the road. He watched as they arrived at the T-junction when one of them let out a stifled cry of surprise.

They had found the dead German sentry. Though Biffo had concealed the greater part of the soldier's body, one jack-booted leg was sticking out through the hedge on the roadside. One of the scouts made a signal, waving both arms aloft and within a minute a group of twenty armed *andartes* came down the road running in a crouched position, rifles at the ready. About two minutes later two men armed with Sten guns, rifles and bandoliers came sauntering along. Clearly these two were the leaders of the Cretan irregulars. Biffo waited no longer. He made a rapid withdrawal along the escarpment and arrived breathless and perspiring at the kibbutz.

"Jerry's in the farmhouse, Sir. There's an officer and seven men somewhere in the farm. There were eight," giving a scissors sign with two fingers at his throat, "but I got rid of the one they left on guard at the top of the lane. I don't know what they're after but they looked all in to me. There's more, Sir. About half an hour after the Jerries arrived about twenty Cretans came down the road. Two of them were covered with bandoliers and had red feathers in their *sarikis*. They may be officers. I didn't wait any longer but I think they're going down the lane after the Germans."

David acted quickly.

"Sergeant Hubbard, take a Bren gun across to the ledge on the other side of the olive grove. Biffo, go back up the escarpment with a Bren and keep the farmhouse covered. Dai and I will stay on this ledge. Load up with grenades and take your Stens. No one is to fire until I have shot first. Maybe they'll fight down at the farmhouse and not come into the olive grove. If they do we may have to get involved."

Sergeant Hubbard and Biffo were hardly in position before the firing began.

Captain Schubert's *Jagdcommando* were temporarily reprieved when one of their members woke with an urgent desire to urinate. He opened the barn door and stepped outside into the yard only to be met by a fusillade of bullets from the *andartes* who were lying concealed at various points around the yard. The soldier died instantly. Within the barn pandemonium broke loose. A corporal charged forwards and barricaded the door whilst the rest took up their positions at the small windows. Captain Schubert peered nervously through one of the windows but a bullet, shattering the lintel above his head, caused him to duck and fall on one knee. His basic instinct was to lie on the ground and cover his head but the urge for survival prevailed. Grabbing his *Schmeitzer* he shouted amidst the din of rifle fire.

"Corporal Krebs and Private Boermann come with me. The rest of you hold them at bay here as long as you can. We'll go out the back and see if we can get behind them."

Captain Schubert had no intention of 'getting behind them'. His sole purpose in escaping from the barn was to make a run for it. He led his two commandos out through a back window, dropped to the ground, waded across the partially dry river bed and turned southwards into the olive grove in the direction of the kibbutz. Captain Schubert reasoned that any pursuers would assume they would make a break northwards towards Piskopiano and safety. His reasoning might have carried the day but for the fact that one of the *andartes*, working his way around the edge of the barn, spotted the captain and two soldiers dashing into the comparative cover and safety of the olive grove.

Rifle and machine pistol firing in the farmyard continued unabated for fifteen minutes and was brought to a halt by two loud bangs, the sound of grenades exploding in a confined space. David could only see the roof of the farmhouse from the ledge outside the cave but Biffo, from his higher vantage point, saw and heard cheering from the *andartes* as they rushed the barn. A minute later two single rifle shots indicated an end to the skirmish and execution of the two remaining wounded *Jagdcommando*. David also heard the two shots and, within seconds, he saw three armed German soldiers weaving in and out of the olive trees crouching as they ran towards the base of the sheer cliff underneath his ledge. One of the three was a *Hauptmann* and David recognised Captain Schubert. He watched with fascination as the Germans began frantically trying to claw their way up the cliff. They were imprisoned by the V-shaped, steep cleft between the two escarpments which were the boundaries to each side of Spiros' olive grove. They crawled into the bottom of the river bed and attempted to conceal themselves amongst the rocks and boulders, in full view of David and Corporal Griffiths and of Sergeant Hubbard on the opposite escarpment.

Within five minutes the baying and shouting of their pursuers grew louder as they dashed and weaved and made a thorough search of the olive grove. And all the time, the Germans, partially hidden, lay cringing, face downwards, in the river bed. One of the searchers gave a loud shout. He had seen the quarry. Letting off one shot in the air he jumped into the narrow river bed and started prodding the Germans with his rifle. The shot brought seven *andartes* to the spot and they stood in a semi-circle, rifles at the ready and pointing towards the prostrate Germans. Someone shouted, "*Hande hoch!*" and Captain Schubert and the two soldiers, dropping their *Schmeitzers*, stood up with arms raised above their heads.

The Cretan *andartes* were excited and congratulated each other on their success. David kept his eyes glued on Schubert, whose face was twitching with anxiety with tears trickling down his cheeks. He began to plead for mercy. Within a minute a diminutive figure with an ugly pock-marked face and a beaked nose, swathed in bandoliers and grenades and carrying a rifle and a Sten gun, pushed his way through the *andartes* and approached the Germans.

"I am Samaritis. At last we come face to face, Schubert. Have you anything to say before I shoot you? You've killed many of my men. You must also die."

Hauptmann Schubert fell to his knees pleading and whimpering with the unpleasant *kapitan*.

"Stop, enough," shouted the irate *kapitan*. "Stand up and die like a man."

Schubert made no move to get to his feet.

"Very well," said Samaritis and, walking to the edge of the trench, he sprayed the screaming Germans with bullets from his Sten gun, encouraging the other *andartes* to do the same, each one in the cordon firing a rifle, or shotgun, into the inert bodies at the bottom of the river bed.

At that moment one of the *andartes* caught sight of Sergeant Hubbard on the ledge opposite the cave. He gave a shout of warning and started firing in the sergeant's direction. Sergeant Hubbard had little choice. He raked the *andartes* with his Bren gun. Bodies were falling everywhere and, when Biffo joined in the carnage, dead and wounded *andartes* lay haphazardly on the ground and in the boulder-strewn dry river bed. Two made a dash for the shelter of the olive grove and escaped in the direction of the farm. Samaritis, the back of his head shot away, and one of his lieutenants, lay on top of Captain Schubert and his two dead commandos in the gully.

From the distant end of the grove came echoes of escaping *andartes* shouting, "Run, run, Samaritis is dead. The *kapitan* has been shot."

At the end of the action Samaritis and five of his followers lay dead at the foot of the cave. Biffo appeared on the hilltop. David signalled him to return to his observation post at the road junction and then, fanning out, they carefully searched the grove for stragglers and made their way to the farm.

Spiros and Anna were standing very still in the doorway. Two *andartes* and a German soldier lay dead in the yard, whilst the bodies of five German soldiers, one mutilated beyond recognition, were found in the barn. Very shortly Biffo appeared to report that eight surviving *andartes* had retreated in the fading light to the south towards Kastelli, carrying three wounded comrades with them. David held a conference outside Spiros' farmhouse door.

"Our hide-out here is no longer safe. We'll have to move out tonight. We'll make for Corporal Griffiths' farm, where we should be safe for a few days. The farmer there can be trusted?"

The question was directed at Corporal Dai.

"Yes, sir," the corporal replied.

"Right," said David, "Let's get back to the cave and load up with as many guns, ammunition and food as we can carry. I'll hang on here for a few minutes and ask Spiros to clear up the mess after we've gone."

David went into the dark living room and sat at the table with Spiros and Anna. They made him drink some *tsikoudia* and milk and offered bread and cheese which David ate with difficulty. He spoke to Spiros in Greek.

"Old man, we have to leave tonight. The Cretan fighters will be back tomorrow to collect Samaritis' body. I have to ask this of you. Will you bring all the dead soldiers from the olive grove and those in the yard back to the barn and keep them there for two days? If no one comes to claim them will you bury them?"

The tired old Cretan understood the request and nodded his agreement.

"I'm sad to see you go, David. You can use two of my mules to carry your equipment. I won't expect the mules to be returned. Anna and I wish you a safe journey and may God go with you"

They both stood up and embraced each other and, as David turned to leave, he again spoke to Spiros.

"When things are settled, Marita will bring your grandson to the farm. She is expecting a baby, my child, and you and Anna will have to take care of them. Please look after my child."

Spiros and Anna were both crying. The embraces were prolonged and poignant but, when he left the farm, David knew that Marita, Stephia's little Spiros and his own, unborn baby, had a safe home in Spiros' farm at Piskopiano.

By the end of March it was evident that Schubert's commando would not be returning. Through informers, Manfred learnt that there had been heavy fighting involving the *Jagdcommando* in the mountains around Males and the report suggested that both Schubert and Samaritis had been killed. On the 4th April he sent a message to General Müller's headquarters informing the general that

Jagdcommando Schubert was now disbanded and that their leader Captain Schubert was 'missing, believed killed in action.

Villa Ariadne: Abduction of General Kreipe

Colonel Manfred Schmidt could not believe his eyes as he read and re-read the cablegram from OKW Berlin relieving General Müller of his command in Festung Kriti and replacing him with General Heinrich Kreipe. Manfred knew little about the new appointee, except that he was an officer who had worked his way up from the ranks. An expert on supply and transportation, he had very little front-line experience, but had spent twelve months in a rear echelon on the Russian front. In any event General Kreipe would be an improvement on Müller who recently had withdrawn into his shell and, fearing assassination by the andartes, refused to venture outside his heavily defended fortress at Khania. Manfred had half a mind to ring Müller, tongue in cheek, and wish him *bon voyage*. The Butcher and his staff left Khania on the 8th April 1944 and his replacement arrived at Festung HQ a week later.

General Kreipe was middle aged, of medium height, balding, with a prominent nose and a stand-offish, diffident manner. He arrived with his entourage at Maleme airport on the 14th April and inspected the Heraklion defences on the 16th where, in the evening, he was entertained by Manfred at Villa Ariadne.

The general proclaimed his satisfaction with the defences of eastern Crete and, to Manfred's discomfiture, declared his intention of using Arhanes as his headquarters and Villa Ariadne as his personal residence. In the general's opinion Arhanes, eight kilometres south of the Knossos excavations, was suitably placed for administration and control of eastern Crete and, the northern coastal strip between Heraklion and Maleme.

Manfred had no choice in the matter. He had to move his staff into Heraklion to share headquarters with Major Oberhaus. *Feldwebel* Schneider was pleased with the move into town with its thriving bustle during the day and some sort of nightlife after dark. Manfred was furious. Not only had he lost the comfort and elegance of the villa, but General Kreipe insisted on keeping Sergeant Schultz and his staff in the cookhouse. Losing the villa was bad enough, but to lose the services of the incomparable Schultz was insufferable. He was not enamoured of the new general's underhand methods but he had to recognise that Kreipe was the boss and he was a mere colonel.

General Kreipe's occupancy of Arhanes and Villa Ariadne lasted exactly twelve days. On the night of the 26th April the general was abducted by SOE agents and, after a complicated adventure in the Cretan mountains, was transported from Crete, on the 14th May, to become a prisoner of war of the British in North Africa.

*

David's new hideout was not at all satisfactory, consisting of three cheese huts at the upper end of a large field of scrubland and grass. The cheese huts were used by shepherds for milking and, during the winter, served as shelters for the animals. Consequently there was a permanent stench of goats' excreta and sour milk inside the small, conical, stone huts. Added to this the huts were a permanent incubation medium for nits, fleas and lice and, after one night, the occupants became infested with the parasites. The cheese huts had one advantage. A towering mountain protected their rear whilst northwards they had a commanding view over the flat valleys south of Heraklion. David, Sergeant Hubbard and Biffo had a cheese hut each, whilst Corporal Griffiths had resumed his tenancy in Spiros' farm about a mile below the hide-out. Their guns and ammunition were concealed in deep crevices on the rocky side of the mountain behind the huts.

In the warm midday sun Biffo was at the farm visiting Dai while Sergeant Hubbard and David sat outside one of the huts scratching and hunting for lice and fleas.

"Sergeant Hubbard, I know I promised I would get you out this month, but I will need your assistance to recce the German headquarters at Arhanes and the villa at Knossos. I can't cover both places at once. Biffo will be needed here to guard the hideout and Corporal Dai hasn't been of much use to us since we moved. I don't know when things will begin to happen but it will involve a patrol every night. I'll take the German HQ. You have a shufti at the villa in Knossos. I expect they'll be heavily guarded, so no heroics. For the next week we'll sleep during the day and turn out at night."

Sergeant Hubbard looked dejected.

"Yes, Sir, I can't sleep at night in any case. I wonder if these damned lice will let us sleep during the day."

Depression was again descending on David's commando. They had been in their new headquarters for only fourteen days and David realised that Sergeant Hubbard was reaching the end of his tether and wanted out. Only Biffo showed a semblance of cheerfulness and made light of their adversity.

"What do you want for supper tonight, Sir? What about some *khorta* and snails? Or would you prefer some lice and chips?"

Sergeant Hubbard was the first to make a positive contact on his third patrol to Knossos. David had been unable to penetrate the heavily protected German headquarters defences at Arhanes. Sergeant Hubbard had positioned himself in a small copse on some high ground about half a mile south of the villa on the left-hand side of the Heraklion-Kastelli road. He had been lying perfectly still for an hour when he heard movement through the undergrowth on his right-hand side and the unmistakable sound of human voices whispering in the darkness. The rustling and crackling sounds in the undergrowth came to a halt some twenty yards to his right, at the edge of the copse, where the intruders had a view of the road and the villa. There was silence for a short while and the whispering re-started. This time the voices were clearer and Sergeant Hubbard realised that the conversation was in English.

"I can't see much through these binocs..."

"Here try mine..."

"That's better", and then silence.

The next conversation started abruptly.

"How long do we stay here, Sir...?"

"We have to be away by 0400 hours..."

"Did you see that Sir...?"

"No..."

"I thought I saw a light flashing at ten o'clock."

Sergeant Hubbard listened acutely for a further ten minutes. There were no Greek, German or Italian words in the conversation. When he was certain that the two men on his right were British he cupped his hands over his mouth and spoke in a loud whisper:

"British soldier over here, Sir. Twenty yards to your left."

Sergeant Hubbard heard the sound of alarm in the darkness from his right and then one of the intruders replied, "Come around and be identified."

The sergeant clutching his Sten gun and half crouching, walked deliberately through the undergrowth to the top of the mound. An authoritative voice in the dark to his right shouted, "Drop your gun and put your hands up."

Sergeant Hubbard obeyed and was conscious of someone standing three paces behind him prodding the small of his back with the nozzle of a Sten gun. He was expertly searched by one of the men and his two grenades and spare ammunition clip were removed.

The man on his right asked, "What's your rank and number?"

The sergeant promptly replied, "Sergeant Jim Hubbard, Royal Marines, Sir, No. 748232."

A figure now appeared in front of him out of the darkness and spoke in a cultured voice.

"Well, I'll be jiggered. What the hell are you doing here, Sergeant?"

"I'm a commando, Sir, and I've been on this bloody island for over two years."

"Good God," the voice replied. "How the hell have you stuck it for so long?"

The voice then ordered the man behind Sergeant Hubbard to move away and instructed the sergeant to crouch down beside him in the undergrowth.

"And what are you doing out here tonight?" the officer asked.

"We've been asked by Cairo to keep an eye on the villa. I don't know more than that, but I could bring my major to meet you."

"That would be a very good idea," and turning to his companion, "Sergeant Galloway, make room for Sergeant Hubbard and give him back his Sten."

The three then settled down together to watch the road and the villa. After about an hour a light vehicle moved on to the road from the villa and disappeared northwards toward Heraklion. The three left the hide together and, before parting company, arrangements were made for a meeting between the officer and David at the same location two nights later.

Sergeant Hubbard's officer contact was Captain Mann of the Coldstream Guards. Captain Mann and David met at the observation post south of Villa Ariadne on the night of the 20th April. The captain explained that there might be a 'show' within a week and that the escape route for the attackers would be northwards towards Heraklion passing through Knossos. He added that the road down to the villa was heavily defended and, at night, the Germans barricaded the main road to Heraklion at a point opposite the Knossos excavation site. He asked if David's force could clear the Germans off the road long enough to allow the attackers to get through. David explained that his force consisted of only four men but they would do everything in their power to assist in the escape. David knew better than to ask the purpose of the raid and the composition of the raiding party. He did however request for Sergeant Hubbard to be evacuated with the attackers and this request was granted by Captain Mann. The date for the commando raid was fixed for the night of the 26th April, 1943.

The Abduction of General Kreipe

By 9 p.m. on Sunday 26th April, 1944 David, Sergeant Hubbard, Biffo and Corporal Griffiths were in position at Knossos in a dry river bed, four hundred yards from a road block on the main road from Arhanes to Heraklion. They were close enough to hear the German guards conversing amongst themselves. There appeared to be four soldiers on duty, a sergeant and three troopers. General Kreipe's staff car was waylaid at a cross roads three kilometres south of the villa. His driver and his aide were disposed of and one of the car's occupants dressed himself in the general's uniform. They drove past the road to the villa to reach the Knossos road block at 10.35 p.m.

David and his commando, now lying alongside the road, saw the dim headlights of an approaching car which was routinely stopped at the barrier. The German sergeant, asserting his authority, turned out the occupants and officiously circled the vehicle. One of the soldiers noticed an irregularity and shouted to his sergeant. The Germans were beginning to unsling their rifles when David ordered his men into action. They came running down each side of the road firing from the hip. The German sergeant crumpled to the floor in front of the car and his companions were mown down where they stood on either side of the automobile. The whole action was over in forty-five seconds. Biffo ran into the guard hut and confirmed that it was empty. The dead Germans were dragged to the side of the road and

Sergeant Hubbard opened the rear door of the staff car and jumped into the back seat.

Through the open window he shouted to David, "Good luck, Sir, and good luck to Biffo and Dai. You won't believe it but my feet are on the face of a German general. I hope it's that bloody butcher, Müller."

The car lurched forwards as David wished Sergeant Hubbard the best of luck and Biffo shouted over his shoulder, "All the best, Hubby."

The car sped northwards into the dark night. Though the glimpse was brief David was certain that the officer in the passenger seat, dressed in a Nazi general's uniform, was Peter Ferman. As they jogged eastwards, back to the cheese huts at Häraso, David wondered if the captured German officer in the Mercedes staff car was, in fact, General Müller.

Meanwhile, Sergeant Hubbard, sitting in the back of the car smelling of perspiration and goat excreta, had both his feet planted on each side of the face of a body stretched on the floor of the German limousine. The gagged German captive was General Kreipe and not General Heydrich Müller. General Kreipe was uncertain, at that moment, of his future. The indignity of his capture outweighed the unpleasantness of the filthy stench which emanated from the feet and legs of the stockily built man sitting on the seat above his head.

*

Manfred was alone, depressed, and sitting morosely in a darkened corner, drinking heavily. The cooking in Heraklion headquarters was diabolical. He was already missing Schultz's culinary expertise. The officers in the mess were deadbeats, dull, uninteresting fellows with equally dull conversation. He was pleased to be alone, lost in his own thoughts, when the orderly-room sergeant suddenly appeared before him.

"Villa Ariadne is on the telephone, Sir. They want you urgently."

The general's staff major was extremely agitated.

"Colonel Schmidt, Sir, the general's car has not arrived from Arhanes and we've heard some firing from the road north of here. I'm very worried about the general's safety. I've sent a patrol out to the roadblock. We can't get through to Arhanes, the telephone lines have been cut."

Manfred exploded.

"Why did the general set up his headquarters in my patch? He should have gone to Khania. Mobilise all the men in the villa and get them out to search the area. I'll have an armoured convoy out to you in half an hour. I'll stay here in the control room and organise road blocks at Heraklion. Major, speed is essential."

But for all the speed, the roadblocks and searches, General Kreipe was whisked away from under the Germans' noses.

General Kreipe's abduction caused an hysterical reaction in Hitler's headquarters in Berlin. Hitler ordered immediate and severe reprisals and Manfred, temporarily promoted to colonel general, was placed in charge of implementing the Führer's orders. Manfred now worked from two headquarters, one at Arkhanes and the other at Khania, commuting regularly by air between the two or, less frequently, by E-boat. The coastal road journey from Heraklion to Khania was fraught with danger of ambush and all convoys using this route were protected by armoured vehicles. At last Manfred felt he was getting the recognition he deserved. His temporary promotion meant that at some stage he would become a full general. In his own estimation he felt he richly deserved this final accolade. He wistfully thought how proud his father would be if he were still alive. But now he had to earn his promotion. He would show the German high command how an efficient paratrooper officer dealt with recalcitrant Cretans.

Chapter Twenty-Nine

Eastern Crete, May 1944 – March 1945
Cheese Huts at Häraso

Cretan Resistance Diary: May – December 1944

The recall of General 'Butcher' Müller to Germany on 8th April, 1944 raised Cretan hopes and their optimism was further enhanced by the successful abduction of his successor General Heinrich Kreipe. The waverers and those who openly collaborated with the Italians and to a lesser extent the Germans, now became openly pro-British, sensing an Allied victory and a chance to drive the hated Germans out of Crete. With the exception of Porphyroyennis all the kapitans were more than anxious to collaborate with British agents.

Porphyroyennis' andartes controlled Ierapetra where they captured and imprisoned two communist nationalist leaders. Porphyroyennis also enjoyed a symbiotic existence in Aghios Nikolaos where, due to Colonel Schmidt's influence, the communist andartes and a small German garrison lived in a spirit of peaceful co-existence. Porphyroyennis had his eye on Elounda where the Germans still had a powerful and well-armed garrison. The wily kapitan felt certain that when the Germans left Elounda he would inherit their armoury and with it become the leader of the most powerfully equipped andartes' group in Crete. At such time Porphyroyennis envisaged he would be made the military supremo of the whole of Crete, and, with his newly acquired armaments, might be able to recruit new members to the communist cause and suppress any rival kapitans who might vie for the position. Colonel Manfred Schmidt's temporary promotion to general in command of Festung Kriti pleased Porphyroyennis but caused a great deal of displeasure amongst all the other kapitans *actively engaged in harassing and fighting the German occupying forces.*

The White Angel of Gournes was now in command of the whole of Crete and the andartes' *hope of a more benevolent German commander were rapidly dispelled. Before he left General Müller had planned to concentrate German and loyal Italian forces in a seventy kilometre beach-head on the north coast of Crete extending from Kastelli in the west to Georgioupolis in the east and enclosing the airfield at Maleme, Soudha and the Akrotiri peninsula.*

Italian troops from Ierapetra, Sitia, Neapolis and Malia were withdrawn in sequence and by the end of the summer some twelve thousand Italians and twenty-five thousand German troops were garrisoned in the northern bridgehead. The vacuum left by the Italian withdrawal was filled by Cretan resistance forces, Porphyroyennis in Ierapetra, Colonel Plevres, the nationalist, in Sitia, Yanni Bodias in Neapolis and Bandouvas in Malia, so that, by early September the only two centres in eastern Crete held by the Germans were Elounda and Heraklion.

Between the 1st and 4th May, 1944, as a reprisal for the capture of General Kreipe, Manfred Schmidt ordered the destruction of four villages west of Heraklion. As the hot summer months progressed Cretan resistance became more positive but successful attacks, mainly by communist andartes *and especially those culminating in loss of German lives, led to drastic reprisals by Colonel General Schmidt's forces. Italian evacuation to eastern Crete into the Khania-Soudha beach-head was condoned by the* andartes *without molestation, but smaller German units were frequently ambushed and sniped at and, as the summer progressed, the frequency and venom of the attacks increased.*

During the first week of August twelve German soldiers were shot at Rethymno and the following week a group of twenty-two infantry men were ambushed and shot at Anoyia. General Schmidt's response was immediate and drastic and between the 21st and 30th August a mechanised force of over a thousand Germans perpetrated the Amari valley massacre, destroying eleven villages and executing over a hundred and seventy Cretans and, at Yerakari, known to be a resistance centre, all forty-three inhabitants were shot.

A conference between the communist ELAS commanders and the nationalist at Arkadi on the 8th September counselled cessation of these attacks to prevent further senseless reprisals. But the ELAS commanders ignored the directive and killed twenty-six Germans at Rethymno on the 11th September and two days later a patrol of fourteen soldiers were shot at Psiloriti. The ELAS kapitans were now almost out of control and prospects of a Civil War in Crete loomed large on the horizon. On the 19th September General Otto Benthag was appointed commander of Festung Kriti and Colonel General Schmidt returned to Heraklion to supervise evacuation of the city. General Benthag's brief was to concentrate all German forces in Crete in Khania – Soudha beach-head and the Akrotiri peninsula. He was a benign commander and all German counter-resistance measures ceased on his arrival in Crete.

By November 1944 General Benthag was firmly in control in western Crete but most of eastern Crete, apart from Heraklion and Elounda, was held by Cretan resistance fighters. On Christmas Day, 1944 Fortress Elounda was evacuated and disbanded and, by the end of January 1945, most of General Benthag's troops in the Khania/Soudha bridgehead had been evacuated to Greece. Germany's occupation of Crete had lasted for three years less two months. The final act of capitulation occurred at Georgioupolis on the 31st March, 1945 when an exchange of prisoners was arranged between the remnants of General Benthag's bridgehead garrison and General Papadakis, the senior resistance kapitan in western Crete.

After Sergeant Hubbard's departure with General Kreipe's kidnappers, the three occupants of the cheese huts at Häraso suffered a distinct anti-climax and missed the influence of the dependable and level-headed sergeant who, at all times, acted as a stabilising factor in day-to-day activities of the hideout. Even the normally cheerful Biffo became morose and irritable and Corporal Dai kept away from the company of the other two commandos as much as possible. David, by nature a reserved and introspective person, sensed that his decimated commando was under great strain and in great danger of breaking up. For the first week after General Kreipe's abduction the roads around the hideout were swarming with German patrols. The small village of Koxari, two kilometres north-east of the farm, had a German platoon

640

in permanent occupation. Cretan resistance fighters in the region fled to their mountain retreats in the Diktis and German infantry were involved in fruitless searches of the foothills and olive groves.

During the daytime David withdrew his two commandos up into the steep escarpment behind the cheese huts where they commanded a good view of the olive grove, part of the farmhouse and the undulating fields and rocky outcrops between the hideout and the village of Koxari. On two occasions German troops were seen in the scrubland, combing and searching through the dense undergrowth. At night the commandos returned to the unwelcoming embrace and squalid stench of their uncomfortable bivouacs. And then on the eighth day the Germans withdrew westwards from Koxari and continued their searches across the plains south of Heraklion and into the eastern foothills of Mount Ida.

By the end of May conditions in the cheese huts were unbearable. David moved his men to a small barn at the edge of Spiros' farm, where the smell was only marginally better than in the huts. The lice and parasitic bugs were equally voracious but they were able to stretch out at night on beds of straw. The farmer at Häraso was not as accommodating as his namesake at Piskopiano and, contrary to Cretan custom, insisted on taking payment for their food and lodging. David sometimes wondered if he could be trusted, but Dai Griffiths insisted that, though he might be mean and over-cautious, Spiros was trustworthy. A monotonous diet, the sordid living conditions and boredom were taking their toll on Major David Green. He began to envy Sergeant Hubbard's escape and wished he had gone out with him and then came the single thought which strengthened his resolve to carry on. He still had a score to settle with the White Angel of Gournes. He would not leave the island until Colonel General Schmidt was eliminated.

By June 1944 the whole pattern of German and Cretan resistance activity in eastern Crete was changing. The Germans, now confined to their garrisons at Heraklion and Elounda, only ventured forth, in heavily armoured convoys, two or three times a week. The *andartes*, openly occupying the main towns, disappeared from view when the convoys passed through, and then reappeared in their former positions as soon as the Germans left. The Germans themselves believed that their policy of armed cordon and search attacks had driven the inhabitants out of the ghost towns. But now they hardly ever veered off the main northern coastal road and never ventured out of the safety of their barracks at night. South of the coastal strip between Heraklion and Aghios Nikolaos the *andartes* had freedom of movement both by day and by night. The town of Ierapetra was openly occupied by Porphyroyennis and, with the remnants of Samaritis' *andartes*, the Cretan *kapitan* also exercised some control at Aghios Nikolaos.

Such was the ferocity of Porphyroyennis' *andartes* that other *kapitans* and nationalist forces steered well clear of the two communist held towns. Yanni Bodias held sway in Neapolis, whilst Bandouvas' nationalists controlled Malia and were the main resistance forces investing and surrounding the German garrison at Heraklion. During the hot summer months of June, July and August 1944 the lesser roads, away from the coastal strip, were crowded with various groups of armed resistance fighters moving between the main centres in broad daylight.

Cretan tradition deemed that these groups passed each other on opposite sides of the road without exchanging words, or even a glance, and daylight skirmishes were a rare event. But during the hours of darkness anyone found abroad, armed or unarmed, was fair game. David quickly adapted to this new rule and conducted his sorties and visits during daylight hours prominently armed with a rifle and a bandolier of bullets with a dismantled Sten gun and a few hand grenades secreted inside his *sakouli* and crap-catcher trousers. Almost every day he left the farm at Häraso and travelled northwards to Gournes or to the suburbs of Heraklion, mixing with the locals and occasionally with bands of *andartes*. Meetings with groups of resistance fighters were always fraught with danger, as they often suspected that the lone, silent, grey-eyed intruder might be a traitor, or an informer. David made sure that he returned to the farmhouse by dusk.

Matters came to a head in mid-July. David had just returned from a sortie to Gournes and was sitting outside the barn looking at the rays of the setting sun when Biffo and Corporal Dai approached him.

"May we speak to you, Sir?" Biffo asked nervously.

"Of course, Biffo," David replied. "Come and sit here next to me. Now what's worrying you?"

"Well, Dai and I have been talking and we wondered if everything's all right with you? Are you feeling unwell, Sir?"

David looked him in the eye.

"I feel fine, Biffo. Come to the point, what's bothering you?"

Biffo blurted out, "Dai and I think we've done something wrong and we can't work it out, Sir."

David squinted at the setting sun and was lost in thought for a few moments.

"No, Biffo, Corporal Dai and yourself have not put a foot wrong. I've got a lot on my mind at the moment. We've been on this island a long time and I think it's about time we all went home." David paused and continued, "My dilemma is that I would go tomorrow if you two would come along but I also have some unfinished business," and David proceeded to tell his commandos about the blood brother ceremony and about his loathing for the blond German colonel whom he had seen destroying Pirgia and about his secret vow at that time to kill the White Angel of Gournes.

"So you see," he concluded, "I still have some work to do on Crete. At the moment my target is in Khania and we're not strong enough to go chasing him there. But I think he'll come back to Heraklion and when he does I'll be ready for him."

Biffo and Dai's attitude now rapidly changed. Biffo's face lit up in a broad smile.

"Why don't we go after him in Khania, Sir? Dai and I are ready for some action," and, looking at Dai, he added, "'ain't we, Corporal?"

The Welsh corporal smiled, his eyes flashing, "I'm sure we could do it if you lead us to the target. In any case I'm not leaving the island till the war's over and Biffo won't go home until you do, Sir."

David leant back against the barn wall and closed his eyes. The enthusiasm of his two companions for what might be a suicide attack was overwhelming. When he opened his eyes again he was near to tears.

"Very well, chaps. It's decided. We'll stay on here in Crete until the job's done. I'll have to do a few more recces to Heraklion and try and find out what the bastard's up to. I'll also be away for a few days to contact Cairo and see what they've got to say. So cheer up. We're in business again."

For the months of July, August and September 1944 the mundane existence of the commandos continued unabated. Biffo generally looked after the hideout. Dai helped the farmer goat-herding, milking and attending to the olive trees, whilst David spent most days on the roads. In mid-July he spent a night at Spiros' farm at Piskopiano. The cave hideout remained undiscovered by the Germans and the stores and equipment were intact. There was no news of Marita and whether she had become a mother.

Spiros explained, "Kastelli has been taken over by about two hundred of Yanni Bodias' men. The citizens, mainly women, have been forced to stay and look after the *andartes*. At the moment no one can get in or out of Kastelli. I advise you not to try and get through to Marita. The baby's due this month, or early next month. She's a strong girl and I have no doubt that she'll come here with the baby as soon as she's free to move."

David reluctantly accepted the counsel of the wise old Cretan farmer.

Contact at Tapes, 20th July, 1944

David reached the small mountain village of Tapes, high in the Diktis, in the early evening on the 20th July. The journey from his hideout at Häraso had taken two full days, walking only in the daytime along secondary earth tracks, but all the while pressing eastwards alongside the Heraklion to Aghios Nikolaos road. He met numerous Cretans, some armed, and on each occasion he obeyed the Cretan code, bypassing them on the opposite side of the road without an exchange of greeting or eye contact. On the second day, between Neapolis and Aghios, he saw a large, heavily armed German convoy proceeding eastwards, raising a cloud of dust as it sped along the road, the noise of revving engines shattering the silence of the hot, peaceful and still Cretan morning.

Tapes was a typical Cretan village perched on a small plateau, nestling under the almost perpendicular face of the eastern Dikti massif. As the crow flies the village was some eight miles inland and to the west of Aghios Nikolaos. Tapes had a small church, a taverna and some thirty one-roomed, whitewashed dwellings clustered around the square. David made his way to the taverna and purchased a *tsikoudia*, bread and cheese from a large, affable, heavily moustached patron. He took his meal and drink to a table in the shade of an orange tree, where he had a good view of the square, which was quite busy with black-clad women carrying water urns and Cretan men, some of whom came to the taverna for a drink and a chat. One or two of the younger men eyed him suspiciously and when the innkeeper came out to replenish his *tsikoudia* he was involved in some innocuous banter about olive crops and goats. The taverna seemed a popular place and David surmised that an ever increasing flow of thirsty male Cretans indicated a curious interest in the stranger who had arrived armed and alone in their village.

David was on his third *tsikoudia*, and had been sitting for over an hour, when two Cretans emerged from the taverna and one of them started whistling 'Greensleeves'. As they passed his table the taller of the two gave David a smile and a broad wink and then proceeded across the square to the only earth road in and out of the village. David settled his bill, thanked the patron, picked up his rifle and followed the men down the road. About four hundred yards outside the village, around a bend in the tortuous road, David found the two men standing in the middle of the path.

The taller man was smiling and spoke with an Oxford accent.

"Sorry, old chap, about the cloak and dagger business at the taverna, but SOE insist on it. We can't be too careful. We met on the beach back in February. This man with me is Psychoundakis, who speaks perfect English, thank God. I can't get the hang of this Cretan lingo."

The two men opposite David burst out laughing and he shook hands with each of them in turn. Paul guided the group into a shady copse on the side of the road and, squatting on their haunches, resumed conversation.

"Since the caper in April, Cairo has been bombarding me with messages for you. The last three have been cryptic and to the point. You are ordered to return to Cairo by the first available means. A few of the earlier wires suggested a recce of Elounda, where the Germans have a seaplane and possibly a U-boat base, but the last two messages were positive. Come home immediately. One of the cables suggested that there might be promotion in the bag."

For a few moments David digested the message and then replied, "Promotion, eh! The crafty powers that be know how to dangle a carrot. I wouldn't mind having a shufti at this Elounda place. It's on my way home and I might pick up some information."

Paul and Psychoundakis looked perturbed.

"Be careful around Elounda. My information is it's garrisoned by a battalion of German Paratroopers and they're first class soldiers. It's the brainchild of Colonel General Manfred Schmidt, the chap they call the White Angel of Gournes. Now he's a nasty bit of goods."

David answered, "I've heard of him, Paul. I'll look out for trouble. Any other news?"

Paul screwed up his red, blotchy face in thought and continued, "Oh yes, we've opened a second front in France. Our chaps and the Yanks landed in Normandy on the 6th June. As far as I can tell they're still stuck there at the moment, some trouble in the bocage, which sounds like the French word for a shithouse. The Russians, though, are pushing the Germans westwards through Poland. It looks as if old Adolf's number's up. Someone had a go at blowing him up a few days ago but apparently they failed. The bastard is still strutting around and shouting his bloody head off. Trust the bloody Germans to botch things up. Now let me think, any other news...? Oh yes, your man Hubby got across safely. He's the one that sent the message about your promotion. He also said that the two men with you can return to Alex without fear. They will not be court-martialled. On the contrary, they will probably be given a gong and sent back to Blighty."

David thanked Paul for the messages, shook hands and began his journey back to Häraso. At first he thought it uncivil of Paul Ransom not to ask him to stay a night or two at his hideout in the mountains above Tapes. But David soon realised that the whereabouts of Paul's wireless transmitter was best kept a close secret. As he retraced his steps to the hideout he had plenty of time to think and make his plans. He resolved not to let the boys know about his promotion. Furthermore, he would tell Biffo and Corporal Dai about the order to return to Cairo and of their immunity from prosecution if they decided to do so. From his own point of view, promotion or not, he intended to stay in Crete and see the job through to the very end. He gave Elounda a wide berth on his way back to Häraso.

As expected, Biffo and Corporal Dai would not hear of deserting their leader. As the Welshman explained, "It's all right for officers, Sir. But for the likes of Biffo and me it would be suicide. With due respect, Sir, I don't trust those bastards in Cairo and Alexandria. If they get their hands on us we'll be goners. After all I came to this island with nothing and I expect to go back to Alexandria with half of bugger-all"

David thanked the two for their loyalty and then announced, "In a couple of weeks we'll go for a trip. Jerry has a heavily guarded base at Elounda. I want to have a look at it."

Biffo, smiling cheerfully, commented, "Here we go again, Dai. A bucket and spade job. I hope we can have a dip in the sea this time. I noticed the other day that even the goats are turning up their noses when you're near them!"

Dai picked up a clod of earth and playfully threw it at Biffo. It was only when Biffo was scraping it off his shirt that they all realised that the missile was a semi-desiccated lump of goat dung.

Festung Elounda, Summer 1944

Before the war Elounda was an idyllic, peaceful, sleepy village some five miles north of Aghios Nikolaos, fringed on its landward side by lofty mountains and guarded on its seaward aspect by the island of Spinalonga, which created an elongated, mile-wide lagoon between the island and the mainland, a safe haven for Cretan fishing boats. The village was approached form the south by a cliff-edge road from Aghios Nikolaos and from the west by a tortuous, trans-mountain road from Neapolis, twelve miles away. By 1943 the occupying German forces had realised the potential of Elounda as a harbour for shipping and U-boats and also as an ideal sea-landing strip for flying boats. Colonel Manfred Schmidt was given responsibility for the development of Elounda as a base for naval shipping and planes and this he had done with energy and Teutonic thoroughness.

By the summer of 1944 Elounda was a true fortress in every sense of the word. There were gun emplacements at Plaka on the northern end of the lagoon and three other emplacements on the mountains ringing the landward approach to the fortress, one of these on the south side overlooking the road running from Aghios Nikolaos. In addition two artillery batteries were positioned at each end of the island of Spinalonga. Both the roads approaching the town were guarded by fortified pillboxes. The harbour was sometimes used by U-boats, frequently by E-boats and throughout 1943 and most of 1944 two flying boat flights from Khania arrived daily at the lagoon.

Since September 1943 Festung Elounda had been garrisoned by the four hundred and fifty strong Fifth Battalion of the *Fallschirmjagger*, but by the beginning of 1944, withdrawal of German soldiers to fight on the home front was taking its toll on the numerical strength of the defenders. By the time David and his two commandos arrived in Elounda in mid-August 1944 the German garrison in the fortress was down to three hundred and twenty men with a further platoon of thirty *Fallschirmjagger* in Aghios Nikolaos, existing cheek by jowl with Porphyroyennis' *andartes*.

On August 13th David led his two man commando alongside the coastal road to Neapolis and continued directly eastwards, skirting the northern slopes of Mounts Xera Xila and Arethiou, to reach the hamlet of Plaka at the northern end of the Spinalonga lagoon and about a mile north of the centre of Elounda. The three were heavily laden with spare Sten guns and ammunition clips, carried a rifle each and had overloaded *sakoulis* containing some food and a dozen hand grenades. Two heavily armed German convoys passed them by on the coastal road without incident. They reached their destination on the 16th August and made camp in a cave on the eastern slopes of Mount Arethiou, directly above the seaside hamlet of Plaka, which was the most northerly defended area in Festung Elounda.

From their vantage point David had an excellent view of the three mile stretch of the fortress and, with binoculars, he could spy on the German garrison in the harbour and in the fortified emplacements, which were arranged in a ring on the mountains behind the seashore, and on Spinalonga island. He observed the daily routine of guard changes, supply convoys from the sea and the arrival of a flying boat each day at dawn and its departure at dusk just before sunset. David soon established that the officer's residence was situated at the south end of the fortress perimeter, on the road to Aghios Nikolaos, and incorporated in a formidable array of bunkers and gun emplacements protecting the southern approach. His recce completed, after eight days at Plaka, David withdrew his commando and they returned to their hideout at Häraso without incident.

On arrival Biffo remarked, "Well, Sir, we're back to our shithouses again. I hope the bloody goats haven't been using them!"

Corporal Dai quickly riposted, "It doesn't matter if they have. The smell's the same with you around Biffo!"

David again resumed his reconnaissances to Gournes and Heraklion and twice called on Spiros at Piskopiano. Spiros was concerned about Marita but the situation at Kastelli remained unchanged. The hilltop fortress was resolutely held by Bodias' *andartes*. During a rare visit to Hersonisos Spiros had heard that two babies had been born in Kastelli in mid-August. He was not certain if one of them was Marita's. He had twice tried to get into Kastelli in broad daylight but had been turned away by well-armed troops at a road-block two kilometres north of the village.

The old man was again near to tears as, hugging David, he said his effusive farewells, "Don't worry. Marita will come to my home as soon as she can and you will then see your baby. Have faith my son."

As David left, Spiros and Anna were crying unashamedly.

*

"The White Angel is back in Heraklion."

The cry spread like wildfire amongst the conglomerate mass of predatory *andartes* milling around the outskirts of Heraklion and Gournes. The news set the whole army of irregulars alight with fervour and demands for revenge against the hated officer, and his men, who had destroyed their villages and was responsible for the death of so many of their comrades and loved ones. The lust for revenge was rife and many of the *andartes* urged their *kapitans* to undertake an immediate frontal assault on the depleted and beleaguered German garrison.

David heard the news in a taverna in Gournes on the 25th September. He returned to Häraso and began preparation for his commando to join in the assault on Heraklion in the hope that he might at least come face to face with his blood brother before the city finally capitulated. Heavily armed they reached the outskirts of Heraklion on the 29th September. The olive and orange groves in the fertile valleys south of the city were jam-packed with belligerent resistance fighters, all straining at the leash and hoping to be the first into the city to fight and destroy the Germans.

On the following morning, leaving Biffo and Corporal Dai in an orange grove, David went into Heraklion and mingled with the *andartes* occupying the buildings and streets inside the city walls. The German garrison of some two hundred and fifty men had withdrawn inside their harbour defences and were pinned down by encircling *andartes*. There was no fighting and both sides lay low, prepared for a cat and mouse confrontation. David pushed into the city as far as he could with safety and took up a position at the junction of two roads, keeping a wary eye open for enemy activity and for any unusual advances from the *andartes* hiding in the houses alongside the road.

The German positions, he was told, were some two hundred yards further along the road towards the harbour. He half lay, half crouched, behind a low wall at the roadside for over two hours, partially shaded from the blazing, noon-day sun by a low parapet. Suddenly three unarmed Cretans appeared walking up the road towards the junction, one carrying a white flag and shouting in Greek:

"I am Colonel Beteniakis. We have come to discuss a surrender. Fetch your senior *kapitan* here to meet us."

David watched, mesmerised, as the three slowly trudged up the road. They were indeed brave men and then, as they approached the junction, David was sure he recognised one of them. Doors and windows opened and, within a minute, the three peacemakers were surrounded by some thirty *andartes* prodding and pointing their loaded rifles at them. David jumped to his feet and gently edged his way towards the front of the militant throng and managed to catch the eye of a Cretan envoy standing to the left of the flag-bearing colonel. By now a commotion at the back of the cordon announced the appearance of a resistance *kapitan* or, at least, a senior officer. David did not bother to look around. He sidled up to the man he had recognised and spoke in English in a loud whisper, "Psychoundakis, where is the blond Angel?"

Psychoundakis' preliminary surprised look was soon replaced with a brief smile of recognition as he replied in perfect English, "He's flown the nest. He left for Elounda today before dawn by sea. We're glad he's out of the way. Now we can get on with trying to arrange an armistice."

The shouting grew louder as David slowly extricated himself from the surging mass around the frightened emissaries. He waited long enough to hear the *kapitan* demanding the head of the blond Angel of Gournes and promising his followers that all armed German soldiers would be shot on sight.

"And what will you do with the unarmed soldiers?" asked Colonel Beteniakis.

The flummoxed *kapitan* had no ready answer.

"We'll deal with them afterwards, but first you must produce General Schmidt for us. It'll be a proud day when we, the men of Yanni Bodias, go out of here with the White Angel of Gournes as our prisoner."

David gently eased his way up the road and out of Heraklion. At least he now knew where his adversary had gone. He would follow with all speed. As he left the town he silently prayed that Georgiou Psychoundakis would not be lynched by his fellow Cretans at the road junction. They would need men of his calibre to look after their affairs at the end of the war.

"Well, chaps, the target has moved to Elounda. We'll pack up camp here and take all the arms and ammunition we can carry to the cave at Plaka. Don't bother packing food. We'll live off the land as we go along. We'll also need ropes and binoculars and plenty of water to last two days. We'll move out at first light tomorrow."

Biffo and Corporal Dai were pleased to hear David's voice reassuming the authority it seemed to have lost since the departure of Sergeant Hubbard. They were both ready for action and packed their armaments and supplies with alacrity. At dawn on the 3rd October, 1944 they crossed the Hersonisos to Kastelli road, moving eastwards, and encountered hordes of Bodias' communists, displaying a red feather in their *sarikis*, moving northwards towards the 'kill' at Heraklion. Three days later Marita came down the same road carrying her six week old baby girl and leading little Spiros by the hand. They reached Spiros' farm at Piskopiano on the 6th October. By that time David and his two-man commando were established in their last and final hideout in a small cave on the slopes of Arethiou mountain, two kilometres above the German fortified village of Plaka at the northern end of fortress Elounda.

Chapter Thirty
Festung Elounda,
October – December 1944
Slaughter on Krikri

Colonel Manfred Schmidt was in a foul mood. He and *Feldwebel* Schneider had returned from Khania by sea on the 23rd September to find the wolves gathering at the ramparts. Many resistance groups, mainly Anoyians, had infiltrated the city. Others were outside the walls – to the west, Petrakageorgis, and to the east, Bandouvas, Yanni Bodias and Colonel Plevres. Manfred was incensed to find that Major Oberhaus had been evacuating troops daily and that there were now only four hundred men available to defend the city. The German bridgehead had contracted into a half-mile area around the harbour excluding the airfield which was by now of little military importance. Major Oberhaus had ensured that the main road from the harbour westwards to Rethymno through Khania gate was well protected. It was the only overland route of escape for the beleaguered garrison. The sea route was still open for smaller supply and naval vessels but, due to increasing British naval patrols and air activity, that route was becoming more hazardous daily. Manfred complimented Major Oberhaus on the disposition of his depleted forces. They both agreed that Heraklion was doomed to fall and Major Oberhaus, through Colonel Beteniakis, the head of the Committee of Civil Advisors, was in contact with the *andartes' kapitans* hoping to arrange an unopposed withdrawal of the German garrison.

Manfred sat on the edge of his bed, drinking compulsively and reviewing the change in fortune which had led to his demotion. General Benthag expected him to oversee the capitulation of

Heraklion, but he was damned if he was going to allow the *andartes* to capture him alive. He recalled how, after the abduction of General Kreipe, he had been promoted to colonel general and became the most powerful German on Crete. He had dealt with the western Cretan *andartes* ruthlessly, personally ordering the destruction of four villages around Yerakari after the abduction and, later in August, he eradicated all resistance at Anoyia and Amari Valley. All these massacres had been conducted with the connivance and approval of OKW headquarters in Berlin and his status with the Führer had been correspondingly enhanced. At the moment he felt it would only be a matter of time before he became a full general. He had basked in the glory of his elevated status and power and then, out of the blue, Berlin had sent out a new general who had never seen active service. General Benthag was a conciliator and compromiser and there was no place in his command headquarters for a man who practised strong arm tactics. General Benthag arrived in Khania on the 17th September and by the 20th had demoted Manfred and sent him packing to eastern Crete, where he would not prove an embarrassment for the Khania command. Well, he, Manfred Schmidt was not going to take all this lying down. He would show General Benthag and OKW in Berlin what a true Nazi commander, with determination and grit, could achieve, despite overwhelming odds. He sipped his cognac and made his plans.

Manfred called for a conference of all officers in Heraklion bridgehead on the morning of the 29th September, 1944 at Major Oberhaus' headquarters. Accompanied by *Feldwebel* Schneider he marched into the small map room and, imbued with the importance of the occasion, he wore his black SS uniform and had re-promoted himself to the rank of colonel general, displaying plum-red flashes on his lapels and an extra star on his epaulettes. As he began to speak he sensed the tension and uneasiness amongst his audience.

"Gentlemen, the situation here in eastern Crete is getting desperate. Demands from Berlin on our garrison at Heraklion have been excessive and have resulted in reduction in our unit strength to three hundred and eighty men, which is not sufficient to maintain an effective defence. Evacuation is inevitable. I have discussed the matter with Major Oberhaus and he agrees with me. It's now only a question of timing. Through his own channels Major Oberhaus has made contact with the Cretan *kapitans* and we may be able to negotiate an evacuation within the next fourteen days. However, my presence here, for various reasons, may compromise the negotiations. I have therefore decided on the following course of action:

"One – as from today Major Oberhaus is promoted to colonel and will command the evacuation. On the appointed date you will leave Heraklion and proceed by road to Rethymno and then on to our fortress in Khania/Soudha where you will come under the command of General Benthag.

"Two – tomorrow I shall leave by sea for Elounda and take command of the fortress there.

"Three – Lieutenant Otto Klemper of the *Kriegsmarine* will take my party in the two E-boats left in the harbour. The E-boats will not be returning.

"Four – before you leave Heraklion you are to destroy all installations, ammunition depots, and any arms and vehicles which you are unable to take with you.

"Five – those officers not on duty are ordered to attend a farewell dinner, prepared by Sergeant Schultz, at this mess at 1900 hours tonight. Be sure to be there as Sergeant Schultz will be leaving with me in the morning.

"And now, gentlemen, all that remains is to wish you the best of luck, and to thank you for your loyalty and exceptional courage in defending this garrison for the past three and a half years. I assure you that your sterling efforts have been recognised in Berlin and by our Führer. Heil Hitler."

Manfred's leaving party was a dismal affair. Sergeant Schultz's food, as always, was excellent but there was little to celebrate and the enthusiasm of the participants was dampened by the impending disaster that lay ahead and chastened by the possibility that they might be captured, or killed, by numerically superior and militant Cretans lying in wait on the road west to Rethymno.

The newly appointed Colonel Oberhaus was only too pleased to be at the dockside at 0400 hours on the following morning to salute and wish *bon voyage* to General Manfred Schmidt. At least, departure of the White Angel of Gournes from the scene, would facilitate his chances of negotiating a successful evacuation for his beleaguered troops. He hastened back to his headquarters and lost no time in ensuring, through informers, that the news of General Schmidt's departure was imparted to the Cretan *andartes*.

Festung Elounda, 30th September, 1944

Colonel Adolf Lindermann was at Elounda harbour a full hour before daybreak on the 30th September, pacing anxiously up and down the jetty, awaiting arrival of a seaplane flight from Khania, which had not materialised for the past two mornings. He was expecting orders from General Benthag and wondered why Colonel General Schmidt, who regarded the paratroopers in Elounda as his own private army, had not contacted him. He was concerned about the safety of his thirty-man platoon in Aghios Nikolaos. They had been forced to withdraw into the town's police station and had a dozen heavy lorries and two troop-carriers under guard in the vehicle compound. Cristos Bourdzalis, Porphyroyennis' lieutenant at Aghios, and his men were getting restless and Colonel Lindermann feared that very soon the German detachment would have to be withdrawn and, if the *andartes* pressed on fortress Elounda, he might be forced to surrender or evacuate the garrison by sea. These were worrisome days.

He continued pacing up and down, deep in thought, when suddenly the officer on watch shouted, "Two E-boats approaching the western entrance at speed and making for the jetty."

Colonel Lindermann snatched the binoculars and, after a few moments scanning and readjusting the lenses, picked up two surface craft appearing out of the swirling, early morning mist. Their progress was rapid and soon he was able to see the number on the bow of the leading vessel, E-533. Colonel Lindermann dropped the binoculars and ran down to the jetty to receive his visitors.

The two powerful E-boats sidled up to their moorings and were secured by the sailors. The first person to disembark was Lieutenant Klemper, closely followed by *Feldwebel* Schneider. The *Kriegsmarine* lieutenant and paratrooper colonel exchanged salutes and greetings and then turned to face the boat, where, at the top of the gang plank, Colonel General Manfred Schmidt stood unsteadily, saluted, 'Heil Hitlered' and walked leaden-legged down to the jetty. Manfred was feeling queasy after the previous night's drinking and the gyrations of the speeding E-boat during the voyage from Heraklion.

"Colonel Lindermann, take me to your command post. I want an urgent briefing of the situation here in Elounda. Get your company commanders to meet me in an hour."

Once alone with his *Feldwebel*, Manfred gulped down two large mugs of strong black coffee, wiped his sweating brow with a handkerchief and spoke.

"I don't like E-boat journeys at the best of times but this morning's mad dash has left me feeling sea-sick. I think that bastard Klemper enjoys giving me a rough ride. I can tell you now, Schneider, Heraklion is doomed and will fall within seven days. We have a better chance of survival here. The troops are largely from our own regiment and they will obey my orders. We will put up a good fight if we have to and can last out the war until the Führer wins in Europe and our forces once again reoccupy the whole of Crete. I fear General Benthag has the wrong idea. He's hell-bent on evacuating the Khania bridgehead. If he does, it will leave us as sole occupying forces. We must build up the spirits and resolve of our *Fallschirmjägger* to defend this small part of Crete to the last man. Colonel Lindermann is a good officer and I can rely on him to carry out my orders. Lieutenant Klemper doesn't know it yet, but his two E-boats will remain with us here in Elounda. That's just in case we need to get away in a hurry. I hope that won't be necessary. I hate the E-boats when they go flat out."

During the time Manfred was speaking they heard a plane circling low over the harbour and, through the window, saw a seaplane swooping down to land smoothly in the lagoon and taxiing towards the jetty. By the time the conference had been convened Colonel Lindermann arrived with a directive from Khania headquarters, which he immediately presented to the newly arrived colonel general. General Benthag's message was short and to the point.

"Start evacuation of Elounda immediately. Send out fifty men each day. Use fishermen's boats and caiques. Abandon Aghios Nikolaos. All troops to be directed to my command in Khania."

Manfred read and re-read the telegram, whilst the other officers remained silently expectant.

"Gentlemen, I will let you know the contents of this message from Festung headquarters later. I am here to defend Festung Elounda to the last man. I have the Führer's authority to do so," he lied and continued, "and the defences of the fortress are such that we will be able to withstand enemy attacks from land, sea and air. On the landward side we are near impregnable and the gun emplacements on Spinalonga will repulse attacks from the sea. We are protected from enemy air strikes by the high mountains behind us and the fortified hills of Spinalonga. We have ample guns, ammunition and food supplies and, if necessary, we could hold out for a year. In my estimation it would take a fully equipped and expertly trained division to winkle us out of Elounda. I supervised the erection of this fortress and now I have returned to defend it to the bitter end."

Manfred paused for a long while and let his words sink in.

"I demand your word as gentlemen and officers that you are with me whole-heartedly in this enterprise." He paused again listening to the murmuring of assent from his paratrooper company commanders and then continued, "Return to your companies and pass on the message to your men. Don't forget comrades – *Rot Scheint Die Sonne.*"

Manfred's moving address had the officers on their feet, pledging their support to the tall, blond, commanding general. Manfred savoured the occasion for a full minute and added, "By the way, I promised to tell you the contents of General Benthag's message. He wishes us to pull out of Elounda as quickly as possible. I shall obtain permission from General Student and OKW in Berlin to fight on. The reply to General Benthag will be delayed for two, or three, days. I'll leave it to your imagination to guess what that reply will be. We shall meet here for a conference every day at 0800 hours. You may now return to your duties. You are all invited to dinner at my residence tomorrow night at 1900 hours. Sergeant Schultz should, by then, have the mess in order. Heil Hitler," and the conference was dismissed.

Colonel Lindermann sat, red faced, on a chair facing the general. Half apologetically he asked the question, "General Schmidt, Sir. You mentioned your residence. What have you in mind?"

Manfred exploded. "In mind, in mind, Colonel Lindermann? You know where I want my residence. I have earmarked the villa at the top of the hill. That's where I want my residence and that's where we will have our dinner tomorrow night."

"But, Herr General," the colonel persisted, "the villa is at the very edge of our defensive perimeter and on the open road to Aghios. Porphyroyennis' men are constantly patrolling the road. I have made my headquarters here in the harbourmaster's house. May I respectfully suggest you take this house and I'll move elsewhere. At least you'll be at the centre of our defences."

Manfred glanced at the unfortunate colonel.

"No, you may not respectfully suggest that I move in here. Get some men up to the villa and help Sergeant Schultz prepare it for me. I will move in tomorrow."

The colonel persisted half-heartedly, "It'll mean displacing a whole company who are using the villa as a dormitory."

By now Manfred was in a rage and shouting.

"I don't care if you have to kick out the whole bloody German army. I want the villa for my personal use."

"Very well, Sir," replied the crestfallen paratroop colonel. "I'll see to it," and he took his leave.

As ordered, the villa was prepared for the general's occupation in two days and Manfred and his staff moved in on the 3rd October. On the 4th October, Manfred received a signal from *Oberkommando der Wehrmacht* headquarters in Berlin approving his plan to hold Elounda at all costs and to fight to the last man and confirming his promotion to full general. He had great pleasure in winging a signal to Khania headquarters on the following day:

"From General Manfred Schmidt to General Benthag, Commander HQ Khania. By direct order of OKW Berlin I have assumed command of Festung Elounda. Stop. Further evacuation from this command will cease. Stop. Elounda will be defended to the last man and last bullet. Stop. Will only accept further orders from Berlin. Stop."

Manfred felt pleased with his handling of the situation. His cable to Benthag's headquarters should put the general's nose out of joint and he imagined the consternation it might cause. There was nothing General Benthag could do about it. He would now have to accept that there were two commanding generals in Crete and that the important one, and the one supported by the Führer, was General Manfred Schmidt, commander of Festung Elounda.

Villa Olous

The villa Manfred had selected as his residence had some good points and some downright dangerous aspects. Villa Olous was a flat-roofed, two-storey building which had been built by a quarry manager in 1937. Quarrying for granite and limestone had been going on in the area for over a century and excavations had left a flat-topped plateau astride the coastal road from Aghios Nikolaos to Elounda.

The villa was built on a large excavated site, fifty metres above the coastal road with a narrow curved earth-road leading down from the courtyard to join the main road. Its front faced the sea and from the flat roof there was a spectacular view of the town and harbour of Elounda and the long, ragged, island of Spinalonga on the other side of the lagoon. When the Germans occupied the area in June 1941 they had commandeered the villa, erected pill boxes and gun emplacements on the rocky spur on the seaward side of the road and also positioned Bofors guns on the villa's roof.

The advantages of the villa were an uninterrupted view of Elounda and Spinalonga, its use in defence from air attacks on the lagoon and proximity to the entrenched defences some forty yards across the road at the front of the villa. Its disadvantage was its nearness to the limits of the fortress defences and limited access by a steep, pitted, earth-road. A sheer fifty metre, excavated, cliff at its western end formed a boundary to the paved courtyard. Twenty metres up the rock face engineers had blasted a ledge into the side of the cliff, sufficiently deep to take a machine gun emplacement, which commanded a field of fire encompassing the courtyard, the front entrance to the villa and the earthen approach road. The courtyard was spacious and on each side of the house there were flattened vehicle parks. The ground floor of the villa had four large rooms, each with a wide marble verandah and on the first floor there were five bedrooms facing the sea. Manfred's taste for comfort and elegance had been stimulated by his occupancy of Villa Ariadne and this smaller version suited his purpose admirably. The dinner on the 4th October, 1944 was to celebrate his new residence and his promotion and he set out to make certain that the participants would remember the occasion for many years to come.

As October 1944 wore on, Manfred's daily routine became established. His orderly, Otto, awoke him at precisely 0700 hours with a mug of steaming black coffee. He then shaved and showered, and dressed at a leisurely pace. At exactly 0750 *Feldwebel* Schneider presented himself at the front door and conveyed the general in a *Kübelwagen*, shepherded by two armed motorcyclists, down the winding hill to arrive at Colonel Lindermann's headquarters at exactly 0800 hours. Attendance at the briefing was compulsary to all ranking officers in the fortress, with the exception of those on duty at Aghios Nikolaos, the road junction at Epano Pines and the barricade on the main Aghios road. The companies guarding these important positions and the platoons at Aghios Nikolaos and on Spinalonga changed every two, or three, days.

At the conference each company and platoon commander reported on activities over the preceding twenty-four hours. Disturbing reports continued to come in about the plight of the garrison platoon at Aghios Nikolaos, where the Germans were virtually held in a vice, confined to the police barracks and parade ground, while Porphyroyennis' armed *andartes* wandered freely around town, which became a no-go area for General Schmidt's paratroopers. Every three days a heavily armed convoy ran the gauntlet to relieve, supply and replace the encircled paratroopers. After the conference the general and *Feldwebel* Schneider returned to Villa Olous for a long leisurely breakfast. At around 1100 the general's small cavalcade moved around the fortress inspecting gun emplacements and bunkers and crossing the lagoon in a motorboat to the defensive positions on Spinalonga. A light lunch was taken in the field and the general returned to his villa by 1500 for a two hour siesta. At 1700 the second visit to Colonel Lindermann's headquarters took place, when the orders for the following day were drafted and any messages from Khania were either dealt with or, more often than not, completely ignored. General Schmidt then drove back to his villa to arrive at around 1800 hours. The general, always in mess dress, dined at 1930, mostly alone, occasionally with *Feldwebel* Schneider and once a week with Colonel Lindermann and off-duty officers. His evening ended with a large cognac, which the general took on to the balcony of his bedroom, or the flat rooftop, and then to bed at 2230. This routine was inflexible and only broken on mess nights when an extra hour's drinking time was allowed for his guests.

At around 9 p.m. one evening in mid-October Manfred and *Feldwebel* Schneider sat out on the balcony in their overcoats, sipping large cognacs and discussing old times, when Manfred leapt to his feet and turned to face his trusty *Feldwebel*.

"Schneider, I'm worried about our platoon in Aghios. It's only a matter of time before the bandits pluck up enough courage to have a go at our boys. It's important we should keep our men in Aghios as long as possible. Their presence there occupies a large number of Porphyroyennis' men and takes a lot of heat off Elounda. Porphyroyennis will not attack here as long as we have a platoon in

Aghios. He doesn't realise that we only have three hundred and forty paras in Elounda. Think of it, Schneider! I'm a general in command of three hundred and forty men. It must be the smallest division in history." Manfred paused and took a large gulp of brandy. "No one else but you knows this, Schneider. I met Porphyroyennis in June 1942. He's a real crooked bastard, cunning and devious, but I managed to do a deal with him then and, if I could meet him, I think I might get him to co-operate with us now. When I last met Porphyroyennis I was a mere captain. Now that I'm a full general I will play with his vanity. But how can we arrange such a meeting?"

Schneider thought deeply for a few moments and sipped his cognac.

"If you give me three days, Sir, I'll go into Aghios with the next convoy and see what I can do."

And so it was arranged. *Feldwebel* Schneider slept in the police barracks at Aghios Nikolaos for four days. Early on he contacted a fat, cross-eyed Cretan police sergeant, who accepted bribes with alacrity and was sergeant in charge of a small office which the Cretan police were allowed to occupy in the compound. At first the sergeant vehemently denied any knowledge of resistance *kapitans* active in Aghios but, within two days, he offered to produce a spokesman. The meeting was arranged in the police sergeant's office. The *andartes'* spokesman from the turned out to be a shifty, verminous runt who was more interested in the bribes being showered on him than in *Feldwebel* Schneider's request. Schneider threw him out of the office.

"Send a senior officer tomorrow. I will only to speak to Porphyroyennis' lieutenant."

On the following evening the runt returned with an equally unsavoury small, vicious looking man whose only badge of rank was a piece of red silk sewn onto the crown of his *sariki*. He was heavily armed and had hand grenades in the pockets of his tunic. His only saving grace was that he spoke some halting German.

Schneider insisted. "I want Porphyroyennis, and only Porphyroyennis, to meet my general."

The Cretan replied, "Impossible, impossible."

Schneider thrust a bottle of cognac into his hands.

"Make it possible. Bring your *kapitan* to meet me here."

The two left in a hurry and were back in ten minutes with a large, handsome, ox-like man with piercing black eyes and a drooping moustache.

"I am Bourdzalis. I am the *kapitan* here, not Porphyroyennis. I will meet your general," and without invitation he picked up two full bottles of cognac and four cigarette packets.

A deal was struck. Bourdzalis would meet General Schmidt in a taverna at Elenika, halfway between Aghios Nikolaos and Elounda. The date of the meeting was 17th October, 1944.

On the appointed day, at twelve noon, a whole company of paratroopers accompanied General Schmidt to the meeting place. They moved south from Elounda and placed machine guns at strategic points along the road. Manfred arrived in an armoured vehicle. The *andartes* were already in position on the south side of the village square and Bourdzalis and two of his henchmen sat, rifles across their knees, at the door of the village taverna. Manfred, dressed in his black SS uniform and accompanied by *Feldwebel* Schneider, strode purposefully across to the seated *kapitan*, while the rival forces, forty yards apart, glowered at each other, guns at the ready. Bourdzalis got up, visibly impressed and overawed by the rank and finery of the blond giant of a general bearing down on him. Manfred was the first to speak.

"Do you represent all the *andartes* in Aghios Nikolaos?"

"Yes," the man whimpered. "I, Bourdzalis, speak for all my comrades."

Manfred looked with scorn at the cringing Cretan *kapitan*.

"So you're Bourdzalis. Where is Porphyroyennis? I will only speak with a senior *kapitan*."

"But I am the senior *kapitan*, Herr General," the cowering *kapitan* replied.

"No," said Manfred using the power of his voice so that all could hear, "Porphyroyennis is the senior *kapitan* in Aghios Nikolaos. I am a *Wehrmacht* general and will only speak to Porphyroyennis. It's an insult to send a minor *kapitan* to meet me. Unless you produce Porphyroyennis there'll be no deals," and with that he turned on his heel and strode back to the armoured vehicle.

The German convoy then withdrew to their Festung to await events. Three days later, on the 20th October, an emissary appeared with a white flag at the southern barricade of the fortress and stated that Porphyroyennis was in Aghios Nikolaos and wished to meet the German general to discuss surrender terms. This request infuriated Manfred. He sent the unfortunate *andarte* packing with a message in reply that there would be no surrender and that the German army was here to stay. Two days later another flag-bearing emissary arrived

"General Porphyroyennis will be pleased to meet General Schmidt at Elenika in two days' time for discussions."

Manfred thought with a grimace, 'So he's promoted himself to general now?'

The meeting between Manfred and Porphyroyennis took place at noon on the 22nd October, 1944 in the taverna at Elenika. The two generals shared a bottle of *tsikoudia* and a bottle of best cognac. Though Manfred could not trust his adversary he had a strange admiration for the man's native guile and cunning. Porphyroyennis did most of the talking.

"As you know, Herr General, Heraklion fell on the 11th and Rethymno was evacuated on the 13th of this month. Your little garrison at Elounda are the only remaining German troops in eastern Crete."

Manfred replied, "Let me remind you, General Porphyroyennis, that my garrison at Elounda is over twelve hundred strong and they're all paratroopers and we're here to stay for a long time."

"I understand," the *kapitan* replied with a sidelong grin. "My interests are in Heraklion and Neapolis. I already hold Ierapetra. I want to be rid of Bandouvas and Yanni Bodias and take Heraklion and possibly Rethymno. I have three thousand men ready to fight. I need arms and ammunition. If you supply me, I'll leave you alone in Elounda."

Manfred thought pensively for a moment.

"And what about Aghios Nikolaos?"

"Well," the *kapitan* replied, shifting his gaze to the floor, "We should be able to live together there. I have promised the town committee that I will liberate Aghios but I will persuade them to change their minds. But let me tell you, Herr General, if the rifles are not coming soon I won't be able to control my men in Aghios and your troops will be eliminated."

Manfred drew himself to his full height and glowered at the Cretan.

"If your men kill or injure one of my troopers I will unleash my division from Elounda and wipe Aghios Nikolaos off the map."

The meeting was at a point of stalemate, neither man prepared to concede an inch, when Porphyroyennis, desperate to acquire guns, suggested that Manfred should withdraw his troops from Aghios and leave their guns for the *andartes*. Manfred played for time.

"I agree to that. We'll fix a date for the withdrawal of our men, but I want all your resistance fighters outside the town when we pull out. We'll leave all guns and supplies in the lorries in the police barracks."

"Agreed," beamed Porphyroyennis and they shook hands and, even as they did so, they were both planning a double cross.

Porphyroyennis would make sure that only a part of his forces left Aghios clear for the German withdrawal and Manfred began making his plans to deny Porphyroyennis the arms he so desperately needed. The date of withdrawal from Aghios was to be the 10th November, 1944.

The Slaughter on Krikri island

On Friday night each week General Schmidt held a mess dinner at Villa Olous for the officers at the garrison and the 5th November, 1944 was no exception. Manfred gathered nine officers at his table, including *Kriegsmarine* Lieutenant Klemper. Sergeant Schultz prepared an excellent meal and the wine flowed freely and by coffee time a heated argument had developed between a young paratroop captain and the naval lieutenant. Captain Grenz, a specialist marksman, and a *Wehrmacht* shooting champion was disdainful of naval training in the art of rifle shooting. The inebriated lieutenant insisted that he could personally out-shoot any paratrooper Captain Grenz cared to nominate. The two young officers became so embroiled and vociferous that General Schmidt thought it best to intervene.

"Come, come now, gentlemen, there's no need for this argument. We can put your abilities to the test. We'll go across to Krikri island tomorrow and see which one of you can shoot the greatest number of goats. Shall we meet on the pier at nine o'clock after the morning conference?"

The two young antagonists backed down and ceremoniously shook hands with each other. The dinner ended amicably with the adversaries placing wagers as to which one would have the largest bag.

Krikri island lies three quarters of a mile off-shore opposite the harbour at Aghios Nikolaos. A small, barren, rocky mass of scrubland, Krikri was the sole surviving habitat for a near-extinct breed of mountain goat. The goats themselves were small, black bearded, agile and elusive and the inhabitants of Aghios had for many decades used the little goat as a symbol on their coat of arms. The town council imposed a ban on hunting, or shooting, these minute wild ibex and, to enforce their decree, paid a miserable pittance to two shepherds to live on the island and guard the flock. The gnarled old men lived in cheese huts, one at each end of the half mile long island. Once a year, led by the mayor, half a dozen inhabitants from Aghios were invited across to Krikri for a selective cull of diseased, injured or elderly goats. It was an honour to be selected by the mayor to accompany him on the shoot. The 1944 cull took place in late September, when the young kids were weaned and were able to forage for themselves through the wet and stormy winter months. The goat population of Krikri was maintained at about two hundred and the Cretan shepherds were there to ensure that the goats were healthy and constant in number.

Manfred's shooting party arrived off Krikri island at around 10 a.m. on the 6th November and, as E-533 edged its way inshore, the party of four disembarked in a dinghy. Each took ashore a rifle and sub-machine gun and adequate supplies of *tsikoudia*, cognac, schnapps, bread and cheese to last the day. The two competitors, Captain Grenz and Lieutenant Klemper, were assigned half the island each and Manfred acted as umpire to the naval officer whilst *Feldwebel* Schneider accompanied the paratroop captain. During the morning many shots were fired, but the Krikri goats proved too shy and elusive and the end result was one kill for Captain Grenz and that, according to Schneider, was a hit from a stray ricochet. The marksmen complained that, though there were plenty of targets available, the goats' natural instinct to jump in the air and leap from rock to rock made an accurate strike impossible.

They declared the vendetta null and void and the whole party settled down to a long, leisurely lunch. After lunch Manfred planned a beat of the island, the four marksmen with machine pistols walking in line abreast and driving the goats across the rocky terrain.

Manfred explained, "There are plenty of the little bastards around the place and we can't really have a good goat stew with the puny little thing you shot this morning, Grenz! Let's see if we can get a few more of the little devils for the pot."

As they were about to leave with their loaded *Schmeitzers*, Lieutenant Klemper asked, "What do we do if the bloody shepherds get in the way? I nearly hit one this morning. He was hiding behind a rock."

Manfred, glassy-eyed and smiling, replied, "If the *Kretos* get between you and the goats let them have it."

The hunt commenced at around two o'clock. The four huntsmen walked slowly northwards across the island shouting, whistling, and beating the small bushes with their machine pistols. Startled goats dashed quickly away, leaping and bounding on the rocks, looking for sanctuary amongst the scrubland and boulders. And still the pursuing gunmen came steadily on, splitting the silence of the dank, sunless November afternoon with their whistles and calls which were clearly heard across the bay in Aghios. Within an hour the main bulk of the frightened, panicking animals had been shepherded into a confined area some two hundred metres square at the north-western end of the island. The ground was alive with darting brown bodies racing for cover, bumping into each other as they tried desperately to scurry away from the huntsmen. Manfred gave a signal and four *Schmeitzers* opened fire simultaneously. They couldn't miss. It seemed that every bullet hit a target and, more often than not, accounted for two, or sometimes three, goats. The fusillade and carnage lasted for three minutes. Bits of goat went flying through the air, a leg, a head, sometimes a whole animal as it leapt high in its death throes. Many of the defenceless animals jumped on to the rocks below, or into the sea, and were drowned.

Towards the end of the massacre a defiant shepherd walked across the line of fire and stooped to pick up two wounded goats, nestling them in his arms. He then deliberately started walking towards the German hunters. The question of who shot the shepherd was never resolved. The four guns were still blazing away when the proud Cretan crumpled in a heap on the dusty footpath, still clutching the injured, bleating goats. He died instantly in a pool of his own blood mixed with the injured animals' entrails and excreta. When the shepherd fell to the ground the shooting stopped abruptly and the Germans retreated slowly, the incessant bleating of the stricken *krikris* ringing in their ears. They left behind them a scene of incredible carnage. The dead shepherd was surrounded by striken and dying goats and there were pieces of goat flesh clinging to the rocks and bushes. On the way back to the E-boat the hunting party fell silent. They were conscious of the plaintive bleats of the stricken animals at their backs. Manfred tried to make light of the situation.

"Cheer up, lads. It's been a good day's hunting. We've got one *Kreto* and about fifty goats in the bag. You can't complain."

His companions were in no mood to be placated. They now felt remorseful and ashamed. Manfred made them drink a toast to celebrate their 'successful hunting operation', but the fiery liquid in their bellies only served to accentuate the guilt they felt at the cowardly deeds they had perpetrated that day on Krikri island. On the return journey in the E-boat Manfred estimated one hundred per cent eradication of the vermin on the island, but the other three were in no mood to argue logistics with the inebriated and slightly mad commander of Festung Elounda.

*

"What's going on?"

Porphyroyennis joined a group of local dignitaries numbly standing at the waterside in Aghios and looking eastwards at the indistinct mass of Krikri island. The mayor spoke.

"The Germans are on Krikri and they're shooting our goats. You can see them on top of that hill from time to time."

There had been some desultory firing during the morning. It was now 2.30 p.m. and, no shots had been heard for over an hour. Porphyroyennis, not being a native of Aghios Nikolaos, made light of the incident

"They're only playing around. Those goats are crafty customers. I don't expect the Germans will be good enough to hit any of them. Not like my Cretan snipers, eh Mayor?"

The Mayor had a worried look on his face. He could hear whistling and shouting emanating from the hilltops of Krikri and this, to the mayor, meant only one thing. The Germans were carrying out a systematic beat and then, at around three o'clock, his suspicions were confirmed when a staccato fusillade of shots at the northern tip of the island continued for three minutes.

"My poor *krikris*," the mayor cried, tears streaming down his face.

He turned to face the *kapitan* and spat out his words venomously, "General Porphyroyennis, the Germans must be made to pay for this. They have killed our sacred *krikris*. The people of Aghios will not stand for it. We want you to attack the police compound tonight. We will not tolerate the presence of Germans in our town a minute longer."

And the mayor's anger was further inflamed when, in the gathering gloom, an hour later, the second shepherd rowed his dead comrade into the small harbour. The mayor screamed at Porphyroyennis, "There's proof that the Germans were not just playing around on the island. Now will you make your men move? My people want revenge."

Porphyroyennis was pushed into a corner. He did not wish to attack the police garrison for fear of a long battle which would use up valuable ammunition, both his own and German bullets. He wanted to delay the action for five days, when, if his plan worked, he would inherit the police station and all its ammunition from the German general. But he had to do something to placate the truculent mayor and to act quickly. That night he brought in extra forces to closely invest the police station and the vehicle compound. His men were literally posted some twenty yards away from the wire fences around the police barracks. He also hastily constructed manned barricades across the Aghios/Elounda road at Xirocombos and Elenika. No further German convoys would be permitted along the coastal road until the 10th November when he would allow the Germans into Aghios, but intended they would not leave and return to Elounda and their arms and ammunition would be appropriated by his loyal *andartes*.

Evacuation of Aghios Nikolaos

In Fortress Elounda there was an air of intense anticipation. On the morning of 8th November a regular relief convoy on its way to Aghios had been turned back at Elenika after a brief skirmish with the *andartes* during which one paratrooper was slightly injured. General Manfred Schmidt was now not at all sure Porphyroyennis would keep his word and allow evacuation of his troops from the police compound. He would have to extricate his men urgently and outlined his plan at the 0800 conference on the 9th November.

"Captain Grenz will command the rescue mission. I have it on authority that the Cretan *andartes* will be clear of Aghios tomorrow. If we are held up at Elenika again we'll have to blast our way through. *Feldwebel* Schneider will lead in the Tiger tank and will be supported by a fifteen-man troop carrier. Captain Grenz will follow with four trucks, two empty and two carrying sixteen men each. Motorcyclist machine gunners will cover the convoy and take up positions along the coast road at one kilometre distance from each other. Once the Tiger reaches the town it will take up position on the bridge across the canal leading to the inland lagoon, to cover our retreat from the police compound. You are ordered to shoot anyone carrying a weapon and to shoot anyone who interferes with our withdrawal. There are twelve vehicles in the compound and they will have been loaded with men and equipment. All these lorries from the barracks are to be driven two hundred and fifty metres to the bridge and then dumped, fully equipped, into the two hundred foot deep lagoon. Our men from the police station, carrying only light arms, will load up in Captain Grenz's lorries and the whole convoy will make a dash back up the road to the fortress. The tank will have to be sacrificed. Dump it into the lagoon if you can, Schneider. An armoured troop carrier will bring up the rear of the convoy. To cover our withdrawal Lieutenant Klemper will position his two E-boats in the narrow straight between Aghios Nikolaos and Krikri Island," and with a sardonic grin directed at the *Kriegsmarine* lieutenant, "You will recall, Lieutenant Klemper, we did a recce there a few days ago. The evacuation plan goes into action at 0600 hours tomorrow. This plan will have to work if we are to rescue Lieutenant Kosterman and his platoon from Aghios."

On the following day the relief operation went without any serious hitches. The *andartes'* stronghold at Elenika offered no resistance to the armoured column. The paratroopers at the police station were expecting to drive their vehicles to the village square and leave them unattended, to be taken, with their valuable contents, by Porphyroyennis' men. They were only too pleased to be ordered to scuttle the heavy vehicles in the 'bottomless' inland lagoon.

Feldwebel Schneider managed to set the Tiger rolling downhill until it also disappeared with a mighty splash into the depths of the lagoon. Two of the lorries were abandoned at the barracks, one from lack of fuel and the other because of mechanical failure. Both lorries were fired and left burning and empty. There was some skirmishing and sniper fire from the hillside on the return journey, but the appearance of the tank had completely unnerved the normally stoic Cretan *andartes*. There were four German casualties. One driver was taken to the bottom of the lagoon imprisoned in his cabin, one paratrooper was shot through the shoulder by a sniper, a third man suffered a severe burn from the boiling radiator of one of Captain Grenz's trucks and Lieutenant Kosterman fractured his thumb when his hand became caught in the heavy metal jamb of a troop carrier. The whole operation was concluded in two hours, without significant interference from Cretan resistance fighters. On the 11th November, 1944 all three hundred and sixty-four German troops in eastern Crete were confined inside Fortress Elounda.

After the evacuation General Porphyroyennis was not clear where things had gone wrong. He had carried out his part of the bargain and withdrew his men from the town, but had not fully done so, and every house along the waterfront and the police barracks had armed observers. The sight of the Tiger tank and two E-boats in the bay unnerved his poorly equipped soldiers. And then the greatest humiliation of all, loss of the equipment which the German general had promised him. The bastard. He had reneged on their deal. Any fond hopes he entertained of re-floating the lorries were soon dashed when he learnt that the inland lagoon was two hundred feet deep and, according to the legend, bottomless. Yes, he had been tricked by the blond Angel of Gournes. Now he would get his own back on the German bastards. If only he had better rifles and plenty of ammunition! On the 11th November he ordered a parade of all his *andartes* at the police barracks. About a thousand men attended to listen to their general.

"I, General Spiros Porphyroyennis, stand before you and swear that I shall lead you to a victory against the German army at Elounda," loud cheers and cat calls. "We have been deceived by the Germans too often. Now we have the chance to strike back. We must move to Elounda and surround the Germans and then slowly, day by day, squeeze them into a smaller pocket until we eventually crush them out of existence. I will not rest until this has been achieved. Every German in Elounda must be shot. Take no prisoners. There will be a prize of two gold sovereigns for the man who brings me the head of General Manfred Schmidt, the one they call the White Angel of Gournes."

After the unopposed German evacuation, General Porphyroyennis' reign over the *andartes* in Aghios Nikolaos began to wane. The hasty dismissal of Bourdzalis and his well-armed militant supporters in late October, the failure of Porphyroyennis to react to the German atrocity on Krikri island, his incompetent mishandling of the German evacuation of the police headquarters and his inability to provide his men with rifles, produced a lack of confidence amongst his followers, who began to desert in droves. Bourdzalis and his group made for Heraklion where they tried to oust Yanni Bodias and take over control of ELAS forces. An argument between Bourdzalis and Bodias resulted in the latter being shot in the arm. Bourdzalis was arrested and, after a summary court martial, was executed by Bandouvas' *andartes*, two days after the fateful altercation.

When German occupation forces pulled out of Aghios on the 10th November, Porphyroyennis' *andartes* gave chase, but it was all too late. The Cretan *kapitan* could only muster about two hundred and thirty armed men and his opportunity of pressing home an attack on Elounda evaporated like the morning mists over Krikri island. The best he could do was to occupy Elenika and set up a formidable road block about two kilometres outside the perimeter of the defensive ring around Elounda, blocking the Elounda – Aghios Nikolaos road. Throughout November bands of loyal resistance fighters were deployed on patrol to the north of Elounda. Skirmishes occurred between *andartes* and German paratroopers and, at Epano Pines, on the mountain road to Neapolis, a pitched battle ensued between the adversaries on the 21st November. Three German soldiers were killed in this action and the *andartes* suffered a dozen casualties and one death.

The days were short, the weather cold and wet and not conducive to active belligerency. And day by day, a few Cretan fighters, their mood mirroring the weather, picked up their empty *sakoulis* and rifles and wandered away westwards, back to their farms and families, away from the battlefield, depressed and completely disillusioned with Porphyroyennis' ability as a field commander. There was nothing

Porphyroyennis could do to stop them. A Cretan peasant, once his mind is made up, is completely inflexible and overwhelmingly stubborn.

As General Porphyroyennis had his problems with manpower and lack of arms and ammunition, so General Manfred Schmidt faced a crisis within Festung Elounda. After the successful evacuation of their comrades from Aghios Nikolaos, morale within the fortress was high for about a week and then, like an inexorable cancer, gnawing doubts about progress of the war in Europe crept in and the home-sick paratroopers, most of whom had not been to Germany for over two years, began to accept the inevitability that Germany would lose the war. The Russians were pouring across the Danube and the Allies in the west were pushing towards the Rhine and into Holland. The battle-hardened paratroopers felt vulnerable and remote from the fierce battles that would soon be raging on German soil. They wanted to be in Germany where they could be effective in fighting and, if necessary, dying for survival of the Fatherland and the Third Reich. They were wasting their energy and risking their lives for a very small part of a remote island in the Aegean and doing so in order to satisfy the ego and fanatic ideology of General Manfred Schmidt.

Reports from the Fatherland that Germany now had a 'secret weapon', which Hitler claimed would bring Britain to its knees, were received with scepticism by the *Fallschirmjagger* rank and file. A victory over the British paratroopers at Arnhem in mid-September had gone some way towards restitution of morale in Festung Kriti but, by late November, talk of desertion and escape was rife amongst the imprisoned *Fallschirmjagger*. The first sign of mutinous intent occurred on the 24th November, 1944. Colonel Lindermann, usually punctiliously prompt, was twenty minutes late for the 0800 conference. He arrived flustered and agitated and immediately spoke up.

"I have to report, Sir, that Captain Brandt and fifty-nine *Fallschirmjagger* are missing. A caique was apparently commandeered last night and I believe they left the harbour in the early hours of this morning. They must be well out to sea by now. I can't imagine why Brandt took this action, but I do know that he comes from Dresden and he may well have felt his place is in Germany to defend the Fatherland."

Manfred took the news badly.

"So you think, Colonel, that Brandt wanted to get away to defend his home? I think he ran away. Captain Brandt and all the men with him are cowards. Where's Lieutenant Klemper? Order him to get out to sea and blast the caique out of the water. If they pick up any survivors, the only one I want to see is Captain Brandt. It will give me great pleasure to have him court-martialled and shot for desertion in front of the whole battalion."

As ordered, Lieutenant Klemper in E-boat 533 put out to sea in a gale and made a half-hearted sweep for thirty or forty kilometres north of Elounda. The caique was not discovered, much to the lieutenant's joy. He had no stomach for sinking a friendly vessel and causing death by drowning of sixty, or more, German soldiers. After four hours' sailing, in poor visibility, he gave up the search and on his return to Elounda suffered a tirade of verbal abuse from General Schmidt.

Manfred was still simmering after the waterborne desertion when, on the 27th November, a platoon of thirty-two men walked away from their strong point at Epano Pines. Their absence was discovered early in the morning when a relief platoon marched to the village only to find the sergeant in charge bound and gagged in a shallow trench. He reported that his platoon had simply walked out into the dark night up mount Xera Xila, taking their arms with them. Manfred's first reaction was that he should send a punitive squad after them but, accepting Colonel Lindermann's advice, he realised that armed Germans wandering around the Xera Xilas in broad daylight would be easy targets for the *andartes*. Within four days Fortress Elounda had lost, by desertion, one officer and ninety-one men and there was nothing General Schmidt could do to prevent this happening. Over the following months the defections continued in dribs and drabs, small groups leaving in rowing boats under cover of darkness and others simply deserting their posts and wandering away at night into *andarte* held territory.

Conditions in Fortress Elounda deteriorated rapidly during December. The Condor seaplane flights became less frequent and supplies brought in by sea were not sufficient to replenish food stocks and, in particular, fuel supplies for the E-boats and caiques. Manfred ordered curtailment of the use of E-boats and Lieutenant Klemper's boat, E 533, was withdrawn from commission, fully fuelled and kept in preparation for a dash to safety.

Christmas 1944 was rapidly approaching and Manfred's garrison strength was now down to one hundred and ninety-four men. Rationing was introduced and the outposts on Spinalonga dismantled and abandoned. The only check points held in any strength by the Germans were those at Plaka, Epano Pines and the Olous Battery protecting the general's villa and facing the main concentration of Porphyroyennis' men. Manfred wondered why the Cretan *kapitan*, boasting a strength of some three thousand men, had not attacked by now.

General Schmidt was aware that Porphyroyennis was having the same problems with desertion and that his effective strength of armed *andartes* was around three hundred. Added to this, Porphyroyennis' troops were in trouble at Ierapetra, where Bandouvas' nationalists attacked in force and drove the communists out of town. Porphyroyennis was in a quandary. Should he further reduce his forces in Aghios to rush off to relieve Ierapetra or should he stake all and hope to capture Elounda with its cache of German arms and ammunition? In the event he procrastinated and did neither and the inactivity on his part compounded his problems. Desertion had so weakened his forces that, at no time, did he feel strong enough to conduct an all-out assault on Elounda. The *andartes* in Aghios, fed up with lack of food and rifles and disillusioned by Porphyroyennis' inactivity, simply picked up their belongings and walked away to the west. Porphyroyennis' credibility as a Cretan general had gone into a sharp decline and even the opportunity for attack, occasioned by the abandonment of Spinalonga and other outposts by the Germans, did not encourage the vain and arrogant *kapitan* to lodge an all out assault. In November and December 1944 Porphyroyennis lost the chance of glory and of possibly becoming a potent post-war Cretan ELAS *kapitan*.

During the week leading up to Christmas 1944 Manfred and Colonel Lindermann had long meetings to discuss the possibility of evacuation of the Festung, or of surrender to the Cretans. Surrender was not an option for Manfred. He realised that his past misdemeanours, which at the time seemed noble actions for glorification of the Third Reich, might cumulatively result in his execution by the Cretans, if he were to be captured. He developed an urgent desire for survival, involving protection of his escape route from Elounda and patronising Lieutenant Klemper and his E-boats.

He had hoped that the Condor flying boats might prove an expeditious way out of the Festung, but, latterly, these flights into Elounda had ceased, as two of the Condors had been shot down by British aeroplanes, which were now operating from a Cretan airfield at Kastelli Pediados.

The final event which led to an irrevocable decision to abandon Elounda occurred on the 24th December, 1944. During the previous night Lieutenant Kosterman and eight of his platoon escaped from the harbour in the second E-boat, E-571 manned by Lieutenant Klemper's petty officer and four *Kriegsmarine* sailors. Loss of the E-boat, and more particularly of its fuel, was a severe blow to Manfred's evacuation plans. He was now left with one serviceable E-boat and two lightly armoured caiques with sufficient petrol to take his garrison possibly to the Greek mainland, but definitely as far as Santorini. At 10 p.m. on Christmas Eve the general convened an emergency meeting at Villa Olous. Six men stood around the table, including Lieutenant Klemper of the *Kriegsmarine* and *Feldwebel* Schneider.

"Gentlemen, I have come to the conclusion that we must evacuate Elounda within the next twenty-four hours. Our means of escape will be Lieutenant Klemper's E-533 and the two caiques. As of this morning our strength in the Festung is one hundred and thirty-nine *Fallschirmjagger*. The men will only carry light packs and rifles. All other equipment is to be destroyed. I'll leave it to you, Lieutenant Klemper, to prepare the E-boat and the caiques for sailing and *Feldwebel* Schneider and four men will mount a twenty-four hour guard on your boats. We shall leave tomorrow evening at dusk and get away under cover of darkness. Lieutenant Krebs will command one caique and Captain Grenz the other. Colonel Lindermann, *Feldwebel* Schneider, and Sergeant Schultz will come with me on the E-boat. The men are not to be told of the evacuation until two hours before we embark. The withdrawal will start in daylight at 2 p.m. with Lieutenant Krebs' platoon coming in from Plaka and the Epano Pines platoon joining them at the harbour, where they will form a defensive ring. At 4 p.m. Captain Grenz's company will evacuate the barricade on the Aghios road and retire past us here at the villa to join the gun battery at Olous and move quickly down to the harbour and board the caiques. Colonel Lindermann will be in charge of loading at the harbour and *Feldwebel* Schneider and I will look after the rear party at Olous. We'll be able to get down the hill very quickly in our

Kübelwagens. Everyone should be aboard fifteen minutes before dusk. Gentlemen, I picked Christmas Day because any British agents active in the area would never suspect that we would do anything silly at Christmas time. And now, Gentlemen, I want you to fill your glasses for a toast. I'm sorry it's only some foul Cretan wine but it's the best I can do. You can have some schnapps afterwards."

The general paused while the officers filled their glasses and then continued, "The toast is to a successful withdrawal from Elounda."

He proposed further toasts to the Fallschirmjagger and the Kriegsmarine. Each officer toasted his regiment but only the general and Lieutenant Krebs thought fit to toast Adolf Hitler, the ailing Führer and military commander of all forces of the Third Reich.

Chapter Thirty-One
Codforce in Festung Elounda
Christmas Eve 1944

When David, Biffo, and Corporal Dai returned to their hideout above Plaka on the 6th October, 1944 very little had changed in the routine of the German garrison at Elounda. The guards at the strong points and machine gun nests along the mountain ridges and the main road barricades at Plaka, Epano Pines and Olous changed every twenty-four hours, as did the artillery emplacements on Spinalonga. The flying boat arrived on schedule every day and the two E-boats in the harbour went to sea regularly for testing and patrolling. David noted the daily 8 a.m. accumulation of German officers outside a building near the harbour and on many occasions he identified Manfred in his binoculars. His pulse quickened at the sight of the tall straight-backed officer, with blond hair and dark glasses. He also noted that the *Kübelwagen* bringing his adversary to the harbour always came downhill from the German battery and look-out point on the flat promontory on Olous plateau and he assumed that the German officer's quarters were in the battery. One day he caught sight of Manfred's uniform and insignia and was taken aback and overcome with disbelief when he saw that he was a general.

'How could they promote such an idiot to this exalted rank?'

A quick mental calculation revealed the startling fact that the man he saw in his binoculars was only twenty-six years old. He must be the youngest general ever in the history of the German army.

Biffo guarded the base, whilst Dai went foraging in the local farmhouses and fields and most days managed to bring home some bread and milk and occasionally meat and fruit. David spent his time at various observation points along the ridges overlooking Elounda and

Spinalonga. The check-point and barricade at Plaka was strongly held and denied access to the fortress from the north. The hamlet at Epano Pines was occupied by a platoon of men whilst, in a semi-circle around the base of the lower slopes of Mount Arethiou and Xera Xila, the Germans had placed machine gun posts, each manned by six or seven paratroopers. Apart from the troops guarding the harbour and dockside, the main concentration of paratroopers was at the southern outlet from the fortress, where a company manned the pill boxes and gun emplacements on the flattened rock plateau opposite Villa Olous, astride the main road leading south to Aghios Nikolaos. Porphyroyennis' forward barricades were about two kilometres south of the villa.

Movement over open ground during daytime was difficult and dangerous and often produced a reaction from German machine gunners, who had orders to shoot at anyone moving around on the mountain slopes and tree covered valleys outside the defensive ring. During the night there was little danger from the Germans, who kept rigidly to their entrenched positions, but there was always the possibility of unexpectedly meeting patrolling *andartes*, who were trigger-happy and ready to shoot on sight, or sound.

David's excursions to and from his observation points were conducted under cover of darkness. By daybreak he hoped to be concealed at a vantage point in the mountains, which offered him the opportunity of observing German activity during the day within the fortress and on Spinalonga. The difficult area to observe was the villa itself, dug into the side of a limestone quarry and protected from view by a hundred and fifty foot rock cliff, which had a machine gun post on its crest. From a higher mountain promontory David identified the machine gun post but access to the villa meant a descent into a narrow valley, crossing a ravine and an ascent up the backside of the cliff in full view of the German machine-gunners.

October 1944 dragged on slowly for the three commandos in their cramped hideout above Plaka. The days were still warm but getting shorter and the nights colder. At least it was dry. Heavy rains and storms were expected in late November and December. David was away from the hideout most nights and luckily Biffo and Dai remained compatible companions. When together they exchanged stories about their younger days. Biffo recounted his school days and subsequent mercenary life on the dockland streets of London with vivid descriptions of his sexual prowess and conquests and brushes with the strong arm of the law. Dai related tales of the hard uncompromising life in a Welsh mining village in the thirties and of the miners' passion for religion, rugby football, choral singing and booze.

In Dai's opinion there was only one rugby club in Britain worth its salt, the Scarlets, Llanelli's team, with its formidable pack of invincible forwards and Albert Jenkins, a footballing full-back of great renown. Most nights Dai quietly sang himself to sleep intoning or humming a Welsh ballad or hymn. Biffo developed a penchant for wood carving, using a sharply honed bayonet as a tool and producing passable reproductions of birds, ships and animals. The pair, from different backgrounds and cultures, were firm friends, a friendship based on mutual trust and spiced with light-hearted banter which only served to strengthen the bond between them. David, by nature serious minded and reserved, remained aloof but was, however, not averse to his men making light of their unenviable surroundings and of the potentially lethal danger which constantly lurked in the background.

Throughout October 1944 there were a few skirmishes between German defence posts and the *andartes*. Bursts of machine gun fire during the day were testament to the established German practice of shooting at anything that moved on the slopes and in the valleys below the mountains. Many a Cretan farmer, or shepherd, met his death in this manner whilst out in the open legitimately tending to his fields and animals. Rarely did the Germans shoot a Cretan resistance fighter as they were infrequently active during the day but, at night-time, they infiltrated between the machine gun posts on to the mountain ridges and fired indiscriminately in the direction of a German strong point, only to melt away and disappear into the landscape before dawn. On two occasions in October British aeroplanes attempted bombing raids on the Elounda lagoon, but on each occasion the dilapidated Tiger Moths were driven away by concentrated fire from Bofors guns on Spinalonga and on Villa Olous' rooftop.

On the 6th November, the British commandos heard concentrated firing to the east in the direction of Krikri island, culminating in a crescendo of machine pistol fire at around 3 p.m. About an hour and a half later E-533 returned to harbour and David saw Manfred Schmidt and three other men, all carrying guns, disembark, followed later by four sailors manhandling animal carcasses. At first light on the 10th November David saw a convoy of troop carriers and lorries leave the harbour area, led by a battered old Tiger tank, and moving uphill and southwards out of sight. Three hours later, and minus the tank, the convoy returned and about forty German paratroopers disembarked from the lorries.

During his observations on the harbour David kept a careful account of the number of ships at anchor. There were two E-boats moored to the jetty, E-533 and E-571, covered with camouflage netting, six caiques of various sizes and about twenty smaller craft, mainly fishing boats. On the 24th November David confirmed that one of the larger caiques had moved out during the night and at around 9 a.m. E-533 raced out of the harbour, to return in a gathering storm some four hours later. Throughout November the number of boats left at anchorage reduced in number and by December two caiques and twelve of the fishermen's craft had disappeared.

Early in the morning of the 27th November the British commandos heard some irregular firing to the south near Epano Pines. When David got near the next morning he saw and heard German paratroopers moving into defensive positions in the village. From snatches of conversation he learnt that a whole platoon of German paratroopers had walked out of the village during the night, leaving their sergeant bound and gagged in a slit trench. So the gallant German paratroopers were deserting their posts!

David now became obsessed with the thought that General Manfred Schmidt might make a dash for safety, probably using one of the E-boats. An attempt on the German general's life would have to be made as soon as possible. The harbour might be a suitable place for his purposes but the Germans had surrounded the area with a ring of steel. The road leading down from the top of Olous hill to the harbour might prove suitable for an ambush. He still, however, had not seen the villa and its immediate surroundings and he now decided to make an in depth reconnaissance of the battery on Olous Hill and of the unseen villa across the bay.

On the night of November 30th David packed his *sakouli* and, heavily armed, started out on his reconnaissance. The direct route from Plaka to Olous promontory, travelling through Elounda, was only five kilometres, but the deviation necessary to avoid German strong points, strategically placed on the mountain ridges, made the journey nearer ten kilometres. At one point he had to break into the German defences into a sloping valley about four hundred metres wide and cross a deep ravine to reach the backward slopes of a limestone ridge which formed the rocky face used for quarrying in bygone years. On the summit of this rock formation the Germans had a machine gun emplacement which covered the valley David had traversed, most of the pill boxes and gun emplacements on Olous plateau, the approach road and the courtyard at the front of a villa. Moving along the crest of the hill in semi-darkness, provided by a waning moon, David found a crevasse at the northern edge of the ridge where he lay concealed from the German strong point with a view of the villa, the approach road and part of the Olous complex. He lay in his crevasse prepared for a long wait, armed with a Sten gun and two full water bottles and a long latex rubber tube strapped to his penis. During his crawl along the ridge he was within thirty yards of the machine gun strong point and heard German voices and an occasional snore emanating from the dugout.

When daylight came David had an uninterrupted view of the courtyard and the main entrance to the villa. The villa itself was two hundred yards away from his hideout, well out of range of his Sten gun whose effective accuracy was only some forty yards. Two *Kübelwagens* were parked in the courtyard. At daybreak he ate a piece of crusty dry bread and goat's cheese, washed down with a gulp of tepid water. The villa sprang to life at around 6.30 a.m. The light was still dim when David heard footsteps in the courtyard and the opening and slamming-close of vehicle doors. A few guttural '*Guten morgens*' were interrupted with an occasional clang of metal and banging of doors from within the villa. By fifteen minutes to seven David saw four, goggled motorcyclists wheeling their machines on to the courtyard and forming a small convoy, one cycle and sidecar ahead of a *Kübelwagen* and another combination at the rear. Each sidecar carried a mounted machine gun. A minute later, from the side of the villa, the burly figure of a sergeant major armed with a *Schmeitzer* slung around his shoulder took up position outside the villa's closed door. At exactly ten minutes to eight the door opened and General Manfred Schmidt appeared in the doorway with a valet fussing around him and removing some unseen blemish on his tunic.

"*Guten morgen, Feldwebel* Schneider. Are we ready to go?"

"*Jawohl*, Herr General," the *Feldwebel* replied.

The German general strode purposefully to the door of his *Kübelwagen* and the motorcycles' engines roared into action. The *feldwebel* took the wheel and with a clattering noise the mini convoy moved forwards in a semi-circle and ploughed its way down the dirt road, disappearing in a cloud of dust, as it joined the coastal cliff road from Aghios Nikolaos to Elounda. David had a brief glimpse of the vehicles as they sped along the road and again disappeared over the brow of a hill to begin their whining, gear-changing, descent towards the harbour. The villa seemed quiet and deserted after the general's departure but, David heard faint metallic sounds and an occasional loud laugh or shout from the western wing of the building. At around 9.30 a.m. the small cavalcade roared its way back uphill and into the courtyard and the general and his *Feldwebel* entered the villa where they remained for two hours, re-emerging at eleven o'clock and proceeding once more downhill into Elounda. The four-man strong point on the ridge to the right and above David's' head changed at 2 p.m. and the general and his entourage returned to the villa at 3 p.m. David distinctly heard the word 'siesta' being bandied about in the machine-gun post and, in deference to the general, the whole place fell into a deathly silence for two hours. On cue, the inhabitants of the Villa became active again at 5 p.m. and the general's convoy left in a flurry downhill into Elounda to return at 6 p.m. General Schmidt disappeared quickly into the villa while the *Feldwebel* busied himself with parking the *Kübelwagens* and the motorcyclists left their combinations out of sight to one side of the villa.

Darkness approached rapidly and the villa became barely discernible, showing dim lights in one or two windows. David heard the faint strains of a Brahms' concerto as he moved out from the crevasse to stretch his legs and release urine from his latex-tubing condom. He again ate some bread and cheese and began preparations for his departure and a return to Plaka. At a few minutes past 7 p.m. a *Kübelwagen* came uphill from Elounda into the courtyard and disgorged four men, followed two minutes later by another vehicle with three occupants. David heard a sharp rap on the closed door which was flung open to reveal the sergeant major silhouetted in a shaft of light, warmly welcoming the visitors. All, except one, were attired in *Fallschirmjagger* mess kit. The exception was an officer of the *Kriegsmarine* dressed in a white uniform. The door was closed firmly behind them and they disappeared into the darkened villa. It soon became evident to David that the officers in Villa Olous were having a mess party. The background music became much louder and from time to time ribald laughter and snatches of song emanated from one of the rooms. He lay quietly, listening intently for a further hour and then decided to pack up and go home. As he skirted the machine-gun post on the ridge he picked up snatches of conversation.

"They're having a good time down there tonight, Heinz. The officers get all the fun. Just our luck to be stuck up here in the dark. We can't see a fucking thing from here. What do you think, Heinz?"

The second paratrooper's reply was mumbled and David was unable to hear his answer but, as he crawled round the bunker, he thought to himself, 'Just like soldiers the world over, bemoaning their lot in life and blaming it all on the officers.'

As he made his way back to the Plaka hideout he concluded that the place to strike at the general would be the villa. If he could get Biffo and Dai and rifles up to the ridge they would have a view of the courtyard and the front of the villa and should be able to pick off the German almost at will. The German bunker on the crest of the ridge would have to be neutralised and he also foresaw difficulties in concealing his commando in the narrow crevasse. The fissure in the rock was quite deep, but only three foot in height in places and it would be a tight squeeze to get three adults into the space available. They would literally have to live cheek by jowl in the claustrophobic tomb.

During the first two weeks of December 1944 it became evident to David that the number of German defenders in Elounda was diminishing rapidly, possibly by night evacuation in the caiques or small boats, but also by desertion. The number of paratroopers occupying the defence points became fewer and fewer each day and by mid-December all the gun emplacements on Spinalonga had been withdrawn and three of the outposts on the mountain ranges around Elounda were unmanned. Each day the number of soldiers patrolling the harbour areas seemed less and activity around the central buildings in Elounda indicated that records were being destroyed, or taken out into the lagoon and dumped at sea.

An hour before dusk on the 17th December a lone Fokker seaplane landed in the lagoon and a dinghy rowed to the jetty where a group of officers, including General Schmidt, met the pilot. After a conversation, lasting about ten minutes, the pilot returned to his seaplane and took off westwards into the enveloping darkness. David was relieved to see the general had not left his fortress.

As Christmas approached the weather deteriorated, with squally showers and frequent gales lashing the seashore. The commando spent most of their days in the cave at Plaka, sitting around, huddled in their damp clothing, wrapped in canvas, soaked to the skin and barely speaking to each other. David realised that if they were to survive as a group something would have to happen soon to relieve their misery. Instinct told him that they should move to the crevasse at Olous, but the thought of exchanging their present cave for the confined hideout influenced his decision to stay put.

The Penultimate Act, Christmas Eve 1944

The day dragged on slowly, a replica of the previous ten days, starting with a cold wet drizzle which abated around noon when a weak, watery sun bathed the harbour in sunshine for about an hour, only to give way to heavy rain squalls carried to the island by strong north westerly winds. By 5 p.m. it was completely dark. David sensed that his companions were at the end of their tether.

"Cheer up, lads, it's Christmas Eve tomorrow."

"Is it, Sir?" Biffo asked in a flat toneless voice.

Dai sat with his back to the wall of the cave, only partially protected by a sheet of canvas sacking from the persistent drips of rainwater from the roof. They were all cold, wet and hungry.

"I'll tell you what, we'll have an early Christmas celebration. There's a few bottles of *Tsikoudia* and some brandy in one of the *sakoulis* at the back of the cave. I'll get them and we'll have a few slugs. I don't think Jerry will be up to any mischief on a night like this," and he went into the back of the cave and returned with the bottles.

Biffo and Dai were taken aback by David's uncharacteristic gesture. Normally he was very abstemious and very much against drinking on duty and certainly against drinking in excess.

"Here we go, lads," they clinked their tin mugs with mock solemnity, "Cheers."

To cap it all Dai asserted his Welshness, *"Iechyd Da."*

The first fiery drink was quickly followed by others and, as an alcoholic inner glow surfaced, so the intoxicant loosened their tongues. Within half an hour the three were chatting uncontrollably, a release of the pent-up tension which had accumulated over the past three weeks. David became reflective.

"This will be our third Christmas on Crete. I can't honestly remember what a Christmas away from here was like. I remember the one in 1939 with the First/Fifth Welch at Portadown. Be damned those boys could sing."

"Sing, sing," Dai interrupted, "You haven't 'erd singing like I remember as a boy. We lived in Hendy then and my father was a miner at Talyclun Colliery. On Christmas Eve us boys used to be taken to the pit head service with candles. Iolo Pritchard, the preacher conducted the service and led the singing. He was a good 'un. He used to frighten 'ell out of us boys. But the singing was tremendous. Always ended up with *Abide With Me*, a song for the poor buggers who had lost their lives in the pit. My father was a one of them in 1937. Mam and all the women cried buckets. Afterwards the women went to the church hall and prepared the tables. By God I can still taste the *bara brith* we used to have. The men went to the Rock and Fountain on the booze and came to pick us up at ten o'clock after stop tap. What a great night. Christmas Day itself was a bit of a damper. Then on Boxing Day Dad took me to Stradey to see Llanelli play Swansea. After the game, whatever the result, there would be a big piss up at the Stepney Hotel. They were bloody good days."

They fell silent for a minute and then Biffo, stifling a giggle, gave his account of a pre-war Christmas in London's East End.

"As a young boy I never had a proper Christmas. They didn't go in for it at Barnardos. I spent two Christmases doing porridge in the Scrubs in 1938 and 1939 and they don't go in for Christmas celebrations in stir. But the Christmas I remember was the first one of the War. I was doing casual jobs at the docks when a couple of us nicked a lorry-load of gifts from Norway. There were all sorts of things like hampers of food and booze and twelve Santa Claus outfits. Well, I organised a gang from Barnardos to go round the pubs in Dockland in their Santa gear begging and, during the week before Christmas they collected fifty pounds. They were given half a crown each and with the rest Joe Fine and I went up west. We had a great night, what with the money and everything. I pulled five birds that Christmas Eve. It was easy game. We blew the lot. Oh yes, Sir, one of the birds I pulled was a girl from our school, the one we used to call Mary Loose."

David could feel his face blushing under his pale tan. He kept a poker face as Biffo continued, "Well, I spotted 'er in a pub off Piccadilly. She was with an enormous sailor, all covered in tattoos 'e was. The pub was 'eaving. Jolly Jack went to the bar to get some drinks and I pulled Mary Loose into the men's toilet. I gave her a good 'un up against the wall, a bloody knee-trembler. She was back in the bar inside five minutes and the stupid matelot didn't know we'd gone."

The three burst out laughing. Biffo turned to David.

"You remember Mary Louise, or Mary Loose, don't you, Sir?"

David wasn't sure if Biffo had, amongst all his amorous conquests, genuinely forgotten the games they used to play in the school yard, or if he was leading him on.

Biffo continued, "I can remember 'er. She was a real goer. I seem to remember you was a bit soft on 'er at school, wasn't you, Sir?"

David felt guilty about the long-past incidents at Pusey Street school. He turned to Biffo and with a smile said, "No, Biffo. I think you've got it wrong. I can't remember anyone at the school called Mary Loose. Now, chaps, I think we should turn in. I'll take first guard and, Biffo, you'll follow on at midnight. I've enjoyed our chat and there's plenty of hooch left for another 'do' tomorrow night. Goodnight Dai. Goodnight Biffo."

He turned about and crawled outside the cave to take up his sentry position lying on a narrow ledge outside in the persistent drizzle.

David was wide awake and alert. He heard Dai's melodious voice from inside quietly humming his favourite song, *Myfanwy* and a combination of alcohol and singing brought back memories of Christmases bygone in his orthodox Jewish household in London dockland when he had to suffer the indignity of refusing invitations to school parties and junkets and his father kept him indoors during the holiday to protect the young Jew from the taunts and jibes of the local Christian community. The celebration of the birth of Christ was indeed a miserable and sour affair at the Grünbergs' apartment in Pusey Street. The only Christmas he had really enjoyed was with the First/Fifth Welch in Portadown in 1939. My God, Dai was right. Those Welsh boys could really sing in unison and harmony. Then his mind wandered quickly to his Christmas leave in 1940 when he had seen Bronwen at Fairwood Isolation Hospital in Swansea. That had not been a particularly pleasant time though Bronwen had tried to cheer him up.

Imperceptibly his mind wandered to the girls he had known and the conquests he had made in his brief lifetime. He recalled Mary Louise O'Rourke and his introduction to sex. He remembered his groping experiences with Hannah, Mr Geldman's niece, 'a good clean Jewish girl' as his father explained, and the tall beanpole nymphomaniac he had encountered at the Oxford May ball. And then, at Llanybydder, and later in Cairo came the real love of his life, Bronwen Elvira Thomas, dear, shocking, vivacious Bronwen, with an insatiable appetite for sex, mollified by a catholic sense of humour and unlimited compassion. And finally there was Marita, now hopefully established at Piskopiano with his own child. How he longed to see the baby! He was not in love with Marita, nor she him, but they had both fulfilled a desperate need for companionship and comfort during those turbulent days at Kastelli. When his business here was finished he silently vowed to return to Marita and the child. It was a matter of honour, but his heart would always belong to Bronwen Thomas.

"Where are you now, my Welsh beauty?" he asked of the leaden, dripping wet sky.

The time was approaching seven o'clock, the wind had dropped, but the persistent drizzle had returned, when David was shaken out of his reverie by the unmistakable sound of powerful E-boat engines moving across the lagoon at speed. He strained his eyes but could not see further than some ten yards in front of him. The engine noise gradually receded into the distance as the fast moving boat reached the open sea.

"Damn it, damn it," David said aloud. "The bastard's done a bunk on us."

He crawled quickly into the cave and woke up Dai and Biffo.

"We've got to move now. An E-boat left the lagoon a few minutes ago going like the clappers and our target may have been on it. We must get across to the villa tonight. We'll need to take two rifles, a Sten gun each and a dozen grenades, a rope and plenty of ammunition. I have to warn you now that accommodation at the villa hideout is cramped. It's certainly not the Ritz. I hope we won't need to be there for too long and that the bird hasn't flown. Once the job is done we will pull out and I'll get you back to Alex."

They packed hurriedly and by ten o'clock they were well on the way to the new hideout above Villa Olous, which they reached, wet and exhausted at two o'clock on the morning of Christmas Eve 1944.

Chapter Thirty-Two

The Final Act, Christmas Day, 1944.

"Blimey, Sir. This bloody hole is smaller than the toilet we had in Barnardos!" Biffo exclaimed as he and Dai were examining the interior of the crevasse.

The two managed to crawl in through the vertical, slit-like entrance but then had to negotiate a four-foot high rock tunnel to reach the interior chamber where two people could be accommodated, one standing at the distant end of the cave and the other flat on the floor. The third person had to lie prone in the tunnel with his head protruding through the crevasse entrance. It was a drizzly pitch-black night and David's three man commando had successfully accomplished their journey to the hideout, carefully circumnavigating the German strong point on the ridge about forty yards to the right, but obscured from their view by two large boulders.

David crouched outside the entrance and whispered from the darkness, "Not too loud, Biffo, keep your voice down. We're only forty yards away from Jerry. So we'll have to keep our voices down to a whisper at all times. Is that clear?"

Two muffled "Yes, Sirs," from within the inky cave confirmed that Biffo and Dai understood.

David continued, "I'll stay out on this ledge until it gets light in about four hours' time. Take it in turns to sleep on the floor. At first light we'll check our equipment. Good night, boys."

David settled himself on the narrow ledge outside the hideout, his back to the rock face, cold, wet and miserable and kept vigil over the area in front and below him, where he knew the villa would appear at first light. It was the longest four hours of his life. He thought he saw a transient flash in the darkness at one stage and distinctly heard a click of metal and an indistinct German oath from the region of the outpost above his head and to the right. The sky became gradually lighter to the east at around six o'clock and about twenty minutes later, the villa was indistinctly outlined in dawn's first rays. He quietly called his two companions out of the hideout one at a time and allowed them to stretch their legs and release their urine condoms.

By daybreak they were all back inside the crevasse. David lay at the entrance with his head and shoulders protruding through the fissured aperture. Biffo was lying flat alongside the lower half of his body examining the two rifles they had brought with them. He urgently tugged the back of David's tunic and whispered coarsely, "Bloody hell, Sir, we're in trouble. One of the rifles 'aint got a bolt and the other's rusted up and the bolt is jammed."

David swore under his breath and asked Biffo to push the rifle forwards. One quick look confirmed that the firing mechanism of the only serviceable rifle was solidly rusted and of no use.

"Pass me the Sten, Biffo," David took the short range weapon and laid it beside his right shoulder, "We'll have to make do with our Stens and grenades. The distance from here to the courtyard is too far for accurate firing. We'll have to move along the ridge nearer the exit drive to be sure of hitting the target. It'll mean taking out the German bunker first."

He had just finished whispering when he heard the unmistakable whine of a revving *Kübelwagen* speeding up the hill from Elounda. When it arrived in the courtyard three men jumped out and ran towards the villa door. One was undoubtedly a *Feldwebel*, the second a paratroop colonel and the third a naval lieutenant. They quickly disappeared into the villa and the door slammed firmly behind them. After twenty minutes the paratroop colonel and the naval officer re-emerged, ushered out of the front door by General Schmidt, swathed in a bright red dressing gown. David took a deep breath at the sight of his adversary and then gave a silent prayer of thanks that the bird had not flown the nest. He was unable to hear their conversation, but two words, "*Heute abend*", came clearly through as the colonel entered his *Kübelwagen* and sped away down the hill towards the harbour.

"A man may be leaving this evening," David relayed the message to his companions in a loud whisper. "We must be ready to move quickly."

Dai's voice came from the depths of the cave.

690

"Sooner the better, Sir. It's getting a bit stuffy in here. Stink's worse than them cheese huts at 'äraso.'"

They took it in turns to keep watch, one man at the aperture, one standing at the back of the cave and the third resting, or sleeping, on the cave floor. There was a fair amount of activity in and out of the villa during the day. Two empty lorries arrived at midday and were loaded up with crates, furniture and paintings supervised by a *Feldwebel* and a fat mess sergeant who David recognised as the cook he had clobbered in the officers' mess at Vai.

The *Feldwebel* journeyed to Elounda twice in his *Kübelwagen* during the course of the morning. The paratrooper colonel again returned in the lunch hour and stayed for about twenty minutes. When he left he was escorted to his vehicle by *Feldwebel* Schneider. As they parted, David heard the colonel's voice.

"Well, that seems to be all in order, Schneider. Be sure to get the general down to me in good time. We must be ready to move before dark."

The stocky, weather-beaten *Feldwebel* saluted and replied, "*Jawohl*, Herr Colonel. I will make certain that the general is with you before dusk."

The colonel was whisked away by his driver. The *Feldwebel* walked across the courtyard to the cliff face underneath the German strong point on the ridge above the villa. He held a conversation with an unseen German paratrooper in the bunker and then returned to the house. At around 1.30 p.m. the two lorries came back from Elounda and picked up eleven soldiers and their kit, many still wearing the shirts and vests of their trade as cooks and servants. David was surprised by the number of personnel employed in the villa. At around 2.30 p.m. two escort motorcyclists brought their machines to the middle of the courtyard. The motorbike engines were started and revved at a standstill for a full minute and then there was silence. At 3 p.m. a German captain came from the direction of Aghios Nikolaos in a motorcycle combination and spent ten minutes in the villa. When he left he took up position at the junction of the earthen road from the villa with the Aghios Nikolaos-Elounda coast road. The captain was seen off by the *Feldwebel*, who, standing in the doorway of the villa, waved his hands in the general direction of the quarry face and shouted, "*Eine, stunde*", and, closing the door firmly, disappeared into the villa.

David turned his head sideways and spoke in a loud whisper, "This is it, chaps. They're going to leave the house in about an hour's time. I think there'll be three or four of them. Fix the clips to your Stens and load up with half a dozen hand grenades. In about three quarters of an hour I'm going up to the cliff-top. Biffo, you follow me a minute later and bring a rope with you. As soon as Biffo leaves, Dai will come on to the ledge and cover the door of the villa and the vehicles in the courtyard. There are two *Kübelwagens* down there and two motorcycle combinations may join the party. Now, Dai, they'll be too far away for your Sten when they leave the house. Don't shoot until you hear us firing first. Then take a pot shot at anything in the courtyard. Biffo, when we get to the top of the cliff I'll take the route along the edge and you go down the slope some twenty yards to my right. We'll be in open country with a few rocks for cover. We'll have to crawl the whole distance. I want to take the dugout without firing a shot. Once we're in the bunker we'll be able to fire at close range on any targets in the courtyard and the track leading up to the villa and we'll be able to drop grenades on the vehicles below. Remember, the prime target is the blond general. I want him dead. Once we've sorted him out we'll make a run for it over the top of the ridge and down into the trees in the valley behind, the way we came up last night. Any questions?"

After a pause, Biffo whispered, "Why do we need a rope? It's a heavy weight and might slow us down!"

"I know, Biffo, but I think I'll take it with me. It may come in handy."

The sweat of anxiety was streaming down David's face as he lay prone on the ledge, his eyes glued like rivets on the white facade of Villa Olous. A peaceful calm settled over the villa nestling in the murky Christmas afternoon drizzle. The forty minute wait seemed interminable. David heard noises of movement and an occasional indistinct voice both from the direction of the outpost to his right and the road junction, which was out of sight beyond the villa rooftop. Soon, very soon he would have to expose himself and his two commandos to the enemy and to kill, or be killed. For a few seconds his thoughts turned to Bronwen, Marita and his little baby. He prayed silently for their safety and for the safety of the two men in the crevasse behind him. One of them let off a loud fart which, at any other time would have been a cause for amusement but, at that particular moment, was a source of irritation.

He snapped tersely, "Cut that out, you two," and then concentrated his mind acutely on the job ahead.

*

The German strong point on top of the ridge was a twenty-foot square, sand-bagged dugout covered with a corrugated roof and camouflage netting, strategically placed to cover the main entrance to the villa and courtyard, the Aghios road junction and, on the reverse side of the quarry, a narrow tree-lined valley and ravine. The German defenders had four portholes along the walls of the dugout, whose entrance was at the rear, facing the ravine, and approached by a narrow path leading up an escarpment from the road junction. The quarry makers had constructed a series of flat platforms hewn into the sheer one hundred foot rock face underneath the ridge. There were four tiered platforms with a twenty, or thirty, foot vertical drop between each stage.

On Christmas Day, 1944, the dugout was manned by a sergeant and four paratroopers. Sergeant Heinz Stettner, a veteran of the Cretan campaign in 1941, knew the Olous encampment would be evacuated that day. His instructions from *Feldwebel* Schneider were clear and, at a given signal from the *Feldwebel*, he was to send his four paratroopers down the escarpment to the road junction and, once the general's car had left the courtyard, he was to follow and join the rear party. They would then conduct an orderly rear-guard action and retire downhill to the harbour where they would board a caique. A stolid, bovine Bavarian, the sergeant wondered why he had been selected for this dirty job. Still it was an honour to be elected by General Schmidt for a most important duty in charge of the rear-guard party. Memories of the carnage which his storm company had suffered at Maleme in May 1941 still lingered in his mind, but the last eighteen months in Elounda had been relatively peaceful and the general seemed to have a soft spot for him. Only a few weeks ago General Schmidt had spoken to him personally.

"Sergeant Stettner, we're both Bavarian, we must stick together."

Yes, General Manfred Schmidt was a great man and a personal favourite of the Führer. Not that he, Sergeant Stettner, was a devout

Nazi. He had sworn allegiance to Adolf Hitler and, at this particular moment, General Schmidt was the Führer's appointed commander in Elounda. It would indeed be an honour to lead the last German paratroopers from Elounda. This would be something he could relate to his children and grandchildren after the War.

Sergeant Stettner had been on duty in the dugout at Olous ridge since daybreak. He witnessed the arrival of Colonel Lindermann and his driver around lunchtime, when he and his troop were feasting on slices of black bread and salami, washed down with schnapps. When the colonel left, *Feldwebel* Schneider walked across the courtyard to tell him the order of withdrawal. At 3 p.m. Captain Grenz and two paratroopers arrived in a *Kübelwagen* and were inside the villa for ten minutes. When they emerged and departed, Schneider waved from the villa doorway and shouted, *"Eine stunde"*.

This was the signal Stettner had been waiting for. He turned to the four *Fallschirmjagger* in the bunker.

"Well, boys, this is your lucky day. You'll remember this Christmas Day for the rest of your lives. Get packed and off you go. There's a boat waiting for you in the harbour. It'll take you home to Hamburg! Good luck, lads. I'm waiting behind for a few minutes and I'll get down to the harbour later. Keep a place for me on the boat."

Even as he spoke Sergeant Stettner saw paratroopers at the road junction moving quietly and in an orderly fashion down the road, past the Olous Battery, towards the port. The sergeant, despite his seniority in the army, was amazed at the orderliness of withdrawal and blind obedience of well-trained *Fallschirmjagger*. Now, however, he concentrated on the two *Kübelwagens* in the courtyard. As soon as they got moving he would pick up his *Schmeitzer* and make a run for the road junction.

General Manfred Schmidt had known the game was up before he convened an emergency meeting at Villa Olous on Christmas Eve. At that meeting plans were made for the final evacuation of Festung Elounda. His garrison, reduced to around a hundred and thirty men, their morale decimated by daily defections, were on the point of mass surrender. He never thought he would see the day when his own men, his coveted *Fallschirmjagger*, would turn tail and run away from the enemy. And the officers? Colonel Lindermann's resolve to stay on was wavering and Captain Grenz appeared to be jittery, though covering up his nervousness with a facade of bravery. Lieutenant Krebs, a young recruit from the Hitler Youth who had arrived at the fortress six months previously, was still fanatically loyal and prepared to fight on, as was his long-standing bodyguard, *Feldwebel* Schneider. But the *Kriegsmarine* lieutenant was a different kettle of fish. He definitely wanted 'out' and as soon as possible and he held the trump card – E-533, the only serviceable, fuelled, fast boat in Elounda. At the morning conference the naval captain hinted he did not know how long he would be able to control his men, especially after the overnight escape of E-571.

Manfred replied with a cold haughty stare, "You will stay as long as I need you. *Feldwebel* Schneider and six *Fallschirmjagger* will mount a twenty-four hour guard on your boat. They will have orders to shoot your men if they show any signs of attempting to move E 533 from its moorings. Is that clear, Lieutenant Klemper?"

The naval lieutenant lowered his head.

"*Jawohl*, Herr General," and was silent for the rest of the meeting.

General Manfred Schmidt spent much of Christmas Day drinking alone in Villa Olous. He drank a whole bottle of Napoleon brandy, brought from Paris and reserved for his own consumption. He sat in front of a large window in the lounge overlooking Olous bay and his thoughts wandered back to Christmases past, to the strict celebrations in his father's house in Munich and his gifts at Christmas time which had always been Nazi insignia and emblems and, very early in his boyhood, as soon as he could read, a dog-eared copy of *Mein Kampf*, personally inscribed by Adolf Hitler. Later, when he joined his regiment, he was on leave over the holiday and spent most of his time carousing and drinking in Willi's bar and eating at Gasthof Den Berliner. The only Christmas he had enjoyed had been in Paris in 1940 at the SS barracks and, at that time, the great attraction was the acts of sexual perversion perpetrated by the SS officers.

Thoughts of their sexual activities stimulated his memory of the women he had known and ravished in his time, countless numbers of them, but a few stood out – Erika on the train to Winterberg, Lise in Paris, a prostitute in Minden, a nurse in Hanover, the Bulgarian officer at the railway station in Sofia and finally Stephia in Kastelli. Poor little Stephia, such a willing partner in his sexual fantasies and now dead, shot by her own people in the debacle at Vai.

He was near to tears, pitifully sorry for himself, frustrated and angered by the thought that he had failed his beloved Führer and that his Festung could not be defended to the last man, or last bullet. Should he do the honourable thing? He toyed with the idea of shooting himself and released his revolver from its holster, checking the chamber was loaded and placing the gun on the arm of his chair. What would his father have advised? Had Colonel Erich von Bulow had the same thoughts before he took his own life? He drank some more brandy and wondered if he would have the courage to pull the trigger and release a bullet into the roof of his mouth, which would tear into his skull and scatter his brain like bloody dew-drops over the walls of the room and the ceiling. His melancholic thoughts came to an abrupt halt when *Feldwebel* Schneider ushered Colonel Lindermann into the lounge. Manfred replaced the revolver in its holster and listened to the colonel's report of the final details for evacuation of Elounda later that day.

"Thank you, Colonel Lindermann. The arrangements are very satisfactory. On one thing I insist. *Feldwebel* Schneider and I will be the last to leave the villa and to board E 533 in the harbour. I have come to regard Elounda as a large battleship and when it finally sinks, as it will later today, I wish to be seen as the ship's captain staying on his vessel to the very last. It is important for the men to see that senior officers take the same risks as they do. I intend to be the last man to step off the island and leave it to the mercy of the misguided Cretan savages."

After Colonel Lindermann and *Feldwebel* Schneider departed Manfred lunched on a plate of cold meat, some crusty bread and mouldy cheese, washed down with a few glasses of foul-tasting *retzina*.

When his servant returned to pick up the tray Manfred asked, "Otto, how many men are left in the kitchen?"

Otto was startled by this unusual question.

"Four, Herr General, Sergeant Schultz, an orderly and two motorcyclists from the mountain regiment. Five including myself"

Manfred replied, "Go and tell them all to pack. We're leaving the villa within the hour. We're being evacuated by boat. Before you go, pack my things, run a bath and lay out my SS uniform on the bed. When you've done that get moving. I'll meet up with you at the harbour."

Manfred did not add that there was no room for Otto in the E-boat. He would have to take his chance with the others in one of the caiques. As soon as Otto departed to deliver the message, Sergeant Fritz Schultz knocked timidly on the general's door and, when permission was granted, entered the lounge. Saluting, he asked for permission to speak.

"Yes, what is it, Sergeant Schultz? Speak up. We've only got a few minutes. I have to get ready to leave."

Sergeant Schultz, attempting to stop his knees from knocking, blurted out, "I wanted to be the last to leave with you, Sir. We've gone through a lot together and I wish to remain with you whatever happens."

The general, feeling he had been rather abrupt with the slow-witted mess sergeant, mellowed.

"I'm very grateful to you, Sergeant, but I think *Feldwebel* Schneider and I can manage. So get packed and leave now with the other cooks and Otto. I'll see you at the boat and we'll have a glass of beer together in Schweinfurt when we get back to Germany."

With mention of his home town the sergeant's face brightened.

"*Danke*, Herr General," and with a backwards, shuffling gait and bowing with each step the heavy-jowled sergeant cook left the general's presence.

'He'll never make a soldier but he's a good man. The salt of the earth,' Manfred mused as he went upstairs to soak in a bath and dress for his departure from Festung Elounda.

By 3.30 p.m., bathed and dressed in his SS uniform, General Schmidt received Captain Grenz's report that troops from the forward barricades were silently withdrawing in small groups and in half an hour the first men from the Olous bunkers would make their way down to the harbour. The captain expected the withdrawal to be completed by 4.15 p.m. and the only German forces on the southern side of the fortress would be the rear-guard at the junction between the road from the villa and the coastal road. General Schmidt drew himself up to his full height.

"Thank you, Captain Grenz. *Feldwebel* Schneider and I will leave this Villa at precisely 4.15 p.m. and make our way down to the E-boat. We have two *Kübelwagens* at our disposal. In the meantime my servant Otto, Fritz Schultz and three other men in the kitchen need evacuation. Perhaps you will take them with you now?"

"*Jawohl*, Herr General," the captain replied, eager to please and anxious to get away downhill to the waiting boats.

Before he left, Otto placed the general's valise in one of the *Kübelwagens* and then, between 3.35 p.m. and 4.15 p.m., the only three persons left in Villa Olous were Sergeant Schultz, lurking in his kitchen, *Feldwebel* Schneider and General Manfred Schmidt, sitting in the lounge finishing off a second brandy bottle. At precisely ten minutes past four the general stood up and walked unsteadily towards the door.

"Well, Schneider, my friend this is it. We must now leave our beautiful villa. You go first in your *Kübelwagen* and make sure the coast is clear for me. Our boys are holding the road junction open for us. I'll follow you after a minute. It will only take us four minutes to get down to E-533. Make sure my kit is on the boat. We should be back in Athens by tomorrow morning. What a Christmas Day to remember! Good luck, Schneider."

They exchanged glances for a brief second and then the *Feldwebel* picked up his *Schmeitzer* and, slinging it over his shoulder, turned to face the general and saluted.

"*Guten glück*, Herr General Schmidt."

In three bounds he ran down the villa steps and jumped into his *Kübelwagen* to find Sergeant Schultz sitting in the passenger seat. "What the hell are you doing here, Schultzie? You should have left half an hour ago. Bugger it, let's get out of here," and, firing the engine, he turned the *Kübelwagen* towards the exit road from the courtyard.

General Manfred Schmidt followed down the same steps at precisely 4.10 p.m. and walked deliberately and sedately to his own soft-topped *Kübelwagen*. With one hand on the door of the *wagen* he turned and took a long, last look at Villa Olous. *Feldwebel* Schneider and Sergeant Schultz were already descending the earthen driveway at speed when the general turned to face the villa, saluted the building and, as he was about to enter the driver's cabin, he heard a burst of staccato small arms fire from the hundred foot high rocky plateau at the southern face of the courtyard, followed some twenty seconds later by the unmistakable crump of an exploding grenade. He instinctively jumped into the driving seat and, after three fumbled attempts, managed to start the engine and the vehicle moved forwards in a wide arc towards the exit road.

Manfred had never been properly instructed to drive a vehicle and the weakness in his left arm made some mechanical manipulations difficult and cumbersome. The *Kübelwagen* was proceeding in an erratic fashion when Manfred became aware that his vehicle was being peppered with bullets from the ridge above his head. With difficulty he managed to manoeuvre the *Kübelwagen* under the quarry face and turn left towards the courtyard exit road, where he slowed down to avoid a boulder projecting from the cliff face. At the very moment, as he was about to re-accelerate, there was a heavy thump on the roof above his head and, looking upwards, he saw the contour of a human body, lying across the canvas canopy. He increased his speed and started zigzagging down the earthen road in a frantic attempt to dislodge the unwelcome encumbrance. He began to panic and, steering the vehicle with his weakened left hand, undid the clasp of his holster with his right and withdrew his *Maüser*. If the man on the roof could not be dislodged by his erratic manoeuvres then he had no choice but to shoot him through the *wagen's* soft top.

*

"Right, lads, I'm going up. Follow me in one minute, Biffo."

Half an hour had elapsed since the German general and his *Feldwebel* re-entered the villa, which was now ominously silent. Two *Kübelwagens* were parked, side by side, at the front of the villa steps. David scaled the twenty foot rock face above the crevasse in a matter of half a minute. He lay face down on the ridge, Sten gun in hand and a rope coiled around his shoulders. The rope was a hindrance to his climb and he thought for a few seconds he should jettison it, as Biffo had suggested. Biffo arrived at his side a minute later. During the brief ascent they had both been exposed to the villa but there were no signs that they had been spotted. From their position they saw the villa, the courtyard, the *Kübelwagens* and, some forty yards straight ahead on the brow of the ridge, the sandbagged parapet of a German bunker. David signalled Biffo to move across the ridge for thirty yards and then they crawled forwards leopard-fashion towards the bunker.

The bunker was silent, with no evidence of activity and David hoped the Germans may have already abandoned their dugout. Within ten minutes they had both slowly and laboriously edged their way across the rock-strewn ridge towards the dugout, fully exposed and easy targets for any defenders.

Everything seemed to be going well and David was within ten yards of the bunker when he heard one of the *Kübelwagens* starting up and, peering cautiously over the edge of the ridge, he saw Schneider drive away with the fat sergeant cook at his side. Within a minute the tall, black uniformed figure of General Schmidt strode down the steps towards the remaining *Kübelwagen*, opened the door of the vehicle and turned to salute the villa. He was out of effective range for David's Sten gun but would be much nearer when he drove down the exit road beneath the hilltop bunker. As he watched his adversary getting into the *Kübelwagen* he noticed a man-made platform hewn into the face of the quarry some thirty feet below. Throwing caution to the wind he got on to his knees and crawled to a solid boulder some five yards back from the edge of the quarry where he safely secured one end of the rope, casting the other end over the cliff edge. Biffo, emboldened by his commander's movements, also got to his feet and began to run towards the bunker, Sten gun at the ready. After three ineffective ignitions the *Kübelwagen* engine burst into life and, with a grating of gears, began to move. David made a dive to the tethered end of the rope and was about to commence his descent down the rock face when he heard a frantic shout from Biffo.

"Look out, Sir, there's a Jerry in the bunker," and Biffo's Sten gun burst into life. Sergeant Stettner spotted David near the boulder and dashed out through the rear entrance, throwing a grenade in David's direction and aiming his *Schmeitzer* at Biffo. But Biffo was quicker and more accurate and, from a range of fifteen yards, his bullets ripped through the German's upper body and neck bringing him down in a mangled, lifeless heap. Biffo continued running towards David and flung himself on to the grenade, just as it exploded, and blew away the middle of his torso. By the time the noise of the grenade explosion had abated David was abseiling down the rope which ended within ten feet of the flat platform. He dropped from the end of the rope landing on his feet and jarring his right ankle. His Sten gun was knocked off his shoulder during the descent.

The rock face platform was some thirty feet above ground level. The Nazi's *Kübelwagen* turned in a wide arc in the courtyard and within ten seconds would pass under David's platform. David sank to his knees and caught his breath, gritting his teeth from the stabbing pain in his right ankle. Almost instinctively he fumbled inside his tunic pocket and pulled out a hand grenade. His first thought was to remove the pin and drop the grenade in the path of the oncoming *Kübelwagen*, but the chances of stopping a vehicle by this means were not favourable. The vehicle was fast approaching and would be directly underneath in two or three seconds. David took off from the platform and hurled his body face downwards out into space to land with a resounding belly-flop on the *Kübelwagen*'s canvas roof, still clutching the grenade in his right hand. The canvas canopy broke his fall but the metal struts supporting the canvas dug deeply into his abdomen and for about five seconds he lay there winded and inert.

The driver of the *Kübelwagen* tried to dislodge David by skewing his vehicle sideways, but he held on firmly and began pulling himself slowly towards the edge of the canopy, at the same time attempting to pull out the pin from the hand grenade. The *Kübelwagen* was by now at the lower reaches of the dirt road where, at a sharp bend, it joined the coast road and where the German rear-guard and *Feldwebel* Schneider were scampering out of the way of the careering vehicle. With a superhuman effort David pushed his head and shoulders over the edge of the canvas canopy and, only a foot apart, looked directly into the steely blue eyes of the German general. There was a moment of instant recognition as Manfred's bellowed:

"*Warum, warum, mein blütbrüder?*"

By now the general had his *Maüser* in his right hand and was steering the *Kübelwagen* with his weakened left hand. David brought his right arm around in an arc and lobbed the hand grenade into the cockpit and, at the same moment, Manfred fired three shots through the canvas canopy, which tore their way, like white hot metal rods, through David's unprotected abdomen. The searing pain in his belly was excruciating and, within ten seconds, his senses blacked out as he sank into unconsciousness.

During those fateful seconds, Manfred, his blond hair covered in blood dripping through the torn canvas top, made frantic efforts to get hold of the grenade rolling about between his feet in the well of the *Kübelwagen*. He completely lost control of the vehicle which went careering sideways into a row of white-painted boulders at the edge of the road, dislodging David off the canopy into space and, a split second later, ejecting Manfred out of the driver's seat. David's lifeless body went hurtling down the two hundred and fifty foot drop to the sea below, closely followed by the screaming Nazi general who bounced off the rocks into the water. The screaming stopped and the unconscious German splashed into the dark, salty water about fifteen yards away from David. The *Kübelwagen* teetered at the brink of the precipice for a few seconds longer and then rolled sideways in an ungainly cartwheel, to crash on the rocks two hundred feet below. The hand grenade did not explode. Its pin had not been withdrawn.

Feldwebel Schneider, standing near his parked vehicle at the road junction, watched in horror as his general's *Kübelwagen* came careering down the dirt road, out of control with a body lying on its roof. As it passed at speed he caught sight of the general struggling with the steering wheel and distinctly heard three shots from within the cabin of the vehicle which continued its erratic progression down the coastal road towards Elounda, hitting the bollards on the roadside, discharging two bodies into space and plummeting over the edge of the cliff and into the sea. He reacted quickly and, calling on Sergeant Schultz and two paratroopers, ran up the steep track towards the villa. At the bend in the dirt road and some eighty yards from the German dugout they were met by a stream of bullets coming from the ridge over their heads. The futility of a counter-attack dawned on the wise *Feldwebel* and he ordered his men back to the road junction and into his *Kübelwagen* to drive at speed downhill to the harbour. Schneider stopped at the spot where the general's vehicle had veered off the road, but it was now almost dark and he saw nothing but a black void at the bottom of the precipice.

Feldwebel Schneider, Sergeant Schultz, and two *Fallschirmjagger* drivers were the last Germans to leave Festung Elounda. They boarded the last caique to leave the harbour, in the light of burning vehicles torched by their departing comrades, and set sail for Santorini. E-boat E-533, with its officer complement, had made a dash out of Elounda some twenty minutes before their arrival.

It struck Schneider forcibly that, had General Schmidt made his way down to the harbour, he would have missed the E-boat and would have had to escape with the rest of them in a slow-moving, unseaworthy caique. Heinz Schneider stood at the rail of the departing caique watching the quayside recede into the distance and the light from the burning vehicles gradually fade into darkness. He was near to tears at the thought of leaving his commanding officer's body on alien soil. Sergeant Schultz, by his side, was weeping unashamedly, salty tears running in rivulets over his chubby cheeks, as he bemoaned the loss of a friend and officer he had proudly served, nurtured and fed for the past two years. And yet, as often happened with Schultzie, his mood changed abruptly and he smiled at the thought of the stories he would tell the boys in the Wildbok in Schweinfurt – a tale of his bravery and how he was the last German soldier to leave Festung Elounda.

Lieutenant Costas Vitalis

Lieutenant Costas Vitalis wondered if he had done the right thing in joining Porphyroyennis' *andartes*. The good looking, dark-haired, twenty-two year old Cretan had been forced into the mountains in June 1943 when the Germans attacked Anoyia and executed all males in the village, including his father. His hatred of the Germans from that time onwards was uncompromising. At first he swore allegiance to Bandouvas' group but, after a month of inactivity in the Dikti mountains, he moved southwards to Ierapetra where he was mobilised by Porphyroyennis. His dedication and bravery became legend and secured him rapid promotion. Within a year he was one of four lieutenants in Porphyroyennis' *andartes* and in July 1944 was posted to Aghios Nikolaos where he took command of the resistance fighters surrounding the police barracks and investing the town. He had always advocated attacks on the German occupation forces in Aghios but the crafty Porphyroyennis, who had now promoted himself general, insisted on patience and a siege policy, waiting for the Germans to withdraw and then moving in to capture their arms and ammunition.

The young lieutenant gradually became disillusioned with Porphyroyennis as a leader and sensed that, at some stage, his *kapitan* had made some sort of deal with the Germans. Porphyroyennis' tactics were targeted at securing enough armaments for his *andartes* to overthrow the nationalists and Yanni Bodias and become undisputed ELAS commandant of the whole of eastern Crete. And then, in August, Bourzalis arrived on the scene. Lieutenant Costas Vitalis was unable to imagine how Porphyroyennis could stomach this autocratic domineering, self-appointed *kapitan*. They were constantly at loggerheads and when Porphyroyennis was away in the south, dictating tactics at Ierapetra, Bourdzalis took command in Aghios and made everyone's life a misery. Vitalis thought many times of leaving Aghios Nikolaos and returning to his family home in Anoyia. But the bitterness in his soul and the desire for revenge against the Germans overshadowed all else and he stayed loyal to Porphyroyennis in the hope that, one day, he would be allowed to come face to face with the enemy and kill a few of his father's executioners.

By mid-October Bourdzalis had become a liability. He completely mismanaged the first meeting with General Schmidt at Elenika on the 22nd October and, as a result, Porphyroyennis was urgently summoned from Ierapetra to take charge of negotiations. Lieutenant Vitalis was present, at a distance, at the meeting between the two generals at Elenika. Vitalis wished he could have been nearer to take a pot-shot at the German general, the one they called the White Angel of Gournes. Confrontation between Bourdzalis and Porphyroyennis continued, exacerbated by the Krikri incident and brought to a head by German evacuation of the police barracks on November 10th, 1944. Immediately afterwards Bourdzalis left with sixty of his staunchest supporters and attempted a coup to overthrow Yanni Bodias in Heraklion. In the event he failed and was executed two days after an attempt to shoot Bodias in a heated argument.

Within twenty-four hours of the German withdrawal from Aghios Nikolaos Lieutenant Costas Vitalis came into his own. He was ordered by General Porphyroyennis to chase the Germans out of Elounda. With a group of sixty armed men he moved quickly northwards along the coast road and took the village of Elenika and, about four kilometres north of the village, his advance was stopped by a strongly defended German barricade protecting the Olous quarry and plateau. The Cretans erected their own barricade across the road two hundred metres short of the German position. The defensive barricades were completed by the 15th November and there the two adversaries lay in stalemate. It was now Christmas Day, 1944 and Lieutenant Vitalis and his men had been permanently anchored at the barricade for nearly six weeks. During that time there were minor skirmishes and a few desultory exchanges of fire and Vitalis had lost three men from gunshot wounds but, of more concern, was the rate of desertion by his *andartes* and, by Christmas Day, his defenders at Elenika were down to eighty men.

One night in early December five German deserters were brought into the Cretan defence post. With a broad grin, showing his fine white teeth, Vitalis ordered his *andartes* to take the captives back to Elenika where they were disarmed, stripped of their clothing and executed without ceremony in the village square. The lieutenant had the dubious satisfaction of personally shooting one of the *Fallschirmjagger*. From their vantage points on the hills and villages around Elounda the Germans had complete control of the area in daylight hours but, at night, Lieutenant Vitalis' *andartes* roamed freely. He personally led four night patrols which achieved very little. Two of his men were killed when they inadvertently walked into a strongly defended German dugout. For six weeks it had mainly been a waiting game. Prospects of a frontal assault along the road were rapidly diminishing and, with nightly defections, his poorly armed defenders were dwindling daily. And then, at about 4 p.m. on Christmas Day, with the light beginning to fade, things started to happen. For most of the day there had been unusual vehicular activity around the villa and across the road on Olous plateau.

A few minutes after four, small arms fire and the crump of an exploding grenade was heard from the direction of the villa, followed by the whine of *Kübelwagen* engines and then more machine pistol firing and silence. The whole action lasted for only ten minutes. Lieutenant Vitalis rapidly recognised that something untoward was happening at the villa. He faced his comrades.

"Come on, lads, over the top. Something's happening at Villa Olous."

And with a bound he was over the barricade and leading his men in a charge on the undefended German barricades and artillery battery on Olous hill.

By the time they got there the birds had flown. The villa, the quarry and the bunkers on Olous plateau were clear of German military forces. Lieutenant Costas Vitalis was hopping mad. He had been caught off-guard and the Germans had withdrawn their forces from Elounda under his very nose. He sent a section of his men to search the villa and the German outposts on the ridge. Very little equipment of military value had been left in the villa. Two bodies near the bunker were found, one a German sergeant almost beheaded and the other an unrecognisable mangle of flesh lying in an untidy heap about fifteen metres from the bunker.

By now it was dark, damp and dismal, and his men were content with the capture of the villa and the Olous bunker. Two miles down the road, at Elounda harbour, flames and smoke billowed into the night sky. Leaving fifteen of his men to occupy the villa, Vitalis took the rest in a headlong rush down to the harbour. The only military equipment in the harbour were the smouldering burnt-out shells of twelve army vehicles and motorcycles. The flames, from time to time, were rekindled by gusts of wind from a probing north-westerly breeze. Lieutenant Costas Vitalis' depression grew when he realised that the waiting at the barricades had all been in vain. The treacherous and hated Germans had escaped from Elounda and denied him the chance of wreaking revenge for his father's death. Now he would definitely pack it in and return to his little village outside Anoyia.

Corporal Dai in Action

Corporal David Griffiths was glad to push his head outside into the fresh air, to clear the fetid body odours which pervaded the inside of the confined space in the crevice. He had not had a whiff of fresh air for twelve hours. He rested his elbows on the ledge, placed his Sten gun at a convenient spot near his right shoulder and concentrated his attention on the main door of the villa and the two parked *Kübelwagens*. Major Green and Biffo had disappeared up the cliff face about ten minutes previously and all was quiet and still. The minutes ticked slowly by.

He allowed his mind to wander, remembering Christmas Day in No. 47 Libanus Street, Hendy, his mother's cooked chicken dinner allowed to get cold, whilst his brother and father slipped across to the Rugby Club for a 'quick pint' before lunch. They brought back flagons of Felinfoel ale, a reserve supply, as his father put it, for the rest of the holiday. And then in the evening, they sat around an open coal fire. His mother was cajoled into taking a glass of sherry which made her tipsy and maudlin. On these nights the family were entertained to the melodious sound of her beautiful soprano voice, complemented by his father's tenor baritone. Duets were the order of the day, rendered with feeling and passion by his mother and father. And, as a boy, Dai used to wonder if his parents did 'you know what' in their bedroom after their passionate duets.

One year, Christmas day fell on the Sabbath, which put a damper on all celebrations. All Wales was 'dry' on Sunday and the pubs were not open. Dai and his seventeen year old elder brother managed to sneak a pint each from the back door of the Rugby Club in common with a dozen other devout Christians. The party dispersed with the arrival of a police sergeant, whose only objective was to clear the field to allow him to have a few pints on his own in the snug. And then it was chapel twice a day and no singing in the house. The singing in the chapel was, as always, superb, but David missed the good old-fashioned sing-song around the hearth. Their Christmas lunch that year was a platter of cold chicken and pork. His mother would not cook on the Sabbath and the cold meats were prepared beforehand. Dai smiled ruefully as he recalled that, during all his Christmas dinners at his home in Llanelli, the chicken was cold.

The time passed quickly and he was meditating on the miserable lunch they had shared in the crevice a few hours previously when a fat sergeant, in a white tunic, appeared from the side of the house and jumped into one of the *Kübelwagens*, followed two minutes later by a burly sergeant major who came bounding down the steps of the villa. In a few seconds the *Kübelwagen* arched its way around the courtyard and came head on towards Dai's hideout. He trained his sights on the *Kübelwagen* as it passed below him but, though sorely tempted, he obeyed Major Green's order not to open fire. His instructions were clear. He was not to act until he heard firing from the crest above his head. And then the general appeared in the doorway, dressed in black, apart from his light-blue service cap.

The general walked deliberately down the steps and across to the *Kübelwagen*, paused and turned to face the villa, and to Dai's amazement, saluted before climbing into the driving seat. He heard the engine of the *Kübelwagen* splutter twice as the general turned the ignition key. Dai, his Sten gun trained on the target, muttered under his breath, "Give 'er more gas, you silly bastard," and his spine tingled at his audacity in calling a senior officer a "silly bastard". On the third ignition the engine fired and the *Kübelwagen* lurched forward erratically, starting its wide turn in the courtyard. Within seconds Dai heard a burst of machine pistol fire above his head and to the right, in the direction of the dugout on the ridge. This was his signal.

He shouted aloud, "Keep coming, you bastard", and kept his finger on the trigger and sprayed the oncoming vehicle with bullets. But the *Kübelwagen* kept coming and passed beneath his position on the ledge. He felt certain he had hit the German general. The

Kübelwagen lurched from side to side and began to slow down, before it disappeared from view behind a rocky bluff. Dai stopped firing and listened intently to the sound of the *wagen* racing down the earth road.

Shouts of "*Achtung, achtung*", heralded its arrival at the road junction. There were three distinct pistol shots and then, about thirty seconds later, a rending crash on the road, out of sight, on the other side of Villa Olous. Dai scrambled up the rock face to reach the ridge and, Sten gun at the ready, he raced towards the German dugout. The light was rapidly fading and he half stumbled across Biffo's body lying draped around a small boulder, his head and shoulders at an acute angle to the lower half of the torso and a gaping hole in the middle of his spinal column, the edges surrounded by strands of Biffo's charred, blood-stained tunic.

Dai cried out in anguish, "Damn and blast it! Major Green, Major Green."

He ran behind the bunker and found the dead German sergeant in a sitting position, his back propped up by the dugout sandbagging and half his head and left shoulder blow away. Corporal Dai ducked low to enter the dugout and looked down the approach road where, in the gathering dusk, some fifty yards away, four German soldiers came running up the road towards him, one of them, the fat sergeant wearing a white tunic. He let out a fiendish Welsh oath and started firing at the approaching figures until they stopped running and took cover at the side of the earthen road. Dai kept firing indiscriminately into the gathering gloom and, when he stopped after half a minute, he could hardly see the villa and the road junction but heard German voices shouting on the coast road and, within half a minute, a lorry started moving rapidly downhill towards Elounda. An eerie silence descended on Olous plateau and the villa. There was a glow of flames in the sky over Elounda harbour but, otherwise, little to see and less to hear.

Dai sat, alone and dejected, in the dugout which smelt of human sweat, salami and schnapps. Poor Biffo, his best pal, lay dead outside the bunker and Major Green had disappeared without trace. The Germans had left and he, Corporal David Griffiths, was the only living person in the quarry. But he was not alone for long. Within ten minutes of the Germans' departure Cretan voices and dim figures appeared on the earth road, running and darting to and fro and chasing across the courtyard to enter the villa, where they rushed from room to room rummaging and looting as they went. Dai reasoned it would not be too long before the *andartes* came up to the bunker. He picked up his Sten gun and ran outside into the darkness. He walked back to where Biffo's body lay and whispered, "Cheerio, Biffo, *bach*. I'll miss you."

He moved smartly off the ridge and made his way down the reverse side of the quarry to the meadow and ravine below. As he trudged through the dark, dank mist he felt salty tears running down his face as he cried unashamedly for his mate, his best friend, the Cockney sparrow he had left in a mangled heap on Olous ridge.

Chapter Thirty-Three

The Beachcombers' Find

Costas Manolis had been a fisherman all his life and, at the age of seventy-three years, he was still plying his trade from Minos, a small secluded beach, half-way between Elounda and Aghios Nikolaos. Military activity along the coast road had not prevented the stubborn, weather-beaten, gnarled Cretan from fishing the bay each day in his dilapidated fishing boat. A bachelor, he lived very simply and alone in a small hovel at the edge of the beach. At daybreak on the 27th December 1944 Costas stepped outside his cottage, a ritual he performed each day ever since he could remember. There was a strong blustery north-westerly gale blowing and, for the second day in succession, Costas realised that there would be no fishing that day. He shrugged his shoulders and, after attending to a call of nature, returned to the relative sanctuary of his one-roomed bachelor hovel, where he brewed a pot of tea and ate some stale bread and dried fish. He cursed the weather and the German conquerors who had prevented him fishing for a whole fortnight in May 1941. They had subsequently harried the old man from time to time, using their E-boats to force him back to shore.

He had soon learned that the unwelcome visitors could be bought off with fish and, in particular, with lobster and crab which abounded in the shallow channels of Mirabello bay and off Krikri island and Spinalonga. The very tea he was drinking had been acquired by bartering with the Germans. Costas wondered what had happened in Elounda on Christmas Day. He had returned form a successful day out in his boat and was cleaning his catch when, around teatime, he heard gun-fire from the direction of Olous ridge and, in the darkness an hour later, he saw a red glow of burning fires above the hilltops somewhere in the region of Elounda harbour. Since the first week of November the Germans had withdrawn from Aghios Nikolaos and he lost a ready market for his fish. His catches were now appropriated by his comrades, the Cretan *andartes*, who occupied Elenika and manned the barricade on the road approaching Olous villa. They were a mixed rabble of men and their commander, the one they called Vitalis, took Costas' catch without payment or even a 'thank you' with promises that:

"Once Porphyroyennis is in command of the whole of Crete, people like you, old man, will be remembered and honoured by my Cretan *kapitan.*"

By mid-morning the winds were still furiously sending large fifteen foot waves crashing on to the small beach and whistling through the rafters of Costas' rickety little cottage. He became worried about his fishing boat, moored in a shallow inlet at the other end of the shelving, sandy beach. Pulling a battered old *sariki* on his head and wrapping his thin, bony frame in a leaky sou'wester, head bent, he set out across the beach. He was only twenty yards from his doorway when he saw two bodies lying face downwards, a yard clear of the water's edge and some fifteen yards apart with their arms outstretched as if they were trying to take hold of each other's hands.

Costas' first instinct was to turn tail and run for help but native curiosity overcame him and, approaching the bodies, he turned each one over and inspected them more closely. The first body was that of a Cretan, but with curious pale grey eyes. There were three bullet holes in the front of the man's belly, small reddish pink holes, washed clean by the salt water. Inside the dead man's tunic were three hand grenades and he had a British army dagger strapped to the inside of his right leg. Costas gingerly removed the grenades and dagger and placed them in a neat pile on the beach, well clear of the crashing waves. He then turned his attention to the second body, a tall blond-haired man with staring blue eyes and a deep serrated wound on the right side of his temple revealing the underlying egg-shell white skull. The body was completely dressed in black, the epaulets and insignia on his shoulders indicating that he was a high-ranking German officer.

Costas' search was thorough. He retrieved a bronze cross from around the German officer's neck, unbuckled the belt and empty holster, removed a ceremonial Nazi dagger from its sheath around the officer's waist and found a pair of dark sunglasses in his breast pocket. The sodden documents in his left breast pocket were of no use to the illiterate Cretan fisherman. He was about to walk away when he noticed the German's black jackboots. He bent down and, after a struggle and a dousing from the angry waves, he removed both boots and placed them with his pile of treasure on the sand.

At that moment Costas decided to inform the authorities in Aghios Nikolaos. But first, wrapping his booty in the sou'wester, he buried the parcel in a sand dune near his fishing boat and took out his faithful, but uncooperative old donkey and rode to the police station in Aghios.

"What brings you to town today, Costas?" asked the fat police sergeant. "If you haven't got any fish for me you can turn around and go home again."

Costas took Sergeant Constantinos' sarcasm with equanimity.

"Get off your arse you fat old bastard. I've found two bodies on Mirabello beach near my cabin, washed in by the storm. One of them is a German officer and the other is one of our own boys."

The sergeant now took notice, conscious of the importance of the 'find'. He shouted for a donkey-cart to be harnessed and personally rode out on another donkey with Costas and two policemen. The bodies were retrieved, thoroughly searched by the sergeant, loaded on the cart and taken to the mortuary at the back of the police station. Sergeant Constantinos was unable to understand why the only retrievable objects on the German's body were his documents, which allowed him to glorify in the knowledge that he had, in his custody, the body of General Manfred Schmidt, the last German commander in Elounda. The identity of the Cretan body was of no concern to the sergeant. He turned to face the gnarled old fisherman.

"You did the right thing to report this find to me, Costas. I can't understand why his pockets are empty and his belt is missing, and," looking at Costas' feet, "whoever took his boots is in for a shock. He has very large feet and I can't think the boots would fit a Cretan." Costas shrugged his shoulders, turned away and walked slowly back down the beach to his little hovel.

Claiming the Bodies

At noon on the third day after Christmas 1944 Corporal Dai Griffiths arrived in Aghios Nikolaos. He had spent Christmas night, after the action on Olous plateau, hiding in the ravine at the bottom of the valley. The hills around Elounda were crawling with *andartes* and an occasional burst of small arms fire attested to the nervousness of the trigger happy Cretans. At dawn, having discarded his Sten gun and grenades, Dai walked boldly from his hide and made for the road leading into Elounda. The town was full of drunken *andartes* still celebrating the victory of the previous day. The harbour area, containing the burnt-out remnants of the German evacuation, was heavily patrolled and defended by Vitalis' men and Dai gave the area a wide berth. He intended making for the commandos' last hideout in the hills above Plaka but the presence of a militant group of *andartes* in Epano Pines forced him to turn around and retrace his steps to Elounda. He felt lonely and insecure and spent most of the morning roaming aimlessly around the small town, mixing with various groups of Cretans, hoping to hear about the fate of his comrades. He knew that Biffo had been killed on Olous Ridge but he was unable to glean any information about the fate of his officer, Major Green. By teatime he made up his mind to return to the ridge above Olous plateau and claim Biffo's body.

Lieutenant Vitalis had made the villa his headquarters and the surrounding plateau was heavily guarded by armed *andartes*. Try as he may, Dai was unable to obtain access to the ridge and, by early evening, he gave up his attempts and joined a group of drunken Cretans making their way southwards towards Aghios Nikolaos. He spent an uncomfortable night in the taverna at Elenika and the next day continued his journey towards Aghios, walking with a straggling group of Cretans, still excited and jubilant over their success in driving the Germans out of Elounda.

Aghios Nikolaos was shrouded in an air of suppressed excitement. A large crowd of some five hundred people had gathered at the police barracks, all clamouring and shouting at the rotund, baggy figure of the police sergeant standing at the top of the barrack steps, legs apart and arms akimbo, selecting members of the crowd to go into the cells to see the body of the German general which he, Spiros Constantinos, had personally found. He dispensed his largesse to the crowd all morning, accepting an occasional bribe, allowing the Cretans to see the prize exhibit in his cells. There were nine bodies in all, the general, a German sergeant and seven Cretans who had been killed in action on Christmas day, including the body of David Green, as yet unidentified as a British officer. General Manfred Schmidt lay alone in a large central cell with a cardboard placard tied around his neck bearing his name and rank and incorrectly assigning him to the SS. In an adjacent, smaller cell the German sergeant, also placarded, but unidentified, lay in solitary splendour. The dead Cretan *andartes* were laid out in a neat row in a third cell waiting to be identified and claimed by their relatives, or comrades. Sergeant Constantinos made the most of his day of glory. Porphyroyennis was expected any minute and when he had identified the dead general he, Constantinos, would be richer by two gold sovereigns. The crowd on the barrack square were getting restless and agitated and, in the right centre, a group of ten or twelve men were being overly abusive and vociferous.

Dai edged forwards through the milling throng and found himself on the periphery of the more militant section of the crowd, whose central figure appeared to be a wizened, weather-beaten, old man in his seventies. Old Costas had recruited a few fishermen friends and some village down-and-outs to come and support him in his claim for the bounty offered by General Porphyroyennis. They had waited patiently all the morning for the Cretan *kapitan*'s arrival. In the meantime they heckled and goaded Constantinos who, by the minute, was becoming more and more agitated and flustered.

It was well past midday before Porphyroyennis and his handsome, smiling lieutenant arrived to take their places on top of the steps next to the obsequious police sergeant. Lieutenant Vitalis silenced the applauding Cretans by firing a single shot into the air and Porphyroyennis stepped forwards to speak.

"Comrades of ELAS Resistance. We have won a great victory in Elounda. We must now move across to Heraklion to take over command and then we'll march on to the Soudha bridgehead and drive the Germans into the sea. But first there is the matter of the SS general in the cells. Police Sergeant Constantinos has laid claim to the two sovereigns I have offered for delivering his body to me. Are there any other claims?"

The shouts from the group around Costas intensified and Dai was propelled forwards to the foot of the steps by his supporters. Porphyroyennis held up his hand for silence.

"Sergeant Constantinos, am I to believe that this old man brought in two bodies to you yesterday?"

Sergeant Constantinos stuttered a negative reply. Porphyroyennis was not happy with the sergeant's explanation and turned to face Costas.

"Old man, you say there are two bodies you brought in, one a German officer and the other a Cretan?"

"That is correct, *Kapitan*," Costas replied.

"Well," Porphyroyennis continued, "If you can identify the two bodies they shall be yours and so shall the sovereigns."

By ancient Cretan custom any bodies not claimed by relatives or friends are the responsibility of the finder who must supervise their burial.

Porphyroyennis continued, "So, come with me into the cells," and turning on his heels, the *kapitan* pushed past the flustered and fawning police sergeant, followed by Vitalis, Dai, and Costas' party.

The old fisherman had no difficulty in identifying the body of General Schmidt and, a few seconds later, David's body lying amongst the Cretans on the cell floor. At the sight of his dead commanding officer Corporal Dai sprang into action. Pointing at the floor he shouted, "Him, SOE, him British *kapitan*." and then he 'la, la'd' the first line of *God Save the King*.

The Cretans were mystified. Porphyroyennis ordered David's body to be moved and laid next to General Schmidt's corpse. Costas received his two gold coins and was ordered to bury his charges in a fit and proper manner. The German sergeant was to be buried in a common grave and the dead *andartes* were to be given a proper military funeral. The *kapitan* general then stormed out of the police station mouthing obscenities at the hapless police sergeant.

About three hours elapsed before the crowd outside the police station dispersed and, in the meantime, various relatives and comrades claimed the bodies of the dead and took them away to be buried. Sergeant Constantinos, his power and authority considerably deflated, disappeared very quickly leaving four of his policemen to look after the funeral arrangements for the dead German sergeant. In the early evening Dai and Costas took away their corpses on a donkey-drawn tumbril and on the following day they were buried with little ceremony on a small hillock overlooking Mirabello beach.

Corporal Dai was made welcome in Costas' primitive fish-impregnated abode. He went out with Costas on his fishing expeditions. At night they sat around an open wood fire in the middle of the earthen floor, which belched smoke and polluted the one-roomed cottage. The old fisherman was useful with his hands and had the ability to whittle intricate wood carvings. Before long Dai had persuaded Costas to carve an inscription on a mahogany driftwood headboard for the grave in the sand dunes.

Major David Green
1st Bn Welch Regiment

———————————

SS General Manfred Schmidt
Paratroopers

———————————

Both Killed in Action, Olous, Christmas Day, 1944

———————————

Blood Brothers in Life
United in Death

———————————

Mewn Heddwch

The latter part of the inscription was a reflection of Dai's non-conformist Welsh upbringing. As a young boy of ten he had been made to attend his father's funeral at Ebenezer Chapel. Subsequently, on his rare visits to the cemetery, the Welsh inscription on the headstone, 'In Peace', brought back sad memories of his father's death in a mining accident in 1934.

This accomplished, Dai set about getting a cross made for Biffo. In the bottom of his *sakouli* he found a small wooden female figure which Biffo had carved with loving care. Biffo called it his 'lucky Mary Loose mascot'. In the middle of January Dai erected the wooden effigy at the exact spot at which he had seen Biffo's mutilated body on Olous ridge. On the cross Costas had etched the words:

Gunner William (Biffo) Wendro
Royal Artillery

———————————

Killed in Action on This Spot

———————————

Christmas Day, 1944

———————————

RIP

With a perverse sense of humour, which he knew the Cockney would have appreciated had he lived, Dai mentally translated the letters RIP into "Rest in Pieces". Corporal Dai Griffiths never found out what became of Biffo's remains.

February 10th 1945. *The Harbour, Aghios Nikolaos*

Corporal Dai Griffiths sat on a bollard at the edge of the quay in Aghios Nikolaos. Costas had sent him into town early to sell their previous night's catch. About an hour after daybreak an armed British supply ship appeared between Krikri Island and the shoreline with its pom-pom guns trained on the harbour. A large crowd of excited Cretans gathered at the quayside and watched the naval vessel letting go its anchor about a mile off the leeward side of the island. Eventually two landing craft were deposited over the side of the ship and approached the harbour at slow speed, each boat laden with green-bereted Royal Marine commandos. The eager young marines, faces blackened, crouched in the bottom of the boats and prepared to jump ashore and scale the quayside wall. They were all young men, raw recruits, on their first landing in combat, their first taste of the 'real thing'. Dai and the Cretans watched with amusement as the boat wallowed in the waves below and three futile attempts were made to secure the craft to the harbour wall. At last, disembarkation commenced.

The first man up the rope ladder was a frightened, bespectacled young lieutenant standing in a half-crouch and brandishing a pistol, uncertain what to do next. A few Marines piled in behind him and the young officer, conscious that he had done nothing so far, shouted, "Corporal Fowler, take three men and secure the right end of the harbour. The rest of you follow me and get these bloody civilians off the bridgehead. Move now, Go, go, go."

The young commandos started rushing in all directions, shouting at the astounded Cretans and urging them off the quay, prodding their backs with the muzzles of their loaded Stens. The Cretans got the message and began to move slowly. But Dai stood his ground, sitting stolidly on his bollard. A pimply frightened young marine commando came up to him and started gently poking the small of his back with his gun.

Dai heard him muttering under his breath, "Please, please go away. Don't make any trouble. I don't want to have to shoot anyone."

Dai stood up and faced the young soldier.

"Look 'ere, boyo. Watch what you're doing with that gun."

The startled young Marine jumped a foot in the air and shouted to his officer, "Lieutenant Hornby, come quickly, Sir, there's a chap here who speaks English."

Lieutenant Hornby appeared in a few seconds, hatred and fear blazing from his eyes, convinced that he was about to capture, or shoot, his first German spy. Using his training in interrogation and remembering the instructor's advice to catch a suspect off his guard he blurted out, "Which school did you go to?"

Without hesitation, Dai replied, "Llanelli Grammar School, Sir, and take that pistol out of my ribs."

The Royal Marine officer was now lost for words and kept prodding his revolver firmly into Dai's midriff. At the top of his voice he shouted, "Sar'n Major, arrest this man. He may be a German spy."

And then within a matter of seconds Dai was looking straight into the eyes of Sergeant Major Hubbard. They instantly recognised each other and, within a second, both men were clasped in a fierce embrace. Sergeant Hubbard was the first to speak.

"It's all right, Lieutenant Hornby. This man is Corporal Dai Griffiths of the RASC. He's been on the island for nearly four years helping the Cretan resistance fighters. I've spent eighteen months out here with him."

The young lieutenant relaxed a little.

"Okay, Sar'n Major, if you vouch for him it'll be all right," and, looking up and down the quayside, he continued, "Well Sar'n Major Hubbard, it's been a successful landing. We've secured our bridgehead with no casualties. The jetty's clear. We will now call in the rest of the battalion."

The experienced sergeant major smiled inwardly and simply replied, "Yes, Sir."

He then reverted his attention to Dai, who was again sitting nonchalantly on the bollard, much to the annoyance of the young marine commandos who were charging around aimlessly and fingering the triggers of their Sten guns. The sergeant major smiled at Dai.

"It's good to see you again, Dai. Is Major, sorry Colonel, Green about?"

"No, Sir," Dai replied. "He copped it on Christmas Day but he took that German general with him, the one we called the White Angel of Gournes."

"And Biffo?" Sergeant Major Hubbard queried.

"Sorry, Hubby. He also caught a packet on Christmas Day. He was blown to bits by a grenade. I miss the little Cockney bastard. He was such good fun!"

"Yes, wasn't he?" replied the sergeant major as he looked wistfully at the tearful Welsh soldier.

"Come on, Dai, let's go into town and tidy things up," and, together, Sergeant Major Hubbard and the RASC corporal marched purposefully along the quayside into Aghios Nikolaos.

Epilogue

In the spring of 1946 Generals Heydrich Müller and Bruno Braüer were extradited from Germany to stand trial for war crimes before a military tribunal in Athens. Both were condemned to death by firing squad. General Müller was shot within seven days of the verdict, but General Braüer's execution was delayed until the 20th May, the anniversary of the German airborne assault on Crete.

Feldwebel Schneider stayed in the army for eighteen months after the Armistice and then enlisted in the *Volkspolitzei* in Dresden where he attained the rank of sergeant and retired in 1966.

Sergeant Cook, Fritz Schultz returned to his home in Schweinfurt and took over his father's bakery. For years after the end of hostilities he proudly wore his white chef's tunic with parachute wings and replica Iron Cross displayed on his left breast pocket. He never ceased to regale his customers and friends with tales of his exploits with the *Fallschirmjagger* in Crete and how he, Sergeant Fritz Schultz, was the last armed German solider to leave Festung Elounda.

Captain Franco Tavana returned to his father's engineering factory in Brescia in 1946. He became active in local politics and was mayor of Brescia in 1959 and subsequently, in 1967, was elected member of parliament for the Maggiore District in northern Italy.

Sergeant William Hubbard stayed on in the Army, was commissioned in 1949 and ended his military career in 1967 as a lieutenant colonel quartermaster at the Royal Marine Depot in Lympstone in Devon.

After demobilisation in 1946 Corporal David Griffiths settled in Llanelli and returned to Talyclun Colliery as a coal-face worker until he was made redundant in 1969 when the colliery was permanently closed following a miners' strike and dispute over pay.

After a peaceful exchange of prisoners at Georgioupolis in March 1945 German and Italian occupying forces left the island of Crete. That a bloody civil war between the nationalists and ELAS did not materialise was a miracle. In April 1945 the climate was ripe for civil confrontation, but the wartime resistance fighters were still poorly armed and preoccupied with their own private vendettas. Development of post-war Cretan policy was largely influenced by events on the Greek mainland, where the monarchy was overthrown and the communist party ELAS was dominant. There is little doubt that if the mainland communists had kept control then there would have been a civil conflict on Crete.

In 1946 General Papadakis emerged as a benign figurehead and helped to defuse the volatile situation, bringing the two antagonistic factors together. It was largely due to Papadakis' diplomacy that Crete emerged, after the war, as a unified country though, even to this day, feuds between families and between communists and nationalist still continue and the bitter memories of wartime killing, treachery and betrayal survive amongst the vendetta-conscious Cretans.